FARM BUILDINGS

Farm Buildings

TECHNIQUES — DESIGN — PROFIT

JOHN B. WELLER
A.R.I.B.A.

VOLUME ONE

LONDON

CROSBY LOCKWOOD & SON LTD

26 OLD BROMPTON ROAD

First published 1965 by
Crosby Lockwood & Son Ltd
26 Old Brompton Rd., London SW7

Printed in Great Britain by Richard Clay (The Chaucer Press), Ltd.,
Bungay, Suffolk

To Ann

CONTENTS

CONTENTS

NOTE: The sub-sections to Part Three, each designated by a capital letter, are further divided in the text under the following sub-headings:

1. Activity
2. Managerial requirements
3. Production techniques
4. Work routines

5. Design data
6. Equipment
7. Environmental control
8. Layout

9. Siting
10. Services
11. Costs
12. References

LIST OF PHOTOGRAPHS

LIST OF PHOTOGRAPHS

FOREWORD

By SIR HAROLD WOOLLEY, C.B.E.
President, National Farmers' Union

At the opening of Agriculture House on the 18th October, 1956 by Queen Elizabeth The Queen Mother, it was announced that to mark the occasion The National Farmers' Union would award a Farm Buildings Fellowship. Mr. Weller was later selected to receive this award.

Economic investment in modern farm buildings is essential to the farming industry, but on account of the complexities of the specialized buildings required nowadays it is often difficult to determine the design and form of construction to adopt.

It therefore gives me great pleasure to introduce 'Farm Buildings', this valuable reference book by Mr. Weller in which he records knowledge acquired both during the period of his fellowship and in subsequent years of architectural practice.

This book should be of great assistance to anyone faced with farm building problems.

March, 1965   HAROLD WOOLLEY

SCHEDULE OF CONTENTS
TO VOLUME TWO*

* Volume Two in preparation.

INTRODUCTION

The design of farm buildings is a controversial subject. Neither food production nor the buildings required for it are standardized. In fact, there are wide differences of opinion concerning methods of production. In some cases, the relation between buildings, especially well-designed buildings, and a profitable enterprise is not appreciated by all farmers. Moreover, for the most part, the data by which buildings should be designed is not easily available and, frequently, has not been confirmed by research. The subject of farm building design is so confused by conflicting opinions and evidence that it is necessary to make a personal statement as an introduction to this book.

In the first place, the subject of food production, even when limited to that part which may need buildings, is so vast that a book on farm building design to be manageable must have many omissions and limitations. Secondly, production of each type of food is becoming specialized and specialist farmers, within each branch of agriculture, require specialized advice.

In the future, there will be less need for a general book on farming or on farm buildings, though there will be a great need for specialized information. In fact, there are specialists more qualified in their own field than I, working in research establishments and on experimental farms, and it would have been possible for each of them to have written respective sections for this book. However, at this point of transition in agricultural practice and organization, there may be some value in one person attempting to cover all farm buildings. Mixed farming is still the norm and there are many people who require some guidance on the design of farm buildings generally.

With one author, it is easier for the text to be uniform in emphasis and presentation. However, inevitably, it must have two main limitations: it cannot be so comprehensive that it gives specialist advice at every level of design, nor, to be of any use, can it generalize and offer quick solutions to problems of design.

Horticulture is intentionally omitted. Poultry and egg production, which is largely outside my experience, has already become so specialized and complex that it no longer justifies a place in a book on farm buildings being, like horticulture, an industry to some extent divorced from normal farm practice. However, within the last few years, development and research in poultry housing has had a profound effect on all other livestock enterprises. Its effect in the future will become more critical and, for this reason, a short appraisal of poultry housing is included. I am greatly indebted to Dr. Sainsbury for preparing a short section on this subject.

I have not attempted to show farmers how to erect farm buildings with their own labour. This subject has been well covered elsewhere [*] by Frank Henderson. I cannot discuss the merits of conversions, since the value of these depend on problems related to individual farms and their buildings. W. G. Benoy has previously shown,[†] by case studies, how conversions can be successful.

I cannot deal with the many examples which exist of individual ingenuity in building economy and this book will not be of direct assistance to the many small farmers struggling to survive by making minimal improvements at a low cost. Verbal advice from local experts or from the Ministry advisors is preferable in such cases. Nevertheless, it should be possible to use some of the design data given in this book even for simple conversions. Similarly, though there is a bias towards farmers wishing to develop intensive production within their enterprises, the data given should be relevant, if considered with discrimination, to any level of production.

The subtitle of 'Techniques—Design—Profit' is pertinent. The basic functions of farm buildings are closely related to many problems of farm management and it is not desirable to consider the design of farm buildings in isolation from production techniques. Unfortunately, it is not possible in a general book on farm buildings to give a detailed analysis of all management problems and production techniques. I have attempted to give sufficient information on the managerial aspects influencing

[*] Henderson, Frank *Build Your Own Farm Buildings*, Rev. Edn. 1963 (Farming Press)
[†] Benoy, W. G. *Farm Buildings: Conversions and Improvements*, 1956 (Crosby Lockwood)

building design, which if not comprehensive, at least should make it possible to ask the more critical questions relating to management policy needing to be answered at the design stage.

For reasons discussed in Part 1, I do not consider it possible, or even desirable, to give 'ideal layouts or building designs'. Therefore, I have attempted to give sufficient data to make it possible to design various layouts to suit the principal variations of management policy. Farm building design is an exercise in economics in which capital cost has to be related both to performance and to the end product. A second volume will deal with the more general aspects of building materials and construction pertinent to agriculture.

I hope that this study will give impetus to more detailed research into a subject of fundamental importance not only to farmers but to the nation. At present, the farming industry is changing rapidly and there is a ferment of new ideas. The book, revealing, as it does, many areas in which knowledge is confused, inadequate and inaccurate will have been of use should it act as a springboard for more serious research into the basic requirements of food production and its buildings.

I have included quotations from or reference to many articles, pamphlets or books, which are listed at the end of each section. It is possible that many of these references will not be of enduring interest. However, they are relevant since much valuable comment on management techniques and building design is at present unco-ordinated or untried by scientific experiment. In addition, it is usually impossible to include as much of the articles as might be of interest to some people, because of space limitations, so that a reference to a journal makes it possible to check the source from which the comment has been taken. A number of selected references are also given to material which is likely to be more comprehensive and enduring. A complete bibliography to such material will be given in Volume 2.

I must express my gratitude to the publishers for financing my travel to visit many farms and institutes in this country. This has been of great value and I should like to thank the numerous people who gave me their time and hospitality both during my travels and in the course of preparing the book. In particular I must thank Mr. John Fletcher, Mr. David Soutar and Mr. Robert Forsyth for giving days of their time in shewing me farms within their area and for their subsequent encouragement. I am grateful to Mr. John Nix for reading and correcting many sections of the book. This has taken a great deal of his time and has been invaluable to me. Likewise, I must thank Mr. Claude Culpin for reading Part 2 and officials at the N.F.U. for reading Chapters 7 and 9 in Part 1. The publishers have been unstinting in their patience and, in particular, I should like to thank Mr. Humphrey Wilson for his advice and encouragement.

LIST OF ABBREVIATIONS

A.I.	Artificial insemination		m.c.	Moisture content
B.S.	British Standard		m.c.r.	Moisture content reduction
B.t.u.	British thermal units		min	Minute(s)
bu.	Bushel		m.p.h.	Miles per hour
C.F.M.	Cubic feet per minute		N.F.U.	National Farmers' Union
Ch.	Chapter		oz	Ounce
C.P.	Code of Practice		p.a.	Per annum
cwt	Hundredweight		P.E.	Protein equivalents
deg.	Degree(s) (for angles: ° for temperature)		Pt.	Part
dia	Diameter		p.t.o.	Power take-off
d.m.	Dry matter		r.c.	Reinforced concrete
f.c.	Foot candles		R.H.	Relative humidity
F.I.S.	Farm Improvement Scheme		r.p.m.	Revolutions per minute
ft²	Foot super = square foot		rt.	Right
ft³	Foot cube = cubic foot		RWP	Rainwater pipe
ft.R.	Foot run = one foot in length		S.E.	Starch equivalents
gal	Gallon(s)		sec.	Second
h.p.	Horse power		sq.	Square = 100 ft²
h.r.	Half round		s.w.g.	Standard Wire Gauge
hr	Hour(s)		T	Tons(s)
ht.	Height		'U'	Value of thermal coefficient
in.	Inch(es)		w.g.	Wire Gauge
kW	Kilowatt		wk.	Week
kW.hr	Kilowatt/hour		wt.	Weight
lb	Pounds		yd²	Yard super = square yard
livewt.	Liveweight		yd³	Yard cube = cubic yard
M	Million		yd.R	Yard run = one yard in length
max.	Maximum		yr	Year

LEGEND : SYMBOLS USED IN DIAGRAMS

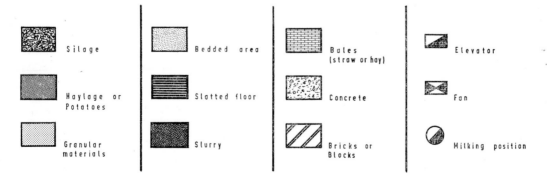

NOTE: Drawings in the text, unless otherwise stated, are by the author.

PART ONE

THE FUNCTION OF FARM BUILDINGS

CHAPTER 1

Capital Investment

Every farm building forms part of an investment. Any part of a building which does not contribute to a profit from the enterprise concerned hinders the success of the farm.

A farmer has many demands on his resources in order to increase the financial return from his farm. He must seek to maintain and to improve the fertility of the soil. This will be limited in value unless the crops give good yields. Capital may be required for improved strains of seed and stock which are able to benefit from the potential fertility of the soil, and new machinery must be bought and maintained. As the investment per acre is increased, so is the need for greater skill and diligence in husbandry. It is easy to waste the benefits arising from improved fertility, crops, stock and machines. A skilled man commands and deserves good wages. Thus, it is difficult to establish the priority for capital expenditure.

It is not surprising, with so many demands on capital, that investment in buildings is subordinate on most farms. It may be that a quicker, if not a better, return on capital will be obtained from investment in the land rather than in buildings. The majority of farms contain a nucleus of traditional buildings which may be made useful with a little ingenuity and not much capital. The need for buildings may be evaded, since some farm enterprises need few, if any, buildings. Moreover, a farmer may sub-contract his work, which can place the onus for providing buildings on other people. Any capital saved from the potential cost of a building can be used to buy better fertilizers, seed, stock or machinery. A building does not, in itself, make money, and it is known that capital spent on buildings is seldom recovered if the farm is sold. However, the benefits from increased investment in the land can reach a point when they are dissipated by a waste of the farm resources due to lack of proper buildings. A building is a piece of equipment which is an aid to the conservation

and better use of the farm resources. The investment in buildings will be economically sensible only if profits are increased in excess of the additional annual building costs. Profits can be raised if the farm product is either improved in quality or increased in quantity. Improved quality may increase the selling price, and increased quantity may reduce the unit cost of production. A building may contribute in either way. For example, calves raised in good housing conditions are likely to be healthier, more valuable and cheaper to raise than those in poor housing. Grain well stored will maintain its quality, whereas badly stored grain will lose much of its value. A man may look after more cows, with a higher average yield, in a well-planned and equipped dairy unit than in a poor building layout.

Throughput is one of the ways in which the efficiency of industrial machines or buildings may be measured. This is also relevant to farm buildings. It can be gauged against several units of measurement, assuming a standard quality in the product considered. Time is one measure. It is important to know how many gallons of milk can be extracted by a milking machine in a unit of time. Power can be another form of measurement. It is important to know how much power will be required to move a ton of grain over a fixed distance. Though both these measurements are required when designing farm buildings, manpower is the usual unit of measurement when assessing the productivity of a farm. The importance of the skilled worker, when designing farm buildings, is discussed in Chapter 4. Thus, when considering the merits and faults of different layouts, the throughput per man obtainable within each layout is a major consideration. The design of buildings and equipment may govern the quantity and quality of material which can be handled or processed by one man within a unit of time.

Throughput has to be related to the annual building cost. A small increase in throughput will seldom justify a large increase in the annual building cost, unless other farm resources besides labour are being conserved. Annual building costs comprise depreciation, interest, maintenance and insurance. Whereas machinery should be depreciated over a period of five to ten years, farm buildings should be depreciated over ten to fifteen, depending on the purpose and construction of the building.

Farm buildings cannot be considered as a long-term investment like some commercial buildings. Interest must be charged on the capital invested and, at 6 per cent compound interest will equal an average annual interest charge of about 3·6 per cent of the initial investment (1). Thus, each £1000 invested in a building depreciated over 10 years will cost £136 p.a. in depreciation and interest. Some allowance should be made for building maintenance even for as short a period as ten years, in spite of the fact that to qualify for grant the building has to be designed to last fifteen years without maintenance. Ingersent and Manning have discussed at length the difficulty of assessing or analysing maintenance costs (2). An arbitrary allowance of $1\frac{1}{4}$ per cent p.a. of the capital cost might not be unreasonable, though, for example, this could be greater in a parlour and less in a straw barn. Building insurance, discussed in Chapter 9, will vary for different situations and uses, but might cost 3s. p.a. per £100 of the capital cost. Thus, on this basis, the annual building cost is about £150 per £1000 capital cost.

The economics of building investment are improved, at present, by the direct grant towards the capital cost made by the Government under the Farm Improvement Scheme (F.I.S.). The grant of one-third of the capital cost of fixed equipment will not be paid on all buildings, and few buildings will be granted one-third of the total expenditure, since some items of the design may not qualify for grant. This grant, and others available, are discussed in Chapter 9, and, when obtained, will reduce the annual building cost to the farmer. Annual building costs form part of the cost of each enterprise and must be deducted from the gross returns as part of the overheads before assessing the net profit. Total costs will include, in addition, such items as labour, raw materials, machinery and a share of general farm overheads.

Labour is not the only farm resource which can be used to better advantage within good buildings. Most farm buildings are used directly or indirectly for the conversion of coarse raw materials into meat or dairy produce. The main exceptions are storage buildings for potatoes and buildings for drying and storing grain, except when grain is used as fodder for livestock.

The manner of housing animals affects the food conversion ratio, i.e. the weight of coarse foods consumed to produce a unit of live weight of food for sale. For example, (Pt. 3, III E, p. 205), pigs fattened in open yards can consume on average between 4 and 5 lb of meal for every pound gained in weight. In contrast, pigs managed in good housing may need as little as 3 lb. If food costs 28s. a cwt. a drop of 0·1 in the food conversion rate means a saving of about 4s. in the food cost of fattening a weaner to bacon weight. Since the average profit is only about £2 per baconer, an improvement of only 0·5 in the conversion rate could increase profits by 50 per cent. Good housing may contribute towards lower mortality rates, especially in young stock. Well-designed silos will reduce the wastage in the conservation of grass for silage or haylage, thus yielding a better conversion for grass into milk. These matters are discussed in further detail in Part 3.

Thus, good buildings can conserve farm resources and allow better conversion rates for coarse foods, thereby recovering their capital cost through improved profitability. Farmers should view the capital cost of a building as a contribution towards higher productivity on the farm. The buildings must be designed to suit the farming system, considering especially whether the enterprises are managed on an intensive or extensive system. The capital costs will be high in intensive housing, but the labour and feed costs should be low. The throughput should be integrated to suit a planned marketing policy. Though individual farmers may have buildings for livestock managed on an intensive system, as part of their farming activities, there is no reason why livestock cannot be managed in units by industrial farmers owning only sufficient land for the layout of the buildings. Intensive livestock systems can be managed as an industrial project divorced from farm land and with purchased feeding-stuffs. (Ch. 3, p. 8.) This can be true in pig and poultry production, and to some extent with beef cattle housed on a feed-lot basis. Dairy cattle, though related more naturally to the fields, can be housed permanently within buildings, and these buildings could be erected as an industrial project to suit a syndicate of smaller farmers.

Buildings owned by syndicates of farmers are discussed in Chapter 9. In addition, it is important to appreciate that contract farming will increase during the next few years. More produce will be grown, reared or fattened by farmers under contract to an established market. On this basis, the investment in farm buildings becomes relevant to the contract. Building design and feeding policies are of vital importance in the even grading of livestock for modern markets demanding produce which is of a constant and specified quality available at regular and specified intervals.

Estimating building costs cannot be an exact science. A price is a personal estimate made by a contractor, and it is not a true basis for comparison. Distance from the works, time of year, size of layout, potential markets in the district, degree of competition and access to a site are some of the factors which will influence an estimate, and will cause building prices to vary between farms. Moreover, few buildings are designed to the same specification even if for layouts of identical size and purpose. Since an analysis of building costs is essential in designing farm buildings, the costs which are given are based, unless stated otherwise, on well-constructed buildings of reasonable specification, and erected in normal situations by contract labour. Therefore, cheaper buildings could be erected for the same farming purposes, but not fulfilling the same design requirements. The costs cannot be related directly to the buildings for any particular farm. Unless stated otherwise, costs when quoted exclude the value of any grant which might be allowed[1].

Costs used for comparative purposes can be considered in a number of different ways. The normal method is to consider the capital cost, or the annual building cost, in relation to each agricultural unit either stored, housed, processed or produced. For example, in milk production the cost may be related either to each 'cow place' available within the building or to an estimate of the number of gallons of milk which will be produced. The cost of storage buildings is related usually to each ton of storage space available. Approximate examples of annual building costs, having allowed for grant, which are considered in further detail in Part 3, in some circumstances might be[2]:

£15 per dairy cow place or $3\frac{1}{2}d$. per gallon of milk produced

£12 per sow farrowing place or 2s. per weaner reared

£1½ per fattening pig place or 10s. per bacon pig produced

£1¾ per ton of grain stored.

However, a building designer must make comparisons using other units of cost in addition to the agricultural units. The capital cost can be divided by the aggregate area of usable floor space, omitting all wall thicknesses. Thus, cattle housing might cost £¾ per ft² (i.e. £45 per cow place if 60 ft²/cow is allowed), but pig housing might cost £1½ per ft² (i.e. £18 if 12 ft²/fattener is allowed). The latter will be an insulated building, and the volume will be as important as the floor area. A well-designed house having only 80 ft³ of space per pig would cost 4½s./ft³ on the same basis. Similarly, the capital cost can be divided into the 'building elements', such as the floor, the walls, the roof, the services, etc. This is useful when comparing different types of construction. For example, it is possible to calculate the cost of 1 yd² of floor taking into account excavation, hardcore, concrete, falls and finish, and then compare it to other types of floor, such as those which are insulated (Vol. 2).

Since, as has been stated, there are many different farming systems suitable for any one enterprise, it is impossible to design 'optimum' buildings which will both give the maximum return on capital invested and be satisfactory on any farm

(Chapter 3). However, in the national interest, as well as in that of individual farmers, it is desirable that there should be greater standardization in unit size and in building design, especially since it seems certain that capital investment will continue at a rate of £30M to £40M per annum.

(1) NIX, J. S. 'Capital Investment in Farm Buildings'. Farm Buildings Association Conference Report. (March 1961).

(2) INGERSENT, K. A. & MANNING, P. 'New Housing for Dairy Cows in the East Midlands'. University of Nottingham. Department of Agricultural Economics (October 1960).

---

[1] When considering the cost of building, it must be remembered that in some sectors of the building industry costs are rising by as much as 10 per cent per annum, though it is probably true that in much of farm building 5 per cent is the average increase. Generally, in the text, costs for building quoted may be considered as those prevailing in the early part of 1964.

[2] For a more detailed study of the annual building costs in relation to livestock production, see the Appendix, p. 251.

CHAPTER 2

Farm Enterprises and Their Buildings

Every farmer must sell at least one product from his farm in order to maintain a living. The activities or operations necessary for each product sold from a farm constitute an enterprise, and the term 'activity' is used to define the series of actions performed by one or more persons within a single defined space and for a specified purpose (1). Normally, the management of a farm is based on more than one enterprise, since usually more than one type of product is sold. The traditional pattern of mixed farming encouraged farmers to have diverse interests, maintaining several enterprises even on small farms. This made it possible to intensify or slacken production in each enterprise to suit fluctuating demands of trade. If one enterprise failed in any year there was a chance that the loss might be balanced by profits from other enterprises.

Part of the economic struggle in post-war agriculture has been between the general farmer, maintaining many different systems of farming, and the specialist farmer who concentrates his resources, in some cases, in order to achieve only one product. The traditional farmer produced from his land as much as possible of the raw material required for each enterprise. In this manner the cost of production was not controlled by factors external to the farm. This approach gave a balanced use of the land, whereby the fields were used in rotation for different purposes, which, in turn, helped to maintain the soil's fertility.

The change to specialized farming has been slower in Britain than in some countries. This has been due partly to the conservative tendencies of traditional farmers, but principally to economic hazards over which the farmer has had no control. There is a natural reluctance to being committed to only one source of income in an industry which has been subjected to sudden and fluctuating changes in world trade and in government policy.

However, experience gained in modern industry and trade indicates that it is essential to specialize when producing for modern markets. This is true in agriculture as well as in other industries. Specialization reduces the cost of administration and of general managerial overheads. It makes it possible to employ a smaller labour force of highly paid and experienced specialists, instead of general labourers; and expensive specialist machinery may be justified to give a high level of productivity per man. The specialist farmer may not attempt to produce his own raw materials, relying instead on his increased farm productivity to justify buying the materials required, even though these may be relatively expensive compared with the cost of producing them himself if he had a mixed farm. Dexter and Barber have illustrated by example that a simple farming system with few enterprises makes it possible for a farmer to keep abreast of new technical advances, and, by intensifying production, to reduce the unit costs of production (2).

It is acknowledged by many farm economists that most farmers still have too many enterprises to be able to keep their unit cost of production to a level competitive with imported produce, even bearing in mind political and trade fluctuations. However, whatever number of enterprises are undertaken by a farmer, each one should be based on several, clearly defined activities required in the development of the final product. Not only is there a tendency for farmers to have too many enterprises, but for the activities on the farm not to be differentiated clearly between each enterprise. This makes the economics of production confused, and it becomes difficult to design buildings which will be a suitable investment.

The production of straw can be a typical example of an activity which may confuse the simplicity of a farming system. A farmer with cattle as one of his enterprises may grow grain to provide straw for bedding the livestock during the winter months. It becomes necessary in this case to collect, transport and store the straw, to distribute it to the livestock, and to lift, transport and spread the subsequent manure on the fields. Moreover, grain production is subject to its own economic laws with regard to land use, cropping and mechanization, and it may seem desirable to dry and store the grain on the farm in order to obtain a better market price. Capital investment and farm resources could become dissipated in fixed equipment, machinery, husbandry techniques and labour, which are uneconomic when related to the scale and throughput of the individual enterprises. It is not sufficient justification to have grain on the basis that its straw can be used to provide manure from the livestock and that the manure will benefit the grassland supporting the cattle. By buying straw, or by using other techniques for bedding, it might have been possible to concentrate the farm resources into the main enterprise, thereby increasing the overall profits. Conversely, concentration on grain production might have shown it to be more profitable to eliminate the livestock from the farm, though grain must be balanced by a crop rotation. This study is not a treatise on crop production of farming systems in the field. However, it is essential that a building designer should question the relevance of each activity, prescribed by a farmer, as being essential to a building layout or necessary to the farm as a whole.

The number and scope of the activities within each enterprise will not be similar on all farms yielding the same product. Any enterprise can be managed by one of several techniques of husbandry, each of which might be suitable for the conditions on a particular farm. The choice of production technique will depend on decisions of farm management policy and each technique may require a different sequence of activities. This makes it difficult to establish precise information concerning the design of farm buildings, since each enterprise can be managed within one of a variety of layouts suitable for attaining the same end product, each layout being suitable for a different management policy combining a different sequence of activities.

For example, beef production is one of the livestock fattening enterprises. A farmer may fatten young stores, which he has not reared, entirely with bought-in feeding-stuffs and within a slatted-floor layout. In this case, the enterprise might be based on only three, clearly defined activities, including the storage of the bought-in foods, the feeding of the cattle, and the storage and disposal of the waste products. The building required to suit these activities is relatively simple. Alternatively, a farmer may feed his stores on grass or grass products, such as hay or haylage, as well as on home-grown cereals, and he may use straw for their bedding. This system of beef fattening will require buildings to suit not only the cattle but also the subsidiary activities of grain drying, storing, milling and mixing, together with the storage of the grass products and of straw. Moreover, this system will require additional machinery, with its related storage and maintenance. There are many permutations of layout which will suit these inter-related activities, since the basic housing of the cattle can be in a totally enclosed building, or it may include open exercise yards in addition to the bedded areas. Similarly, food can be distributed in several different ways.

Each variation of management policy will require a different sequence of activities, thereby fundamentally affecting the basis of the design which will be most suitable for the enterprise. For this reason, it is better to study the different activities rather than to give a description of each enterprise with all the numerous variations which may occur to suit different management policies. There are many ways in which the activities might be examined in order to give data to facilitate the design of farm buildings. The farmer normally will think in terms of grouping the activities within the requirements for each enterprise. As has been shown, this will lead to some confusion due to the differences between farmers in managing each enterprise. It is the intention of this study to group the activities within their basic functions, irrespective of the enterprises which they are designed to serve.

The basic function of farm buildings may be for one of three purposes. All farm activities which concern buildings will be for:

   I. Storing foods, materials and equipment
  II. Processing foods or materials to improve their quality or to change their physical state
 III. Converting coarse foods into foods for human consumption.

Some enterprises, such as cabbage growing, may require no buildings other than a general storage shed for implements; others, such as milk production, directly or indirectly may require a complex of buildings. The buildings required for some of the activities within various enterprises may have their function limited to requirements arising from the internal needs on a farm, particularly when more than one activity is required in the production of a final article for sale. For example, a building required to store silage is not related directly either to the sale of milk or of cattle for slaughter, but is used for subsidiary activities within those enterprises.

The storage of food, materials and equipment is required in one form or another for all the enterprises. It is a basic function on all farms, and some of the storage buildings, such as hay or straw barns, may be required for more than one enterprise. However, it must be realized that storage is a form of inactive capital, and it should be included only when there are definite financial benefits. Inadequate or misplaced storage can be wasteful of resources, and some materials may be bought and stored more cheaply out of season.

The buildings in which foods or materials are processed may be related closely either to the storage buildings or those in which coarse foods are converted into food for human consumption. For example, grain drying may take place within or near its point of storage, and milk extraction and storage can be within the same building in which hay and grain are converted into milk. However, in the processing of foods and materials, to improve their quality or to change their physical state, the machinery required for one process may be required in others. One fan may be suitable for drying grain, grass, hay and for ventilating potatoes; and milling and mixing grain machinery may be required for all the livestock enterprises.

The conversion of coarse foods into those for human consumption, even though these may be processed further in factories off the farm, includes all the livestock enterprises, but has a common requirement in that the food conversion ratio is important. The basic function of converting coarse foods may include the subsidiary activity of rearing the young animals which will be used in the process of obtaining meat or dairy produce. It might even be argued that this is in fact a fourth activity, especially since many farmers rear animals for sale for others to fatten.

No analysis of the requirements for farm buildings can be either complete or entirely satisfactory, due to the lack of uniformity in the production techniques, which means that many permutations of the basic layouts can all prove satisfactory. However, a study of the requirements for the basic functions in each enterprise, whether they have to be included or not in any particular scheme, shows a greater uniformity for presenting design data than a study of the enterprises. This is discussed in detail in the introduction to Part 3.

(1) *Architects' Journal Design Guides* planned for 1962–6 giving data for all building types, including a study of 'activities' common to all building types and of specialized 'activities' unique to each type. Most agricultural activities are unique to farming.

(2) DEXTER, K. & BARBER, D. *Farming for Profits*, pp. 59–65. *Penguin Handbook* (1961).

CHAPTER 3

Specialization and Multi-purpose Buildings

The trend towards specialization was discussed in the last chapter. Specialization can influence building design, since manufacturers can concentrate their resources to make building components, or even complete buildings, designed to precise requirements and based on an analysis of the agricultural functions the building has to enclose. This can lead to efficiency not only in the use of materials, manufacturing processes and site erection, but within the farm enterprises. The latter, in turn, can lead to increased investment in buildings, which is the incentive to manufacturers to improve and to co-ordinate their products. However, the technique of prefabrication, which should eliminate the site cutting of materials as well as all wet construction, has had limited development, and it has been observed that the design of prefabricated farm buildings generally is inferior to that of industrial buildings (1), (Vol. 2). This is true whether prefabrication is used for specialized or for multi-purpose buildings. Prefabrication is discussed in more detail in Chapter 6.

Buildings designed for specialized intensive farm systems need considerable initial capital in order to yield high annual gross returns from raw materials used with maximum efficiency. Specialized buildings, in which full control over the product or commodity within them is obtained, are inevitably more expensive than multi-purpose buildings in which the farm enterprises, using the raw materials less efficiently, yield a lower annual gross return. All other factors being equal, the latter should yield a net return per £ invested less than that from intensive farm systems. However, it may be contended, as a safeguard against price fluctuations, that most of the general farmer's investment in fixed equipment should be concentrated in multi-purpose, flexible and adaptable buildings, even though he may not obtain the maximum return possible from his investment. This viewpoint frequently appeals to landlords, since their capital investment may have to be planned for possible changes in tenancy (2).

This has led to the consideration that the majority of farm buildings should be in the form of a large area covered by asbestos-cement sheeting and supported by as few structural uprights as economically possible. The eaves height at the sides of the building should be between 10 ft and 12 ft, and generally the floor should be of concrete. A building of this design is multi-purpose in that, if required, several alternative activities could be performed within it. It could house most of the storage activities, except perhaps those for haylage and for slurry. It could be suitable for all the processing activities, except for the extraction and storage of milk. It could be used in the conversion of coarse foods, especially in the case of cattle, and to some extent in that of pigs and poultry. Therefore, it is flexible in that these activities can be expanded, contracted or inter-changed within the space covered. It is adaptable in that few modifications need be made to the basic structure to maintain flexibility.

Thus, a building of this kind has been described as an 'umbrella' to cover many farm activities. Such a building, to be successful, should have a central span of between 40 and 60 ft, with a lean-to of up to 30 ft on each side of it. Alternatively, with some extra expense, it might have a single clear span of 70–120 ft (Vol. 2). The length of the building should be between 75 and 150 ft. The walls should be considered as panels between the uprights to the frame, to be erected and dismantled as required in order to contain specific activities within the building.

An example of a building which might be termed an 'umbrella' is given in Figure 1. The building is 120 ft × 120 ft, comprising a central span of 50 ft, and a lean-to on each side of it of 35 ft span. At the south end of the building is accommodation for 100 cattle, with a clamp silo within the central span, with straw storage on top of the silage and with a bedded area for 50 cattle within each lean-to. Within the central span at the north end is a grain unit with 8 bins, each of about 60 tons capacity, complete with intake pit, elevators and drying equipment. The ventilation ducts to the bins can be arranged so that subsidiary ducts could be taken across the floor of each lean-to. These lean-tos can be used to dry and store additional grain in bulk, or for potatoes, or for a combination of various storage activities. Alternatively, additional cattle could be housed within the lean-tos at the north end, or there could be extra storage and fewer cattle at the south end, or extra grain bins could be included.

The building is multi-purpose, flexible and adaptable, and it is a reasonable solution to the general requirements for the various activities.

Moreover, the frame should prove cheaper and more effective than those required had the different activities been housed in separate buildings. A successful building of similar design has been erected in Lincolnshire (3).

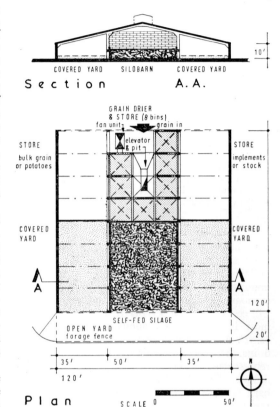

Fig. 1. An 'umbrella' building which is to some extent multi-purpose, flexible and adaptable

Though many farmers could make use of at least one umbrella building, a design of this kind has its own limitations, if agriculture is to be considered an efficient industry. The C.o.I.D. report has shown from a study of existing buildings that a farmer asking for a general-purpose building is unlikely to realize his aim for flexibility, unless his general requirements are studied in detail and the manufacturer briefed with an accurate specification (4). These conditions seldom prevail; and the technical literature provided by manufacturers is considerably inferior to that generally found within the building industry, though even that of the latter is frequently criticized for its poor quality.

The limitations of multi-purpose buildings should be considered:

1. Some activities require the roof to be ventilated, but others are better with an insulated roof.

2. Some buildings should exclude natural light, but others should have rooflights.

3. Some activities require a high unobstructed headroom, but others need the least volume possible.

4. Some activities may need fittings to be attached to the frame, others an unobstructed space.

5. Sometimes there should not be any internal supports, but at other times these may be useful for supporting panels, machinery or services. In some cases, it is better not to have any supports around the perimeter of the building.

6. Some floors need a damp-proof membrane, others should be porous; some should have a fall, but others should be flat; and some surfaces should be rough and others smooth.

7. Some activities need slots, dowels, tunnels, ducts or services in the floor, but others none.

8. Some walls need foundations, but others can rest on the floor.

9. Some walls have to withstand lateral thrusts, others vertical loads and some may be light-weight panels. The economic spacing of the frame uprights will vary in each case.

The benefits derived from a general-purpose building tend to be misleading, since the building may serve no purpose efficiently. It is important to relate these disadvantages to the economics of the investment. The frame and roof will cost only about £$\frac{1}{3}$ per ft^2 covered, which at most is equal to an annual building cost of 1s./ft^2. A concrete floor with 4 ins. concrete on 6 ins. hardcore, suitable for general purposes, represents another 2s./ft^2, or only 3$\frac{1}{2}$d./ft^2 p.a. Simple, sheeted walls at the sides and end of a barn 90 ft × 90 ft × 10 ft to the eaves might represent another 2d./ft^2 p.a., whereas perimeter walls of 9 ins. blockwork 10 ft high and with sheeted gables might equal 6d./ft^2 p.a. An annual building cost of between 1$\frac{1}{2}$s. and 2s. per ft^2 will be but a small part of the total annual costs required for any enterprise. It is possible to design a general-purpose building of this kind which will be capable of housing two or more enterprises at one time, and which may give some economy in the structure. Such a building may be, to some extent, flexible and adaptable. However, planning a building to be suitable for unspecified future changes in farm management policy may mean that it will be inefficient in its structure and layout for the immediate needs. The sacrifice may prove to be valueless, especially considering depreciation over ten years, though it is possible for successful planning to suit a long-term policy of specified change and expansion. In some cases a small increase in efficiency may be sufficient to cover the additional cost of a specialized building above that of a general-purpose structure. For example, a fattening house for baconers justifies an extra £4 per pig place provided the food conversion rate is lowered by 0·1, a factor discussed in Chapter 1. Part 3 examines the specialized buildings designed to suit the requirements for each farm activity. It will be seen that there are few activities which can be performed as successfully in a multi-purpose building as in one planned for a specialized purpose, directed and controlled in all its parts. The size, design and siting of the specialized building probably should be governed by the requirements of the enterprise. The enterprise, in turn, should be governed by the farm system to suit the land, labour, physical resources and capital available. It is unlikely that co-ordination and control could be obtained as effectively within a general-purpose building as within a specialized building, but the former could be justified if the net return from each £ invested should prove to be the greater, but industrial experience indicates this to be improbable. Moreover, it might be argued that the nation should not allow its raw materials to be used wastefully, but should make capital available to conserve its agricultural resources and to reduce the need for imports. This is relevant, in particular, to the conversion ratios for coarse foods, which depend on good buildings in order not to be excessive.

(1) 'Report on Prefabricated Farm Buildings', Council of Industrial Design, p. 2 (Autumn 1962).
(2) LONG, D. 'Basic units to last on larger farms', *Farmers Weekly*, pp. 84–85 (29th Mar. 1963).
(3) LONG, D. 'The accent is on flexibility', *Farmers Weekly*, pp. 80–81 (12th Apr. 1963).
(4) C.o.I.D. Report. Ibid., p. 3.

SELECTED REFERENCE
a. 'Multi-combination Farm Building Design Interim Report'. Agric. Engng. St. Joseph, Mich., pp. 545–7 (Aug. 1956).

CHAPTER 4

Skilled Labour

Since the war labour has continued to leave the land. It has become critical that the farmer should plan his labour force in relation to the work content of his enterprises.

In traditional arable farming, certain seasons of the year, such as harvest, caused a peak demand on farm labour, and the farmer maintained a labour force large enough to handle that demand. At other seasons, there would be surplus labour on the farm, which enabled such tasks as hedging, ditching, cleaning yards and carting feeding-stuffs to be done by hand. With this slack labour available, it was seldom profitable for a farmer to have a fully mechanized building in order to eliminate some of the work content of an enterprise.

The specialist farmer aims to plan his farm so that there are no disproportionate periods of heavy demand on his labour, except in some cases, such as pea-picking, when seasonal labour can be employed. Therefore on the specialized farm there will be a small labour force; most of the men will be specialists with very few general labourers. The farmer can pay his labour well, which in some districts is essential to prevent the men leaving for higher industrial wages.

In the mid-1950s, Sturrock and Brayshaw (1), investigating traditional farms, showed that tending livestock in buildings accounted for about half the man-hours spent in British farming, and that up to 90 per cent of the stockman's time was spent in feeding, littering and cleaning, if special operations like milking and egg collection were excluded. Therefore, drudgery, rather than stockmanship, accounted for much of farm work, and frequently this was carried out in remarkably poor physical conditions. Moreover, labour is one of the major farm expenses, accounting on average for 15–30 per cent of total costs (2). The efficient use of labour is therefore important.

The nature of farm work has to be considered in relation to two factors. The population working in agriculture represents only 4 per cent of the total working population, whereas in no other country is the percentage less than 10 (3). Secondly, the Agricultural Returns for March 1962 showed that the employed labour force of regular workers in England and Wales numbered 372,000, whereas in 1945 it was 549,000, showing an annual decline of about 10,000, and, moreover, Clark (4) has said that this regular farm staff could be cut to 150,000. More important, perhaps, is the fact that nearly three-fifths of farms employ no labour; and, of the 162,000 farms that employ full-time workers, 67,000 employ only one full-time man, and another 60,000 only two or three men with fewer than 7,000 farms employing ten men or more. Moreover, the land farmed per male agricultural worker in Britain is far higher than in other European countries. On a rough calculation of one arable acre being equivalent to two acres of permanent pasture and four of rough grazing, land farmed is about equal to 30 acres per man, compared with 22 in France, 20 in Denmark and 13 in Western Germany (5).

Minimum wages and average earnings of farm labour, being £10. 2s. and about £13½ per week respectively, are considerably less than comparative industrial wages, and this is not in itself an attraction to work on the land. But a skilled man on a specialized farm can receive wages as attractive as in many industries, taking into account his basic wage, incentive schemes and such assets as cheap housing. The recognized differential between agricultural and industrial wages is likely to be reduced during the next few years.

The effect on farm building design of a smaller labour force commanding a higher wage will be of fundamental importance in this decade. There is a trend towards buildings for specialized enterprises of sufficient size to be managed by one skilled man or by multiples of skilled men. This is emphasized particularly in animal husbandry. As the size of livestock units become greater, the skill and organizing ability of stockmen become more valuable. It is probable that even today a skilled stockman managing a large unit is worth £1000 p.a. including overtime and incentive schemes. Nearly 15 per cent of cowmen averaged over £15 per week in the July to September period of 1961 (6). A few earn up to £24 per week (7). Planning livestock buildings for the future should be based on the skilled operator costing the farmer at least £1500 and probably £2000 p.a. This might be assessed on the man receiving £1000 including an incentive scheme and overtime, plus a subsidized house worth up to £200, and perhaps with farm overheads for his work including his insurance, secretarial help and occasional management supervision or direction worth up to £400. It must be assumed that the future worker will have a 40-hour 5-day week, and

11

that a relief worker to manage the enterprise for the remaining 120 days will cost up to £400.

Therefore, in order to absorb the cost of skilled labour, productivity per man is becoming a crucial factor on the farm. It is important to appreciate that the skilled man may be managing an enterprise within buildings which cost £20,000, and with livestock, feeding-stuffs and machinery worth at any time another £20,000. With the assessment of fixed and running costs at this level, the skill of the stockman cannot be dissipated either in drudgery or in enterprises in which the stockman is less skilled. Enterprises, and the buildings for them, must be designed to suit a cowman, or a pigman, or a shepherd, or a poultryman, but not a general stockman, and they must be of sufficient size to allow the maximum throughput to equal the maximum productivity possible.

The skilled man might be helped by part-time assistance, but only if the assistant can be made available from other duties at planned times. For example, a man with a tractor may be made available from his normal work in the fields to assist in moving fodder for a livestock enterprise. This might be organized as a specified job to take place at a fixed time either every day or every week. However, if there is a possibility that at some peak time of the year the tractor and man cannot be spared from urgent work in the fields, then the system is unlikely to be satisfactory. It would be better for the livestock enterprise to be mechanized sufficiently to enable the skilled livestock man to manage without part-time help. Moreover, the stockman's time must be planned so that the relief worker, taking over in his absence, will have only the daily routine to perform, whereas all the jobs which have to be done once a week or once a month are carried out by the skilled man. In a few cases it is becoming the practice for two or three farmers to combine in the employment of an extra man, whose time can be shared and who can act as the relief worker. Other workers are available for employment on a 'locum tenens' basis. Large estates, with several herds on different farms, can employ their own relief worker.

Most farm buildings, with the exception of some of those designed for grain or potatoes, are directly or indirectly required for the livestock enterprises. No livestock enterprise will be successful unless it is designed to be managed for at least one-quarter, perhaps one-third, of each year by a relief worker. The buildings must be designed to eliminate drudgery, in order to give the maximum time to stockmanship, to give good working conditions and to allow a high level of productivity. The size of the enterprise will be governed by the labour force. One skilled man may work alone, or he may have a semi-skilled part-time or full-time assistant for specific jobs. Alternatively, there may be two

skilled men, and the unit must be designed to employ both men. A skilled man is entitled to skilled wages, and there is no point in using him for unskilled work in order to keep him fully employed.

The size of the enterprise will be governed also, to some extent, by the size of the farm. Whereas, traditionally, one dairy cow was maintained from 2 acres of land, good grassland may reduce this to 1¼ acres, and a few farmers have managed with ¾ acre per cow.

Similarly, grassland can be improved for beef cattle. Pigs and poultry, and even beef cattle, can be managed indoors with bought feeding-stuffs, thereby requiring no more land than that needed for the buildings. It is uneconomic to employ a skilled stockman if his productivity is restricted by the limited capacity of the land. If the enterprise is to be maintained, then the farming system must fully justify the employment of the skilled stockman.

The size of unit to give the maximum productivity and throughput per skilled stockman is difficult to assess, and in any case, is being rapidly revised due to modern changes in farming. Yard and parlour units planned a few years ago for up to 60 cows, and considered efficient being managed by one man (8), now could be designed to hold 80–90 cows, and even a few larger units have been considered. Buildings for dairy production, perhaps, should be designed for units that could be expanded up to 100 cows per man. Milking would have to take place at a rate of at least 50 per hour, and three-quarters of the cowman's time would be in the parlour and dairy. A unit of this size might justify mechanical feeding arrangements. Calf-rearing may become an enterprise in its own right in many more cases than envisaged today. In a pig enterprise one man could manage 70 or 80 sows and their progeny fattened for bacon or pork. In fattening houses, complete with mechanical equipment for feeding and cleaning, one man could manage up to 2000 pigs. Such high levels of productivity depend on good management as well as good buildings. The size of unit will be discussed further in Part 3.

Within recent years there has been a trend to use skilled labour on contract. Usually, this has been for seasonal work, especially in the harvesting of grain when the combine harvester and other tackle represent considerable capital. Sometimes contract work is extended to include other field work. It is possible, perhaps even economic, for a farmer to contract out all his field work. More recently there has been a trend to include livestock husbandry in contract work, especially for the milking of a dairy herd. Terms vary, but may be based on 6d. per gallon (9). If this practice becomes prevalent, as it might, then the design of buildings could be profoundly affected.

(1) STURROCK, F. G. & BRAYSHAW, G. H. 'Planning the farm to save labour', *University of Cambridge, Farm Economics Branch Report No. 47*, p. 4 (1958).

(2) STURROCK, F. G. 'Planning farm work', *Ministry of Agriculture Bulletin No. 172*, p. 1 (1960).

(3) MCCRONE, G. *Economics of Subsidising Agriculture*, p. 24. Allen & Unwin (1962).

(4) *Farmers Weekly*, p. 71 (3rd Aug. 1962).

(5) 'Farm Labour costs and the Common Market', *Land*, No. 13, p. 42 (Autumn 1962).

(6) 'Agriculture', *The Times*, 4th June 1962.

(7) 'Farming Notes', *Country Life*, p. 867 (11th Oct. 1962).

(8) NIX, J. S., BELSHAW, D. G. R. & WELLER, J. B. 'The yard and parlour', *University of Cambridge, Farm Economics Branch Report No. 58* (1962).

(9) HEYWOOD, C. 'Cowman under Contract', *Farmers Weekly*, p. 95 (11th Dec. 1964).

SELECTED REFERENCES

a. STURROCK, F. G. 'Planning farm work', *Bulletin No. 172*. Ministry of Agriculture (1960).

b. *The Farm as a Business*. Section M. Ministry of Agriculture (1958).

c. CAMM, B. M. 'Farm planning data.' Farm Economics Branch School of Agriculture. Section D. Cambridge (1962).

CHAPTER 5

Mechanization and Building

The Ministry of Agriculture has published a series of pamphlets, following its Post-War Building Study on Farm Buildings in 1945, concerning different aspects of farm buildings. The series is titled 'Fixed Equipment of the Farm'. It is important to appreciate that, to the farmer, a farm building is similar to any other equipment on the farm, except that it is fixed. Because it is fixed, the farmer may consider it less flexible and desirable than his other machinery.

On the modern farm it is difficult sometimes to establish what is a building, in the traditional sense, and what is a machine Some structures are clearly in the nature of a building, having frames, walls of cladding or of blockwork and roofs of asbestos-cement. Other structures, made of sheet metal and with machinery attached, may appear to be machines. In some cases, both structural types may serve the same purpose. For example, grain can be stored in prefabricated bins erected inside a barn or in bulk directly on the barn floor. These would be grain storage buildings. But prefabricated bins can be single-skin units, supporting their own roof as an integral part of the bin, and with mechanism for filling and emptying attached as part of the unit. Similar in technique, but more pronounced, are the vertical steel silos for grass or grain, glass lined, hermetically sealed and completely mechanized in use. But grass can be stored in clamps within a modern barn.

Each building should be a structural and mechanical solution to an agricultural problem. Each problem should be analysed to establish the real requirements. In such cases the building may become a piece of mechanical equipment. However, it is doubtful whether too much emphasis should be placed on the term 'fixed equipment' to define an agricultural building. Both the farmer and the designer of his equipment should be interested in the farming process or activity, and it is perhaps a limitation to consider that any particular activity must be undertaken with fixed equipment. Milking may take place both within a fixed parlour and within a portable bail. Hay can be dried within a barn, either with a fixed or a portable fan unit, or in the fields with a portable fan unit. Similarly, meal, which is prepared normally within a barn, can be delivered to or handled on a farm with a lorry plus a built-in mixer, not unlike pre-mixed concrete vehicles. Grass may be harvested and chopped in the fields, or it may be chopped at the buildings prior to storage.

All farm buildings are equipment, even if they are not actually machines. However, some buildings will have machinery integrated with the structural components. In grain drying and storage, for example, the ducts to circulate the air, together with the control mechanism, may be an integral part of the bins. In other buildings the machinery will be attached superficially to the structure, as with the equipment for milking or with the rotating cutters suspended from the dome of a tower silo. In addition, most farm buildings have to be designed for working in conjunction with unfixed machinery.

Machinery is used to process materials in order to change their physical state or to improve their quality. Machines extract milk from a cow and cool it for safe storage. Other machines will remove unwanted moisture from grain or grass, or will mill and mix grain to form meal. Such processes, and their effect on building design, are discussed in Part 3, Section II. However, most machines used within or between buildings are used to transport materials, and these are discussed in Part 2.

The mechanical handling of materials is the crux of all modern farm design. No farm process or activity can be planned without making a detailed study of the requirements and machinery for handling materials within that process. Moreover, the farming system should be based on a co-ordinated policy for the mechanical handling methods used for all the different activities.

The Scottish Agricultural Industries Ltd. have studied the quantities of materials which have to be transported on traditional 100-acre farms (1). (Part 2, I.2.) Sturrock analysed the transport which might be required on a traditional mixed farm within its farmyard, and showed how an improved layout could reduce the daily transportations of food, litter and manure, from 17 to 2 by increasing the occasional transportations from 10 to 14 (2). On a specialist farm, all movement of materials can be achieved by a push-button technique. Few farms are mechanized to this extent, and the majority rely on handling materials with unfixed machinery which need a man to operate them, such as a tractor or a portable auger. Mechanical handling should not only control the building layout but also the detailed designs.

Since the mechanical handling of materials is the basis of all farm building design, Part 2 of this study is devoted to it. Thus, mechanical handling is considered before a detailed study is made of each of the specialized buildings, and the latter are referred back to Part 2 as required. However, Part 2 cannot attempt to give an assessment of the mechanical efficiency of the different machinery. This would be a vast subject requiring its own detailed research and study. It is possible to consider handling as the basic, functional requirement occurring in all layouts, and to study the materials which have to be handled, together with the journeys they have to make, in relation to the methods available for transportation. Any handling requirements particular to individual buildings, or the effect of the general requirements in each case, are considered in Part 3.

It must be remembered that farm machinery is backed by considerable research at a national level and at that of individual manufacturers. Such institutes as the National Institute of Agricultural Engineering and the National Institute for Research in Dairying do much to test machinery and to introduce prototypes. Numerous institutes or groups carry out work into animal physiology, feeding techniques and work routines. The research undertaken is to some extent related to building design, construction and materials, and is to a limited degree co-ordinated by the A.R.C. (Chapter 10). It is not surprising that those farm buildings most akin to machinery generally prove to be the most efficient in specification and in use. Buildings which are manufactured and erected entirely by one firm tend to have the building components co-ordinated to a greater degree than those which are erected piecemeal by different contractors, unless an independent designer gives considerable time to the project. However, anyone connected with the design of farm buildings is aware that the fixing of one material to another is wasteful of material and labour due to an unco-ordinated approach to the manufacture and erection of the building components.

Though mechanical handling of materials has transformed farm work methods in the last decade, mechanization has had only a limited effect on the structural design of farm buildings. Building, as well as farming, must become more scientific in its approach. This is considered in the next chapter.

(1) FLEMING, I. J. & CUNNINGHAM, J. D. 'Materials Handling on the Farm', Scottish Agricultural Industries Ltd. *A.W.S. Reports.* (1960).
(2) STURROCK, F. G. & BRAYSHAW, G. H. 'Planning the Farm to Save Labour', University of Cambridge. *Farm Economics Branch Report No. 47*, p. 4. (1958).

CHAPTER 6

Building Techniques and Specification

The design, specification, manufacture and erection of farm buildings are in their infancy. Farm buildings are not unique in this respect. All building types are in a state of flux due to the increased demand for building which has arisen from the changing needs of society.

In building, as in farming, the planned use of labour is vital if production costs are to be kept to the minimum, especially since the cost of labour is continually increasing. Work on building sites must be restricted in order to prevent waste of time due to bad weather, and to reduce the cost of transporting workmen to and from the site. This factor is particularly important in rural building. All spheres of the building industry require building components which are co-ordinated in size within a module, prefabricated in units for easy transportation and designed for simple erection on a site. Normally, it is assumed that work below ground and for the floor will require traditional sitework, since for small projects it is not easy to prefabricate many of the building components required for these parts, though prefabricated foundations have been the subject of some research.

It is surprising that the prefabrication of farm buildings has had little co-ordination (Chapter 10). Many farm buildings are of framed construction, and most are prefabricated to some extent—if a loose definition is accepted for the term 'prefabrication'. A prefabricated building should be designed so that no materials need be altered after delivery to the site. All cutting, shaping and drilling of the components should be carried out in the factory. The number of site operations should be kept to the minimum, being limited to an assembly of prepared components.

The interim report prepared for the Council of Industrial Design, referred to in Chapter 3, has indicated some of the limitations within the available prefabricated frame components (*b*). Ex-amples of lack of co-ordination between the components for farm buildings are without number. Though the term 'prefabricated' buildings is used, it is generally a misnomer.

The normal building frame is spaced at 15-ft centres. The basic covering width of asbestos-cement roof sheets is 3 ft 4 in. centres, which is a suitable module for frames spaced at 10-ft or 20-ft centres, or, if required, at 13 ft 4 in. or 16 ft 8 in. Therefore, the two most commonly used farm-building components are unrelated to each other. Moreover, bolting the roof to the frame is a complicated process. A roof slope of 18 ft at a single bay spacing of 15 ft will require five purlins fixed at each end to the frame, ten roof sheets with a total of forty fixings on to the purlins, each fixing being composed of a bolt, washer and cap and including a hole drilled through the sheet. If frames are required at 15-ft centres it would seem desirable for the roof cover to be in panels 15 ft long, complete with sheeting and purlins ready for fixing to the frame. Many frames require wall sheeting. Prefabricated wall panels, 15 ft long, could be available with a choice of material suitable for different situations, either asbestos-cement, or galvanized iron, or various types of timber boarding or plywood, and these panels could be interchangeable on standard frames.

Insulated roofs and walls could be in prefabricated panels. The present method is wasteful, since normally a base sheet is fixed, followed by a damp-proof membrane, followed by insulation, and followed finally by a top sheet, each requiring a separate site operation. The provision of openings for ventilation, doors or windows, and the fixing of downpipes and of machinery, mainly depend on elaborate sitework, though these could be integrated with the design of frames and panels.

Most farm buildings probably could be prefabricated. At present, sitework is required for most walls which have to withstand horizontal thrusts either from livestock or from stored materials. However, prefabricated storage buildings are available, and a prefabricated milking parlour has been marketed. The main requirement is for greater co-ordination between the manufacturers of the existing building materials and components. This has been emphasized by the C.o.I.D. report.

The design and specification for a farm building will depend on the accuracy of management control within the enterprise justified by the economics of food production. Control will be required over both the physical and chemical state of the processes concerned and over the work routines for the enterprise. Circulation of men, machines and materials must be planned to establish the best work method. The labour force will be assisted by mechanization, and the level of mechanization justified must be related to the productivity per man. This design process is no different from that required for any industrial building, except that it will be influenced by whether the investment is made by an owner farmer, by a landlord or by a tenant. Their differences of attitude will be expressed in their budgets for capital and maintenance expenditure, and for fixed and portable equipment. Such factors determine the standard of construction required and should be ascertained at the outset of the design process.

The standard of construction required is difficult to assess. It is true that the cost of a farm building generally is depreciated over a period of ten years. However, it is impossible to design a building which will fulfil its functional requirements, but have a useful life of only ten years. Most modern farm buildings will have a useful life, as far as their materials and construction are concerned, of at least one generation. Building frames, and some buildings, may have a life span of fifty to one hundred years. However, it is possible to consider the economics of a building life on the basis of a short-, a medium- or a long-term investment, and this could influence the standard of construction required.

A building erected on a short-term investment policy lasting, perhaps, for 10–15 years without collapse, might be required as a temporary expedient prior to a major farm reorganization. Construction for this purpose could be mainly from second-hand materials, perhaps with the use of farm labour, with the capital cost kept to the minimum. The building would be unlikely to present an efficient solution to the farming requirements, nor would it conserve the farm resources. Buildings of this nature are likely to be designed with spans of under 20 ft, which is a planning limitation, since buildings with wider spans, perhaps between 30 and 60 ft, must be constructed in order to maintain stability using methods which inherently will last considerably more than a decade.

Normal standards of construction, with reasonable use, result in most buildings still being reasonably sound even, perhaps, after 30 years. Hard usage might mean that some parts of the building would have to be repaired or replaced before that time. It must be appreciated that little extra capital cost may be required to give a building an effective life of 60 rather than of 20 years, and that the annual building cost would be probably considerably less if depreciation for the former was assessed over 20 years rather than over 10 years for the latter. Even an asbestos-cement roof in most regions would be reasonably free from defect for 40 years (*f*), and some might last for 60 years without becoming too brittle, provided there was almost no movement within the structure of the building. Therefore, most buildings must be assumed to have an effective life span of up to 30 years, though some buildings, or some parts of a building, could have a long life in excess of 60 years.

It is difficult to relate the potential life of a building to a depreciation period of 10 years or to the knowledge that farming requirements change rapidly every few years. It would prove important for farm building economics if a common module could be used as the basis of design. The latter should be related to the module being developed in the building industry, that is one based on 4 ins., with many components on multiples of 3 ft 4 in. The module should be standard for building components within all three dimensions and the manufacture of the components should allow for prescribed tolerances. As many of the components as possible should be prefabricated and should require the minimum of labour for site erection, being interchangeable for different purposes and positions, thus providing maximum flexibility. In particular, the module for building frames should be related to those for various types of panel and for fixtures and fittings.

Revised British Standards and Codes of Practice, if related specifically to agricultural requirements, together with suitable periods of depreciation for the different activities, could be of immense value in the specification of farm buildings. The lack of suitable structural standards for farm buildings means that many materials are used in the wrong situations, either because they are inadequate or because they are too robust in relation to the intended life of the building. Both the building techniques and the specification of farm buildings need further research (Chapter 10).

SELECTED REFERENCES

a. GEARY, R. 'Work Study Applied to Building', *The Builder* (1962).

b. *Council of Industrial Design. Report on Prefabricated Farm Buildings* (1962).

c. This section is based on articles by the author in *Farm Mechanization*, 'Prefabricated building frames and panels' (March & April 1963).

d. CORKER, E., & DIPROSE, A. 'Modular co-ordination, a modular primer', *The Architects' Journal*, pp. 279–92 (1st Aug. 1962).

e. IREDALE, R. 'Prefabricated building, the Nenk method in operation', *The Architects' Journal*, pp. 569–76 (13th Mar. 1963).

f. Code of Practice. C.P. 143, Pt 6: 1964.

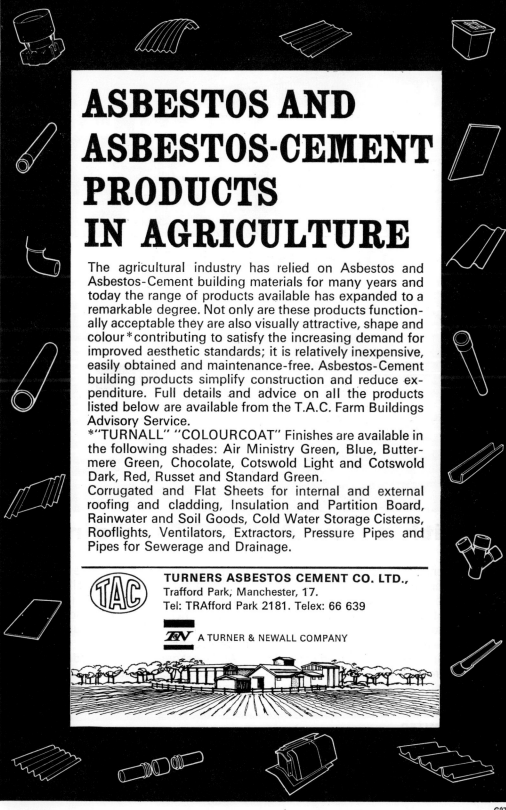

MODERNIZE NOW...

with a new ATCOST building

Atcost understands your needs—how best to meet them quickly and economically. Our wide general practice in farm building is growing steadily, giving you an accumulation of valuable experience for which we don't charge a penny.

We build in pre-cast reinforced concrete. Our structures are long-lasting, maintenance-free and fire-resistant. Our construction methods provide adaptable and quickly erected farm buildings for all purposes. They make the best possible use of your space and help you to apply the new farming techniques which make your operations more economic.

All Atcost quotations are made on a time/cost basis which includes foundations, delivery and erection; and all work is carried out by our own specialized personnel.

ATCOST LIMITED

PADDOCK WOOD, KENT (*Paddock Wood 333*)
ST. IVES, HUNTS (*St. Ives 2491*)
ST. HELEN'S AUCKLAND, CO. DURHAM (*Bishop Auckland 3961*)
100 NORTHGATE STREET, GLOUCESTER (*Gloucester 26861*)
1 MELVILLE TERRACE, STIRLING (*Stirling 2183*)

1: REMOTE CONTROL FROM THE OFFICE

Mr. T. F. Blackwell, Hall Farm, Langham, Suffolk

A farrowing crate is covered by a transistorized television camera and is lit by a floodlight. Farrowings can be watched on a screen either in the farm office or in the home of the pigman. This system can save fatigue, especially for observation during night farrowings, and it is possible that several piglets may be saved per dozen farrowings which otherwise would die due to lack of prompt attention. Television can have other applications in the control of farm operations. [SEE PAGE 90] Courtesy of Pig Farming.

2: STRESSED SKIN CONSTRUCTION

Alton Hall Farm, Holbrook, Suffolk

Most farm buildings depend on prefabrication in their construction and relatively simple forms for their structural frames. However, it is important that individuals should experiment with new structural techniques or adapt those familiar in other building spheres. The hyperbolic paraboloid stressed timber skin, though often used for some types of building, has had little application on farms. In this case, four sections give a clear floor area of 80 ft × 65 ft with good headroom to form a general-purpose building of pleasing appearance in view of the Hall. The roof is formed with three layers of $\frac{3}{4}$-in. boarding with the top course tongued and grooved and fixed above a layer of roofing felt. The boards are laid to curves in two directions and are restrained by 1-ft × 1-ft timber beams at the edges and by 1-ft × $\frac{1}{2}$-ft beams at the internal junction of the four roof sections with transverse straining rods. The roof is supported only by an ex-electrical transmission pole at the apex along each side, one of the four poles being visible. [SEE PAGE 27] Courtesy of C. H. Smith & Partners.

3 & 4: PREFABRICATED PANEL CONSTRUCTION: EXTERIOR AND INTERIOR

Prefabrication of farm buildings is being developed by a number of manufacturers, especially for such specialized buildings as storage silos and pig fattening or poultry houses. Prefabrication of building units will become more prevalent and co-ordination of the units is desirable. Panel wall and roof construction is one aspect of prefabrication and can be developed in timber, concrete, metal or composite materials. Shown in the photographs are 10 ft wide wall panels of deeply corrugated galvanized steel which can have a length, unrestrained laterally except by being bolted to an eaves angle and to foundation bolts, of up to 90 ft by being bolted together. Each panel is assembled on the ground from four 3 ft wide sections, allowing for overlaps to form a panel 10 ft wide, and is lifted into place. Door, window and gable components are available and the roof, also, is formed in panels. Reinforced concrete strip foundations are required for the walls. The roof is braced and supported by a post-and-beam structure, which can be arranged in various ways, though clear spans may be limited in one direction by posts at 30 ft intervals. Wall heights of up to 14 ft are available. [SEE PAGE 15] Courtesy of Butler Buildings (U.K.) Ltd.

CHAPTER 7

Legal Requirements in Building

All building is subject to the law. No new building, conversion or alteration may be made without the fulfilment of certain statutory requirements. In many cases there is a formal procedure enforced to ensure that building work complies with these requirements. Legislation, for the most part, has been made either to protect certain general principles of national planning or to ensure that buildings conform to specified standards of construction. Agricultural buildings, in addition, have to comply with various other Acts because of their specialized use. The principal regulations are listed below.

I. TOWN AND COUNTRY PLAN-NING ACTS

Certain Acts prescribe that permission must be obtained from the County Planning Authority before any building is erected, though, by virtue of an Order of 1950, this is not the general rule as regards the erection of farm buildings, except for certain farm buildings subsequently classified as requiring planning permission. Application for planning permission must be made to the Local Council, who will provide application forms and will state the number of plans required. An 'outline application' can be made, without detailed plans, to find out whether building will be allowed on any particular site before a scheme is prepared.

1. The Town and Country Planning Act, 1947

The Act made it necessary for planning permission to be obtained before any building or engineering operation is carried out, any material change made in the use of buildings or land or any new access made on to a trunk or classified road, and under Section 30 was compiled a list of buildings of interest which require special permission before alteration.

2. The Town and Country Planning General Development Order, 1950
Statutory Instrument 1950. No. 728

Farm Buildings, provided they are for an agricultural unit of more than 1 acre and are designed specifically for the purpose of agriculture, were exempted from the Town and Country Planning Act of 1947 provided that:

1. The height of buildings or works within two miles of the perimeter of an aerodrome does not exceed 10 ft.
2. No part is within 80 ft of the metalled portion of a trunk or classified road.
3. The view of anyone on a road which is used by vehicles is not obstructed.
4. Notice is not served on the owner or occupier of land that other restrictions have been made under Article 4 of the G.D.O.

3. The Town and Country Planning (Landscape Areas Special Development) Order, 1950
Statutory Instrument 1950. No. 729

Local Authorities will advise whether an area has been designated as a special area of beauty, in which planning permission is required before building.

4. The Town and Country Planning Act, 1959, Section 37

The Act made it necessary for all applications for planning permission to be accompanied by certain certificates, to ensure that all owners of land and tenants are given notice of applications relating to their land. The forms for the certificates are obtainable from the Local Councils. This is important, particularly when land is held on a tenancy.

5. The Town and Country Planning General Development Amendment Order, 1960
Statutory Instrument 1960. No. 283

The Order prescribed that all agricultural buildings erected or extended to give a total aggregate area of 5000 ft^2 within 100 yards of one another and erected in any two years require planning permission.

6. The Town and Country Planning Act, 1962

The Act consolidates the statutory requirements of the 1947 Act, together with the many subsequent amendments and variations. The Act describes the procedure for the administration of planning submissions and of appeals against planning orders and refusals.

II. PUBLIC HEALTH ACTS

Under the Health Act of 1936, Local Authorities have made Building Byelaws which are enforceable within each local area and to which all buildings must comply. Model Byelaws were compiled in 1953 with amendments in 1954. All new buildings, extensions, alterations, drainage, services and changes in use must be granted Byelaw approval before building work is started. Application for approval has to be made to the Local Council, who will provide application forms and will state the number of plans required. Though at present each Council formulates its own building Byelaws, there is a possibility that a standard Byelaw may be introduced to provide uniform standards of construction throughout the country. The Public Health Act of 1961 made it necessary to have the consent of the Local Council before farm effluent is discharged into a public sewer, such consent being subject to their conditions and charges, and generally bringing requirements for farm effluent into line with those for trade effluent as contained by the Public Health (Drainage of Trade Premises) Act, 1937.

III. RIVERS (PREVENTION OF POLLUTION) ACTS, 1951
and 1961

Persons responsible for making a discharge of trade effluent from farm buildings must obtain permission from the River Board and adhere to their conditions, before unclean water may be discharged into any ditch or watercourse which eventually drains into a river. Both Acts, and the Public Health Act, 1961, permit a farmer a right of appeal to the Minister of Housing and Local Government. Applications must state the composition, maximum temperature, maximum daily quantities and maximum rate of discharge of the effluent. Discharges commenced before 1951 are covered by legislation within the 1961 Act, enforced from June 1st, 1963, whereas discharges commenced since 1951 are covered in the 1951 Act and in the 1961 Act.

IV. PETROLEUM (CONSOLIDATION) ACT, 1928
also: Petroleum Spirit (Motor Vehicles) Regulations, 1929

The Act makes it necessary for a Licence to be obtained from the Local Council before petrol is stored in excess of 2 gallons, and conditions are made concerning its storage.

V. FOOD AND DRUGS ACT, 1955
The Milk and Dairies (General) Regulations, 1959
Statutory Instruments 1959 No. 277

Part V of the regulations prescribes general provisions relating to buildings and water supplies and Part VI special provisions applicable to the production of milk and the treatment, handling and storage of milk. The regulations prescribe certain finishes to the structure of milking parlours and dairies. Briefly, the principal requirements which affect the building design state that:

1. Those parts of the surface of the floor liable to soiling by cows are to be impervious, to make possible the removal of any liquid matter.
2. The floor is to be sloped and provided with gutters or channels of some impervious material, to ensure that liquids will be conveyed to a suitable drain outside the building.
3. Those parts of the surface of any walls liable to soiling by cows are to be impervious and capable of being readily cleansed.
4. Any room in which milk is handled, processed or stored shall have its floor constructed with an impervious surface sloped to convey liquids to a trapped drain, and shall have any part of its walls liable to splashing by milk smooth and impervious.
5. The milk shall be cooled without delay either to a temperature not exceeding 10° C or, if the temperature of the water supply available for cooling is 8° C or above, to a temperature not more than approximately 2° C above the temperature of that supply. (60° F, 45° F, 5° F respectively).

VI. THE AGRICULTURE (SAFETY, HEALTH AND WELFARE) ACT, 1956

The Act made it possible for the Minister of Agriculture to introduce safety regulations enforceable on all farms, some of which affect building design.

1. The Agriculture (Ladders) Regulations, 1957 and Agriculture (Safeguarding of Workplaces) Regulations, 1959
Statutory Instruments 1957 No. 1385 and 1959 No. 428

'Commonsense' regulations concerning the design of ladders, openings and pits are set out, principally stating that:

1. There should be a handrail on the open side of all stairs which are not less than 3 ft high and not 30 deg. or less from the vertical. If the stairs have two open sides, handrails to both sides are necessary.
2. All enclosed stairways should have at least one handrail.
3. Stairs set at 30 deg. or less should have a handhold at the highest point.
4. Pits or openings in floors more than 5 ft deep should have a rail.

2. The Agriculture (Stationary Machinery) Regulations, 1959
Statutory Instrument 1959 No. 1216

All stationary machinery must be protected by guards so that:

1. A worker is safe from contact with that machinery which includes shafting, pulleys, fly-wheels, gearing, sprockets, chains, belts, blades, feeding inlets and outlets.

2. Every prime mover has a cut-off switch on or near it, with clear indications showing how the machine may be stopped.

3. There is adequate natural or artificial light where a prime mover or machine is used.

SELECTED REFERENCES

a. Ministry of Agriculture. Fixed Equipment on the Farm No. 28. 1956. Procedure for Building and other work on Farms and Estates.

b. Ministry of Agriculture. Farm Safety Regulations. Explanatory Notes. (Various.)

CHAPTER 8

Administration of the Building Contract

Building can be a simple process requiring little administration. A farmer may enjoy the process of designing for his own requirements and of supervising the erection of the building. Occasionally, the farmer may undertake the building work himself. However, a building project may involve considerable work in the consideration of the requirements, the preparation of a sketch plan, final drawings and specification, as well as in the organization and administration of the contract. As outlined in the previous chapter, building is governed by legal requirements in its planning and design. Moreover, the law relating to the contractual relationship between a building owner and a builder can be difficult to interpret. The farmer may prefer to delegate the work to an agent, especially when the project is complex. Usually the latter will be an Architect or Surveyor, but can be an unqualified consultant.

It is important that the normal procedure in building should be understood, whether a farmer manages his own building project or delegates it to an agent. Most farmers review their enterprises during the winter months. At that time ideas formed during the previous season for the development of the farm begin to be considered in detail. The proposed development might be for a small conversion, or it might include a complete reorganization of the farm buildings. Therefore, the time required, from the consideration of the first ideas to the start of work by the builders on the site, can vary considerably.

If the problem is simple the farmer might prepare the design himself or in consultation with a local builder or manufacturer. The latter might offer an 'all-in' service, and the farmer would need to ask only for an estimate and for confirmation of a starting and completion date for the work. However, in order to obtain the best investment, a farmer might seek advice from an independent consultant. Before consultation, the farmer should prepare his brief and, if unsure of his requirements, should list all the basic management factors within the enterprise concerned. The initial design, which might be in the form of a simple line drawing, could take an afternoon or a year, since decisions will be necessary which will govern management, finance and investment policies, and whether a conversion of existing buildings or a new layout would be required. A detailed survey might have to be made, not only of the buildings but of work routines, circulation routes and markets.

Work study, which can be an aid to management, may be of assistance in planning a new or converted layout. It is also essential for basic research in farm-building design (Chapter 10). It can be used as an aid in assessing the economics of a proposed building, to improve work routines, to reduce circulation routes, to save labour, to improve efficiency and to increase throughput and productivity. It can be used to help determine the optimum level of mechanization as an aid to labour. Therefore, it can be of assistance in planning buildings. However, this study is not a work study manual, the principles of work study being described in certain standard works (Ref. a).

The line drawing will be inadequate for obtaining competitive tenders from different builders. A surveyor or architect might produce a detailed drawing and specification within a few days, but a more realistic allowance of about a month should be made for normal schemes, and of two months for major projects. This should allow time to check detail, to make trade enquiries for materials and to have a preliminary meeting with the Ministry of Agriculture, if the scheme is to be submitted for an Improvement Grant (Ch. 9, p. 22). In most cases the drawings should be submitted to the Local Council for Byelaw Approval, and, occasionally, to the County Council for Town and Country Planning Approval (Ch. 7, p. 17). Since these Councils meet once a month, and the application should be made at least one week prior to the meeting, three weeks might normally be the minimum time for approval to be granted, but two months might be required if some minor point required clarification.

While the scheme is before the Council, the specification and detailed drawings should be completed, prices obtained for specialist equipment and builders asked whether they would be interested in tendering for the work. A few farm-building schemes will require a Bill of Quantities. A builder will be justified in asking for a Bill for any scheme valued at more than £8000. However, most builders will be content without one, due to the relatively simple nature of most farm work. Normally, specialist work, such as a frame or milking or grain fittings, can be excluded from the estimate. Large areas of concrete flooring, walling or drainage might be excluded, but if the estimate for the building work requiring the usual tradesman is much over £8000 when these exclusions have been made, and if the work is at all complex, then a Bill should be prepared. A Quantity Surveyor might need three to six weeks for this work on receipt of the drawings and specification. When Council approval has been granted the documents can be given to the builders, allowing two or three weeks for tenders to be prepared. When these are obtained the scheme can be submitted to the Ministry of Agriculture for approval for an Improvement Grant (Ch. 9, p. 22). Though this may be obtained within a week in rare instances, two or three months, occasionally longer, should be allowed, especially with schemes representing a major investment for a modern farmer, who may not be as conservative as the 'Prudent Landlord'. Since the period required to obtain a grant will be unknown, a farmer may find that the builder who gave the lowest price will have taken on other work in the interim period, and several weeks or months might elapse before work can commence on the site.

Four to six months might be a realistic time to allow for most farm-building work from the acceptance of an initial design to the start of the contract. In the case of a standard building, this might be only two to four months. The time required will not depend on the cost of the project. A £1000 scheme might take as long as one of £10,000, but the time required will depend not only on the complexity of the scheme but on the farmer's interest in detail in order to save labour and improve efficiency when the building is in operation. Speed in planning may allow an early completion date, but the usefulness of the building may be impaired, causing waste in the future, excessive in value to that of the time saved.

Before the builders start work the Contract must be established in writing. The exact work required by the builders for their tender must be confirmed. Since the Ministry will have examined the documents, the work should be clear in every detail, even if no consultant has been employed. However, it will be easy for the builders to have excluded from their price items of building, especially around the perimeter of the new work, unless the specification is very detailed. Normally, the drawings, specification, tender and acceptance are the basis of the contract between building owner and builder. If an architect is employed, especially for works of complexity, he may advise that the contract should be based on the standard form of Contract prepared by the Royal Institute of British Architects. This will be a safeguard for all the interested parties, should difficulties arise during the course of the work.

In appointing the Contractors, if more than one is involved, it is important that each should understand the sequence of the work and their responsibility one to another. Frequently, there will be the erector for a frame, a general building contractor, a machinery specialist, such as for a milking parlour, and other specialists, such as an electrician or blacksmith. The frame erector might leave the site before the other contractors have made a start. However, he might rely on the general contractor to prepare the footings and to lay some hardcore on the site. Similarly, the general contractor might not be able to start his work until the erector had finished. The specialists might have to wait until the general contractor had finished, or they might need the general contractor to secure their machinery or the electrician to provide power. If one contractor is delayed, the overall work programme might be upset. Moreover, should any material be damaged on the site, it may be difficult to establish which contractor was at fault.

The General Contractor might be placed in charge of all the contracts. He would be responsible for the work programme and the completion of all the work. The Contractor would expect the quotations from his sub-contractors to include a discount of $2\frac{1}{2}$ per cent to himself, allowing for monthly payments. He would charge another $2\frac{1}{2}$ per cent for his attendance on the sub-contractors and for the use of his plant in their work, and a further $2\frac{1}{2}$ per cent to allow for profit on the work carried out by the sub-contractor, for which he will have taken responsibility. Usually, this $7\frac{1}{2}$ per cent in addition to the basic cost of part of a scheme will prove to be money well spent for the success of the project.

There are few contracts, even when well planned at the start, in which the farmer will not want to make some variations as the work proceeds. Even a simple alteration can affect many craftsmen. Therefore, it is important for all amendments to the contract to be recorded by letter immediately an order has been given, and it is best that the Contractor should confirm his variation of price.

Farm buildings do not justify the employment of a Clerk of Works, nor is an Architect or Surveyor employed as one. Therefore, a builder cannot be supervised in every detail of his work, even if a farmer administers the contract himself. If a farmer has an agent he should establish the approximate number of site visits which the agent would make for his fee. The number required will depend on the nature of the work, and some parts of the contract will require more frequent visits than others. On average, as a rough guide, one visit might be needed for every £1000 value of general building work.

The Contractors will have to be paid during the course of their work, probably at monthly intervals. Payment should be made on the value of work completed, and sometimes for any materials delivered to the site. A sum of 10 per cent of this value is retained, by prior arrangement, in case of defects occurring. When the builder has completed his work a sum of 5 per cent of the total Contract may be withheld, usually for a period of six months, in case of latent defects. The Contractor should submit all his receipts for materials and his detailed accounts, including any variations, and each of these should be checked before payment and before they are submitted to the Ministry for obtaining the Grant. At the end of the maintenance period a final inspection should be made and the last account paid.

SELECTED REFERENCES

N.B. This chapter is based on articles published by the author in *The British Farmer*, 10th February 1962 and 3rd March 1962.

a. CURRIE, R. M. 'Work Study', *British Institute of Management* (1962).
HARVEY, N. 'Farm Work Study—a basic guide', *Farmer and Stockbreeder* (1958).
CULPIN, C. 'Farm Mechanization Management', Chapter 4. Crosby Lockwood (1959).

b. 'Bibliography of Work Study in Agriculture'. British Productivity Council.

c. WILLIS, A. J., GEORGE, W. N. B. 'The Architect in Practice'. Crosby Lockwood (1964).

d. CRESSWELL, W. T., & GREIG, N.P. 'The law relating to building and engineering contracts.' Pitman.

e. 'Working with your Architect.' Royal Institute of British Architects (1963).

CHAPTER 9

Financing the Improvements

The source of finance for farm improvements is as complex as the structure and ownership of agricultural land. Approximately, there are one-third of a million farms of more than 5 acres and, if rough grazing is excluded, these represent rather less than 29M acres (1). The average farm size is only about 60 acres, but most of the cultivated land is held by large farms, as is shown by the following figures:

Size of farms (acres)	Total cultivated land (per cent)
15–30	10
30–60	10
60–120	40
120–300	15
over 300	25

Though half the farms have less than 60 acres, representing 20 per cent of the land, one-twentieth have more than 300 acres, representing 25 per cent. There is a trend towards fewer farms of larger size.

Denman has shewn that rather more than half the cultivated land is let in 120,000 holdings of at least 15 acres each and that these are divided into the following categories of ownership (2):

	Percentage of Total	
	Acreage	Holdings
Private persons	45·8	38·9
Companies	10·2	8·4
Trustees	11·9	9·7
Charities	8·3	5·5
Local Authorities	9·9	24·7
Government Departments	13·9	12·8

Nearly 40 per cent of the let acreage is within estates of at least 10,000 acres, 25 per cent in estates of between 4000 and 10,000 acres, and 25 per cent in estates between 1000 and 4000 acres. In contrast, only 5 per cent of the owner-occupied land is held in estates of over 1000 acres. During this century the number of owner-occupiers compared to tenants has increased from 1 in 8 to one half, and it has been suggested that this trend has been exaggerated by the 45 per cent rebate of death duties on agricultural land, though this had been intended to stabilize the ownership of the land (3).

The farming land is worth £2300M, but the Radcliffe Report of 1959 showed that the total loans to farmers amounted to about £700M, of which only 32 per cent came from banks and under 5 per cent from the Agricultural Mortgage Corporation, the remainder coming from merchants, dealers and private lenders (4). The report reckoned that at most £570M were backed by securities, of which no more than £200M were mortgages of farmland. One estimate has suggested that, for agriculture to remain efficient, further capital expenditure of £300M will be needed within the next decade, representing an increase of about 7½ per cent on the capital of some £4000M already invested in farming (5). This estimate may be conservative, since in 1961 a total of £155M were invested in fixed assets, nearly one-third of which was invested in buildings and works.

It is probable that at least £35M are invested every year in farm buildings, and £50M in buildings and allied equipment. Part of this investment is made from capital, either in the form of a direct capital grant from the Government or as an investment of capital made by various companies. A small percentage of the total may be paid by individuals from their own capital or on the basis of a short-term loan. It is probable that most of the capital required will be raised on the basis of a long-term loan.

FARM IMPROVEMENT SCHEME

The Government will give a direct grant of one-third of the approved cost of providing or improving permanent fixed equipment, as provided for in the Agriculture Act of 1957. Applications are made through regional offices of the Ministry of Agriculture, on the basis of the lowest of three competitive tenders or on a schedule of standard costs prepared by the Ministry to cover various building elements. The latter are intended mainly for farmers who erect buildings with their own labour. The grant is made subject to the proposals fulfilling certain conditions. The scheme must be of a kind that a prudent landlord would plan; it must be related to the size of the farm; it must not rely on intensive production which cannot be supported by the farm itself; the cost of the improvement must be reasonable in relation to the benefit derived from it; it must be of value to the farm irrespective of changes of occupier; and it must be designed to last at least fifteen years without maintenance.

SILO SUBSIDY

Buildings to house grass silage do not receive an improvement grant, but an application to the Ministry for a silo subsidy may be granted to a maximum of £250 per holding.

EXPERIMENTAL FARM BUILDINGS

Buildings which are experimental in structure or designed to accommodate experimental farming techniques do not receive an improvement grant. However, an application may be made to Agricultural Research Council and, at their discretion, a grant of up to 50 per cent of the cost may be allowed, subject to their conditions and to a three-year contract during which the A.R.C. may test the building for prescribed purposes (Chapter 10).

FARM WATER-SUPPLY SCHEMES

A grant of 25 per cent of the actual cost of installing a water supply from a public source, or 40 per cent from a private source, may be made by the Ministry, if the installation is not covered within an improvement grant for a building layout. Alternatively, a grant might be allowed for a comprehensive scheme under the Hill Farming and Livestock Rearing Acts.

IMPROVEMENT LOANS

The Improvement of Land Acts empowered the Agricultural Mortgage Corporation and the Lands Improvement Company to advance loans for long-term improvements on agricultural property up to the full cost of the works, possibly in the latter case against the security of a rent charge on the land being improved, provided that the loan is repaid in under 40 years and provided also that the proposals are approved by the Ministry of Agriculture and give sufficient return on the investment. Short-term loans may be obtained from the N.F.U.'s Agriculture Credit Corporation, Banks and Hire-Purchase Companies.

MORTGAGES

Loans on mortgages can be obtained from Mortgage Companies, Banks and private sources, against the security of a freehold or leasehold of the property. The loans may be used for any purpose and the amount lent will depend on the value of the property. The Agricultural Mortgage Corporation will make loans for up to 60 years on a maximum of two-thirds of the certified value of the property.

TAX ALLOWANCES AND RELIEFS

Capital expenditure on new works and improvements may be granted an allowance of tax on one-tenth of the expenditure in each of the ten years following the investment, and an investment allowance of 10 per cent of the net cost may be granted in the first year after the investment is

made. Relief may be granted on the interest paid on a loan from a recognized source.

PROVISION OF CAPITAL

Capital for improvements may be provided either by a landlord or by a tenant. Normally, the tenant will be responsible for mobile equipment, and auxiliary fixtures and fittings, whereas the landlord will pay the cost of the permanent structure on the basis of an increased rental charge to the tenant. Substantial discounts may be obtained by purchasing equipment, and even prefabricated buildings, through a co-operative trading association. In 1961 the co-operatives within the U.K. had a trading turnover in excess of £200M. Organized trading can help to reduce the capital cost of building and, if the demand for building components through these trading organizations was co-ordinated, it is possible that a standardized building system could be introduced, as suggested by the C.o.I.D. report (6), thereby reducing the manufacturing costs of production.

A development in recent years has been the formation of Syndicate Credit Groups of farmers and nearly 300 machinery and building syndicates exist, all of which have been promoted by the N.F.U. Of this number, under ten of the syndicates, which own buildings, have invested capital in grain-drying and storage plant, though others have erected buildings to house their jointly owned machinery. However, co-operation among farmers is possible without formal financial backing. Syndicates can be formed to rear weaners on a centralized co-operative farm, in order to supply the weaners for fattening to individual farmers within the group. Similarly, calves for beef fattening may be reared on a co-operative basis. Other types of syndicate-owned buildings are possible. Some syndicates may be formed for co-operation in management, rather than for building co-ownership. The syndicate usually has to provide 20 per cent of the capital from the members, if financed by the N.F.U., the remainder being available on a short- or long-term loan. The syndicate makes it possible for small and medium-sized farms to own equipment which is more expensive, but more efficient, than would be justified on individual farms, thus making it possible to have lower production costs which may be competitive with the large farms. Co-operative trading and syndicate farming probably could do much to reduce capital building costs and to improve the flexibility and design of the building components available.

INSURANCE

All farm buildings, including any produce, livestock or equipment within them, should be insured, and existing policies should be reviewed after any major building scheme has been completed, to see whether they are adequate for the new conditions. Terms depend on individual Insurance Companies. Generally, an allowance of 3s. per cent p.a. for the building is normal for fire insurance. Construction is unlikely to affect the policy, but if the building is sited near fire hazards, then an additional premium may be required. For example, straw storage within 20 yards of a building containing fire heat or within 50 yards of a railway line may be considered an additional risk. Similarly, the use of electrical motors combined with auxiliary fuel engines, or the concentration of machinery and equipment under one roof, may need an insurance rate of 5s. per cent p.a., and stored produce which is inflammable one of 7s. 6d. per cent p.a. Insurance for livestock within the building might be 2s. per cent p.a. Adequate fire precautions, such as fire hose reels, foam fire extinguishers and a good water pressure should be planned to suit the buildings. There should be additional policies to cover accidents to men and to livestock.

RATES

Rates do not have to be paid on farm buildings on agricultural holdings when the enterprise within the buildings is supported by or connected to the adjoining farm land. Rating demands have been made on certain intensive farm-building units, particularly for poultry, when these units have been supported entirely by bought produce, sometimes having been built on small areas of land not within a larger farm unit. The legal position has not been established. However, it is doubtful whether all farm buildings should be exempt from rates indefinitely, especially since heavy rating assessments are made on other industries and on other sectors of the community. Agriculture is an industry. Modern farm buildings can be planned to be efficient, and they could support an annual payment of rates as part of their overheads without prejudice to the success of the enterprises within them. However, it is doubtful whether an assessment could be made equally on floor area or volume. Perhaps all buildings used for purposes internal to the farm might be exempt, whereas those used to produce the saleable commodity could be assessed on the basis of throughput in relation to area. Thus, production buildings, as described within Part 3, Section III, could be assessed, whereas storage and processing buildings, with the possible exception of those for potatoes and grain, could be exempt.

(1) MCCRONE, G. 'The Economics of Subsidising Agriculture', p. 34. Allen & Unwin. (1962).
(2) DENMAN, DR. D. R. 'Who owns the land?', *Farmers Weekly*, p. 72 (20th Nov. 1959).
(3) READ, H. E. G. 'Landlords that never die', *Farmer and Stockbreeder*, p. 65 (17th April 1962).
(4) DENMAN, DR. D. R. 'The money under our boots', *Farmers Weekly*, p. 95 (5th Oct. 1962).
(5) THORNTON, R. G. 'Capital investment in farm buildings', *Farm Buildings Association Report*, p. 6 (March 1961).
(6) *Council of Industrial Design. Interim Report on Prefabricated Farm Buildings*, p. 4 (Autumn 1962).

SELECTED REFERENCES
a. Ministry of Agriculture. Fixed Equipment of the Farm. Leaflet No. 2. *Financing Improvements to Land and Buildings*.
b. 'Farm finance', *Farmers Weekly Bulletin* (25th Nov. 1960).

CHAPTER 10

The Need for Research

The national annual investment in fixed equipment probably exceeds £35M. In the five years since the Farm Improvement Scheme was inaugurated in 1957 grants totalling £45M have been allocated for farm buildings. This represents an annual investment of £27M, to which must be added the cost of buildings receiving other grants, such as silos, water installations and experimental buildings. Moreover, many buildings do not comply with the 'prudent landlord' clause of the F.I.S. and are erected without any grant. These include most of the poultry and some of the pig units, as well as all layouts excessive in size when related to the farm and those which are unorthodox in design or structure. In addition, the cost of unfixed machinery used in conjunction with the buildings forms part of the investment. A total of £155M was spent on fixed assets in 1961, of which £50M was for building and works, £79M for machinery and £26M for vehicles.

It is probable that at least £500M will have been invested directly or indirectly in farm buildings during the decade since 1957. Nearly one-fifth of this amount will have been contributed by the nation in grants to the farmers. This investment will have been made without any co-ordinated research to examine the basic requirements, structural techniques and economics of farm buildings and the relation of their design and development to agricultural practice. Agriculture must be one of the few modern industries prepared to make a large capital investment without research. Practically every sphere of agricultural practice in Britain has a research institute, wherein both long- and short-term work is supported by Government expenditure, with the exception of farm-building design.

It is important to appreciate that there are research institutes for farm buildings in most Western European countries other than the U.K. In 1960 two European Documentation Centres for Farm Buildings were set up at Lund, Sweden, and Bari, Italy. These are controlled by the Organization for Economic Co-operation and Development (O.E.C.D.) and include about twenty Member countries and reporters in many other nations throughout the free world. The U.K. is a member and has a correspondent to the Centre. There are state farm-building research institutes, for example, in each of the Scandinavian countries, the Netherlands, Germany and Italy. France and Spain carry out building research in centres including other agricultural interests. Moreover, Denmark has a special research building to test the climatic environment suitable for pigs and Germany one for agriculture work study, including the use of labour in buildings, in addition to their main institutes.

In the U.K. the situation is confused by diverse and unco-ordinated research, of which only a small part is financed directly by the Government. The main organizations which promote research can be summarized as follows:

1. MINISTRY OF AGRICULTURE
Though principally concerned in conducting an advisory service to farmers, including the publication of information to record current building design and practice, also has eleven experimental husbandry farms which may carry out incidental farm-building research.

2. AGRICULTURAL RESEARCH COUNCIL
To some extent co-ordinates all research, including that for farm buildings, and has made a survey of existing farm buildings and of all relevant information published between 1945 and 1958, with supplements for the years 1958–61 in preparation, and through experimental farm-building grants is able to study new ideas in practice. However, their authority, finance and facilities preclude research and development on a national scale.

Studies being made at present over three years under the experimental farm-buildings scheme, though others are contemplated, include the following: (1)

Methods of economizing straw and labour in cattle yards.
Investigation of merits of different types of floor construction for cattle yards designed to economize in the use of straw or other materials for bedding cattle, and thereby to reduce labour requirements. Matters considered include capital and maintenance costs, design, performance of stock and labour requirements in use.

25

A comparison of the performance of laying houses with slatted or wire-mesh floors with the performance of a deep-litter house.

Investigation into the capital and maintenance costs of the buildings, the labour requirements and the production and hatchability of eggs under the different systems.

Methods of housing hill sheep.

Investigation of methods of housing used to avoid the need to send sheep away from hill farms in winter. Capital and maintenance costs of the buildings, and the comparative performance of sheep wintered in houses or sent away are being studied.

Bulk storage of fertilizers on the farm.

Investigation of capital and maintenance and other running costs of buildings and equipment for the long-term bulk storage of fertilizers on farms, the length of time fertilizers can be stored and the economics of this practice.

Structures and ancillary equipment used for handling and feeding bulk cattle foods.

Study of the ways in which design of buildings is affected by new or recently introduced methods of feeding the bulky part of the ration to cattle. Investigations include the capital, maintenance and other running costs of buildings and equipment used, the labour and power requirements of the different systems, the control of quantity fed, the factors affecting the handling of the fodder and the design of the buildings used.

Pig housing.

1. Study of capital and maintenance costs of slatted and partly slatted floors, and performance of pigs on such floors.
2. Study of the effects of floor feeding on capital and maintenance costs, labour requirements and pig performance.
3. Study of capital and maintenance costs and atmospheric conditions in high-temperature and high-humidity houses and pig performance in them.

Chitting houses.

Investigation of the performance and capital, maintenance and other running costs of buildings and ancillary equipment for chitting seed potatoes.

Potato storage in buildings.

This project covers the design, equipment, capital, maintenance and running costs and efficiency of potato stores, with particular reference to the problem of maintaining quality and preventing losses in late stored potatoes.

Multi-purpose buildings.

Investigation of the procedures and information required in the planning of multi-purpose farm buildings in order to obtain general rules for guidance of those considering erecting such buildings.

N.B. With the exception of the last project, publication of reports concerning the various studies is expected in 1964 and 1965.

3. NATIONAL RESEARCH INSTITUTES

Several national institutes, such as those for Agricultural Engineering, for Research in Dairying and those for animal genetics, promote research which may influence building design. The Building Research Station is limited mainly to the structural problems in the use of materials.

4. UNIVERSITIES AND AGRICULTURAL TRAINING COLLEGES

Many Universities and all Training Colleges possess a demonstration farm. In many cases finance is restricted and the farm buildings do not demonstrate the best modern practice. However, limited experimental work is carried out and the results published in bulletins. In addition, some Universities have departments for agricultural economics which conduct economic and labour surveys on existing farms.

5. INDUSTRY

Many major industries, particularly those concerned with animal feeding stuffs and meat marketing, possess research farms where the requirements for farm buildings are studied. At least one industry is reputed to spend more than the Government on farm-building research. The use of work study in agriculture, including that within farm buildings, has been promoted by another major industry, and this has encouraged the Ministry of Agriculture to have its own work-study officers.

6. COUNCIL OF INDUSTRIAL DESIGN

A farm-buildings advisory panel has studied existing prefabricated farm buildings, reported on their defects and recommended the research which is desirable.

7. NATIONAL FARMERS' UNION

Though essentially engaged in the administration of the interests of farmers, the Union has an education and scientific development department which inaugurated a farm-buildings research Fellowship under the direction of the former Nuffield Foundation's Division for Architectural Studies. This Fellowship was held by the Author.

8. FARM BUILDINGS ASSOCIATION

A private organization of those interested in farm buildings, promoting greater interest and knowledge in the subject and convinced that finance should be made available for national research in farm-building design. In 1964, the Association in conjunction with the Royal Society of Agriculture formed a Farm Building Development Centre, with a Director, at Stoneleigh, Warwickshire.

It is clear that there is diverse interest in research. The Documentation Centre recorded twelve experiments in the U.K. in 1961 (2), though this was by no means an exhaustive summary of the research in this country. It is obvious that this research is unco-ordinated and that there is a serious gap between research, development and practice. Equally, it is evident that the investment in research is disproportionate to the investment in the industry. This situation is not peculiar to agriculture, but is endemic to the building industry as a whole, as has been studied by Llewelyn-Davies and Cowan (3). Though 0·7 per cent of the net output of agriculture is spent on research and development work, only a minute part of this is spent on research into farm buildings. At present in the building and construction industry with an annual net output of £1500M, only £2½M, that is 0·16 per cent, is spent on research and development. In contrast, in the manufacturing industry the percentage in 1958 was 2·6 per cent, and this has been increased in the last few years. Moreover, the national percentage of research and development work to the Gross National Product is 2·7 per cent. If agriculture is to be as efficient as other manufacturing industries, then the expenditure on research, including that for buildings, must be increased.

The consequence of this lack of co-ordination and research is that the national resources are being dissipated. Therefore, the need for imports is increased and the farmers' potential income is held in check. Though the situation in 1965 is better than that in 1960 and shows a revolutionary advance since 1955, nevertheless few farm buildings are designed to make the maximum use of modern agricultural methods, machinery, building materials, structural techniques and manufacturing processes. The basic requirements and data necessary for efficient buildings are largely unknown. Any study of farm buildings has to rely on empirical observation more often than it can on established fact. This is one of the limitations made obvious in the 'research' for this book and is emphasized in the presentation of its information. Modern methods of marketing food probably will make it essential for farm-building research to be treated as a necessary part of a modern industry.

Research in farm-building design is needed not only to increase efficiency in food production and to make the maximum use of national resources but also to improve the appearance of farm buildings. No architect should write a book on farm buildings and be so insensitive as not to mention the appearance such buildings make in the landscape. However, this is almost the only place in this study in which appearance is discussed.

The traditional farmstead, for the most part, enhanced the landscape and the buildings, because of an innate functional tradition in their design, were satisfactory in use and in appearance. Few buildings were designed to a preconceived aesthetic discipline, but, following regional patterns of agriculture and of building materials, they had a natural harmony. The charm of this functional tradition has been lost for ever. The modern linear plan, suitable for mechanization, disrupts the traditional courtyard. The scale of modern enterprises is unsympathetic to the traditional buildings and there are fewer materials suitable for the exteriors. But above all such considerations is the fact that the modern economy cannot support the same individual attention to detailing the buildings on the site with time-consuming craftsmanship. Moreover, the buildings reflect the uncertain nature of agriculture, which, under economic pressures and fluctuations, is in a period of rapid transition, in which there has been little opportunity to study the basic requirements.

The functional tradition can be regained, albeit with modern materials and scale of building, as soon as research has shown sufficient uniformity in the requirements of design. Building components, mass produced in factories, to suit an established market with precise and scientifically specified requirements, can be manufactured to form well-detailed and economic buildings, using materials to their best advantage and reducing site erection to the minimum. Steel, concrete, timber, light-weight sheets of various materials, plastics, aluminium and all modern materials are suitable for the countryside, provided that some attention is given to siting, massing, colour and detailing. It is the present clumsy detailing, enforced by the lack of established requirements, which makes it appear that the majority of farmers are insensitive to the environment they create.

The inauguration of a Farm Buildings Research and Development Centre would give the stimulus to the economic development of farm-building design, and would contribute to the national agricultural progress (4). Moreover, the appearance of new farm buildings would then reflect an industry which had become sure of itself in a modern mechanized age. Such a centre would need architects, engineers of all sorts, work-study experts, statisticians, chemists and physicists, as well as agriculturists and economists among its team of experts.

Some research and development comes from industry. In fact, much of the real progress made in recent years has depended on the enterprise and financial risk taken by individual manufacturers—

often without support from official sources. However, such development is unco-ordinated. The capital required to produce full prefabrication of components for many farm buildings is too great for any one manufacturer. It depends, to be economic, on a large, guaranteed market outlet spread over several years. In other fields of building, such as schools, a guaranteed market has been made by groups of Local Authorities forming building consortia. This has made it possible for manufacturers to invest in large production lines producing well-designed components. This could be copied in agriculture by farmers getting together, perhaps through the N.F.U., to form their own consortia. For example, it would not be difficult to establish how much p.a. was spent on dairy buildings and to guarantee such a sum for five years. This would be a major step forward for farm-building design, giving an impetus for research, development and prefabrication with profound repercussions for the agricultural industry.

(1) MANNING, P. 'Research in progress at various centres in the British Isles', *Architects' Journal*, pp. 676–77 (27th Mar. 1963).
(2) Agricultura No. 2. *European Documentation Centre for Farm Buildings*, pp. 32–4 (1961).
(3) LLEWELYN-DAVIES, R. & COWAN, P. 'How much Research?' *R.I.B.A. Journal*, pp. 158–62 (April 1963).
(4) *Farm Buildings Association Journal*, pp. 1 and 2 (Dec. 1959).

SELECTED REFERENCES
a. SOUTAR, D. S. 'Research and development in farm building design', *The Scottish Farmer* (2nd Dec. 1961).
b. WELLER, J. B. 'The appearance of the modern farm', *Industrial Architecture* (April, May & July 1962).
c. 'A Bibliography of Farm Buildings Research, 1945–1961.' Agricultural Research Council.

N.B. This section is based on an article by the author in *Farm Mechanization* (Nov. 1963).

PART TWO
MECHANICAL HANDLING OF MATERIALS

farms. Therefore, there is little information, based on research, which indicates the best aids to mechanical handling for certain types of farm, whereas there is information available to help the selection of a machine for handling materials for a specific job. Capital costs of machinery are not considered in this Part, since there are wide variations due to the different capacities and performance of machines, even when used for similar tasks, and up-to-date cost lists are given in several technical magazines.

QUANTITY OF MATERIALS HANDLED

The Scottish Agricultural Industries have carried out several investigations on various dairy and beef farms of about 100 acres. Their report has shown that one farm supporting 36 cows and followers, to a total of about 52 cow equivalents, required nearly 1200 tons of material to be handled each year, but that the total tonnage actually handled was nearly 9000 tons (1). The farm was managed with traditional stocking and cropping. By making revisions to the work procedure with the provision of better equipment and by dressing the potatoes in the buildings rather than in the fields, it was possible to reduce the materials handled to under 6000 tons a year. Therefore, each ton required, on average, had to be handled five times each year. An analysis of the materials handled is given on page 32.

It is interesting to note that $\frac{3}{4}$ of the total tonnage actually handled was moved about either within or to and from the buildings. Other 100-acre dairy farms investigated also required about 1200 tons of material each year, but in their case total handling was only about 3000 tons, due to the use of slatted floors for the cows and simpler methods of feeding. Similar examinations of 100-acre beef farms showed that 600 tons of materials were required every year, but 6000 tons might be handled, though this could be reduced to 4000 tons with improved methods (2). In the latter case each ton required, on average, had to be handled over six times each year.

Introduction

The chapter on Mechanization and Building (Pt. 1, Ch. 5, p. 14) showed that the mechanical handling of materials has transformed farm-work methods in the last decade, but that this mechanization has had a limited effect on the structural design of farm buildings. In fact, the development of materials-handling techniques, with its effect on work routines, storage methods and building layouts, has been neither as rapid nor as far-reaching as in industry, where new ideas have been gathering impetus ever since the war. In agriculture a similar impetus is now gathering momentum. Every year many new machines for materials handling on the farm are being marketed, and there is an increasing interest in handling materials in bulk.

The aim of mechanical handling is to eliminate all unnecessary handling of materials and to mechanize the remainder. However, mechanization has to be a planned aid to the use of labour. It must be economic in that it improves the value of the overall throughput from the farm in excess of any machinery costs greater than the value of the labour saved. Moreover, labour must be costed in terms of the agricultural wages which will be paid within a few years. Machinery must be considered in relation to the building layout in order to obtain its maximum efficiency, and any labour saved by using a machine must be put to other productive uses.

Handling materials on a farm can form a considerable part of the annual work required for the various farm enterprises (Pt. 1, Ch. 5, p. 14). Handling materials is unproductive in itself. There have been many studies, for the most part of an advisory nature, to improve work methods for particular jobs, and, in some cases, for streamlining production within one complete enterprise. These studies have led to improvements in mechanical handling and occasionally in relating mechanization to the structural design of buildings. Very little study has been made, however, concerning the mechanical handling of materials as a fundamental part of planning farm work within complete

DESIGN FACTORS IN HANDLING

The background to the handling of materials on traditional farms is of interest. But modern farm layouts can be designed to reduce the number of times each material has to be moved and to eliminate the manual work of transportation.

The tractor and foreloader has revolutionized farm work, and today the tractor with its various attachments is the basis of the modern farm. However, it might be that the cost of using a tractor with an attachment for handling materials may be greater than using other methods, such as blowing, sucking or overhead conveying systems. More information is required concerning the comparative capital and running costs of different mechanical handling equipment. This is a matter for detailed analysis and study.

Before considering the mechanical tools which are available and their method of use, it is necessary to consider the materials that have to be moved and the nature and purpose of the movement involved, together with the method of making the movement. The design of each building must be made on the basis of this analysis. These three factors governing mechanical handling are tabulated below.

CHAPTER

1 MATERIALS
  A. Solids (non free-flowing).
  B. Free-flowing solids.
  C. Liquids.

2 CIRCULATION
  A. Delivery to the buildings.
  B. Circulation between or within the buildings.
  C. Despatch from the buildings.

3 POWER
  A. Gravity.
  B. Tractor driven.
  C. Electrical.

The types and physical state of materials which are handled on the farm have changed during the last decade. There will be further changes in the future. To some extent, the physical state of materials can be altered to suit the method and purpose of transportation. This is considered in Chapter 1. Secondly, in order to reduce the number of times a material has to be moved, it is necessary to consider the purpose of each journey. This is examined in Chapter 2. Thirdly, the development of electrically powered methods of transportation, together with those powered from a tractor, have made it possible for all materials to be moved, for whatever purpose, by machine. The pitchfork and other hand tools are out of date. However, it would be desirable for all mechanical-handling systems to be examined critically on a comparative basis and for some co-ordination between the manufacturers of the equipment and those producing the standard building components to be achieved.

Material	Tons Required	Original Method			Revised Method		
		a	b	c	a	b	c
Oats	33	$521\frac{1}{2}$	271	15·8	$250\frac{1}{2}$	179	7·6
Straw	31	498	357	15·8	315	186	10·2
Hay	36	602	216	16·7	528	216	14·7
Silage	100	978	852	9·8	819	693	8·2
Swedes	220	2090	1650	9·5	1320	1100	6·0
Kale	15	90	60	6·0	75	60	5·0
Potatoes	32	486	92	15·2	$250\frac{1}{2}$	$218\frac{1}{2}$	7·8
Milk	$136\frac{1}{2}$	$880\frac{1}{2}$	$880\frac{1}{2}$	6·5	$11\frac{1}{2}$	$11\frac{1}{2}$	0·08
Dung	320	1905	1265	6·0	1585	1265	5·0
Bought foods	30	180	180	6·0	130	130	4·3
Fertilizers	31	217	68	7·0	186	124	6·0
Lime	28	56	0	2·0	56	0	2·0
Seeds	$6\frac{1}{4}$	46	24	7·4	$37\frac{1}{2}$	25	6·0
Fuel	$4\frac{3}{4}$	$9\frac{1}{2}$	$9\frac{1}{2}$	2·0	—	—	—
Water	134	212	212	1·6	91	91	0·7
Sawdust	6	30	30	5·0	24	24	4·0
Total Tons	1164	8801	6147		5679	4323	

  a. Total tonnage handled in buildings and in fields.
  b. Total to and from fields and within buildings.
  c. Number of times handled.

5: REMOVING MANURE BY SLURRY TANKER

Mr. B. Robinson, Lolworth Grange, Cambs.

Slurry, like other free-flowing solids or liquids, can be removed by suction. Vacuum tankers for handling slurry are frequently used. In this case, a proprietary fattening house for heavy hogs has a slatted dunging area alongside the external walls over a dung channel which holds sufficient slurry for 6–8 wks housing. The tanker has a flexible suction hose which is placed through a small outlet in the external wall to empty the channel. The tanker is coupled to a tractor, the latter driving the suction pump. Tankers holding up to 700 gal are available. Access is required alongside the building. [SEE PAGE 47] Photo: Courtesy of Agripress Publicity Ltd.

6: HANDLING GRAIN ROUND CORNERS

An auger with a flexible steel plastic-cover around two concentric counter-revolving spirals makes the handling of grain and some other free-flowing solids easy, even around corners and over obstacles. This implement makes the planning of layouts for grain, meal, etc., less restricted than when fixed, straight run conveyors are used. [SEE PAGE 44] Courtesy of Lundell (G.B.) Ltd.

7: MOBILE MILL/MIXER

Though not widely used, the advantage of being able to mill and mix rations in transit from a food store to the point-of-use is obvious, especially if different mixes using the same ingredients are required for different batches of livestock. In this case, a self-feeder for a pig fattening unit is filled from the inclined auger boom attached to the mill/mix plant towed by a tractor. [SEE PAGES 40 & 129] Courtesy of Rustproof Metal Window & Eng. Co. Ltd.

8: HANDLING HAYLAGE BY AUGER

Mr. G. D. Rivis, Boythorpe, Malton, Yorks.

Mechanical feeding of cattle can be automatic. On the left is a covered yard, beyond which the base of a tower silo is visible. An inclined auger picks up the haylage from the base of the silo and lifts it into a small hopper from which it is conveyed by an open auger and deposited into a manger. The latter is about 5 ft wide, with cattle feeding from both sides. The sides of the auger are protected and the cattle cannot touch it. Alternatively, the auger can be housed in a tube with slots so positioned that each animal receives exactly the same quantity of feed. [SEE PAGES 45 & 187] See also Photo 13 Courtesy of Farmer and Stockbreeder.

ii. *Short.* Cut, sometimes wilted. Handled by buckrake or blown into trailer. Used for silage, or after chopping for haylage.

Depends on season machinery, and m.c.

iii. *Lacerated.* Cut, sometimes wilted blown into trailer after laceration. Used for silage.

" " "

iv. *Chopped.* Cut, wilted, chopped and blown into trailer. Used for haylage, or possibly dried for hay.

" " "

b. CONSERVED GRASS

i. *Silage.* Average d.m. content of grass 20–25 per cent, then compressed in horizontal bunkers. Used for self-feeding or for cutting and carting as fodder.

Long grass—45–50 lb/cu ft. Lacerated grass—50–55 lb/cu ft. (15 lb/cu ft d.m.)

ii. *Haylage.* Average d.m. content of grass 50 per cent, then compressed in vertical silo. Cut and conveyed for fodder.

30 lb/cu ft. (15 lb/cu ft d.m. irrespective of m.c.)

iii. *Hay.* Dried bales at 20 per cent m.c. Bales opened at manger. Chopped self-feed.

250 lb/cu yd.

c. PEA-HAULM

Pea-plants placed in stacks or bunker silos and compressed. Cut and carted for fodder.

45–50 lb/cu ft.

d. POTATOES

Lifted either by hand or mechanically, handled in trailers or containers into store.

56 cu ft/T.

e. ROOTS

Lifted either by hand or mechanically, handled in trailers, normally swedes, fodder beet, mangolds and potatoes, not usually stored, sometimes chopped and used for fodder.

50–60 cu ft/T.

f. KALE

Cut mechanically, handled in trailers, used for fodder.

Depends on crop.

g. BEET TOPS

Sugar and fodder beet tops —as kale.

" " "

CHAPTER 1

Materials

INTRODUCTION

Materials can be divided into the classification of solids, free-flowing solids and liquids, each group becoming progressively easier to handle, though not necessarily cheaper. (Gases seldom have to be handled on farms except in cylinders.) It is possible to change the physical conditions of the material in order to facilitate handling. Straw can be chopped and mixed with dung and water to make a free-flowing slurry. Fertilizers, which are granular and free-flowing, can be mixed with water to become a liquid. The division between each physical state is not clearly defined. Normally solid materials, such as straw, grass, or haylage, can be chopped, and, since they can be blown or conveyed by auger when chopped, they could be described as free-flowing. It may be important to remove water from a material to reduce the costs of handling. Normal grass for silage contains about three parts of water to one of dry matter, but grass for haylage may be in the ratio of 1 : 1. In the latter case two tons less water for each ton of dry matter stored will be carried from the fields to the buildings.

The following table is a summary of the normal materials which have to be handled on a farm. Each material is tabulated, together with a brief description and data giving the average dimensions of the material when transported. More detailed information is given in the individual sections in Part 3.

A) SOLIDS

a. GRASS

i. *Long.* Cut, sometimes wilted, baled. (Rarely handled loose.) Bales dried in field or in buildings. Used for hay.

36 in. × 18 in. × 14 in. bale at 45 per cent m.c. 350 to 400 lb/cu yd

h. STRAW
Cut, and normally baled. *Depends on crop.*
Handled in bales. Used for
bedding or fodder.
Wheat straw (twine baled) *450 cu ft/T.*
Oat   „   „ *375 cu ft/T.*
Barley „   „ *400 cu ft/T.*

i. SHAVINGS
Wood shavings used for *375–400 cu ft/T.*
bedding (semi-compressed).

j. SAWDUST
Used for bedding. *325–350 cu ft/T.*

k. FIBRE
Coconut fibre used for *300 cu ft/T.*
bedding.

l. LIVESTOCK
Normally driven or lead,
sometimes taken in box or
trailer.
i. Pork Pig   for slaughter. *120–160 lb.*
ii. Bacon Pig „   „ *200–220 lb.*
iii. Heavy Hog „   „ *260 lb.*
iv. Ewe Sheep „   „ *160 lb.*
v. Bullock   „   „ *10–14 cwt.*
vi. Veal Calf „   „ *250–400 lb.*
vii. Dairy Cow Adult *9–11 cwt.*
viii. Bull   „ *20–30 cwt.*

m. WOOL
Sheared for sale. *Depends on method of packing.*

n. MANURE
Straw and dung com- *35–50 cu ft/T.*
pressed.

B) FREE-FLOWING SOLIDS

a. GRAIN
Combine harvested, dried
and stored. Density at 14
per cent m.c. with angle of
repose at 30°. Stored for
sale, or for mill/mixing for
feeding-stuffs.

Wheat	*46 cu ft/T.*
Barley	*51 „*
Oats	*70 „*
Rye	*51 „*
Peas	*46 „*
Beans	*43 „*
Linseed	*51 „*

b. MEAL
Various mixtures of meal are
available, and bulk densities
vary. Stored for feeding-
stuffs.
Meal *70–75 cu ft/T.*
High protein concentrates *52 cu ft/T.*
Pellets *60 cu ft/T.*
Cubes *56 cu ft/T.*
Large pig nuts *52 cu ft/T.*

c. FERTILIZERS
Various granular fertilizers. *35–38 cu ft/T.*

d. LIME *30 cu ft/T.*

e. SLURRY
Depends on solids present. *40–50 cu ft/T.*

C) LIQUIDS

a. MILK
Stored for sale. $\begin{cases} 10.1\ lb/gal. \\ 6\frac{1}{4}\ cu\ ft/gal. \end{cases}$

b. WHEY
Stored for feeding-stuff. *„   „   „*

c. SKIM MILK
Stored for feeding-stuff. *„   „   „*

d. WATER
Stored for drinking, mixing *„   „   „*
with meal, or for cleaning.

e. FERTILIZERS
Stored (occasionally). *„   „   „*

f. EFFLUENT
Drained from silage. Gluti- *„   „   „*
nous.

g. PETROL *8 lb/gal. approx.*

h. DIESEL OIL *„   „   „*

CHAPTER 2

Circulation

INTRODUCTION

Most materials which have to be handled within the environment of buildings are those which are put into and taken out of storage. Other movements are caused by the necessity for changing the physical state of materials, such as the milling and mixing of grain to form compound feeding-stuffs. The change in physical state can sometimes take place within the place of storage, thus eliminating the handling operations either from the storage to the place of change or from the place of change to the store or even both journeys. Grain, for example, can be dried whilst in store. Sometimes, the physical state of a material may be changed whilst in transit, as in the case of grain within a mobile mill/mix unit. In a few cases, materials are handled only once. Slurry can be moved from under the livestock in slatted layouts direct on to the fields or kale may be carted from the fields direct to the cattle mangers.

Circulation of materials should be reduced to the minimum. Moreover, if materials have to be stored, the place of storage should be adjacent to the point of use and the material should be conveyed mechanically, preferably by gravity, over the shortest distance from the store. These observations are a matter of common sense.

The circulation of materials can be classified into the basic types of journey made: delivery to the buildings either from the fields or from the public road as bought commodities, handling either between or within the buildings, or transference from the buildings either to the fields or to the public road as commodities for sale. Each of these types of journey will require a different relationship between the materials handling machinery and the building design.

A) DELIVERY TO THE BUILDINGS

The materials delivered from the fields have been listed in Chapter 1 above, most of which are put into storage and a few taken direct to the place of use. The tractor, plus its attachments, is the normal form of transport and the trailer is the most flexible and commodious of the attachments. However, various other forms of bulk container are being developed, especially boxes and pallets. Normal methods of handling materials from the fields are (discussed further in Part 3):

a. GRASS TO SILOS
   i. Lifted by buckrakes, and placed in clamp silo.
   ii. Blown into trailer from forage harvester, and tipped near to or into silo, and spread by buckrake.
   iii. Blown into trailer from forage harvester, tipped into hopper at base of tower silo, chopped and blown into silo.
   iv. Chopped and blown into trailer from forage harvester, tipped into hopper at base of tower silo, and blown into silo.

b. GRASS TO FORAGE FENCE OR MANGER (ZERO-GRAZING)
   i. Blown into self-unloading trailer or forage box, automatically emptied at fence or manger.
   ii. Blown into trailer, forked from trailer along fence (2-man operation).

c. HAY TO DRIER OR BARNS
   i. Bales in stacked trailer loads on fixed-bed trailers.
   ii. Bales in tumble-stacked loads on fixed-bed or moving-bed trailers.
   iii. Bales in tractor hydraulic carriers ready for barn stacking at low heights.
   iv. Chopped and blown into trailers.

d. ROOTS, KALE, BEET TOPS, ETC., TO FORAGE FENCE OR MANGER
   i. Picked up by buckrake, or by fork, placed into trailers, hand forked or mechanically distributed at fence or manger.
   ii. Kale forage harvested and mechanically distributed.

e. POTATOES TO STORE
   i. Hand loaded into stillages, lifted by tractor on to trailer, and by tractor or fork-lift truck from trailer, tipped into store.
   ii. Hand loaded into trailer, tipped into store, stacked by elevator.

f. STRAW TO BARNS
   i. As for hay, chopping and blowing more developed.
   ii. Chaff blown into forage trailer, tipped into barn in block of material, perhaps 10 ft × 8 ft × 7 ft high, or blown.

g. GRAIN TO GRAIN DRIER OR STORE

i. Combined into bags, loaded on to trailers, hand emptied into intake pits or on to drying platform.

ii. Combined into bags or boxes on pallet or trailer, pallet fork-lifted into store.

iii. Combined into trailer or tipping tanker, tipped into intake pit, or augered into store.

On some farms the materials listed above will be bought commodities and will not be delivered to the buildings from the fields. Hay and straw for cattle are the normal materials which may be bought when the farm produces insufficient to maintain its herd, though grain, too, may be purchased to supplement a feeding policy. Most farms will have considerable merchandise being delivered, usually seeds and fertilizers and feeding-stuffs for livestock farms. In addition, deliveries will be made of machinery, spare parts, fuels and livestock. Numerous representatives, experts, officials and other personnel will call at the farm for various purposes. The process of relating these interruptions to the normal farm routine is important. Many of the deliveries and visits should be based on a regular time-table. There should be a central office for checking all arrivals and departures connected with the farm (Pt. 3, I K, p. 89). Large farms may find that time can be saved by checking vehicles on a weighbridge. The following additional materials may be delivered to the buildings, usually from established merchants:

h. FERTILIZERS TO STORE

i. Paper bags of 80 lb., or 1 cwt., delivered by lorry, and lifted or elevated into store.

ii. Bulk delivery by tipping tanker or tanker with blower.

iii. Bulk liquid delivery by tanker, pumped into store.

i. SEEDS TO STORE

i. Sacks or bags of 80 lb., or 1 cwt., delivered by lorry, and lifted or elevated into store. Sacks are returnable to merchant.

ii. Bulk delivery by tipping tanker or tanker with blower.

j. FEEDING-STUFFS

i. Paper bags or sacks of 56 lb., 80 lb., 1 cwt. or 1¼ cwt., delivered by lorry, and lifted or elevated into store. Sacks are returnable to merchant.

ii. Bulk delivery by tipping tanker or tanker with blower or auger.

k. SHAVINGS AND SAWDUST

i. Normally by tipping trailer into store.

ii. Occasionally in sacks by lorry.

l. LIVESTOCK

i. One- or two-storied livestock lorries with ramps for letting animals out into yard or pen.

m. FUELS

i. Bulk tankers, pumped into store.

ii. Drums, rolled into store.

n. SKIM MILK AND WHEY

i. By bulk tanker, pumped into store.

B) CIRCULATION BETWEEN AND WITHIN BUILDINGS

Most of the handling of materials occurs either between or within buildings. Sturrock suggested that on traditional livestock farms 80 to 90 per cent of all work other than the specific jobs of feeding, cleaning and milking, etc., were concerned with carrying materials around the farmyard (Pt. 1, Ch. 5, p. 14) (3). This would not be true on modern, mechanized farms. Large cattle and pig layouts can be planned where all the materials required for the livestock are mechanically handled. On livestock farms one of the most important planning problems will be the decision to have one centralized food store, with a system of distribution to individual stores at each livestock building, or no central store, but for all feed to be delivered direct to the individual stores. If a farm has its own mill and mix unit a centralized storage point will be essential (Pt. 3, II E, p. 124). However, if feed is a bought commodity, it is better to omit the central store in order to save double handling. The following materials are handled either between or within buildings:

a. SILAGE FROM CLAMP SILO TO FORAGE FENCE OR MANGER (RATIONED FEED)

i. Cut, lifted by fore-loader into mechanically unloading trailer.

ii. Cut, lifted by elevator into mechanically unloading trailer.

iii. Cut and elevated by automatic auger (U.S. development).

iv. Cut and lifted and carted by buckrake.

b. HAYLAGE FROM TOWER SILO TO MANGER

i. Cut and deposited into mechanically unloading trailer.

ii. Cut and conveyed by auger.

c. HAY FROM BARN TO RACK OR MANGER

i. Chopped and blown or augered (also straw for fodder).

ii. In bales, lifted on to and off a trailer (or fore-loader).

iii. In bales, by hand, preferably by gravity.

iv. In bales, via overhead conveyer.

d. STRAW FROM BARN TO BEDDED AREAS
As for hay.

e. FEEDING-STUFFS FROM STORE TO
MANGERS OR FEEDERS
i. Blown or augered through pipes or conveyors.
ii. By gravity into hoppers on monorails, powered by hand or by electricity.
iii. By gravity into trolleys or trailers, powered by hand or by motor.
iv. By gravity into sacks, handled in trailers or by buckrake.
v. Auger or elevator instead of by gravity into hopper or trolley.

f. GRAIN FROM DRIER TO STORE, OR FROM
STORE TO MILL/MIX UNIT
As for feeding-stuffs.

g. SHAVINGS, SAWDUST, ETC., FROM STORE
TO BEDDED AREA
i. By tractor and scoop.
ii. By hand trolley.

h. SLURRY AND MANURE FROM DUNGING
AREAS TO STORE
i. Hand-operated or small motor-powered scraper blades, with widths of 3–5 ft, for cleaning passages.
ii. Motor-powered barrows, capacities up to 15 cwt.
iii. Tractor-mounted scrapers into slurry pit or over ramp into dung trailer.
iv. Automatic scoop and chain or scuttle-type scrapers into slurry pit or over ramp into trailer.
v. Gravity flow through channels or pipes.
vi. Pumped through pipes.

i. MILK FROM COWS TO STORE
i. Automatic milkers via pipe-line into bulk-tank.
ii. Automatic milkers via pipe-line, over cooler, into churns.
iii. Automatic milkers via pipe-line, to churns.
iv. Automatic milkers to churns, churns moved by hand, by monorail, by trolley or on rollers.

j. SKIM MILK AND WHEY FROM STORE TO
TROUGHS
i. By gravity through pipes.
ii. By gravity into trolley.

C) DESPATCH FROM THE
BUILDINGS

Materials can be handled from the buildings to the fields in the normal course of farm work. Seeds and fertilizers are the usual commodities, together with slurry and dung. The despatch of goods from the buildings to market, merchant or factory is the most important aspect of farm work, since it is the basis of income to the farm. In many cases the commodity is fetched by the merchant or factory. Free-flowing solids and liquids may be handled in bulk tankers. Other solid materials may need packaging and certain produce may be pre-packed on the farm ready for the markets. The importance of pre-packed goods from the farm is likely to increase, though this may be carried out by farming syndicates in buildings away from the farm (Pt. 3, II K, p. 162). The following materials may be handled from the buildings:

a. FERTILIZERS AND SEEDS FROM THE
STORE TO FIELDS
i. Hand loaded in bags on to trailer, and towed by tractor.
ii. Hand loaded in bags on to pallet and lifted by rear-mounted buckrake or transport box.
iii. Gravity loaded into fertilizer spreader.
iv. Gravity loaded into tipping bulk tanker or trailer.
v. Lifted by fore-loader in bulk.

b. HAY FROM STORE (FOR FEEDING IN
FIELDS)
i. Hand loaded on to trailer, towed by tractor.

c. MANURE FROM STOCKYARD OR MANURE
PIT TO FIELDS
i. Lifted by fore-mounted buckrake into spreader or trailer.

d. SLURRY FROM COLLECTING PITS TO
FIELDS
i. Power driven through pipes.
ii. Sucked into vacuum tankers.

e. GRAIN AND SEEDS FROM STORE TO
MERCHANT
i. In sacks, hand loaded on to lorry.
ii. In bulk in detachable lorry body, filled prior to arrival of lorry and chassis.
iii. In bulk in bulk tanker.

f. LIVESTOCK FROM YARDS OR PENS TO
MERCHANT OR ABATTOIR
i. In livestock lorries, as for delivery.
ii. In detachable livestock box mounted on trailer.

g. MILK FROM FARM DAIRY TO DAIRY
i. By gravity or pump into bulk tanker.
ii. In churns, lifted onto lorry.

h. POTATOES FROM STORE TO MERCHANT
i. Elevated into lorry.
ii. Packed into boxes on pallets, fork-lifted on to lorry.
iii. Pre-packed into bags packed into boxes.

CHAPTER 3

Power

INTRODUCTION

Previous sections have indicated the materials usually handled on farms and the normal journeys made with them. This section is not intended either to study the mechanics of handling materials or to give a comprehensive study of the machines which are available. These factors are studied in several standard reference books (Selected references). A critical study of the mechanical efficiency of materials-handling machinery in relation to building design is overdue, but should be undertaken by a team of experts, since there are many machines available for each of the specific jobs of handling which have been listed in Chapter 2, and some of the machines can be used for several purposes.

It is possible, however, to consider the normal machinery used for handling materials and to indicate some of the principal effects these machines can have on building design. As has been stated (Pt. 1, Ch. 5, p. 13), machinery may be either fixed to the building, as a permanent addition to the structure, or it may be portable, being placed in different static positions within the buildings, or it may be mobile when in operation. In many cases a building can be designed in detail only after the machinery has been chosen, since the manufacturer of the machinery may have definite requirements in order to obtain the maximum efficiency and safety with his machine. Package-deal buildings, especially those for grain storage, are sometimes provided complete with machinery for handling materials.

Electrical power and the hydraulic attachments for tractors have made it possible to perform almost any desirable operation for transporting materials. Not only can all farm materials be used without being touched by hand, but the majority within buildings can be transported automatically without even a worker in attendance. Sometimes manufacturers will adapt their machines for specific requirements.

Many factors have to be taken into account in the choice of a machine other than its mechanical efficiency. A farmer may have a preference for a particular manufacturer. The most important personal factor will be the problem of maintenance. As far as possible, a farmer should restrict the number of machines which will require different specialist services for the provision of spares and for maintenance. For example, it is best for a farmer to have only one make of tractor, and this might limit the choice of tractor attachments (Pt. 3, II J, p. 158).

The power required for handling any material, together with its intrinsic qualities, must be the basis of choice of handling method taken into account when comparing the capital and running costs of a machine. There is a critical speed for the various materials at which they begin to sustain damage, and this will limit the throughput of the machine. The quantity of product that is transported over a fixed distance within a fixed time is the throughput: (Pt. 1, Ch. 1, p. 3). This will be significant for most handling tasks and may govern the basic choice of layout and plant. Storage units should be placed where the materials can be handled at the least cost. Other factors which must be considered are the amount of material to be handled, the distance to the point of use and the best method of handling over that distance within a fixed time.

Sources of power are of three main categories. Gravity should be used wherever it is practical. Secondly, the tractor can perform many of the handling tasks with its attachments, and it can be adapted fairly easily from the performance of one task to another, but it requires at least one operator in use. For example, with well-designed modern equipment, one man should be able to assemble a foreloader on to a tractor within $\frac{1}{3}$–$\frac{1}{2}$ hr. The tractor is an essential machine for tilling the fields, and the cost of most of the attachments, in order to adapt the tractor for handling materials, is not excessive. However, the running cost of the machine and operator is likely to be considerably more than that of electrically powered machinery. Electricity is the third main source of power. (A p.t.o. drive from a tractor can be useful, especially as an emergency source of power, should there be an electrical fault. In fact, power from a tractor frequently is used for driving various farm machines, particularly barn or drying equipment, some of which may include handling devices, but generally this method is economic only if electrical power is unavailable.)

A) GRAVITY

Gravity handling can be used for solids, free-flowing solids and for liquids, whenever the available height makes it possible. Traditional buildings containing an upper floor or loft often can be converted for this purpose. Usually with a new building the cost of an upper floor would not be justified when compared with the use of mechanical elevators and conveyors, though the use of framed catwalks can be an alternative and cheaper type of floor. However, at least one specialist pig-house, which is prefabricated, includes a raised feed store in the design.

Gravity handling is desirable, particularly for loading a bulk transport tanker with free-flowing solids such as grain and meal (Pt. 3, I D 4bi, p. 65). The economic use of tankers depends on the minimum of time being wasted in loading and unloading. Half an hour might be a reasonable allowance for each operation, though twenty minutes is desirable. Since 20 T. tankers soon may be in common use (4), loading machinery (i.e. elevators and conveyors) with capacities of 40–60 T./hr would be required from normal grain storage bins, and the cost of achieving this speed without damaging the product would be excessive. Therefore, either the tanker must wait for 40 min. with conveying equipment rated at 30 T./hr or overhead storage bins of 20 T. capacity are essential. The latter can be filled more slowly prior to the arrival of the tanker, which then can be filled by gravity within 30 min. Storage bins for this purpose can be obtained complete with their own supports to act as independent, weather-tight structures. The bins may be filled from an overhead conveyor or by blowing the material into them from a lower level. The outlet from the storage bin must be 12 ft above road level and the distance between the supports must be at least 10 ft, to allow the tanker to be positioned for filling (Fig. 2) (5). Alternatively, high-speed augers might be used to convey grain either direct from a special bin at ground level into the tanker, the bin being filled before the tanker's arrival, or direct from floor storage (Pt. 3, I D, 4b, p. 65). Bin outlets can be operated by a shutter combined with a lever-arm. It is best to empty a storage bin near its centre and, to facilitate emptying, at least two of the sides to the bin should be sloped to the outlet. With dry grain, 30 deg. is its angle of repose, though most self-emptying bins will have a floor slope of 45 deg., and 60 deg. should be used for meal with one side of the bin vertical. Smooth plastic-faced boards for the bin floor will assist the grain flow (6). In the process of filling and emptying a bin both grain and meal tend to separate into their heavier and lighter particles, the latter leaving the bin last. In filling, there will be an additional problem in that the grain will be shaped in a pile under the inlet. A spreader

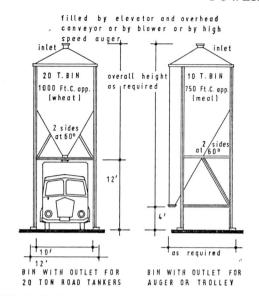

Fig. 2. Bulk storage bins for gravity unloading into tankers, conveyors or trolleys

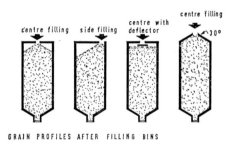

Fig. 3. Problems in filling bins

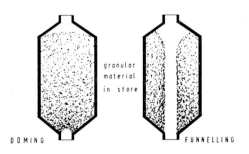

Fig. 4. Problems in emptying bins

or a conical roof will increase the storage capacity, the latter will also shed rain from the roof (Fig. 3). In emptying, an obstruction may be created by the material doming or funnelling (Fig. 4). The problem of flow or non-flow of bulk solids out of storage is primarily one of strength of the bulk material, which is increased by the compacting pressures due to its own weight and from its impact in filling, as well as from vibration, until the strength is sufficient to resist the pressure to flow. Grain is less of a problem than meal in this respect. The risk of obstruction occurring can be reduced by vertical partitions at the centre of the bin, by shelves at intervals on the bin wall, by a spreader to reduce impact when filling and by insulation against vibration (7). There will be some damage to pellets and cubes by the bulk discharge, which can be kept to under 2 per cent by a well-designed installation (8).

Both grain and meal can be handled by gravity for other purposes than filling a road transport tanker. Gravity can be used in the preparation and delivery of feeding-stuffs to livestock. Storage bins can be used for filling a milling and mixing plant from overhead and they can be used in the same manner for filling hoppers in milking parlours or piggeries, whether the hoppers are fixed, used on a monorail or pushed by hand. Fertilizers can be stored in overhead bins in a similar manner, being released by gravity into the field transport.

Straw for bedding can be dropped into cattle yards from raised storage spaces, particularly on top of bunker silos. Similarly, hay can be dropped into mangers. However, both these movements involve a manual operation. Such produce as potatoes can be damaged if excessively handled by gravity. Water can be handled by gravity to useful effect. Independent storage tanks controlled by ball valve can supply a range of drinking bowls by gravity, keeping them filled whenever the livestock drink. This eliminates the need for tongue-operated levers in the bowls and can be useful, particularly in pig housing. Milking-parlour floors can be cleaned easily if they are flooded by a volume of water, pumped perhaps from a milk cooler and stored in an overhead tank, being released quickly by gravity through a large outlet. Milk is handled by gravity at the end of the dairy pipe-line where the vacuum pressure is released. The milk either flows over a surface cooler into the churns or through a pipe-line into a bulk tank. With in-churn cooling it will flow directly into the churns. Most sludge-handling techniques involve gravity movement through carefully graded pipes. The handling of molasses into silage of feeding-stuffs and the supply of skim milk or whey to pigs will both be by gravity from raised storage tanks. Storage bins for free-flowing solids and liquids, and designed for emptying by gravity, can be obtained in a wide range of sizes and designs suitable for any requirement, and for discharging into tankers, hoppers, barrows, sacks or pipes. Storage tanks for these purposes of up to 1000 gal. of liquid are a normal commodity and storage bins for grain and meal up to 100 T. can be obtained.

B) TRACTOR DRIVEN

Some farms may have no fixed materials-handling equipment and very little portable equipment, except perhaps a simple auger conveyor, since it is possible to rely on the tractor and its attachments as the sole mechanical handling aid. The tractor can be used in the traditional manner, towing a trailer, the modern counterpart of the horse and wagon, or it can be made to move materials by a number of hydraulically operated attachments, powered directly from the engine, as if it had its own arms to push, scrape, dig, cut, lift and carry. Obviously, the former method is capable of handling larger unit loads than the latter, which, therefore, tends to be economic only for short distances. Finally, power can be taken directly from the engine, either when the tractor is stationary or when it is moving. The capacity of a tractor to handle materials will depend on its own size and power and there are numerous types of tractor available.

a. TOWED ATTACHMENTS

The traditional attachments towed behind a tractor are various types of cultivation tool or a trailer, both of which have been revolutionized in design during the last few years. Though small unit loads can be economically handled over short distances by such tools as a foreloader, which also can pick up and put down the load, as Holt has said (9):

'The mechanized movement of a product or material over distances greater than two or three hundred yards generally involves more than one piece of equipment and often more than one operator for loading, transport and unloading, tipping or stacking.'

Because of this factor, the National Institute of Agricultural Engineering has devised an experimental self-loading vehicle for materials handling, capable of picking up and loading on itself a number of unit loads, such as five $\frac{1}{2}$ T. 40 × 48 in. pallets, transporting them at 30 m.p.h., and unloading them on to the ground, on to another vehicle or of stacking them. The vehicle has been tested during 1962 for work in orchards, but it may have a wider application for transporting fuel, fertilizers, bales, potatoes and many other materials suitable for handling in units or pallets.

Normally, with few exceptions, towed attachments should be used only for handling materials from the fields to the buildings or from the buildings to the fields, and not for journeys between buildings within the farmstead. Exceptions can be made for handling silage or haylage in a self-unloading trailer to a forage fence or for handling feed from a mill/mix unit to individual stock houses, provided all loading and unloading is mechanized. In contrast, for example, it should not be necessary to load bales from a barn on to a trailer and then to have to manhandle them into stockyards from the trailer, since this is an expensive method of handling materials. However, the self-loading vehicle could be a valuable tool for handling unit loads between buildings, but its total length will be about 25–30 ft, with loading at one end, and this means that its manoeuvrability is limited.

Many cultivation tools are designed with containers, such as seed drills and fertilizer spreaders, with carrying capacities of up to 2 T. and with a working delivery spread of up to 50 ft, depending whether the spreader has a plate and flicker, a spinning disc or some other type of mechanism. However, transport widths are mainly under 6 ft, with a few exceptions of up to $11\frac{1}{2}$ ft, and with loading heights ranging from 2 to $6\frac{1}{2}$ ft (10). Some drills and spreaders have widths for storage of about 14 ft, though the machine may be swivelled so that it can be stored in the other direction (Pt. 3, I J 5b, p. 88).

Farm lorries or trailers can be obtained in various sizes up to about 25 ft in length and 7 ft in width, able to carry loads of up to 20 T. Many types of trailer are available, the simplest of which are designed as travelling platforms, usually used for handling bales or sacks, and are not a versatile method of transporting farm materials. Most platforms, however, can be fitted with side and end walls, which makes them as effective as most farm trucks, and in many cases both platforms and trucks can have extension pieces to increase the height of the walls. Similarly, trailers can have hinged or detachable walls or extension pieces, and the latter may be in the form of deep-panelled sides increasing the overall travelling height to 9 or 10 ft, used particularly for handling cut or chopped grass. Farm trailers can be similar in design to commercial bulk trailers, or they can be shaped at one end like a 'dumper' trailer used by builders and eliminating the need for a tailboard or they can have a shaped floor for self-emptying grain through an outlet in the bottom or side. Trailers can be equipped with an hydraulic, tractor-powered jack to tip the platform for unloading, which saves labour in handling some materials. Normally, the latter would limit the length of a trailer to a max. of 15 ft, carrying loads of up to 6 T. Popular-sized tipping trailers are about 10–12 ft long by 6 ft wide, with loading capacities of 3–4 T. The trailer can be formed from timber or sheet steel, and most trailers tip towards the end, though a few tip to the sides in addition to the end. The angle of tip is normally 40–60 deg., though a few trailers tip to 90 deg. A 12-ft trailer tipping at 60 deg. needs a working ht of about 14 ft, but if the trailer has extended sides about 6 ft high, which is normal practice for transporting grass or grain, about 16 ft clearance will be required. Most trailers have their floor about $2\frac{1}{2}$–3 ft from the ground. Tipping dump boxes of 2–3 T. capacity can be mounted on ordinary trailers.

Several proprietary self-emptying trailer hoppers, fitted with an auger for unloading, are available for transporting grain, mostly in loads of up to 3–4 T. Off-loading with some equipment can discharge the grain at hts of about 10 ft, and, depending on the height and angle of the auger when unloading, have emptying rates of 20–30 T./hr. A smaller auger-feed truck, for example, of 3 T. capacity, measuring about 8 ft × 6 ft, can handle about 12 T./hr of pellets or 10 T./hr of meal. Some machines also can be used as a mixer, and recently one or two machines have been developed which will mill and mix grain on a vehicle and which will discharge the feed via a side-mounted auger into a trough (Pt. 3, II E 6g, p. 129).

Other types of trailer are fitted with a moving chain and scraper floor which, when operating, will move material in the trailer to one end, where it can be distributed directly on to the fields. These can be used for fertilizers, lime and manure. In the latter case a chopper spreader is attached which increases the length of the trailer by about 3 ft. Normal carrying capacities are 2–3 T., or up to 5 T. in the case of large models, and with spreading widths of 12–15 ft. Some spreaders are power driven directly from the tractor engine, which means the turning circle may be based on a vehicle 25 ft long, since they cannot turn independently of the tractor.

Some vehicles, similar in principle to the spreaders, can carry, chop and distribute silage or haylage to one side at the end of the trailer directly into a feeding position or manger. Large vehicles may hold 5–7 T. of silage, and distribution rates of $\frac{1}{2}$ cwt./yd.R/2 sec. may be obtained, perhaps capable of feeding about 20 lb. d.m. haylage/2 sec. to dairy or beef cattle (Pt. 3, III A 2a ii, p. 166, and IIIB 3a). Though small self-unloading trailers may need passages only 6–7 ft wide, a large trailer may need 8–9 ft for safe operation with a 7-ft clearance. Other trailers of a similar kind can be used for delivering either grass or grain to a trough or forage fence. Usually, the discharge point is about $2\frac{1}{2}$ ft from the ground.

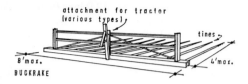

Fig. 5. Tractor attachment for handling grass, etc.

Fig. 6. Tractor attachment for handling bales, etc.

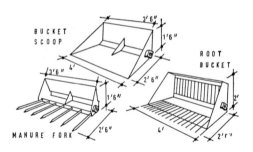

Fig. 7. Tractor attachments for lifting solids or semi-solids, etc.

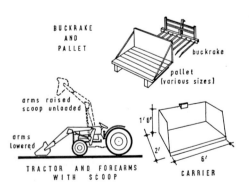

Figs. 8, 9, 10. Tractor attachments: various

Liquid manure spreaders can be towed behind a tractor, and large sludge tanks will hold up to 700 gal. Most of these tanks operate under suction, powered from the tractor engine, and are fitted with a spreader for distributing the manure on the fields. Most machines can operate at a rate of 1000–2000 gal./hr and are fitted with pick-up suction hoses of 10–20 ft. The hoses are placed in the sludge holding tank or can be fitted with a special hand-operated scraper blade and suction outlet for cleaning yards. One large tanker can be used to circulate 700 gal. of water through a sludge or slurry pit in order to agitate and dilute the muck and which can draw the diluted effluent back into the tank, which later, having an irrigation pump on the tanker, can be coupled to irrigation pipes in the fields (Pt. 3, I G 6, p. 78). The rate of extraction of the slurry by tanker is considerably less than that of an organic irrigation plant, where about 6000 gal./hr may be handled, though the material has to be diluted to a greater extent. Some systems can handle unscreened organic matter through a cutter with outputs of up to 13,000 gal./hr at a max. total head of 185 ft.

b. ATTACHMENTS MOUNTED FORE OR AFT ON HYDRAULIC ARMS

The lifting capacity of a tractor depends on the hydraulic pressure and output of the tractor pump as well as on the size of tractor. Some market-garden tractors may have no hydraulic system. Many types and sizes of buckrake are available today for mounting on the hydraulic fore-loaders or three-point linkage of a tractor. The number, size and strength of the tines will vary for different purposes. A buckrake used for picking up grass or hay may be $8\frac{1}{2}$ ft by $4\frac{1}{2}$ ft with 12 tines. A smaller tool might be 6 ft $\times$ $3\frac{1}{2}$ ft with only 7 tines (Fig. 5). The buckrake may be fitted with framed sides to a height of 5 ft for carrying and stacking up to 16 bales (Fig. 6).

The hydraulic fore-loaders have a normal lifting capacity of about $\frac{3}{4}$ T. to a pivot point for discharging at approximately 10 ft, but an overall clearance of up to 12 ft from the ground is required. Loads will seldom be transported at the full height of the fore-loaders. A counterbalance weight may have to be attached to the back of the tractor. Alternatively, the tractor may be equipped with fore- and aft-mounted loaders.

Equipment other than a buckrake can be attached to the hydraulic loaders. Variations on the buckrake design can be obtained with manure forks, scoops or buckets for roots (Fig. 7). Dimensions will vary with different makes, and the tools can be used for filling a trailer or container, either with fore or rear loaders (Fig. 8). Some fore-loaders can be fitted with boom arms for lifting about $\frac{1}{3}$ T. up to 20 ft. Rear loaders may prove more useful on difficult ground and may do more work in a given time, but many factors have to be taken into consideration.

A rear loader can be modified for lifting pallets for transportation (Fig. 9). Alternatively, a carrier can be attached to the rear of the tractor for carrying small loads (Fig. 10). In both cases loads are restricted usually to $\frac{1}{2}$ T., but $\frac{3}{4}$ T. can be carried with some tools. A rear-mounted tractor fork-lift is available and it can raise loads of 1 T. up to heights of 6 ft. This is useful, particularly for pallets (Fig. 11).

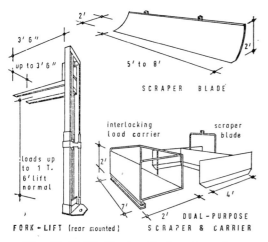

Figs. 11, 12, 13. Tractor attachments: various

Scraper blades can be attached fore or aft to a tractor and are used for cleaning yards. Most blades have lengths of 5–8 ft (Fig. 12). Some blades are designed for a dual purpose, having an interlocking carrier for transporting materials (Fig. 13). There are other attachments which can be used with a tractor, but the majority are operational tools rather than those for handling materials.

c. POWER DIRECT FROM THE TRACTOR ENGINE

The engine of a stationary tractor can be used in several ways to power other machinery. The normal method is to apply power from the engine with a power take-off coupling. Provision for this is important, especially in cases where an electric motor is used for essential work, which can be coupled to the tractor engine in an emergency, such as a power failure. The electric motors of most modern milking equipment will be positioned so that an emergency counter-shaft is available through an external wall for coupling to a tractor. The drive belt is taken sometimes from the end of a tractor and sometimes from the side. Liquid manure or sludge tanks can be mounted on the

back of a tractor, with capacities of up to 100 gal., or they can be towed behind the tractor, with capacities of up to 700 gal. as discussed above. Similarly, power may be taken from the tractor engine to operate a manure spreader.

C) ELECTRICAL

Electricity is an important and economic source of power for the mechanical-handling of materials, though the tractor sometimes may be more flexible and mobile for some jobs. Stationary diesel engines can be used in some positions to power mechanical-handling equipment; and are useful, particularly if an electrical supply is not easily available, for such equipment as the motor for driving the agitators in an organic irrigation tank or for powering some of the mobile sack elevators. However, they may cost more than electricity to use. The operating cost of a 5-h.p. electric motor is about two-thirds that of a 5-h.p. stationary diesel engine (11). Generally, electricity is used for what is normally termed 'barn machinery', which includes most of the mechanical-handling methods within buildings.

Electrically powered mechanical-handling can include elevators, conveyors and suction and blowing equipment. Several forms of each method of handling materials are available. However, the main distinction is between portable and fixed handling equipment, as far as planning farm buildings is concerned, even though the same type of equipment may be used in each case.

a. PORTABLE CONVEYING EQUIPMENT

Portable electrically powered equipment for handling materials is available, and this can be plugged into a power socket. Such equipment is designed to be flexible and capable of doing different jobs in different positions. Two main types are available. The auger is similar in design to fixed augers, and the bale and sack elevators may be similar in construction to the fixed bale conveyors.

i. Portable worm conveyors or augers are an asset on most farms, several types of equipment being available with the auger screw housed in a metal tube and with an electric motor attached on the outside. The tubes have diameters of, normally, between 3 and 6 ins., with a few, heavier models of up to 9 ins. They are suitable for handling free-flowing solids such as grain, meal and fertilizers. Augers for handling stiff sludge are used widely in Scandinavia and a 9-in. screw auger, 16 ft long, operated at 85 r.p.m. by a $1\frac{1}{2}$ h.p., 3-phase motor, can move 17 T./hr (12). Augers are an alternative method to vacuum tankers for handling slurry from under slatted floors, and recently have become accepted practice, though the advice of the manufacturer should be obtained, since not all augers are suitable.

Research into the efficiency of augers has been made by the National Institute of Agricultural Engineering (13). Most augers have the pitch of the screw approximately equal to its diameter. The speed of rotation and the angle of work, as well as the condition and type of the material conveyed will affect the throughput in relation to augers of stated diameter. For example, tests have been made with a 5½-ins.-dia. and with a 3-ins.-dia. auger and, when operating at the optimum speed for each auger conveying the same material at the same elevation, the throughput of the former will be approximately 2½–3 times that of the latter. Throughput when the auger is vertical is about 40 per cent of that when horizontal. Therefore, when the maximum throughput is desired the auger should be as near horizontal as possible, though requiring more floor space, which may not be practical. Denser materials may be conveyed more quickly than those which are lighter. Thus, 12 T./dry wheat might be handled by the same auger within the same time as a little over 8 T./dry oats. Similarly, and of great importance in practice, drier materials can be handled more efficiently than those which are wet, the efficiency declining sharply when the m.c. of grain exceeds 20 per cent. At 24 per cent m.c. using a 3-ins. auger at 45 deg., the throughput is only 70 per cent of that obtained with dry wheat and the power consumption is increased by 50 per cent. Conveying very wet grain could overload a motor which was capable of handling normal harvested materials (Fig. 14) (14).

The size of motor depends on the drive ratio of the screw; and the h.p. required/ft.R has to be related to the overall length of the conveyor. Conveying capacity is almost in proportion to the speed of an auger, and normally larger augers run considerably slower than smaller ones (500–750 r.p.m. compared with 1200–1500 r.p.m.). An auger conveying 10 T./hr at 400 r.p.m. will move 12½ T./hr at 500 r.p.m. (15). Power consumption will increase sharply if an auger's speed is increased above a critical point at which a given throughput can be conveyed economically, and most augers are set at a speed just below their critical point. A 6-ins. auger, required to give nearly 1000 r.p.m., might need a 3-h.p. motor for 12 ft, 5 h.p. for 21 ft and 7½ h.p. for 40 ft. Similarly, a 12 ft 6 ins. auger at 45 deg. might need a 2-h.p. motor to move dry grain at 760 r.p.m., but 3 h.p. for wet grain. In ideal conditions a 6-ins. auger might convey 40 T./hr, but a normal rate for dry grain would be not more than 20 T./hr at 30 deg. and 15 T./hr at 60 deg. elevation. Damage to grain passing through an auger two or three times should be negligible, but pulses may be damaged except at low speeds,

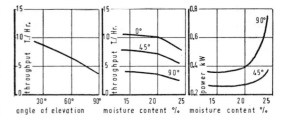

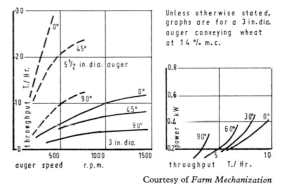

Unless otherwise stated, graphs are for a 3 in. dia. auger conveying wheat at 14 % m.c.

Courtesy of *Farm Mechanization*

Fig. 14. Auger performance 2nd power consumption at various angles of elevation

and cubed concentrates might have more than 5 per cent damage. The exposed auger flight must be guarded.

Many types of portable auger are available, suitable for vertical, horizontal or inclined positions, and some are telescopic and carrier mounted, others can convey round corners, and in some cases one motor can convey round three rt-angle corners. One manufacturer has 13 basic models with a wide range of attachments. Augers can be used for complete feed handling to livestock. They can be used instead of bucket elevators, though less efficient but requiring no excavation for a boot intake. Sweep augers can be installed to empty floors of grain storage bins, the screw and motor to the auger being taken from one bin for use in another (Pt. 3, I D 4b iii, p. 66).

Portable augers are available in lengths of about 40 ft max., though 20 ft is more manageable for handling. Various wheeled and mounted augers can be obtained, perhaps of up to 45 ft in length discharging at a max. ht. of 25 ft, and suitable for filling grain storage bins or bulk vehicles (Pt. 3, I D 4a i, p. 65). For example, a 6-ins. auger, with angles of elevation varying between 15 and 50 deg., might have a max. output for dry wheat of 45 T./hr. The delivery end of an auger can be fitted with an adjustable spout, to control the grain flow in any direction, or with a two-way bagging-off spout for sacks. Augers are available with a flexible steel, plastic-covered tube containing two concentric, counter-revolving spirals, with normal lengths of up to 20 ft, and 3 ins. in dia. with throughputs of up to 10 T./hr, and capable of being bent in any direction at any point on a radius of about 2 ft.

ii. Simple chain and flight elevators for bales or sacks are available, set in a light metal frame of about $1\frac{1}{2}$ ft $\times$ $\frac{1}{2}$ ft cross-section. Lengths of up to 42 ft elevate to a ht of 35 ft at 60 deg. max. Therefore, in normal use, they require at least 30 ft of floor space from the overhead conveyor or stack (Pt. 3, I A 6a, p. 55). For mobility, lengths of up to 30 ft may be mounted on a wheeled tripod, giving a loading point 6 ft from the floor and elevating to a max. ht of 30 ft at 45 deg. More robust sack elevators are made with a series of slats travelling over a metal frame, mounted on a wheeled tripod, with a max. off-loading ht of about 20 ft at 45 deg. These can be used for handling roots. Light bale elevators have a normal h.p. requirement of 1 and the heavier models $2\frac{1}{2}$ for sacks or $3\frac{1}{2}$ for roots.

b. FIXED CONVEYING EQUIPMENT

The fixed equipment for conveying is mainly of three distinct types, the horizontal conveyor, the elevator and pipes for the suction or blowing of materials both horizontally and vertically.

i. The auger may be a fixed tool, instead of being portable, both for conveying and for elevating. It is used in grain and feed installations and may be used for handling feed to the troughs. They are not such sturdy machines as other forms of conveying, though heavy duty augers are used for handling either haylage from a silo or chopped silage or roots to the feed troughs. The latter are mostly of 7–9 ins. dia. Some are not enclosed, except by two side-boards forming a trough, though some are enclosed in a metal tube with adjustable slot outlets. The latter can be adjusted either to give a uniform ration from each outlet, perhaps with an outlet at every 2 ft, irrespective of the length of auger or to vary the amount of the ration. Similar augers can be used for conveying rolled barley. They are usually available in units of up to about 12 ft and can be coupled up to form runs of about 100 ft, powered by a 4 h.p. motor at about 150 r.p.m., or 200 ft with $7\frac{1}{2}$ h.p., depending on make, and conveying between 1 and 2 cwt./min. (8–16 ft³) (16) (Pt. 3, III B 5b, p. 188).

ii. The chain and flight conveyor has many uses, both for conveying and for elevating, and can be designed to convey and then to elevate from one motor, though the normal use is for long straight runs. The chain and flight is supported from an enclosing tube or trough, the moving chain supporting cross-flights which keep the material in motion. The design and construction of the conveyors can vary within the basic principle to suit different situations. They are suitable either for conveying grain or meal and, in the latter case, should not give rise to uneven distribution in a mixed meal. The conveying capacity will depend on the material, the design and size of the conveyor, and on the motor. It is easy to arrange distribution outlets along the run of conveyor. The conveyor is convenient for handling meal from a central mill/ mix unit to different points of use and can be used in pig houses for distributing meal along lengths of several hundred feet or in milking parlours to the various hoppers in the stalls. Throughputs with a 2-h.p. motor of 20 T./hr along 100 ft are normal, though this might be reduced to 5 T./hr if the conveyor was set at 30 deg. Normal throughputs are about 10 T./hr per 50 ft with a 1-h.p. motor. Special chain and flight elevators will raise 5 T. of grain or 3 T. of meal to 25 ft for the same power. Few of the conveyors are self-cleaning. Other fixed conveyors can be used for handling bales of hay or straw, in conjunction with mobile elevators, and over distances of 120 ft (Pt. 3, I A 6b, p. 55). (See below, iv.)

Dung channels in piggeries and cowsheds can be cleaned mechanically. Piggeries can have their dung passage cleaned with a proprietary mechanism based on a winch-operated scoop which, in theory, has a movement similar to a chain conveyor with one large flight (Pt. 3, III E 6b, p. 213). In cowsheds two main types of channel cleaner are available. One cleaner has a reciprocating rod carrying a series of hinged slats which are raised as the rod is pulled, pushing the dung forward, and then hinge and fold back behind the dung as the rod is pushed back. Another type of cleaner is operated with slats on an endless chain. Both cleaners are inclined up a ramp for part of their run, dropping the dung over the end of the ramp into a trailer or spreader (Fig. 15). One modern cleaner will operate over 200 ft.R with a 5-h.p. motor, at about £6/ft.R, with a conveyor-elevator for the ramp, operated by a $1\frac{1}{2}$-h.p. motor, cleaning at a rate of 95 ft/min. A ramp 16 ft long will raise the dung 7 ft, one 22 ft long 10 ft. Most discharge elevators will give a max. rise of about 25 deg. Channels vary between 1 and $1\frac{1}{2}$ ft in width, and up to 1 ft in depth. Motors for the driving unit may have to be set in the floor. Endless chains operate round corners over a pulley wheel which has to be set in the floor.

iii. Endless belts for conveying materials horizontally are used throughout industry both for solids and for free-flowing solids. They are usually 3–15 in. wide, carried on rollers and moving in a shallow trough. The belts may be flat or troughed. They tend to be a little more expensive than chain and flight conveyors. They are self-cleaning, which can be important for conveying seed corn, and do not cause uneven distribution of mixed meals. Off-loading deflectors can be used to change

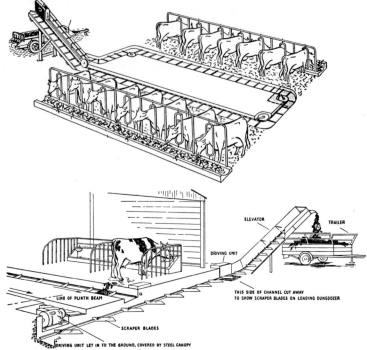

Fig. 15. Mechanical cleaning of dung channels.

(*top*) Courtesy of S. M. Wilmot & Co. Ltd.,
(*lower*) Courtesy of Simplex Dairy Equipment Co. Ltd.

direction or to convey to more than one point. Throughputs are similar to the chain and flight, i.e. 1 h.p. may convey 10 T./hr/50 ft. A 15-in. belt can convey 35–40 T./hr over 120 ft with a 3-h.p. motor at each end. Some trough belts can be inclined to 30 deg. for low throughputs. The belts should be guarded. Some endless belts have been used or adapted for cleaning cowshed dung channels.

iv. The vibrating belt or jog-trough has limited application today, though, if floor mounted, it can be a cheap, though sometimes noisy, method of conveying, with high rates of throughput for low power requirements. New forms of vibrator may be developed. A recent machine combines a single-chain elevator and conveyor with a bale separator and a jog-trough feeder manger so that bales can be loaded, stored and fed by machinery, the only manual work required being the placing of the bales on the storage elevator and the feed conveyor (17). The elevator-conveyor with 100 ft.R of conveyor suspended from a barn roof and powered by 1-h.p. motor can random stack up to 2500 bales/day using a movable push-off plate controlled by a rope from the ground. This unit costs about £400. For feeding, the operator places the bales on the conveyor, removes the springs and sets a time switch, the cattle being fed automatically via a bale separator and vibrator-feeder at a rate of 8 lb./head to fill a manger 60 ft long in about 5 min. A manger 50 ft long requires a 2-h.p. motor, one 100 ft long 3 h.p. The first 20 ft costs about £350, thereafter £6/ft.R.

v. The bucket elevator, which has buckets attached to an endless belt, is the normal heavy duty grain elevator, with high throughputs for low power requirements. Naturally, the unit is larger than other conveying systems, the size being increased by the up and the down runs of belt, and an area 6 ft × 1½ ft may be required, though this will vary with make. The normal size of bucket may be up to 12 in. The buckets are enclosed in a timber case, which should have an access panel. The intake point may be 1–2 ft above the base of the elevator, which means that a pit may be required, and 2–4 ft may be needed above the delivery point. Elevators up to 60 ft high are available, with throughputs of up to 50 T./hr. Normal units will raise 8 T./hr/25 ft for 1 h.p., or 15 T./hr/16 ft.

vi. Suction is used for conveying or elevating liquids and, to some extent, for free-flowing materials. Milk, by an alternating arrangement of suction and pressure, is extracted from a cow and moved along a pipe to the point of storage and cooling. The earlier milking machines had a pulsation ratio of 1 : 1, but modern equipment is based on 4 : 1 with an initial vacuum mercury gauge at the cow of about 15 w.g., and the speed of suction and pressure in relation to the diameter of the pipe-line will be important in the design of machinery suitable for large herds (Pt. 3, II F 2c, p. 135). Lengths of milk pipe-line may exceed 300 ft. Bulk tankers will suck the milk from a bulk tank through a length of flexible coupling hose. Vacuum tankers will lift water or sludge from collection tanks. Grain can be sucked from a heap or from a bin with attachments coupled to a normal pressure conveying system for distances of up to 150 ft. Grain must not pass through the fan mechanism.

vii. Mobile blowing units are standard equipment for filling vertical silos and will blow between 10 and 40 T./hr. of chopped grass for heights of 70–90 ft through ducts of about 9 in. dia. Motors of 5–10 h.p. are required for the lower throughputs and of up to 35 h.p. for the max. Small 3-h.p. blowers are available for 4 T./hr capacities. The smaller units are used mainly for blowing grain and meal into storage bins from bulk transporters. They can be used for blowing grain and meal for distances of up to 200 ft, but with meal there will be some displacement of the particles. The units are made up from a fan, an injector and the run of pipe or duct, and can include an inlet hopper into the injector. The resistance of vertical piping is roughly twice that of horizontal piping. A cyclone may be required at the distribution point to filter the air away from the grain.

(1) FLEMING, I. J. & CUNNINGHAM, J. D. Scottish Agricultural Industries Ltd. A.W.S. Report 6. September 1960. 'Materials Handling on the Farm—Dairy Farming'.
(2) Ibid. A.W.S. Report 7. October 1960. Beef Arable Farm.
(3) STURROCK, F. G. & BRAYSHAW, G. H. University of Cambridge. School of Agriculture Report No. 47. May 1958. *Planning the Farm to Save Labour*, p. 1.
(4) CULL, R. *Bulk Handling and the Merchant*, p. 70. *Agricultural Merchant*, April 1962.
(5) NATIONAL ASSOCIATION OF CORN & AGRICULTURAL MERCHANTS. *Bulk Handling of Grain Feeds and Fertilizers.* July 1963.
(6) *Farmers Weekly.* Report on Farm Buildings Conference. 10 October 1962.
(7) JENIKE, A. W. 'Flow of bulk solids in bins', *Utah Engr. Expt. Sta. Bulletin* 64, March 1954.
(8) CULL, R. *Bulk Handling and the Merchant*, p. 72. *Agricultural Merchant*, April 1962.
(9) HOLT, J. B. 'A self-loading vehicle for materials handling', *Farm Mechanization*, July 1963, p. 65.
(10) 'Fertilizer spreaders', *Farmers Weekly*, 1 December 1961, pp. 94–98.
(11) CULPIN, C. *Farm Mechanization Management*, 1959, p. 80.
(12) North of Scotland College of Agriculture. April 1962, Report on Demonstration of Sludge Handling.
(13) STEVENS, G. N. 'Performance tests on experimental auger conveyors'. *Jour. Ag. Eng. Res.* Vol. 7 No. 1, 1962.
(14) STEVENS, G. N. 'There's more to an auger than meets the eye'. *Farm Mechanization.* June 1963, pp. 37–39.
(15) HINE, H. J. 'Through the tube', *Practical Power Farming*, May 1962.
(16) MORTIMER, P. G. 'Push-button silage', *Dairy Farmer*, June 1962, p. 34.
(17) 'Bales loaded, stored and fed—all by machinery'. *Farm Mechanization.* January 1963, pp. 34–35.

SELECTED REFERENCES
a. CULPIN, C. *Farm Machinery*, 7th Ed., 1963.
b. CULPIN, C. *Farm Mechanization Management*, 1959.
c. 'Mechanical Handling of Farm Materials', *Farmers Weekly Supplement*, May 1960.
d. *British Tractors and Farm Machinery. The Green Book.* (1962). (Annual.)
e. HAMMOND CRADOCK, T. *Farm Mechanization Handbook*, 3rd Ed. (1962). (Annual.)
f. Materials Handling Conference Issue. *Agricultural Engineering*, September 1958.
g. 'Automatic Feeding'. *Farm Electrification Handbook No. 9.* Electrical Development Association (1964).

9: LOADING BALES MECHANICALLY

There are various mechanical methods of loading bales into a barn. Not only are bale elevators available, but, as shown here, a foreloader attachment on a tractor can lift 6–8 bales to hts of 12–15 ft, place them on a stack and the tractor driver can release the foreloader grip on the bales. The tractor needs a concrete block rear weight to counteract the load. In this case the straw barn is of simple timber pole construction. [SEE PAGES 42 & 55] Courtesy of Practical Power Farming.

10: ELEVATING BALES

Baled hay can be elevated into a barn on a portable inclined chain-and-flight conveyor from a trailer towed from the fields. One man is required for loading and one for stacking (the others shown examining the elevator are not required). The hay barn is a traditional Dutch barn with curved roof. The elevator is mounted on an adjustable tripod and can be moved with a tractor. Straw bales can be handled in the same manner. [SEE PAGES 45 & 57] Courtesy of British Farmer.

11: LOADING A TOWER SILO

A self-unloading trailer can discharge 3–4 T of wilted and finely chopped grass within 10–15 min into a hopper. A short auger in the hopper takes the grass into the blower. The grass can be blown 50–80 ft vertically into the top of the tower silo. In this case, the tower is made of vertical concrete staves around which are tension wires. Space is required at the base of the tower for the tractor and trailer to manoeuvre. [SEE PAGES 46 & 59] Courtesy of Rustproof Metal Window and Engineering Co. Ltd.

12: LOADING TOWER SILOS: SEALED AND UNSEALED SILOS

Two different types of tower silo are shown together; one is a hermetically sealed, glass lined, stove enamelled silo 50 ft high and the other is formed from precast concrete staves bound together with external tension rods, complete with a galvanized steel dome 70 ft high. The latter is being filled by a self-unloading trailer, the grass being discharged into a blower, from which it passes up a vertical $\frac{3}{4}$ ft dia. external pipe into the silo near the top. A spreader in the top of the silos distributes the grass evenly, which becomes compacted under its own weight. Cat-ladders give access to the top of the silos. The sealed silo is unloaded by a cutter in its bottom, whereas the concrete silo is not air-tight and a cutter suspended from the top discharges the haylage down a chute on the far side. [SEE PAGES 46 & 59] Courtesy of Rustproof Metal Window and Engineering Co. Ltd.

PART THREE

THE SPECIALIZED BUILDINGS

Storage for these commodities may be required prior to their being used in the buildings or in the fields, or prior to their sale from the farm (Pt. 2, Ch. 2, p. 35).

Bulk handling into and out of storage is important and the correct siting of the store in relation to the other relevant spaces may eliminate double handling.

Introduction

The chapter on 'Farm Enterprises and their Buildings' (Pt. 1, Ch. 2) showed that farm buildings could be examined in three main groups according to the nature of their basic function, even though, in practice, some of the functions tended to overlap between the groups. The basic function of any farm activity requiring the enclosure of a building is either for storage, for processing or for converting coarse foods. Each of these activities is performed within a defined space and such a space may form a complete building, a number of buildings being required to form the layout for an enterprise. However, the space required for an activity may form only a part of one building, the complete building being composed of a number of inter-related spaces. For convenience, each of these spaces is referred to as a specialized building.

Part 3 of this study will consider each of these defined spaces, or specialized buildings, separately. An attempt will be made to give sufficient data for it to be possible not only to design the space to enclose its specified function, but to relate the space correctly to the others required in a layout to suit any particular farm management policy. It is necessary, however, first, to consider in more detail the three main groups of activities which occur within farm buildings.

I. Storage buildings are designed to maintain foods, materials or equipment in a satisfactory and convenient state, without changing the condition of the stored commodity. Storage is a subsidiary activity to those of processing and of converting coarse foods. Buildings for storage form Section I and include storage for:

IA. Straw	IG. Manure and
IB. Hay	slurry
IC. Haylage and	IH. Potatoes
maize	IJ. Implements
ID. Grain and seed	IK. Records and
IE. Feeding-stuffs	office
IF. Fertilizers	

II. Processing buildings for foods or materials on the farm are designed in order to improve the quality or to change the physical state of foodstuffs or materials either prior to their use on the farm or their sale from the farm. These buildings form Section II, and include facilities for:

IIA. Grass drying	IIF. Milking
IIB. Hay drying	IIG. Dipping and
IIC. Ensilage	shearing
IID. Grain drying	IIH. Potato chitting
IIE. Milling and	IIJ. Workshops
mixing	IIK. Packing

Again, bulk handling of the materials and the siting of the buildings in relation to the other relevant spaces are important. The processes involved require machinery for their performance, and, to some extent, each process is a technical problem over which considerable control may be required.

III. Production buildings are designed to convert coarse foods, including grass and grass products, roots, grain and skim milk, into flesh or dairy products. Though the techniques of livestock fattening and of milk production are related principally to the food conversion ratio between the coarse foods and those for human consumption, there are numerous methods of obtaining this transformation. Unfortunately, there is little scientific knowledge available which relates the breed and physiological requirements of livestock to the design of buildings and to the management within the buildings. This is one important reason why so many types of livestock building are used in practice. These buildings form Section III, and include production units for:

IIIA. Milk	IIIF. Weaners
IIIB. Beef	IIIG. Mutton and
IIIC. Calves	lamb
IIID. Veal	IIIH. Poultry and
IIIE. Pork, bacon	eggs
and heavy	
hogs	

It can be seen that there are more than two dozen types of specialized building. Each of these specialized buildings may need an analysis of several different basic layouts, since there may be variations in farm management policy to attain the same goal, and each of these layouts may require a choice from one of several structural forms suitable for the same purpose. Some of the buildings are governed in their design principally by their relationship to the system of farming the land, some more particularly to the labour routines performed within them and some to the machines which are used to assist the work methods. Others, in contrast, will be governed by the physical requirements of the commodity housed within them or by the structural techniques economically available. The cost of the building and its value as an investment will govern the final choice (Pt. 1, Ch. 1), since most buildings have to be a compromise between conflicting requirements.

In order to examine the basic design requirements for the many different specialized buildings, the data must be presented in a disciplined manner. This facilitates cross reference between the different buildings, which is essential, since many have design problems or requirements similar to other buildings. Each specialized building will be considered under twelve headings, numbered from 1 to 12 inset to the text. Cross-references are given by the group classification of the building, as listed above, followed by the relevant numeral. The twelve headings are defined below:

1. *Activity*. The description of the farm activity governing the basic function of the specialized building will be given briefly and will be related to the overall farming system. The major variations which may be encountered are also given, in so far as they affect the building design.

2. *Managerial requirements*. The factors outlined in (1) above will be expanded to give in more detail the managerial decisions which may influence a farmer's requirements for a specialized building. The main actions and processes that are varied to suit different farm policies will be considered. These create variations in the basic layout, which in turn cause differences in the throughput attained.

3. *Production techniques*. An analysis will be made of the main variations in the farming techniques in relation to the specified activity and for which the specialized building has to be designed. Thus, the managerial requirements (2) will be translated into terms of the physical requirements for the layout.

This section is not required to any great extent for storage buildings.

4. *Work routines*. The principal work requirements within each activity, in so far as they affect the building design, will be considered, including the frequency of operation, the method of performance and the work and circulation spaces required. This section, however, will not be a work study examination of the correct work methods for doing a particular job.

5. *Design data*. The minimum or basic dimensions, volumes or weights compatible with good management will be given, together with any physical measurements of change in the commodity or product held within the specialized building. Data may be based on approximations and averages from empirical observation or on scientific measurement, the limitations to accuracy being stated.

6. *Equipment*. The equipment used within the building for purposes related to the activity will be considered in relation to its effect on the building design. The equipment may be used to assist the work routines (4) or may influence the design data (5). The equipment may be mobile, may be attached to the building or may be part of the building structure.

7. *Environment control*. Data concerning the control of the physical environment required for the commodity or product, as outlined in (5), will be considered. These will include such factors as heating, ventilation, humidity, moisture extraction, insulation and lighting.

8. *Layouts*. Line drawings and descriptions of the specialized building will be given in sufficient detail to suit the managerial requirements (2), production techniques (3), work routines (4) and design data (5).

9. *Siting*. The basic layout will be related to factors which may influence the choice of site and orientation. Indications will be given briefly as to how the specialized building should be related to the other spaces required for the enterprise in which it occurs. It is not the intention to give optimum layouts suitable for all conditions, since this is in fact impossible.

10. *Services*. Most specialized buildings will have definite requirements with regard to the services required. This section will consider such factors as electricity, water, light, heat, ventilation, drainage, etc. The distribution and installation of these services may influence the layouts (8) and the siting (9).

11. *Costs*. Cost is part of the data required when considering the design of a specialized building. It is impossible to give accurate costs for each layout for reasons discussed in the chapter on Capital Investment (Pt. 1, Ch. 1). Moreover, it depends on the choice of structure, materials and finishes (Vol. 2). However, certain levels of cost, which can be considered in the broadest terms, are found to occur in normal practice. They can be taken as a rough guide on a unit cost basis (Pt. 1, Ch. 1), and are given on the basis of contract labour and a reasonable to good level of specification and execution. They cannot be taken as the maximum or minimum level of capital investment which is reasonable. Each design should be costed in relation to a particular farm.

The annual building costs are taken as the capital cost multiplied by 150 per cent to cover interest, maintenance and insurance, and divided by 10 to allow for depreciation (Pt. 1, Ch. 1). Similarly, machinery costs are taken as the capital cost multiplied by 150 per cent and divided by 6. Labour costs are rated at £¾ per manhour to cover the basic wage, bonus, housing, insurance, relief assistance, supervision and other overheads (Pt. 1, Ch. 4). Machinery running costs have to be rated on fuel consumption. Though these assessments of cost may be higher than those normally made in the past, it is essential, in considering buildings which have to be proved economic over a number of years, that costs should be taken which may still be relevant in about five years time.

12. *References*

References are given to the text. Some of these references are to standard works, others to various articles in magazines. Not all the references will have lasting significance, but they are given not only to sources of technical data but to various ideas and techniques discussed in greater length than is possible in the text. In addition, certain other references are given to selected works which give further information on current practices.

SECTION I

STORAGE BUILDINGS

Introduction

Half of the storage buildings considered are used principally in conjunction with the production units described in Section III. Their design and efficiency will affect the unit cost of production either for meat or for dairy produce. Many livestock enterprises require also three of the other storage buildings, those for fertilizers, implements and records, and sometimes, in addition, that for grain. In contrast, intensive production buildings may require storage only for feeding-stuffs, slurry and records.

Two of the storage buildings, those for fertilizers and for implements, are used principally in conjunction with fieldwork, two are used for crops and one for farm administration. Storage, since it is a subsidiary activity to those for processing and for production, does not contribute directly to the profit from an enterprise, with the exception of that for grain and potatoes. In the latter two cases, unless the crop is intended for consumption on the farm, storage may make it possible to obtain a higher price when the peak marketing period at harvest has passed.

The principles of storage are changing rapidly and radically and it is essential to re-examine them constantly, considering storage as a temporary and expensive delay between production and consumption. Should a winter grass be perfected, fewer buildings for grass conservation and storage would be required. Modern means of transport and the organized means for distributing goods no longer make it as necessary to have storage near the point of production and near the point of use as when the means for distribution were disorganized and difficult. The design and cost of modern machinery and buildings tend to make large storage units more efficient and cheaper than numerous smaller units.

Many merchants believe that grain storage on the

farm is inefficient, and centralized grain storage, except on large grain-producing farms, is becoming more prevalent. The growth of contract and of co-operative farming will tend to centralize the storage of machinery and fertilizers. The production and storage of straw may prove to be an excessive burden on the unit cost of producing meat or milk. Regional farming may be developed, in which case crop production will become more centralized, and, with efficient techniques for harvesting and for distribution, the storage of fodder might be at any point between the fields and the animals.

IA. Straw

1. *Activity*. Straw is a by-product of grain production. About 60 per cent. of the straw is collected and stored after harvesting, 30 per cent. being ploughed directly into the field and 10 per cent. burnt before ploughing (1). In the West, where the livestock density is high in relation to the cereal acreage, most of the straw is collected, but in the East the opposite conditions prevail. Straw may be stored for the following reasons:

a. To be used for the bedding of livestock, both for their comfort and for the farmyard manure thereby produced. Capital and handling costs for producing manure in this manner can be considerable and other methods for bedding livestock are available. Some recent research has shewn that this method for returning the straw into the soil has had little effect on subsequent yields (2) and since the slurry produced by livestock can be applied to the fields in a liquid or semi-liquid state (IG1, p. 76), it may become less popular to store straw to act as bedding. This problem requires further research.

b. To be used as cattle food. Straw, particularly oat straw, is to a limited extent fed to older cattle, mainly as part of the maintenance ration.

c. To be sold for bedding when prices for straw rise during the winter months.

d. To act as a cover for potatoes during storage (IH5, p. 81) and, sometimes, as a cheap roof insulation over netting for livestock.

2. *Managerial requirements*. The main requirements are to maintain the straw in good condition and to make its handling easy.

3. *Production techniques*

a. The quantity of straw to be stored on a farm will depend primarily on the acreage of grain and the proportion of the straw conserved. Yields of straw per acre may be up to 3 T, but $1–1\frac{1}{4}$ T are most common. The yield may vary due to:

i. Type of grain, variety of seed and fertilizer policy.

ii. Weather, particularly rainfall, and moisture content when harvested.

iii. Height at which the crop is cut; the higher the cut, the quicker the combine harvester can work. Most straw is handled from the fields in bales, but it can be collected in bulk.

b. Some combine-harvesters have low density straw balers (or bunchers) attached at the rear. However, most straw is baled by a separate machine, the pick-up baler. Most balers produce rectangular bales bound with twine, but some produce circular bales and some bind the bales with wire. The density of the bales varies according to the machine and its setting, and therefore the volume per ton of straw also varies.

c. Straw can be collected from the field in bulk and handling techniques now being developed allow for the straw to be chopped, either with a chopper and pick-up attachment on the combine or with a flail type forage harvester blowing the chopped straw into a forage box. In the future the method of handling straw will determine the method of storage. It has been shewn that labour costs can be reduced by half with chopped straw storage (1). For example, loads of $1\frac{1}{2}–1\frac{3}{4}$ T of chopped straw can be blown into a hooded trailer from a forage harvester in under $\frac{1}{4}$ hr. These can be blown in $\frac{1}{8}$ hr through a $\frac{3}{4}$-ft-dia. pipe into a barn. Therefore, to harvest, cart and store over $1\frac{1}{4}$ T of chopped straw from fields at some distance from the barn, using only 1 man and 2 tractors, should take less than $\frac{3}{4}$ hr. Other than saving labour, advantages are (3):

i. Corn and straw can be cleared from a field within the day without requiring additional labour.

ii. Grain is harvested without running over the straw.

iii. Straw is harvested before it is damaged by the weather.

iv. Undersown seeds are not smothered by straw, chaff or balers.

v. Ploughing, spraying, grazing or cultivation if required can start immediately after harvesting.

4. *Work routines*. The work routines connected with straw storage are in filling and emptying the store.

a. FILLING

i. Bales usually are delivered from the field on a trailer, often in 3-T loads. (Approximate size of loaded trailer, 10 ft × 7 ft × 10 ft high.) The bales are unloaded by hand and may be stacked in the store:

1) By hand.
2) By elevator, with hand stacking.
3) By elevator, with random, tumble stacking.

ii. Bales also may be delivered from the field on fore or rear loaders attached to a tractor. The tractor transports, lifts and places each load into the stack. Sizes of load vary between 8 and 20 bales per loader.

iii. Chopped straw can be mechanically unloaded into a blower to fill the store.

b. EMPTYING

i. By hand from stack direct to point of use (particularly with some cattle layouts).

ii. By hand on to an overhead conveyor to point of use.

iii. By hand into a trailer for conveyance by tractor to livestock.

iv. Chopped straw may be handled by a tractor and scoop, or by a blower, or by an elevator, and may be conveyed by a belt or auger conveyor or forage box.

5. *Design data.* The size of individual bales depends on the machine and the setting of the bale chamber. Lengths may be varied from 18 to 42 in., but 36 in. or 42 in. are normal Cross-sections will vary, but are normally about 14 in. × 18 in. for twine-bound bales, 20 in. × 24 in. for wire-bound bales and 14–22 in. in diameter for circular bales. Weights of straw bales may be between 20 and 30 lb./bale for low density buncher bales, 35–45 lb./bale for medium-density bales and 60–100 lb./bale for high-density bales. Average volumes for stacking may be taken as (4):

	In bales	Loose
Wheat straw, yd³/T	17	23
Oat straw, yd³/T	14	25
Barley straw, yd³/T	15	30

Semi-compressed chopped straw can have an approximate volume of $\frac{2}{3}$ of the volume for baled straw (1), but, due to the normal uncompressed nature of chopped straw, it might have a volume of $1\frac{1}{3}$ that of baled straw. Further research is required. If blown into a tall barn, chopped straw will settle under its own weight to a semi-solid mass (3).

6. *Equipment.* Proprietary bale elevators and conveyors are available, though ordinary sack elevators may be used.

a. BALE ELEVATORS (Part 2, IIICa, ii, p. 45).

b. BALE CONVEYORS

Chain and frame unit, as before, in horizontal sections, suspended at a max. of 16-ft centres and weighing about 6 lb./ftR. Bales may be diverted off the conveyor at any point. Maximum conveying length about 120 ft.

c. BALE LOADERS

Mechanical loading by tractor can reach max. heights of about 12–14 ft. Greater stack heights can be attained only by hand loading.

d. STRAW BLOWERS

Straw is usually blown by using a forage blowing unit, which will blow 20–25 ft into the store, the unit being moved as the store is filled. Thus normal heights of about 20 ft are possible. Distances and

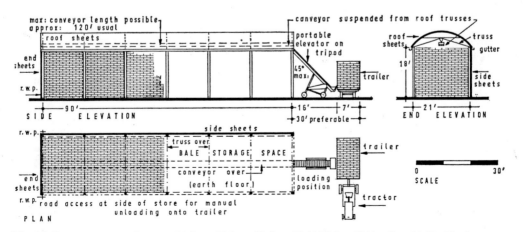

Fig. 16. Straw storage: volume — 90 ft × 20 ft × 18 ft = 32,400 ft³ = 1200 yd³ = 80 T of barley straw

heights can be increased by using tube extensions to the blower.

7. *Environment control.* Exclusion of rain and snow from the top of the stack is the main requirement and this necessitates either a roof or plastic or tarpaulin sheets. On sites exposed to driving rain, there should be protection on the sides.

8. *Layouts.* Baled straw is usually stacked for cheapness in Dutch, or other simply constructed, barns. If a conveyor is used it can be suspended from the apex of the barn. Barn spans of about 20 ft are convenient, with access from one end for loading and from one side for emptying. One end and one side may be sheeted with galvanized iron against the weather. The floor, except on wet sites, can be of earth (Fig. 16). Chopped straw produces considerable dust and the best methods for storing it have not been established. A cheap method is a barn with chicken netting at the sides.

9. *Siting.* It is preferable for straw to be stored away from other buildings, due to the fire risk, and large quantities should be stored in two or more well-separated barns. However, labour-saving layouts are today more important, and for this the store needs to be adjacent to the point of use, especially with cattle yards (IIIA and IIIB). Straw barns are sometimes sited to act as a wind break for other buildings.

10. *Services.* An electrical supply is required for mechanical elevating, unless petrol engines are used. Roof water should be drained clear of the site.

11. *Costs.* The store shown in Fig. 16 might cost £10 to £11/T stored, plus another £2 if the floor had to be concreted. The conveyor and elevator would add another £3¼ to £4/T. For costs of baling and carting straw see IIIB 26 p. 184.

12. *References*

(1) EDDOWES, M. 'Alternatives to Baling'. *Practical Power Farming*, p. 6 (June 1962).
(2) *High Mowthorpe Experimental Husbandry Farm Guide* (Ministry of Agriculture), p. 18 (1962).
(3) 'Speeding up the straw harvest,' *Farm Mechanization*, p. 52 (March 1963).
(4) *Farm Buildings Pocketbook* (Ministry of Agriculture), p. 22. (Revised figures.)

IB. Hay

1. *Activity.* Hay is conserved grass for winter feeding, mainly of cattle (IC Haylage and IIC Ensilage). In 1957, 84 per cent of the grass con-

served was made into hay (1), but since then silage has increased in popularity. Nevertheless, hay is likely to remain the main fodder crop, even though it may have to be handled six, or occasionally twelve, times between field and stock (2).

In order to store hay, it is necessary to reduce the moisture content from a normal 75–85 per cent when cut to between 15–20 per cent. This reduction can be achieved, if the weather is perfect, by tedding the grass after cutting, and the feeding matter produced is as good in quality as that obtained by artificially dried hay. However, frequent tedding and turning of the grass increases labour requirements and, more important, a moderate shower of rain can reduce the value of the hay. It was shown at the Drayton Experimental Husbandry Farm in 1961 that the reduction in value reduced the liveweight gain of beef cattle by ¼ lb/day, and this was worth £3½/T of hay produced (3) (IIB 2a, p. 97).

To reduce the risk of nutrient losses, barn hay drying is being increasingly practised. In this method the grass is allowed to wilt in the field for up to 48 hours after cutting (24 hours being preferable), in order to bring the moisture content down to under 45 per cent, if possible to 30 per cent. The hay is then baled and artificially dried. Very little hay is dried loose rather than in the bale (4). Hay drying is described in IIB, and may take place either within the place of storage or prior to storage in a separate place. This section is concerned only with the storage of baled hay, whether sun or barn dried. Hay can be harvested and chopped in the field (IIB 3a, p. 100), but it is then likely to be artificially dried within its place of storage, having been handled in bulk from the field (see below).

It should be noted that a method is being developed in America to mechanize the handling of hay, in order to reduce the labour costs of producing bales. In this method, the crop has to be tedded until the moisture content is about 25 per cent, when it is picked up, chopped and passed through a press, giving a pressure of about 5000 lb/in.² to produce a hay wafer. The wafer has a minimum density of 25 lb/ft³ and a maximum of 35 lb/ft³, and weighs about ⅛ lb. The wafers can be handled with a trailer in bulk to the store. Bulk storage and mechanical conveyance to the troughs is possible. This form of wafer hay may replace the baler on large farms, especially if it is proved that it is possible to produce wafers with 40 per cent m.c. (moisture content) and dry them artificially down to 20 per cent m.c. (2, 6). This is a matter for further research.

Recent experiments in the United Kingdom have shown that it may be possible to combine rapid field wilting with chopping to under 6 in. length together with pneumatic loading into a storage hay drier. This method would eliminate the need for bales and allow complete mechanization from field to feeding, but depends on artificial drying (6).

2. Managerial requirements. As for Straw (IA).

3. Production techniques. The quantity of hay required to be stored will depend on the feeding policy. Yields of hay per acre depend on the grass varieties, the soil, the weather, fertilizer usage and the cutting policy. Yields are normally between $1\frac{1}{2}$ and 2 T/acre, with possible yields of more than 3 T, but the weight of the yield is not an indication of the quantity of protein and other nutrients, since, as the crop matures, the moisture content falls. The types of bale are similar to straw bales (IA 3), but are heavier.

4. Work routines. The work connected with filling and emptying a hay store is similar to that with straw bales (IA 4). One U.S. machine automatically picks up the bales in the field into $3\frac{1}{2}$ T loads on a hydraulically operated trailer, which is capable of being tilted at the barn, forming a stack about 10 ft high. Alternatively, modern bale accumulators and loaders can collect from the field and load into a barn at a rate of 1000 bales/day without manhandling (8).

5. Design data. Sizes of bales are similar to those for straw (IA 5), except that a small 18-in. × 28-in. × 14-in. half-bale is popular for its ease of handling. The density and weight of the bales will vary with the moisture content and the baler, but average figures can be given (9):

> At 40–45 per cent m.c. 18-in. × 14-in. × 36-in. bale ($\frac{1}{5}$ yd³) weighs 70–80 lb.
> Dried to 20 per cent m.c. 18-in. × 14-in. × 36-in. bale ($\frac{1}{5}$ yd³) weighs about 50 lb.
> Thus, dried hay weighs 8–9 yd³/T.

6. Machinery for handling bales—(IA 6 and Pt. 2) (8). The method of loading hay into storage will depend on the harvesting machinery and drying system.

7. Environment control. Hay, when dry, should be protected from all damp. Hay, if subjected to changes of temperature and moisture, can overheat until it smoulders. Ventilation is required to prevent combustion, and the stack should be inspected with a plunger. For this reason, farmers sometimes restrict the width of a stack of undried hay to about 18 ft. Alternatively, a feeler probe can be left in the stack which can have an electronic connection to an alarm bell, operated should the hay overheat (10).

8. Layouts. See IA 8.

9. Siting. See IA 9.

10. Services. See IA 10.

11. Costs. The store shown in the diagram for straw would hold about 130 T of hay. Therefore, the cost, equipped with elevator and conveyor, might be about £10/T. However, it might be necessary to sheet down the other sides, to provide hatches for throwing out bales along the side and to provide gable ventilation. This might add another £2/T to the cost.

12. References
(1) 'Grass conservation and handling'. *Farmers Weekly Supplement*, p. 18 (3rd April 1958).
(2) MINSON, D. J. 'Alternatives to baling'. *Practical Power Farming*, p. 6 (June 1962).
(3) CULPIN, S. 'Modern methods of making hay'. *Scottish Institute of Agricultural Engineering Report*, p. 2 (14th March 1962).
(4) 'Modern haymaking'. *Farmers Weekly Supplement*, p. xxvi (21st April 1961).
(5) MINSON D. J. 'Pelleted and wafered hay: summary of experiments'. *J. British Grassland Society* (March 1963).
(6) GRUNDEY, J. K. 'Will the wafer oust the bale'. *Dairy Farmer*, p. 55 (April 1962).
(7) 'Chopped hay'. *Farm Mechanization*, p. 25 (Sept. 1963).
(8) 'Field to barn—untouched by hand'. *Farm Mechanization*, p. 43 (Sept. 1963).
(9) 'Green hay'. *Lister Publication* 104H, p. 12 (April 1962).
(10) *Farmers Weekly*, p. 43 (10th August 1962).

IC. Haylage and Maize

1. Activity
a. Production of haylage is one of several methods for conserving grass as a fodder for cattle. The term 'haylage' is used here to differentiate the method of production from either that for silage or for hay. Good-quality silage and hay largely depend on certain physical changes in the grass planned to occur within buildings, whereas haylage largely depends on these changes occurring in the fields (Silage—IIC; Hay—IB and IIB).

Haylage is produced best if grass is wilted in the field to about 45 per cent m.c., though in normal practice grass is harvested at as high as 65 per cent m.c. However, as the m.c. is increased, the quality of the haylage will be reduced, becoming, perhaps, no better than good-quality silage. It is important to obtain the maximum nutritional value from the product, since the capital and running costs may be greater than those for other methods of grass conservation. Costs for harvesting, storing and feeding should be considered in conjunction with the nutritional value when comparing the different methods. Unfortunately, comparative costs are not available for grass conservation in the United Kingdom. Though some U.S. costs are available, they are not specifically relevant to conditions and modern practice in this country (Ref. (*a*)).

Many different machines, techniques and sequences of operation can be used to make haylage. Wilted grass is collected in the field, is chopped to under 1 in. in length, preferably to under ½ in., and is blown into the top of a tower silo. The shorter cuts give better compaction with more uniform density, and reduce the strain on the cutting arms of the unloaders. Haylage compacts under its own weight, whereas silage requires artificial compaction. With either material, not only is the percentage of dry matter important, but the proportion of crude fibre, crude protein and starch equivalent within the dry matter will control the nutritional value. Moreover, the percentage of matter lost either in the field or within the silo, by seepage, fermentation and spoilage, is important. Haylage in a tower silo can have three advantages when compared with silage:

i. The nutritional value as a bulk fodder can be greater.
ii. The grass can be handled mechanically from the field to the cattle.

iii. The use of the fields and the crops can be planned more efficiently.

b. American research has estimated the percentage dry matter losses in the field and in the silo, with forage harvested at different moisture contents and stored in different types of silos (see table below) (1).

Considering these figures, which are not claimed to be conclusive, a sealed bunker silo can be as effective in retaining dry matter as an unsealed tower, and the additional field losses in wilting the forage to 40–50 per cent m.c. for a sealed tower are greater than the dry matter which is saved by sealing the storage. However, it is not possible to accept these figures without reservation for United Kingdom conditions, particularly with regard to the field losses, and the nutritional losses are not given.

The Ministry of Agriculture published the following figures for the loss of feeding values which occurred with different methods of grass conservation. The figures are based on experiments in the northern region in 1961/62 (2).

	m.c. per cent	Dry matter, per cent	Starch, per cent
Badly made wet silage	85–75	23	44
Well made wet silage	85–75	17	33
Normal wilted silage	75–70	10	22
Wilted haylage	55–50	6	16
Barn-dried baled hay	45–40	9	15

Type of silo	M.c. per cent	Field	Per cent d.m. lost Seepage	Per cent d.m. lost Fermentation	Surface	Total
Hermetically sealed tower	85	2	10	10	0	22
	80	2	7	9	0	18
	75	3	3	8	0	14
	70	3	1	7	0	11
	65	4	0	6	0	10
	60	6	0	5	1	12
	50	10	0	4	2	16
	40	13	0	4	3	20
Unsealed tower	85	2	10	10	3	25
	80	2	7	9	3	21
	75	3	3	8	4	18
	70	3	1	7	4	15
	65	4	0	8	5	17
	60	6	0	9	5	20
Bunker (sealed)	85	2	8	11	2	23
	80	2	5	10	2	19
	75	3	2	8	2	16
	70	3	1	7	4	15
	65	4	0	9	5	18

The haylage had a nutrient loss of starch equivalents of 5 per cent in the field and 11 per cent in the tower, the quality being comparable with that of barn-dried hay. On this basis, haylage should have about 8 per cent more feeding value than stored silage, though the quality of the latter might be improved by a better seal around the store, as discussed below. The nutrient losses can be reduced, perhaps to about 10 per cent, by wilting the grass to 45 per cent and by storing in a sealed tower, though field losses may be increased disproportionly.

The quality of fodder is important, since not only does it become more digestible as the quality is improved, but more cattle can be kept on the same acreage and, moreover, it can affect the value of the type of silo used. As a tentative conclusion, it would seem that well-made silage in a sealed bunker can be about as satisfactory as haylage, though this does not take into account any losses occurring after the bunker has been opened. Further research is required to establish the feeding value of haylage made from different grasses, wilted at different moisture contents and stored in different types and sizes of vertical silo, and these should be compared with different techniques for silage.

c. Haylage is handled mechanically into the tower; one man, for example, being able to load 3 T of grass in under 8 min. However, with silage, the tractor probably spends nearly half an hour for the same quantity stored in handling and compacting the grass in the silo, and this takes place at a peak labour time. Moreover, grass harvested at 50 per cent rather than 75 per cent m.c. means that only half the weight of material is transported from the field, and this represents a considerable saving in tractor and manhours, though part of this saving may be absorbed by extra fieldwork to reduce the m.c. of the grass. These are matters requiring proper time studies. With a tower silo, it is necessary to cut the haylage mechanically, loading directly into a trailer or on to a conveyor, whereas cutting silage may take 24–37 min/T (3). With self-fed silage, the labour requirements are not as acute, being about 7 min/T, though self-fed silage may be less satisfactory than rationed silage. The ability to ration silage with low labour requirements is a major advantage in using a tower silo.

d. Tower storage can be used in several ways. It is possible to have a tower with a bottom unloader, which means that the tower can be emptied as it is filled. Alternatively, with two towers and top-unloaders, one can be emptied as the other is filled. In this manner it is possible to harvest and to feed at the same time from one field. Grass yields can be increased when the cattle do not poach the crop by grazing, and up to 4 crops/field p.a. can be harvested in some areas. Yield of d.m. from grassland can be more than 5 T/acre (IIC 1, p. 105). Thus, it is possible to plan the cropping of the fields and to house the cattle for any part of the year or for the whole year. Maize silage can be used in the tower. Maize can yield a valuable crop which can be harvested as late as November in some areas. This means that additional bulk foods can be stored after the grass harvesting has finished, obtaining perhaps as much as 5 T d.m. from 30 T/acre of harvested maize in a good year.

2. *Managerial requirements.* Tower storage has several functional requirements. It has to maintain the food in good condition with as little loss of nutrients as possible. Therefore, it is important to reduce or eliminate oxygen from entering the silo. The walls must be airtight. The roof may be constructed to ventilate the top of the tower, but to exclude rain, or the complete tower may be sealed hermetically. The walls must resist the thrust of the material. Drainage should be provided to remove effluent from the base of the silo, though this will be very slight with material ensilaged at 50 per cent m.c. The materials used must resist the acids in the silage. Filling and emptying the silo should be made as easy as possible.

3. *Production techniques.* The techniques for making haylage are discussed above. The quantity required and, therefore, the size of the tower will depend on the number of cattle, the feeding policy, the period of housing and the acreage of crop available (IIIA and IIIB). Generally, not more than 25 lb d.m./day/beast are required, less if there are other supplementary rations. Two towers with top-unloaders are more flexible than one with the same storage capacity. If the haylage is too wet, especially with a bottom-unloader, the cutting mechanism may get blocked.

4. *Work routines.* Work with a tower silo can be completely mechanized, both in filling and in emptying.

a. Filling

The wilted grass can be chopped in the field, or it may be chopped at the base of the tower. In the first case a chopper harvester is used, with a blower at the tower. Alternatively, a flail-type harvester is used with a chopper-blower at the tower. The material is brought from the field in a trailer (usually up to 5 T capacity), which can have a mechanized floor, feeding the material into an auger to place it in the blower. Alternatively, the material can be tipped from the trailer into a holding box, which automatically

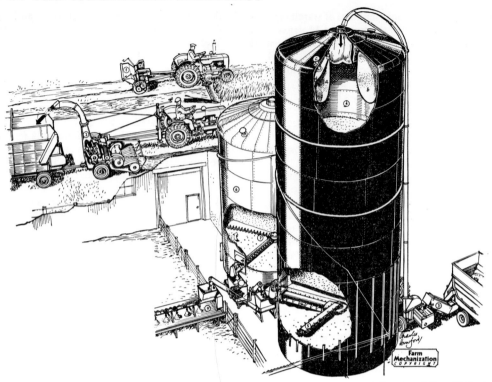

Courtesy of *Farm Mechanization*

KEY:

1. Tractor with mower and crimper.
2. Forage harvester.
3. Forage box emptying into blower.
4. Tower silo (hermetically sealed).
       a, *b*, *c* breather bag, *d* air vent.
5. Bottom cutter unloader.
6. Tower silo for grain (hermetically sealed).
7. Bottom auger unloader.
8. Automatic roller mill.
9. Automatic auger feeder for haylage and rolled grain.

Fig. 17. Tower silo system for haylage and grain

feeds the blower. The tube, through which the material is blown into the top of the tower, can be part of the blower or it may be a fixture on the tower. The dry material can be lifted 80 ft with a motor of about 25 h.p. at rates of up to 20 T/hr. In most cases a load can be filled from a trailer in 10–15 min. The cutting, conveying and filling rates have to be planned to prevent any labour bottlenecks. It is essential to get an even distribution of material inside the tower, and therefore a top distributor is important (Fig. 17).

b. Emptying

The majority of towers are equipped with cutters, suspended from the roof, which rotate, discharging the cut haylage into an external chute fitted on to the tower. The chutes terminate about 8 ft from the ground. Some towers have the chute internally down their centre, the haylage being cut and dropped down the chute on to a conveyor in the floor of the tower, and this can be coupled to mechanized feeding arrangements if required. Alternatively, cutters can be

included at the bottom of airtight towers (Fig. 17). This is a more expensive mechanism that works best with well-wilted material. The output rates vary between 3 and 10 T/hr, and in all cases the material can be delivered either into a trailer or on to an horizontal conveyor.

5. *Design data.* A number of proprietary tower silos are available with diameters varying between 15 and 30 ft, and with their heights for the most part between 20 and 60 ft. They are normally in the form of a cylinder topped by a dome. The manufacturers will give advice on the size required. An estimate can be made of the number of cattle to be fed and their ration of haylage per day over a predetermined period to give the overall storage requirement. Considerable research is still required to give an accurate estimate for the density of haylage in order to determine the size of silo to store a given quantity. There will be a wide difference of density in the haylage between the bottom and the top of the tower, since the latter receives no compaction. The following might be taken as an average guide until further tests are made (4):

60

	per cent	lb/ft³
Dry matter at 50–55		30
Dry matter at 40–45		40
Dry matter at 30–35		45

It would appear that the drier the material is stored, the less compaction occurs and that an average density of about 15 lb of dry matter per cubic foot will be obtained irrespective of the moisture content. This is confirmed by American research (5). If the ration of dry matter for adult cattle is 25 lb/day, 50 ft³ will store enough feed for one beast per month. It is best to consider costs of storage on the basis of the cubic content in relation to the tonnage of dry matter stored. Storage becomes considerably cheaper for the silos with greater diameters and heights compared with smaller silos. Generally, no storage occurs in the domed roof of the tower cylinder.

The only restriction on height may be the requirements of the local County Planning Officer. The restriction on diameter might be taken as a rule-of-thumb that a depth of at least 3 in. storage should be fed per day in ventilated silos to prevent secondary spoilage. On this basis, for example, towers of 20 ft diameter may be suitable for 50–60 cattle, or a greater number if a depth of more than 3 in. is fed per day (dry matter at 48 per cent, and 50 lb/beast of haylage fed per day). The tower silo has to be designed to withstand the thrust from the stored material. This is a matter to be considered by the manufacturers of the proprietary towers. Similarly, the foundations will be designed by the manufacturers, even though the farmer may be responsible for their erection. Weights of about 1 T/ft² may be encountered. Most foundations will be formed with a mass concrete beam under the silo wall skin and with a concrete floor on a well-compacted depth of hardcore draining to a sump in the centre. The concrete surface should be painted (Fig. 18). The cylindrical walls provided

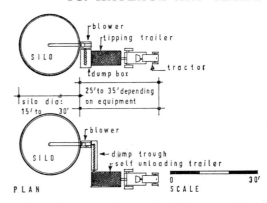

Fig. 19. Space requirements for filling tower silos

by manufacturers can be classified generally by their materials as follows (6):

i. Heavy-gauge (12–16 gauge normal) hot-galvanized steel sheets, bolted on site.

ii. Glass-fused surfaced steel sheets, bolted on site.

iii. Reinforced, interlocking dense concrete panels, restrained by external tension wires round the tower at prescribed centres.

iv. Interlocking, pressure-treated timber staves, restrained as above.

Types *i* and *iii* may require internal painting every two or three years with bitumen or plastic paint, and this can be done in stages while the tower is being emptied, which saves the cost of internal scaffolding, but may cost as much as £$\frac{1}{2}$/T stored if farm labour is used—say, 3s. to 5s./T stored p.a. Roofs are of galvanized metal sheets, glass fibre or timber. Some towers are erected from internal scaffolding, but structural types *i* and *ii* may be jacked up using a Land Rover or tractor.

6. *Equipment.* Space is required at the foot of the tower for the portable or fixed equipment for filling and emptying. Space requirements can vary. Filling will require a blower or chopper-blower adjacent to the tower and normally there is a portable holding receptacle and conveyor to take the grass from the trailer. This may be in the form of a large box, about 6 ft × 4 ft, or of a long trough, about 10 ft × 2 ft, but it may be possible for the trough to be raised vertically, allowing tractors to pass. Some trailers can tip the grass into the receptacle, other trailers are self-unloading. The main requirement is that the layout should allow easy circulation for the tractor and trailer (Fig. 19).

Top-unloading silos empty the haylage down a permanent chute attached to the side of the tower (4b, above). This can be at any point on the circumference of the tower in relation to the filling

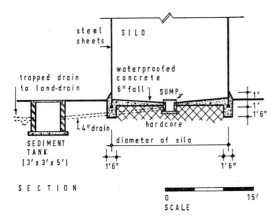

Fig. 18. Typical foundation and floor to tower silo with steel sheeted sides

position. The chutes are large enough to take a man and contain ladder-irons inside them to give access to the top of the silo. Bottom-unloading silos have a hatch at the base of the tower. (For conveying mechanisms and layouts from the base of the chute or tower: IIIA and IIIB.) There are many blowers and self-unloaders available (6).

7. *Environmental control.* The best environmental control is given by towers which are glass lined and hermetically sealed. These reduce nutrient losses in the haylage (1a above). Other towers should prevent air flow through their walls. Galvanised metal and concrete should be protected from the acids in the silage, and advice should be obtained from the manufacturers. Silage produces acetic acids, which have a pickling effect on mild steel, but cause stress cracking and corrosion in hard steels and which react with carbonates in concrete, causing leaching. The wetter the silage, the more serious the acid damage (7). Haylage may be formed with crimped grass wilted to about 50 per cent m.c. and stored in a clamp lined with poly-vinyl-chloride sheeting, the edges of the latter being heat sealed after the clamp has been filled. In experiments, d.m. losses have been less than 10 per cent. Fermentation has been limited, the temperature not rising above 45° C (113° F) (8). This might be considered a superior form of silage.

8. *Layouts and* 9. *Siting.* Layouts and siting for towers as storage units are simple, being shaped as tall cylinders and requiring only access at their base for filling and emptying. However, they are usually designed in conjunction with cattle layouts (IIIA and IIIB).

10. *Services.* An electrical supply will be required, as directed by the manufacturers. Three-phase supply is preferable for all installations, though single-phase may be practical. Silos with diameters of up to 20 ft normally require a motor for the unloader of about 5 or $7\frac{1}{2}$ h.p., but the 30-ft-diameter silos with a top cutter unloading down a central flue may need only one 3-h.p. and one 1-h.p. motor.

11. *Costs.* Costs for tower silos have not reached a stable level. However, the cost for storage will vary with the type and size of silo as well as with the equipment chosen to go with it. Unsealed towers of above 10,000 ft³ storage capacity will cost (erected with foundations) about 2s. 3d. to 2s. 6d./ft³, increasing to about 3s. for stores of 6000 ft³. Completely sealed towers may only cost about 3s./ft³, but this can be increased to about 4s./ft³ in some cases. An average cost of £18/T dry matter stored compares favourably with a cost of about £28/T for a clamp silo (IIC 11, p. 112). However, the mechanical unloader may cost another £300 to £600, depending on size and throughput (6), and this might add another 1s./ft³ to the costs. Bottom unloaders may cost about £800–£1200. The chopper-blower may cost another £300–£500, though this can be used for more than one silo. Therefore, it would appear that a tower silo may cost approximately the same as a clamp silo, or possibly a little more, with all the extra field equipment taken into consideration. The latter may not be true when best-quality silage is made. Since the nutritional values of the fodder are about equal, whether good haylage or silage is made, the determining factor in the selection of a silo must be the labour costs and general design requirements for any particular layout.

12. *References*
(1) Selected reference (*a*), p. 21.
(2) Grass Conservation Leaflet. Ministry of Agriculture. Royal Show 1962.
(3) NIX, BELSHAW & WELLER. 'The yard and parlour'. *Farm Economics Branch Report* 58, Cambridge University School of Agriculture, p. 49.
(4) TRINDER, N., ADDISON, J. & JOCE, E. H. Personal communication.
(5) U.S. Bureau of Dairy Industry Information Bulletin 149.
(6) MORTIMER, R. G. 'Push-button silage'. *Dairy Farmer*, p. 31 (June 1962).
(7) EBBINGHAUSE, J. H. 'Silage Handling Techniques'. *Agricultural Engineering* (*U.S.*), p. 556 (September 1958).
(8) OADES, J. M. & BROWN, W. O. 'Haylage in plastic'. *Farmers Weekly*, p. 101 (15th February 1963).

SELECTED REFERENCE
a. HENDRIX, A. T. & CALMONT, J. R. 'Harvesting, Storing and Feeding Silage'. *Symposium on Modern Construction Technique in Agriculture.* State Research Institute, Sweden. (June 1962.)

ID. Grain and Seed

1. *Activity*
a. All grain (with one important exception) harvested at over a certain moisture content has to be dried, if it is to to be stored, in order to maintain its quality. A few farmers manage to store without drying, turning the grain, if necessary, to keep it in condition, though this is impracticable with very wet grain. A new technique discussed below (2b), which is the main exception, is the high moisture storage of grain, principally barley, used for feeding-stuffs. Not all the harvested grain is dried and stored on the farm. In some cases it is sold immediately after harvesting, or the farmer may send it away to be

dried and possibly stored on contract. Occasionally, the grain is dried and stored in a building owned by a syndicate of farmers. A farmer stores his grain either to use it as feed for his own livestock or to sell it between January and June, when prices are usually higher. Seeds have to be dried, in most cases, before storage, whether they are grown for sowing on the farm or for sale. Seed storage is to some extent similar to grain storage, the main differing requirements being given in an appendix to this section.

b. Most grain harvesting is done by combine harvester. There were 50,000 combine harvesters in England and Wales in 1960. This was an increase of 40,000 compared with 1950 (1). Combine harvesters can have cutter-bars with widths from 4 to 14 ft, though one recent model has an 18-ft cutter-bar. The width chosen depends mainly on the acreage to be cut, but the capacity of the threshing drum and the locality of the crop are important, and the width of cut is no longer a good guide to combine output; 10 cwt/ft cut/hr is a general assessment and the combining season probably will be limited to 15–20 days (2). In wet districts 15–20 acres/ft cut may be the maximum capacity for most combines, with 25 acres for normal and 30 acres for ideal conditions (3). Not only are there several types of grain, such as wheat, barley, oats and rye, but there are many varieties of each type. Each variety grown by a farmer has to be handled, dried and stored separately, though a few mixed crops are sown. However, the trend is to have few varieties, even though this tends to concentrate harvesting into a short period. The estimated tonnage of grain produced in England and Wales in 1962 and the average yield per acre are given at foot of page (4):

Yields vary considerably according to type of seed, fertilizer used, weather and terrain, but yields of 40 cwt/acre or more are not uncommon, with exceptional yields recorded at over $3\frac{1}{2}$ T/ acre. Harvesting averages $1\frac{1}{2}$–2 T/hr with 8–10-ft cutter-bars, but large-capacity combines may have throughputs of over 5 T/hr, with 8–10 T/ hr claimed for the largest harvesters. Since large grain farms probably will have one combine per 200–250 acres, the intake of grain at the drying and storing point can be considerable. It is important that the machinery which handles the

grain from the field to the store is planned to prevent delay, since time is of vital importance in harvesting. Grain harvested in bulk is usually taken from the field in tipping trailers, normally of 2–3 T capacity, though on large farms lorries with greater capacities may be used. If grain is bagged on the combine the sacks are taken away on a trailer, either during or at the end of the day. Handling (and drying) in sacks is sometimes economic for yields of under 100 tons of grain or as an additional method on large farms harvesting seeds and grain.

c. In the design of buildings, grain storage is seldom considered separately from grain drying, especially since it is possible to dry grain while it is being stored. (For Grain Drying and Grain Drying in Storage: IID.) However, it is important to consider the technical requirements of grain storage, since the building design for pre-dried and *in situ* dried grain can be very different. In addition, grain can be stored wet if held in airtight containers (2b below).

2. Managerial requirements

a. Dried Grain Storage

The length of time for which grain can be stored safely will depend on its moisture content. The table below gives the recognized maximum percentages of moisture (5):

Period of storage	A per cent	B per cent
Until 4 weeks from harvest	17	18
Until February	16	17
Until April	15	16
Beyond April	14	15

A. In bulk or in closely stacked bags without turning or forced ventilation.
B. In bags standing upright and freely exposed to air, or in bulk with forced ventilation, or in bulk with frequent turning.

Many farmers will store with higher moisture contents than these figures. In the latter case, frequent inspection of the grain is desirable. It is obvious that grain must be stored in dry conditions, otherwise its moisture content will be increased. It is

	Wheat	Barley	Oats and mixed corn
Millions of tons produced	$3\frac{1}{3}$	$4\frac{3}{4}$	1
Yield in cwt/acre	35	32	27
Yield in cwt/acre (Min. of Agric.)	30·8	27·2	23·7

The average yields estimated by the Ministry of Agriculture are adjusted for moisture content, for unharvested portions of fields, as well as for a number of marginal fields outside the main corn-growing areas.

important to protect the grain from mice, rats, birds, insects and mites. The method of handling grain into and out of storage should be designed to suit individual requirements as given below.

b. Wet Grain Storage

An important development within the last few years has been the storage of undried grain over long periods without deterioration in hermetically sealed containers. Though wet grain, when taken from its storage, is considered unsuitable for human consumption, it can be rolled and fed to livestock. Barley is the principal crop stored in this manner, though there are experiments at present to hold wheat for the same purpose. The technique of storing wet barley has changed the method and economics of livestock fattening and has an important bearing on the design of some modern livestock housing (Section III). It can have other advantages as shows an editorial in *Farm Mechanization* (6):

'A formidable number of advantages can be quoted for sealed grain: increased acreage per combine; field losses reduced; harvest peak work eased; lower storage cost; no wastage from vermin and respiration; less damage in handling; no dust during milling; and lower concentrate bills—showing a saving of £10 per cow per year. It can be fed to pigs, cows, calves, bullocks and sheep; it is more palatable and digestible (calves can be put on it in three weeks); small farmers can afford it as even a 10-ton bin is claimed to be economical; it would encourage cereal growing in the north and west. Barley is easy to handle when moist and it can be fed 'ad-lib'. This promises the end to daily stockfeeding and removes the need for complex mechanical feeders.'

It has been claimed that the cost of storing moist grain, if all plant and equipment is depreciated over ten years, should not exceed £1/T p.a., whereas the total cost of drying and storing grain on a similar basis is about £4/T p.a. (7). Since about four-fifths of the grain grown is for stockfeeding, wet grain storage has wide implications.

Barley can be stored in hermetically sealed containers at 25 per cent m.c., or even at 30 per cent m.c. if required, and can then be used for feeding to livestock after being rolled, without drying, but it will keep only for about 3 days after removal from the silo, whereas, if stored at 18 per cent m.c., will keep for longer. The aim should be to store grain with an m.c. of 17–24 per cent.

c. Temporary Wet Grain Storage

In one experiment grain with 16 per cent m.c. was stored on a 24-ft-wide 500-gauge polythene sheet, to a depth of $1\frac{1}{2}$ ft, in an external clamp (8). The clamp was 16 ft wide, the edge of each side having the sheet turned up over the top of a straw bale to form a dwarf wall. Dry straw was humped over the grain and was covered by another polythene sheet, forming a watershed, and held at the sides

by a second layer of bales, secured by twine taken across the clamp from one layer of bales to the other. With storage until December, less than 5 per cent wastage occurred, mainly due to rodent damage. Alternatively, some farmers have stored grain in plastic bags for 9 months without mould growth, especially when the m.c. is less than 21 per cent (15).

3. *Production techniques.* Grain can be handled from the field as discussed above either (a) in bulk or (b) in sacks, depending on the type of harvester. Handling of grain is a matter of economics, capital outlay and efficient operation, but many layouts contain improvisations which cause uneconomic handling (9).

a. Bulk Handling

If grain leaves the field in bulk it should be dried, stored and conveyed either for sale or for feeding to livestock in bulk.

b. Bag Handling

If a bagger combine is used the bags can be:

i. Emptied into a pit, the grain being handled thereafter in bulk for drying and storing.
ii. Dried, stored and conveyed in bags either for sale or for feeding to livestock.

c. Hermetically Sealed Containers

Though wet grain can be stored in airtight tower silos, formed from treated metal plates and normally used for haylage, it is usual to store in smaller types of tower silos made specially for the purpose, though similar in basic design, and holding 100–150 T of grain, being, perhaps, 20–30 ft high with diameters of under 20 ft.

Experiments have shown that wet grain can be stored in plastic bags, normally formed from 500 gauge polythene sheets (10). There are several proprietary methods for sealing the bags. However, not only can bags of this kind easily be punctured, but they are subject to rodent attack. Giant polythene bags can be used to line some of the circular grain storage bins (5b, below), the bags being blown up by a fan and a fan or auger being used to load the grain into the bag (11). The same fan can be used to draw off the grain, a twin-pipe system maintaining the vacuum. When the bag has been loaded, excess air is drawn off to leave the grain in a vacuum. For prolonged storage, nitrogen can be drawn through the grain.

4. *Work routines.* The design of intake pits to receive grain as conveyed from the field is discussed in IID. Bulk filling and emptying grain into storage can be a simple operation, but sack handling involves manual labour, which is arduous and sometimes inconvenient. With bulk storage, the

whether it's
SILAGE
OR GRAIN

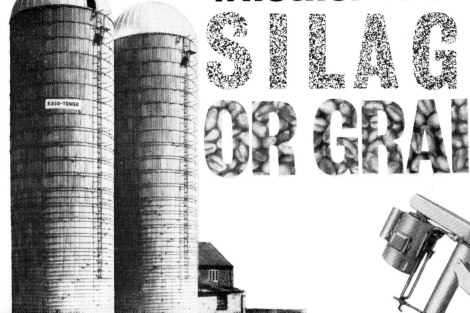

RECO-TOWER FORAGE SILOS are of concrete stave construction of American design, with a domed roof of aluminiumized steel and translucent fibreglass cap. The cost of this type of silo brings it within the scope of even the smaller farmer.
RECO SEALED SILOS FOR HIGH MOISTURE BARLEY are available in galvanized or vitreous enamel finish.
RECO GRAIN CONVEYORS—$3\frac{1}{2}''$, $4\frac{1}{2}''$, $5\frac{1}{2}''$ diameter in lengths up to 49' 6". Compare the robust construction of the Reco Conveyor with any other, and prove to yourself that Reco offer the finest value for money.
Now available:
    THE NEW RECO-LIFT TROLLEY MOUNTED CONVEYOR $4\frac{1}{2}''$, $5\frac{1}{2}''$ diameter.

RECO

SUPPLY A FULL RANGE OF MECHANICAL FEEDING EQUIPMENT

FORAGE HARVESTER

BLOWER

DUMP BOX

SILAGE SPREADER

SILO UNLOADER

FEEDERS *of different types to suit specific installations*

FEED METERS

RECO
can handle it

Illustrated literature sent without obligation

RUSTON'S ENGINEERING CO LTD

ST. GERMAIN STREET, HUNTINGDON

Telephone: Huntingdon 1372/4

13: UNLOADING A TOWER SILO

Mr. G. D. Rivis, Boythorpe, Malton, Yorks.

Some tower silos have a bottom cutter-unloader. In this case, the unloader empties the haylage on to a chain-and-flight conveyor, which connects with three towers, and in turn the haylage is augered into a hopper filling a horizontal feed auger. Concentrates can be automatically added to the feed under cover in the work area within the end bay of the steel portal framed barn, the remainder of which is used as strawed covered yards. The cattle feed from the manger in the open yard. A tower blower-loader is visible used for filling a tower beyond the one in the foreground. [SEE PAGES 45, 62 & 193] See also Photo 7. Courtesy of Farmer and Stockbreeder.

14: WET GRAIN STORAGE: HERMETICALLY SEALED SILO

Undried grain can be stored in hermetically sealed silos. Several proprietary makes are available using different types of material or detail in their design. The silo shown is under erection and test, being formed from prefabricated curved mild steel plates erected on a concrete base and welded together and painted on site. The silo includes an extraction outlet for an auger at the base, an inspection manhole, top inlet, access ladder and guard rail. The conical roof suits the natural slope of stored grain. Diameters for silos for wet grain storage usually do not exceed 20 ft with heights up to 40 ft, though larger silos are used in some cases. Grain can be stored with little fermentation with a m.c. of over 24%, even up to 30%. Wet grain storage is not used when the grain is required for human consumption, but is suitable when used in conjunction with livestock enterprises, especially for storing barley as fodder for beef cattle. [SEE PAGES 64 & 186] Courtesy of Lawrence Engineering Co. Ltd.

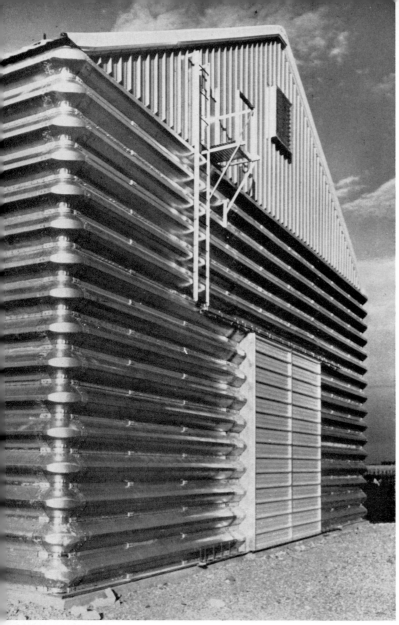

15: BULK GRAIN STORAGE

MacRae Farms Ltd., Bury St. Edmunds, Suffolk

Grain can be stored in bulk on the floor, but, unless it is coned, the surrounding walls must be capable of withstanding the thrust from the grain. Reinforced brick or concrete walls can be used. Alternatively, a rigid steel frame can be used with corrugated horizontal galvanized sheets, in 20 ft long × 3 ft high sections having corrugations $\frac{1}{2}$ ft deep at $1\frac{1}{2}$ ft centres, which require no additional rails or supports to the internal steel portal frames at 20 ft centres. The interior of the structure is designed to make self-cleaning easy during removal of the grain: corrugations are sloped at 43 degrees and corners are rounded. Sliding doors, access ladders, access traps, gable panels and gable louvres are incorporated as part of the prefabricated units. Internal overhead augers, catwalks and floor outlets can be included. The building is of 40 ft span, 60 ft long and 15ft to the eaves and will hold 950 T of wheat. Panel walls up to 24 ft in ht. are possible. The roof space can be used for storage. Units for 500 T to over 50,000 T are possible, the cost per T being less as the storage capacity is increased. [SEE PAGES 15 & 66] Courtesy of Butler Buildings (U.K.) Ltd.

16: CIRCULAR BINS FOR GRAIN INSTALLED IN A BARN

Relatively cheap grain bin storage can be installed in existing or new barns with circular, galvanized corrugated sheets held by simple framing and some internal cross-bars. They are easy to erect, but require more floor space per ton than interlocking square or rectangular bins. The barn shown has a typical lattice and triangulated roof truss strong enough to support transverse steel joists carrying the necessary overhead catwalk. The discharge chutes from the overhead central conveyor, used for filling the bins, are shown. This emphasizes the need for sufficient headroom above the bins for the conveyor and chutes, which should discharge at about 30–45 degrees into the centre of the bins. Dust wraps for each bin are shown hanging from the roof. These not only hold the dust but can prevent bird contamination. [SEE PAGE 67] Courtesy of Gordon Felber & Co. Ltd.

17: GRAIN STORAGE

Proprietary pressed steel panels can be assembled to form grain storage bins on a concrete raft floor. They can include ventilated floors for drying in store. Sliding doors give access to a grain handling area. At the near end, is an independent 20 T hopper which can be filled from the overhead conveyor. The hopper has two sides at 45 degrees and discharges 12 ft above ground level for loading bulk tankers. [SEE PAGE 67] Courtesy of Northgate Studio.

18: GRAIN BINS FILLED AND EMPTIED BY A TOP CONVEYOR

National Institute for Research in Dairying

An auger conveyor or the tube for an auger can be installed in a grain bin at an angle, preferably of 45–60 degrees, with the base set in a sump in the concrete floor to the bin. If an auger is used, permanently fixed in each bin, one removable head unit complete with motor, drive, delivery spout and short length of auger casing can be coupled to the top of the auger shaft to empty a bin, later being removed and transferred to other bins for the same purpose. To save time, the motor unit can be also permanent, one to each bin, at some extra expense. Alternatively, as an economy, empty tube casings only need be permanent, short lengths of auger being inserted and coupled together, thus needing little headroom, before the head unit is fixed. The auger can be used, as shown, to discharge into a top conveyor, which could also be used for filling the bins with a reversible belt and discharge outlets. This method eliminates the need for a bottom conveyor. Square bins with overhead cat-walk are shown installed in a simple Dutch barn-type structure. [SEE PAGES 44 & 67] Courtesy of Practical Power Farming.

19: BULK GRAIN STORAGE IN A MULTI-PURPOSE BUILDING

A concrete portal framed building, 90 ft long and with a central span of 40 ft plus a lean-to on each side of 22½ ft, complete with a concrete floor and perimeter walling and having vehicle access from the ends, provides an 'Umbrella' which is reasonably adaptable and flexible. Grain can be stored cheaply in bulk or in sacks on the waterproofed floor, provided the external walls are reinforced. Grain can be easily handled in bulk with a portable auger mounted on a tripod, but handling grain in bulk will produce dust. Sacked grain can be handled on sack-barrows and lifted on to lorries with an inclined elevator. Grain drying plant is beyond the sliding doors. [SEE PAGES 8–9, 43–45 & 66] Courtesy of Turners Asbestos-Cement Co. Ltd.

20: FEED STORAGE

Three 20 T external bulk storage hoppers for a weaning enterprise standing with metal legs on a concrete base. The tops of the hoppers are sloped at 45 degrees to shed rainwater and to allow the hoppers to be filled to the inlet point. They also include an inspection hatch. Two sides are sloped at 60 degrees to allow complete self-emptying to occur without doming or funnelling. The bins have an inlet and an air-control pipe. Outlets are at barrow or motorized truck height. A bulk delivery lorry is in the process of blowing the meal into the hopper through a flexible coupling. The space required for a bulk lorry to manoeuvre and the clearance while tipping is emphasized. In the background is the provender mill. [SEE PAGES 72 & 39] Courtesy of The Southburn Estates, Yorks.

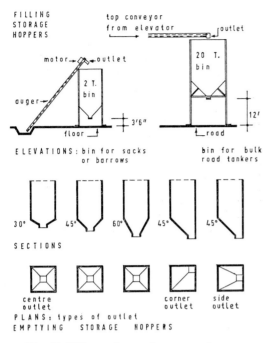

FILLING
STORAGE
HOPPERS

ELEVATIONS: bin for sacks
or barrows

bin for bulk
road tankers

SECTIONS

PLANS: types of outlet

centre
outlet

corner
outlet

side
outlet

EMPTYING   STORAGE   HOPPERS

Fig. 20. Filling and emptying storage hoppers
(see also Fig. 22, p. 72)

grain may have to be turned while in store if it begins to deteriorate, and the bins or storage space should be cleaned after use. The grain should be tested while in store for temperature, moisture and keeping quality. This may be achieved from an overhead catwalk by reading a thermometer set into the grain, or the installation can be recorded automatically on to a graph or dial outside the storage area. Barley rolled for livestock should have a m.c. of 18 per cent. Therefore, with dried barley, water should be sprayed on to it after it is removed from unsealed silos and 24 hr allowed to elapse before rolling, the following quantities of water being required:

M.c. of grain from store	Gal/T of water to give 18 per cent m.c.
14	10·4
15	7·9
16	5·4
17	2·7

a. Filling

i. After drying on a continuous flow or batch drier (IID), the grain is elevated and conveyed overhead, being deposited into the stores by means of adjustable chutes from the conveyor. Alternatively, it can be augered or blown from the drier to the top of the store, but this is usually done for only small amounts. (For equipment: see Part 2.) High moisture barley

is normally stored in hermetically sealed tower silos, which are filled as given in IC 4 (p. 59).

ii. Alternatively, after continuous or batch drying the grain may be conveyed by tipping trailer from the drier for floor storage.

iii. Sacks are lifted from a platform drier to be stacked in the store. Storage to heights of more than 5 ft can be assisted by a sack elevator.

b. Emptying (Fig. 20)

i. The simplest method of emptying grain from a store for conveyance to its point of use is by gravity and this method is used for emptying overhead storage hoppers into bulk tankers, into farm tipping trailers or into sacks. In these cases the maximum size of store required and the height of the hopper outlet above the floor is as follows:

	Storage capacity (in tons)	Height of outlet (in ft)
For bulk tankers	20	12
For tipping trailers	5	8
For sacks	2	$3\frac{1}{2}$

Gravity emptying of grain can be used for storage bins of any capacity. However, for full self-emptying, wet grain needs a floor slope of 45 degrees decreasing to about 30 degrees for dry grain (in practice, 45 degrees is preferred for dry grain as well) in order to flow, and this substantially increases building costs for large bins. Clean and dry wheat and barley has an angle of repose for emptying or funnelling of 27–28 degrees and for filling of 16 degrees, and for oats of 32 and 18 degrees (12). Alternatively, the floor can have a lower slope, allowing the majority of the grain to self-empty, the last few tons being removed by shovel. The use of smooth plastic-faced boarding for the floor can facilitate the flow. Grain from storage bins can be discharged on to a conveyor and taken up an elevator, in order to fill the overhead storage hopper from which the bulk tanker is filled. Alternatively, a high-speed elevator can be used, emptying direct into the tanker, or the conveyor may take the grain to some other point of use.[1]

ii. If the grain is stored in bulk on the damp-proofed floor of a building it can be emptied either by a tractor and scoop or by an auger into a trailer or lorry. Clear working heights of at least 12 ft will be required for the scoop. Alternatively, a loading elevator of 30 T/hr capacity can be used to fill a bulk tanker, but a height of 15 ft will be required, or a tractor and scoop working in conjunction with an elevator.

[1] Recently, a slotted metal bin floor has been marketed whereby, with air blown through the slots, grain can be moved to a discharge outlet.

iii. Grain can be removed from the base of a tower silo or a storage bin either by inserting a flexible auger through a small opening of about 6–8 in. diameter or by a sweep auger, or by a sweep and under-floor auger, the latter being moved from bin to bin. The outlets can be just above ground level. Dry grain can be removed at about 7 T/hr with a double motor of about 2 h.p. and 1 h.p. for the outer and inner auger coils respectively.

iv. Sacks have to be lifted from the store by hand either directly to a mill/mix unit or on to a trailer or lorry. In the latter case it is desirable to have the road 4 ft below the floor of the store.

5. *Design data.* Storage densities and volumes of dry grain average (13):

	lb/bushel	Ft³/ton	lb/ft³
Wheat	63	46	48
Barley	56	51	43
Oats	42	70	32

In a clean and uniform sample of wheat or barley the bulk density varies inversely with the moisture content, as follows:

	Cappelle wheat			Proctor barley		
M.c., per cent	14	20	26	14	20	26
Density, lb/ft³	46·8	44·0	40·75	43·0	42·1	41·1

About 10 per cent reserve space should be included in a layout in excess of the estimated normal annual storage requirements. Bulk storage of dry grain in circular or rectangular silos can be calculated as follows:

Dia. Circular Silo (in ft)	Floor area Rectangular Silo (in ft²)	Wheat	Barley	Oats
		(Capacity in tons)		
8	50	1·1	1·0	0·75
9	64	1·3	1·2	0·9
10	78	1·6	1·5	1·1
11	94	2·0	1·8	1·3
12	112	2·4	2·2	1·6
13	131	2·9	2·6	1·9
14	152	3·3	3·0	2·2
15	174	3·8	3·4	2·5

Circular bins will waste about 20 per cent of the floor area, which is important with indoor storage. The volume required for sack storage will increase the ft³/T required compared with bulk by about 15 per cent. Densities for uncleaned, wet grain when stored have not been established.

6. *Equipment.* Equipment for moving grain is considered in Part II. The most important requirement for storing large quantities of grain is ease and flexibility in handling. Grain may have to be moved from one part to another of the store. Therefore, the storage space is best divided into a series of compartments. The size of compartment, usually of between 20 and 100 T capacity, will depend on the overall size of the store in relation to the number of grain varieties to be stored, taking into consideration the fact that the larger bins are cheaper per ton stored.

7. *Environmental control.* Grain can be stored in rustproof and watertight metal containers to maintain the condition satisfactorily. All storage should be impervious to external moisture, and floors should therefore include a damp-proof membrane. Alternatively, non-watertight containers can be erected within a dry building free from condensation, preferably protected from birds, rats and mice. Storage in a dark building will help to deter birds. There will be some dust when handling dry grain, and this should not be allowed to penetrate into livestock buildings. Wet grain storage depends on the exclusion of air within a hermetically sealed environment: as soon as the oxygen within the grain has been used by respiration, further aerobic micro-organisms are prevented from developing; other micro-organisms cause some slight fermentation, and a little alcohol will result (14). Since the wet grain is held in carbon dioxide, care must be taken that the latter is not inhaled when the store is unloaded. Moist grain sealed in plastic bags should be stored at as low a temperature as possible, since moulds can become active at high temperatures.

8. *Layouts*

a. The cheapest storage layout will be for the grain to be kept on a waterproof floor to a building. Normal 9-in. walls should be able to hold the pressure from the grain to depths of 4 ft and reinforced walls to depths of 6–10 ft, which are the normal depths for convenience. The bigger depths will create considerable pressures on the retaining walls. The lateral pressures of grain are not easily determined, being a combination of a horizontal pressure similar to fluids, together with a frictional load caused by the granular consistency of the material against the wall surface. Detailed information is given in *The Design of Walls, Bins and Grain Elevators*, by M. S. Ketchum, (McGraw-Hill). The formula to calculate the pressures is complex, a matter for a qualified engineer. This is a subject which could be clarified by an authoritative research publication showing certain structural solutions for storage at different heights. The main advantages for bulk floor storage are economy, both with regard to the building and the elevator and conveying equipment, and the possibility of using the store for other purposes in the spring and early summer. The disadvantages are the time required to turn the grain while in store and to remove it from the store, and the difficulties in storing more than one or two varieties of grain. Proprietary wall units, about 5–8 ft high, are available for bulk grain storage. These can be either r.c. pedestal units or braced timber panels, the weight of the grain on the pedestal or brace holding the wall in place against the lateral pressures. A store 40 ft wide can have the grain heaped to a depth of 16 ft at the centre using 8-ft-high pedestal walls.

b. Proprietary and watertight storage bins are available, complete with their own roof, for erection on a concrete base. They can include arrangements for drying the grain (IID), and they can be erected without their own roof within a building if required. Normal types are:

i. Corrugated aluminium or galvanized steel circular stores with conical roofs, top hatches for filling by blower or auger, and bottom emptying chutes, complete with an auger if required. Normal sizes vary between 10 and 24 ft dia., and 11 and 24 ft ht., giving storage capacities of 15–270 T. Giant bins, holding up to 1800 T, are available, being up to 60 ft dia. and 40 ft ht.

ii. Square silos formed from steel plates, which can be either dip painted or hot-dip galvanized. Some plates are made about 3 ft 8 in. square with 2-in.-wide edge flanges for bolting and sealing together, and the bins have internal ties for restraint. Other plates can have 4-in.-deep corrugations in sheets of up to 10 ft long. Maximum bin sizes normally are 10 ft × 10 ft × 18 ft (40 T wheat), but sizes of about 15 ft × 15 ft × 22 ft (110 T wheat) may be obtained. The bins can carry roof trusses and an asbestos-cement roof.

iii. Resin-bonded plywood circular or square silos, normally up to 10 ft dia. or 12 ft square.

iv. Stove-enamelled and glass-lined (or other treated metals) circular hermetically sealed silos, similar to those for haylage, with a dia. of 15–25 ft and a ht. of up to 60 ft, though usually the latter is restricted to less than 30 ft.

c. Several proprietary storage bins are available for erection within a building. They can include arrangements for drying the grain (IID).

i. Pre-cast, reinforced, interlocking concrete panels, usually 2½–3 in. thick, either for circular or square silos, restrained by rods at intervals around their perimeter. Normal maximum sizes are 15 ft dia. or 12 ft square, with heights up to 18 ft.

ii. Expanded metal circular silos, with diameters of up to 15 ft, restrained by rods at intervals around their perimeter, or circular wiremesh bins lined with hessian or waterproof building paper, diameters usually being limited to under 10 ft.

iii. Tongued and grooved timber boarded square or circular silos, with timber braces on the outside, and internal steel rod ties, with maximum sizes of 12 ft square by 18 ft high. Scandinavia uses timber silos which are up to 60 ft high (both for storage and drying), this makes it economical to have a self-emptying floor and some of the silos can be erected in the open.

iv. Circular silos of 4½-in. brick reinforced with wire in the joints. Erection is a skilled job, and advice should be taken from a brick manufacturer—see Reinforced Brick Grain Silos, issued by the London Brick Company (Nov. 1958).

d. All the bins, except bi above, are normally placed in rows two deep, so that they can share an overhead and bottom conveyor, which are thus able to circulate the grain to any position in the store. Circular, and sometimes square, bins normally have a central passage of 2½–4 ft width to take the conveyor. However, two rows of square bins can be put together, the bottom conveyor being

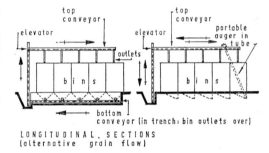

LONGITUDINAL SECTIONS
(alternative grain flow)

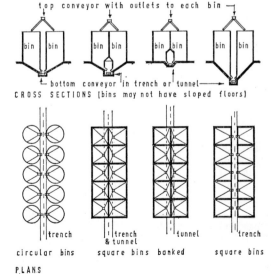

CROSS SECTIONS (bins may not have sloped floors)

PLANS

Fig. 21. Layouts for grain storage bins

placed in an underground tunnel. Alternatively, the bins can be made to include the tunnel within the nest of bins. The top conveyor should be placed to discharge the grain to the centre of each bin via a chute, and this is normally at 30–45 degrees to the horizontal. Height is therefore required above the bins to accommodate the top conveyor, and this space can be used for a catwalk. The bottom conveyor can be omitted by having an auger from each bin, returning the grain into the top, reversible conveyor. Unless the grain for sale can be removed from the store at 30 T/hr direct to a bulk tanker, it should be conveyed into a holding hopper of 20 T capacity ready for the tanker (Fig. 21). The size and number of storage bins required on a farm will depend on the number of varieties of grain to be stored, but larger bins are cheaper than smaller bins per ton of storage space.

e. Polythene lining bags for circular bins are limited to stores of about 100 T capacity.

f. Polythene sacks normally are of up to 100 lb capacity: used fertilizer bags holding about 60–70 lb if well sealed, but only about 50 lb if the neck is tied.

9. *Siting.* The siting of the grain store must take into consideration the nature of the farm. The store is usually integrated with the drying arrangements. If the grain is for sale the drier and store can be central to the fields, provided that there is access for the bulk tanker. If the grain is for feeding to livestock, then the store should be adjacent to the mill/mix unit (IIE), which in turn should be near to the livestock unit. The point of delivery from the store, which can be a holding hopper, may be either at the same end of the store as the intake pit or at the opposite end. In either case there must be good access.

10. *Services.* Electrical power for the mechanical handling equipment is essential (Part II).

11. *Costs.* Costs of storage can vary over a wide range. Storing grain on the floor or in bins within an existing building can prove relatively inexpensive. Floor storage, using r.c. pedestal walls 8 ft high, to a width of 40 ft, might cost less than £5/T storage space including a barn cover. Storage in outdoor circular bins may cost, complete with foundations, £2½–£5/T, mainly depending on the size of silo. Steel plate silos, including their own roof, will probably cost at least £6/T for 100 tons stored in 25-T capacity bins, but only about £4½/T for 1000 tons stored in 100-T storage bins. Indoor bin storage will cost about £3–£5/T. All mechanical handling costs will be extra to these amounts. The 20-T holding hopper might cost about £400. Total storage and handling costs may be £10–

£15 T, including the building but excluding drying costs, and some hermetically sealed silos will also cost from £10 to £15/T. A polythene lining bag for a circular bin will cost about £2½/T, including a 10 h.p. fan, for a 100-T store and £5/T for a 30-T store with a 3-h.p. fan.

12. *References*

(1) *Land* 12. Spring 1962. 'Farming Equipment and the Common Market'. p. 44.
(2) 'Building for Grain'. *Farmers Weekly*, p. 84 (12th October 1962).
(3) 'Grain and Seed Harvesting'. *Farmers Weekly Bulletin*, p. xvi (19th May 1961).
(4) 'Cereal yield estimates'. *Agricultural Merchant*, p. 104 (October 1962).
(5) 'Farm Grain Drying and Storage'. *Ministry of Agriculture Bulletin* 149, p. 19 (1959).
(6) 'Wet grain'. *Farm Mechanization*, p. 29 (October 1963).
(7) FRIEND, I. J. C. 'Sealed grain storage'. *Farm Mechanization*, pp. 35–36 (October, 1963).
(8) 'What's new in farm research'. *Dairy Farmer*, p. 91 (October 1963).
(9) COLL, R. A.M.I.T.A. 'Bulk Handling and the Merchant'. *Agricultural Merchant*, p. 70 (April 1962).
(10) HOPE, H. 'Plastic sacks for undried grain'. *Farmers Weekly*, p. 79 (23rd August 1963). 'Moist Grain in bags'. *Dairy Farmer*, p. 86 (October 1963).
(11) JONES, P. 'Machinery and methods'. *Farmers Weekly*, p. 39 (12th July 1963).
(12) UNITED STATES DEPT. AGRICULTURE. 'Grain Bin Requirements'. *Circular No.* 835 (1950).
(13) MINISTRY OF AGRICULTURE. *Farm Buildings Pocketbook*, p. 24 (1960).
(14) FRIEND, I. J. C. 'Barley stored damp'. *Farmers Weekly*, p. 84 (13th July 1962).
(15) HOPE, H. 'Undried grain in plastic bags.' *Farmers Weekly*, p. 79 (7th August 1964).

SELECTED REFERENCES
a. 'Grain drying and storage'. *Farmers Weekly*, pp. 53–76 (28th December 1962).
b. 'Building for grain'. *Farmers Weekly*. Report on 7th Farm Buildings Conference. pp. 84–6 and pp. 128–9 (12th October 1962 and 19th October 1962).
c. 'Farm grain drying and storage'. *Ministry of Agriculture Bulletin* 149. (1959.)
d. NIX, J. S. 'Drying and storing grain on the farm'. University of Cambridge. *Farm Economics Branch Report* 44 (1956).
e. AGRICULTURAL RESEARCH COUNCIL. *Bibliography of Farm Buildings Research* 1945–58. Pt. V. Buildings for drying and storage of grain (1961): also, 1958–61 (1964).

Seed Appendix

The Seeds Regulations (1922) specify the quality required for the main certified seeds, which for most farm seeds are grouped under three main headings: (*a*) grass and clover seeds, (*b*) cereal seeds, and (*c*) field seeds. Seeds are a specialized crop, requiring great care in harvesting and storing. In 1958, 325,000 tons of seed were required from importations and home production, the latter being derived from about 35,000 acres (1). Normal crop yields vary from 2 to 5 cwt/acre, with a few yields of about 7 cwt/acre. There are three main types of grower:

    i. Intensive.

    ii. Side-line.

    iii. Occasional, as a restorative crop, which is used for grazing, cutting, as well as seed.

Most of the seed is combined, which may pick up dirt with the seed or cause mechanical damage to it, but some is cut, conditioned and threshed. The seed may be handled to the store in the same manner as grain, though there have been experiments for handling in $\frac{1}{4}$-T boxes (2). In one case, the boxes measured 3 ft $\times$ 3$\frac{1}{2}$ ft $\times$ 3$\frac{1}{2}$ ft deep, with a base of mesh and sacking, so that they could be placed over a tunnel through which cold air was blown in order to keep the seed cool until ready for hot air drying.

    Since seed may be harvested with an m.c. as high as 40 per cent, it may need considerable drying before storage (IID). Storage should provide:

    i. Relative coolness.

    ii. Relative dryness.

    iii. Very gentle ventilation.

    iv. Uniformity of *i, ii, iii.*

Since seed may be harvested in small quantities, a number of small storage bins of 10–20 T each may be adequate for most growers, though small-tonnage crops may be stored in bags without excessive labour requirements. The list below gives the weights and the m.c. required to restrict germination and to maintain the quality of the seed for some of the normal crops. Some growers may store with higher moisture contents, and the m.c., except for carrots, parsnips and, possibly, sainfoin, may be 2 per cent higher when stored in bags.

IE. Feeding-stuffs

1. *Activity.* The following list indicates some of the variety of foods which may be fed to livestock (1):

Barley, wheat, oats, rye, maize, flaked maize, wheat bran, weatings, brewers' grains, beans, peas, soya beans, coconut, groundnut, palm nut, linseed, bone or meat meal, fish meal, separated milk, whey, mangolds, swedes, beet, potatoes, cabbage, kale, beet tops, straw, grass, dried grass, hay, haylage, silage, molasses, chemical and mineral trace elements and water.

Not all these products have to be stored prior to feeding, in particular the roots, root tops, kale and grass are normally fed either in or direct from the fields. Most of the nuts, seeds and meals are fed in the form of proprietary concentrated foods. Storage of barley, wheat, oats and rye is considered in ID, straw in IB, haylage and maize in IC and silage in IIC. Water requirements are considered in each of the livestock sections in Section III.

    This section is concerned mainly with the concentrated foods and the liquids. Some of the concentrates are fed to the livestock as bought, whereas other foods are prepared on the farm, storage being required for the ingredients before preparation, and sometimes in addition for the compound after preparation and prior to feeding. The milling and mixing of feeds is considered in IIE. Several manuals are available concerning feeding policies for livestock, including the Ministry of Agriculture's Bulletin 48, *Rations for Livestock.* Each ration has to provide sufficient nutrient both to maintain the animal and to produce some additional commodity, such as liveweight gain or milk

| Grass and clover seeds | | | Field seeds | | |
Seed	lb/bu.	M.c.	Seed	lb/bu.	M.c.
Clover, red	65	10·2	Cabbage	55	8·0
Clover, white	65	9·5	Carrot	30	9·6
Cocksfoot	22	10·9	Kale	55	8·2
Fescue, meadow	30	11·9	Mangold	22	11·6
Lucerne	64	9·5	Parsnip	18	8·5
Ryegrass, Italian	22	11·3	Peas, field	64	14·3
Ryegrass, perennial	28	11·3	Rape	52	7·3
Sainfoin, milled	70	10·0	Sugar beet	19	11·8
Sainfoin, unmilled	28	10·6	Swede	56	7·9
Trefoil	66	10·0	Turnip	50	7·4

(1) N.I.A.B. Report on Herbage Seed Production Conference (November 1958).

(2) *Farmer & Stockbreeder*, Machinery section (21st August 1962).

and the nutrient composition is divided primarily into Starch and Protein Equivalents (S.E. and P.E.), which are considered together with their digestibility. However, it is not necessary to assess here the qualitative values of different fodders, but only the quantitative, since only the latter directly affect storage requirements.

2. *Managerial requirements.* The quantitative values for the major bulk fodders can be summarized as follows:

	Silage	Haylage	Hay	Grain
Dry matter in lb per 100 lb material	25–35	35–55	80–85	86–87

It must be appreciated that the nutritional value of d.m. per 100 lb material can have an S.E. of 70 lb for barley, 50 lb for good hay, 25 lb for poor hay, 15 lb for good silage and under 10 lb for poor silage, while the P.E. can vary as well. Therefore, the average d.m. requirements for livestock, given below, which are the average weights that can be consumed with comfort, do not indicate the nutritional values nor the wide variation in appetite of individual animals. With dairy cattle, the winter bulk fodders seldom give energy for more than maintenance plus 2 gal/day milk production, and poor silage or hay little more than maintenance. Additional milk production has to be derived from concentrated foods, most of which have a barley base.

Average d.m. requirements per day in lb (2)

Dairy cattle	Beef cattle	Sheep	
Jersey 23	5 cwt★ 14½	Lamb (60 lb)	2
Ayrshire 30	7 cwt★ 19	Ewe (110 lb)	3
Friesian 34	10 cwt★ 23½	Ewe-in-milk	6
	★ Liveweight		

All feeding-stuffs, with the exception of self-feed silage have to be handled to the livestock or to the livestock self-feeders. The handling can be completely mechanized, though in many cases it will require either partial or even full control from a man. Most bulk fodders are handled by a tractor and attachment, and concentrates by some form of barrow or hand-operated container (Part II). In all cases the siting and design of the store should be planned to assist the processes of filling and emptying the store and of conveying the food to the livestock.

The principal requirements for storing most concentrates is similar to other granular substances such as grain, i.e. it must be free from moisture, birds, rodents and insects, and should be handled as a free-flowing solid. Skim milk and whey can be handled as a liquid and piped to the point of use. Molasses, which are used as an additive to compound foods and to silage or haylage, need more

control, since their rate of flow as a liquid depends on their temperature. The method of feeding the rations will affect the store design.

3. *Production techniques.* Grain is fed to livestock either crushed, rolled or ground, in various granular sizes and mixtures depending on the class of stock. Farmers growing their own grain will probably dry it (IID) and store it (ID) prior to the preparation of the feed in a mill-and-mix unit (IIE). In addition, in 1961 merchants in Great Britain (less Northern Ireland) produced 8M tons of compound foods: poultry (45 per cent), cattle (36 per cent), pigs (17 per cent) (3). In some cases the meal will be compressed to form cubes or pellets, since these help to improve and speed digestion, eliminating waste and dust (IIE 2*b*, p. 125). Therefore, feed may be delivered to a storage point either from a merchant, or from a farm mill/mix unit, or from both sources either as a meal, pellets or cubes. Delivery may be made in sacks or in bulk, but bulk delivery from merchants represents at present only 10 per cent of the sales, though this method is more efficient (3) and should become more popular. Skim milk or whey will probably be delivered in a bulk tanker from a dairy, unless a dairy farmer makes his own cream or cheese, in which case the separated milk can be piped directly to the livestock. Skim milk is the residue of milk after the cream has been removed, and whey is the residue after making cheese. About 1¾M gal of skim milk per month were used for stock feeding in the second half of 1962, most of which would be consumed by the large pig units around the major butter-making centres, though some would be used for calf rearing.

Molasses are normally delivered in 50-gal drums, though a few farmers will receive molasses in bulk. Minerals and concentrated foods are delivered in bags, and mineral bricks in boxes.

4. *Work routines.* Work required to handle feeding-stuffs into and out of storage should be reduced to the minimum. Bulk handling and mechanical conveying combined with gravity flow are therefore desirable. (Parts 2 IIIA *i* and IIIB *e* for meals and concentrates). In many cases, rather than conveying the feed from the store to the trough or manger, it may be desirable to store the feed above the livestock, so that it can be gravity-fed into the mangers with a meter or ratchet control. However, generally, as in milking parlours (IIF), it may prove cheaper to install conveying equipment rather than to build a loft, especially since the poultry feed conveyors have been adapted for pig and cattle feed. However, mechanical conveyance of cubes rather than of meal may prove to be disproportionately expensive.

The frequency of filling a store, which is one factor determining the size required, will depend on several managerial requirements. Mill/mix units for compounding home-grown grain should be operated on a planned work routine, which might mean that compounding would take place once a day, once a week or once a month, and storage facilities to hold rations for that period would be required. This storage might be adjacent to the mixer, especially if the layout makes it practical to convey the feed to the livestock from that point. But in many layouts it will prove more efficient to have the storage points at or near the point of use. Therefore, the layout must include the best method of taking the feed direct from the mixer to one or several storage points some distance away. This can be done by blowing, mechanical conveyor, tractor or barrow.

In some cases, particularly with pig fodder, it will be necessary to allow a thin trickle of molasses to be added to the compound during mixing, which may make it impractical to store the mix in large quantities or for long periods away from its point of use, since the molasses must remain fluid. Nearly all feedstuffs, having cereals for the bulk of the compound, will need a small percentage of special concentrates, minerals and other additives to the mix, but though these will nearly always be a bought commodity, they will not affect the storage of the compound after mixing.

Those farmers buying their feed ready mixed will have a different principle for its storage. In the first place, the feed will be bought to obtain the maximum discount from the merchant. Only a few large layouts will have deliveries as frequent as every week, most having deliveries at between monthly and quarterly intervals, since the economic load will be the full capacity of a lorry or tanker, which may vary between 5 and 20 T at a time, or, with skim milk and whey, up to 2000 gal. However, skim milk and whey should be delivered weekly. In designing service roads, allowance should be made for the fact that the delivery vehicle may add another 5–10 T to these loads, and the vehicle should be able to draw alongside, or back up to, the entrance to the store, unless the feed is to be blown or pumped, when 20 ft of hose is normally available on the vehicle, though 30–40 ft may be available, and where the vertical lift required does not exceed 30 ft delivery may be at 15–20 T/hr, the former rate being for $\frac{1}{2}$-in. cubes. Some lorries will have a belt or auger stored on the vehicle for mechanical unloading and, normally their reach will extend in a 15–20 ft arc from the rear of the lorry, unloading at rates of 15–20 T/hr. Holding bins or tanks can be designed to have a stand-pipe from their top to 4 ft from the ground, with a coupling for connection to the tanker. Usually, connecting pipes are 4 in. dia. and should

not have a sharp bend of under 4 ft radius. A tipping lorry may have its discharge point about 3 ft from the ground, with its top perhaps at 18 ft, but a large tanker may need 25 ft clearance. Bags should be off-loaded on to a platform about 4 ft above road level. Turning circles for vehicles normally range between 30 and 50 ft, but a 30-ft-long rigid or articulated bulk tanker or lorry may need 70–100 ft.

Cubes may cost more for delivery, perhaps an additional £$\frac{1}{4}$/T ex works. The economics of bulk delivery are difficult to establish, as there are variations between merchants and districts. However, the cost ex works of bulk meal might be about £$\frac{5}{8}$/T cheaper than meal in bags or £$1\frac{1}{4}$/T in hessian sacks, but delivery charges may be greater, depending on distance. The charge for a 6-ton load ex works might be as much as £1/T for a 25-mile radius from the works, and over £2/T for 100 miles. However, the additional charge has to be judged in conjunction with the ease of handling.

5. *Design data.* Average densities of meal, skim milk and whey are given in Pt. 2, Ch. 1, B and C (p. 34). A more detailed analysis has been given (3):

Food	lb/ft³	ft³/T
Whole wheat	50	45
Whole barley	44	51
Whole oats	33	68
$\frac{1}{2}$-in. Dairy cubes	40	56
$\frac{1}{4}$-in. Weaner pellets	38	59
$\frac{3}{16}$-in. Calf pellets	42	53
Poultry crumbs	37	40
Maize meal	40	56
Barley meal	33	68
Bran	13	172

Problems concerning the storage of granular bulk materials are given in Pt. 2, Ch. 3A (p. 39) and Part 3 ID Grain (p. 65). Sacks or bags as delivered weigh about $\frac{1}{2}$ cwt, $\frac{3}{4}$ cwt, 1 cwt or $1\frac{1}{4}$ cwt. Generally, the trend will be towards 70–80-lb bags. Sizes of bags vary with different merchants, but one merchant gives the variation in bag size holding different types of ration when stored as:

	$\frac{1}{2}$-cwt bags (paper)	1 cwt-bags (hessian)
Length	30–35 in.	32–35 in.
Breadth	16–18 in.	20–24 in.
Height	$4\frac{1}{4}$–$5\frac{1}{2}$ in.	$6\frac{3}{4}$–$7\frac{3}{4}$ in.

Closely packed meal bags have an increase in volume of 5–10 per cent when compared with equivalent bulk storage, and other rations one of 10–15 per cent. The bags can be stacked flat, as with fertilizer bags, but pellets, nuts and cubes may be damaged under compression. Therefore, storage is made more often with the bags upright.

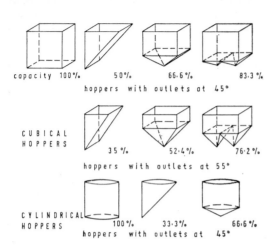

capacity 100%   50%   66.6%   83.3%

hoppers with outlets at 45°

CUBICAL
HOPPERS

35%   52.4%   76.2%

hoppers with outlets at 55°

CYLINDRICAL
HOPPERS   100%   33.3%   66.6%

hoppers with outlets at 45°

Courtesy of *National Association of Corn & Agricultural Merchants*

Fig. 22. Hopper capacities with different types of outlet

Bulk storage can be in proprietary feed hoppers or bins, but can be in a feed storeroom. Bins to be self-emptying are wasteful of space (3) (Fig. 22). The quantity of fodder stored will depend on the period between deliveries, the number of stock, the quantity fed per animal, plus perhaps 10–20 per cent emergency supply. However, arrangements should be made for existing feed stocks to be used before a new supply is started. The quantity fed per animal is considered in each of the livestock sections, but a summary may be made:

a. Dairy cattle rations are normally based on maintenance plus 1 or 2 gal from bulk foods, with perhaps $2\frac{1}{2}$–$3\frac{1}{2}$ lb (in many cases $3\frac{1}{2}$–4 lb) of concentrates fed per additional gallon. For example, assuming a herd averaging 800 gal, with bulk feeds giving maintenance plus 1 gal, and with the peak yield/cow occurring within a period of 2 months, then 3 gal/cow/day must be obtained from concentrates during that period. Therefore, maximum storage of about 10 T/month would be required for a 60-cow herd, though since not all the cows may be in milk at one time, in practice, 8 T max./month may be adequate. (IIF, 2*b*, p. 135.)

b. Beef fattening may be obtained from bulk fodders, though, in most cases, between 5 and 10 lb/beast/day of cereals will be given, at least during part of the fattening period. However, beef can be fattened almost completely on cereal, perhaps with an 85 per cent barley/15 per cent concentrate mix, and 3–$3\frac{3}{4}$ cwt/beast/month might be required. (IIIB, 3*a*, p. 186.)

c. Pig fattening may require an average of $4\frac{1}{2}$ lb/day, or 1–$1\frac{1}{4}$ cwt/month, of meal, or $\frac{3}{4}$ gal/day

of skim plus some additives, though this depends whether fattening is for bacon, pork or heavy hogs and on the conversion rate. Gilts and sows when farrowing may have 2 gal/day of skim, and 3 gal/day during lactation, and proportionally increased meal rations. Generally, it is considered that the sow and creep feed averages $2\frac{1}{2}$ cwt/month. (IIIE 3, p. 208.)

Storage for skim milk or whey must be designed to suit the dairy from which it is obtained. Since they keep for not much more than a week, weekly deliveries are usual. Tanks, which may be hired in some cases, normally have open tops and are erected about 7–8 ft from the ground outside each piggery, though it is desirable for the tank to be in the shade. Skim tanks should have an outlet flush with the tank bottom for complete drainage, with a valve on the outlet coupled to a tee connection, each with a valve and with one connection for mains water and one for the supply to the troughs. The outlet should be $1\frac{1}{2}$–2 ins. dia. Two tanks should be used alternately. After feeding, the feed pipeline should be washed out, and the storage tank should be washed out after emptying, the quantity of water being used equalling the amount required to add to the skim to provide the pigs with adequate liquid. The tanks can be filled with skim or whey by tanker, and there should be a 2-ins.-dia. supply pipe, complete with connector for the tanker, which discharges over the top of the tank. A ladder for inspecting the tank will be required. Whey, and sometimes skim, may be allowed to become sour prior to feeding; in this case, the outlet should be about 6 ins. above the base and the tank should not be washed out (5).

6. *Equipment.* Equipment for filling and emptying the stores is described in Part 2. Proprietary free-standing external storage hoppers for meal of various sizes are available, though most give storage volumes of 200–600 ft³, holding about 4–10 T of food. Usually, they are of galvanized steel, circular cylinders on legs, complete with self-unloading outlet chutes to 3 ft or $4\frac{1}{2}$ ft from the ground, and with intake pipes to the top for coupling to a tanker plus an air-inlet control pipe. Larger hoppers, as used for grain, can be used, but there should be two sides vertical and two sides inclined at 60 degrees towards the outlet, plus inlet and air control pipes, with internal meal distributor plates to prevent blockages or funnelling. Hoppers should have a concrete base and holding-down bolts into the concrete.

Tanks for skim and whey are similar to water storage tanks in sizes ranging from 100 to 3000 gal.

7. *Environment control.* All meal and compound foods must be kept dry. Skim milk and whey con-

tain solids which undergo changes with age, forming lactic acid and lumps of curd, which attack zinc galvanizing and concrete, and these should be treated with bitumastic paint or anti-corrosion paint, though one authority claims to have had no trouble in using galvanized tanks (5). As discussed in Part 2, handling feed must be designed to prevent it shattering or separating and to restrict dust if conveyed pneumatically. Vermin must be excluded and stale material removed.

8. *Layouts* and 9. *Siting.* Layouts and siting of food stores are considered in conjunction with the livestock units.

10. *Services.* Electrical supply for lighting and conveying equipment will be required. All rainwater should be drained well clear of a feedroom.

11. *Costs.* Proprietary external storage hoppers, including erection and a concrete base, might cost up to £35/T storage space for a 4-ton, or £20/T storage space for a 10-ton store. Side discharge outlets might add £15–£30 to these costs. If the store is filled monthly, then the building cost per ton stored over 10 years will be about 8s. and 4½s. respectively. Internal storage hoppers constructed from hardboard on framing might cost as little as £10–£15/T storage space. Feed storerooms are seldom separated from part of a larger building. Assuming that the store might be on the corner of a building, 8 ft to the eaves, and designed to hold 20 tons, with a shaped floor to suit an auger supply to the livestock, and with the meal on average 6 ft deep, therefore requiring a plan area of 20 ft × 15 ft, the cost might be about £15/T storage space. Normal storage costs of £10–£25/T storage space may be assumed, i.e. approximately half the cost of freestanding storage hoppers.

12. *References*

(1) MOORE, H. I., Ed. by. *Agricultural Notebook.* 14th Ed. *Farmer & Stockbreeder,* pp. 377–87 (1962).
(2) 'Off the grass'. *Farmers Weekly Supplement,* p. xxi (14th September 1962).
(3) NATIONAL ASSOCIATION OF CORN AND AGRICULTURAL MERCHANTS. 'Bulk handling of grain, feeds and fertilizers'. (July 1963.)
(4) Personal communication from REEVE, B. E. of B.O.C.M. Ltd.
(5) D. W. TAYLOR & SONS LTD. *Skim or Whey,* p. 14 (1962).

IF. Fertilizers

1. *Activity.* Artificial fertilizers are an important commodity on nearly every farm. Though organic farming can prove completely successful (1), it is not favoured as the sole method of fertilization for intensive, commercial production, but organic irrigation can reduce the quantity of artificial fertilizer required. On most farms many tons of several different fertilizer compositions may be handled each year. Fertilizer requirements on most farms average between 3 and 4 cwt/acre, though some intensive grass production and root crops may need 10–15 cwt/acre.

The fertilizers may not need to be stored. Field applications can be made by contractors, the fertilizer being delivered directly to the field, perhaps in 2-T containers, prior to use. Recent experiments have shown that fertilizers delivered in sealed polythene bags can be stored in the open, either in the fields or near the farmstead, without deterioration unless the bag is punctured. It is too early to know whether there may be any climatic limitations to their use, but it could be that fertilizer storage in buildings will not be required in the future. Fertilizers, moreover, can be delivered from the merchants as a liquid, which is easier to handle, spread and place on the land than granular fertilizers. Delivery can be made direct by bulk tanker to the field, where the liquid may be stored, perhaps temporarily, in portable light-weight fabric tanks of up to 500-gal capacity. However, the use of liquid fertilizers is not widespread.

2. *Managerial requirements.* Granular fertilizers, which are delivered either in bulk or in paper bags when not in polythene, must be kept dry and well ventilated during storage. The different varieties of bagged fertilizer should be kept in separate heaps to facilitate handling. All fertilizers should be kept apart from feeding-stuffs.

Fertilizers are bought from merchants, most of whom offer substantial discounts for those fertilizers bought out of season. This is the main incentive to store fertilizers on the farm. Moreover, buying fertilizers in bulk rather than in bags normally proves cheaper for those farms which require more than 50 T p.a., and this can save at least £1½/T for larger quantities, due to the merchant's reduced labour costs (2). Bulk fertilizer use, though increasing, is still not in widespread practice.

3. *Production techniques.* Fertilizers, whether granular or liquid, are spread on to the fields by tractor-drawn containers (Pt. 2, Ch. 3B, p. 41). Small spreaders may have 5 cwt storage boxes and bulk spreaders may hold up to 2 tons.

4. *Work routines.* Though bags of fertilizer can be mechanically handled both into and out of a store, using a sack elevator, it is important that the bags should not be damaged. Fertilizers are not normally stacked above a man's reach, except on large farms. Thus, elevators are seldom used unless the

bags are taken into a loft for emptying into a hopper, to fill a trailer by gravity. On large farms, in any case, it may be desirable that fertilizers should be handled in bulk to reduce labour requirements.

Bulk delivery of granular fertilizer can be made by a tipping lorry, perhaps of 15-T capacity. If the fertilizer is tipped on to a barn floor it can be pushed into a heap by a tractor and scraper. When required for use, it can be lifted by a tractor and scoop into a trailer or into the hopper of a bulk spreader, at a rate of $\frac{1}{2}$ T/min using a 5-cwt scoop (3). Alternatively, the fertilizer can be tipped into an intake pit, from which it can be augered into an overhead store, and a 5-h.p. 6-in. auger can lift $\frac{1}{3}$ T/min (4). Though fertilizers can be either scooped with a foreloader or augered into the spreaders, it is better to have a trailer filled by gravity from an overhead fertilizer storage bin or hopper, since it is undesirable that the spreader should have to return from the fields to the store to be filled. An even better system is to have a tipping tank mounted on a trailer, so that it can be filled from the hopper and which can tip the fertilizer into the spreader in the field. A 4-T tank could fill a large spreader twice without returning to the farmstead (Fig. 23).

5. *Design data.* Fertilizer densities vary mainly between 35 and 38 ft³/T when stored granulated and in bulk, and 6¼ gal/ft³ or about 29 ft³/T when stored as a liquid. Granulated fertilizers have an angle of repose of about 35–40 degrees. A 1-cwt bag measures about 30 in. × 18 in. × 6 in., and densely stacked bags need a volume 10–15 per cent greater than when in bulk, i.e. about 38–41 ft³/T. However, bags are best stacked on a duckboard if they are to be stored for more than a few weeks, with at least 9 in. between the bags and the walls, and with $\frac{1}{2}$ in. between the bags and 1½ in. between blocks of bags (5) (Fig. 24). Normally, fertilizer is not stacked above 5 ft with manual handling, and 7 ft at the most, that is, about 12 bags high, due to solidification of the fertilizer when compressed, though 12 ft is claimed to be satisfactory. With a stack 7 ft high, floor loading is about 1½ T/yd². Bulk fertilizers will exert considerable pressures on

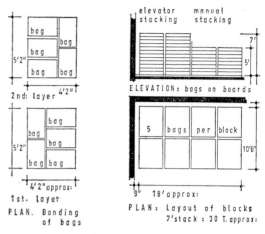

Fig. 24. Bag storage in barn

retaining walls, as with grain (ID 8a, p. 66), and all 9-in. walls should be reinforced when storage is above 4 ft. Allowance should be made for tipping granular fertilizers, in some cases, a bulk tanker of 30 T when loaded requiring 25 ft headroom.

6. *Equipment.* Normal augers and elevators can be used (Part 2), though fertilizers can have a corrosive effect on metals. Equipment and bins should be cleaned after use. Liquid fertilizers can be stored in portable rubber and fabric containers, holding perhaps nearly 4 T in 9-ft × 5-ft × 2½-ft high containers which weigh only about 1 cwt when empty. Portable bins for granular fertilizers are obtainable, but expensive. Patented, 2-T bulk containers with telescopic legs for delivery on a platform lorry require about 10 ft width and 11½ ft height clearance. These are used by merchant/contractors (6).

7. *Environment control.* Storage should be made on a damp-proofed floor, preferably of 6 in. concrete. If it is not possible to include a damp-proof membrane in an existing floor, polythene sheet can be used over its top. Bulk storage can be made within a series of three-sided cubicles in a barn, but each cubicle should be labelled to show the variety of fertilizer stored. Heavy gauge (say 6-mm) 500-gauge plastic sheet should be used to line the walls to the store and should also be laid over the top of the fertilizer. Controlled gable ventilation across the top of the storage is desirable. Galvanized steel sheeted roofs are not as desirable as asbestos-cement sheeted roofs, due to the greater risk from condensation in humid weather. Granular fertilizer in storage must be kept completely dry.

8. *Layouts.* Existing buildings are normally used for fertilizer storage. Existing lofts can be used for

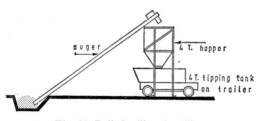

Fig. 23. Bulk fertilizer handling

storage and gravity filling into trailers, provided the floor can take the load required. Cubicle walls can be formed with sleepers laid horizontally in the webs of 6-in. × 3½-in. steel stanchions, placed at 8-ft 7-in. centres and set in concrete foundation blocks, in order to take granular storage to a height of 7 ft. The sleepers should be lined with plastic. However, this walling might cost £1¾–£2/ft.R, but it could be used within a barn which has external light wall cladding.

9. *Siting.* Good access for vehicles is essential, especially if 15- or 20-T bulk tankers are used for delivery. Doors at least 12 ft high are required for tipping trailers. A store in a central position relative to the fields is desirable, though normally the existing farmstead will be the storage point.

10. *Services.* Electrical supply for lighting and for conveying equipment will be required. All rainwater should be drained well clear of the store.

11. *Costs.* Since most stores are in existing buildings, costs are not easily assessed. Conversion of existing dry barns by the addition of division block walls, lined with plastic, and including general minor alterations might cost as little as £½ to £¾/T storage space. Fig. 25 shows three 20-T cubicle bunkers which might be erected within an existing barn. The cost, including steel stanchions and sleeper walls lined with plastic, concrete foundations to the stanchions and a 6-in. concrete floor,

including a damp-proof membrane, with plastic sheets to cover the top and end, might equal about £4/T. If the plastic sheet was replaced every 3 years, and the cubicles were depreciated with interest over 10 years, the annual building cost might equal a little more than £½/T stored. A new building for sack storage to 7 ft might cost over £9/T storage space, which would give an annual building cost of about £1¼/T. If the building was used for only one load of fertilizer p.a., without any secondary uses, the annual cost of £1¼/T would be almost equal to the incentive discount for storing fertilizer and the investment might not be worth while. A grant would improve the position.

12. *References*
(1) 'The Haughley Experiment' 1938–62. Soil Association. (June 1962.)
(2) MOTTRAM, R. S. 'Bulk fertilizer'. *Dairy Farmer Supplement*, p. 59 (March 1962).
(3) 'In bulk all the way'. *Practical Power Farming*, p. 33 (April 1962).
(4) ATTLEE, P. 'Fertilizers in bulk and pocket'. *Farmers Weekly*, p. 89 (1st September 1961).
(5) SHELL CHEMICAL CO. LTD. *Fertilizers*, p. 5 (1962).
(6) 'Bulk handling of grain, seed and fertilizers'. National Association of Corn and Agricultural Merchants (July 1963).

IG. Manure and Slurry

1. *Activity.* All livestock farms produce effluent, the disposal of which is governed by legal requirements.

a. The Public Health Act 1961 has classified the effluent from cattle and pig buildings as trade effluent, and therefore it cannot be discharged into a public sewer without consent from the Local Council and subject to their conditions (Pt. 1, Ch. 7, II, p. 17).

b. The Rivers (Prevention of Pollution) Act 1961 has made it necessary to obtain permission from the Local River Board and to adhere to their conditions before unclean water may be discharged into any ditch which eventually drains into a river (Pt. 1, Ch. 7, III, p. 18).

The effluent can be in the form of dung and urine, sometimes mixed with rainwater from open yards, and sometimes mixed with water used for hosing down yards and milking parlours. Effluent can be produced by water used to clean milking equipment, especially bulk tanks, or by liquid draining from silage. The effluents contain organic matter which, when discharged into streams, is broken down into inorganic or mineral matter, absorbing

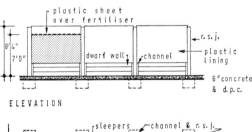

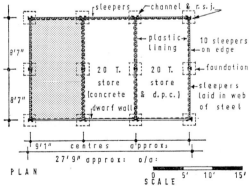

Fig. 25. Bulk fertilizer bunkers in barn

the oxygen in the water in the process. Silage effluent is 220 times more potent than average settled domestic sewage (1), and might need 20,000 gal of water to absorb 1 gal of effluent (2). Each gallon of drainage from cows and pigs might need 1000 gal of water (2). The acidity and alkalinity of different effluents need further research to confirm these figures. It is possible to drain the effluent from livestock buildings into a soakaway, if the subsoil is sufficiently permeable. This is difficult with large livestock units and with the majority of soils. Moreover, there is a risk of contaminating underground watercourses. One solution to the problem is to store the effluent and return it to the land. This process can be of great benefit to the fertility of the soil. The effluent can be stored and returned to the land in five ways:

i. It can be mixed with an absorbent (straw or sawdust), and then it can be lifted by mechanical loader or be pushed into a trailer or manure-spreader to be taken on to the land for shredding and distribution (Pt. 2, Ch. 3B, p. 40). Alternatively, it can be placed on the land either in small heaps from a trailer, subsequently being spread by a separate machine, or in a large heap, subsequently being loaded and spread by any of the methods described above. These processes require more labour than the use of a manure spreader.

ii. It can be stored as a semi-liquid slurry and periodically sucked from the store by a vacuum tanker which also spreads it on to the land (Pt. 2, Ch. 3B, p. 41). Water can be added to keep the slurry diluted to between 25 and $33\frac{1}{3}$ per cent dry matter.

iii. It can be stored as a semi-liquid slurry, before being pumped through pipes on to the land. This method should use least labour and, compared with ii above, avoids running over the land with heavy machinery in winter. The slurry should be diluted to a ratio of 1 : 1. Water may be added and agitated under pressure with the slurry in a pit immediately prior to removal.

iv. It can be stored to induce anaerobic decomposition in a digester, releasing a methane and carbon dioxide gas which can be stored in a gas holder. The residue in the digester will decompose to produce a semi-dry fertilizer, which can be handled as such. Very little experience has been gained concerning this method (4).

v. Alternatively, effluent, particularly from pigs, can be drained into a lagoon, where evaporation equals the rate of drainage, but bacteria will not break down in cold weather. Residue may be returned to the land as a semi-liquid when required. Decomposition of the effluent is normally inoffensive, but little experience of the

method has been gained in this country. Maximum dilution should be 1 : 1, so rainwater should be limited.

Straw as a bedding for livestock is popular with grain producers. However, the majority of loose cattle housing includes one-third or half of the yard as an unbedded area, especially adjacent to the feeding positions, and it is possible that as much as two-thirds of the dung and urine from cattle is drained from the unbedded yards (3). On this basis, the straw absorbs only a small part of the dung and urine and the maximum value is not obtained from the manure. Moreover, part of the liquid deposited on the straw will drain away and other losses will occur from leaching, especially if the manure is exposed to the elements. These losses are important, considering that the urine is rich in nitrogen and potash, whereas the dung has most of the phosphorous voided by the cow, as given in the following percentages (3):

		Nitrogen	Phosphoric acid	Potash
Cow	Dung	0·32	0·21	0·16
	Urine	0·95	0·03	0·95
Pig	Dung	0·6	0·5	0·4
	Urine	0·3	0·1	1·0
Poultry	Faeces	1·5	1·1	0·5

Ministry of Agriculture and NIRD figures suggest that a cow gives an equivalent value per annum of:

	Ministry	NIRD
Sulphate of ammonia, cwt	$6\frac{3}{4}$	$9\frac{1}{4}$
Super-phosphate, cwt	2	$3\frac{1}{4}$
Muriate of potash, cwt	$2\frac{1}{3}$	3

It is desirable, as shown by these figures, to retain the liquid deposited by cows and pigs, if the farmer values organic fertilizers, rather than to drain away the liquids and use a bulky manure low in nitrogen and potash content. This is particularly important in relation to the experiments in ploughing straw back into the land after combining, which have shown that subsequent yields have not been affected (IA 1a, p. 54). Therefore, storing effluent as a semi-liquid slurry has much to commend it.

2. *Managerial requirements.* As soon as dung and urine is voided, fermentation will commence and will release ammonia gas. If effluent is discharged into water the organic matter will decay and will use the oxygen in the water. Storage of the muck with bedding can be managed in the bedded areas by the regular addition of bedding, or the muck can be scraped (usually from open yards) on to straw or shavings in a pit or midden.

It is desirable to keep rainwater from the manure, though this is seldom achieved in practice. If the semi-liquid is held and emptied by a vacuum tanker it is stored normally in a pit a few feet deep under the animals, water being added only if the material appears to be solidifying. If the semi-liquid slurry is to be piped to the fields it will be stored in an open underground tank, and it is essential for it to be diluted with water. Since the fermentation will release ammonia gas, it can be held in solution and will not be wasted if water is added to the muck as soon as possible. The solids must be kept in suspension by mechanical agitation, since the tank is not a cesspit and a crust should not be allowed to form.

If the effluent from animals is stored in a static condition with warm temperatures, is diluted and also has a depth not greater than 5 ft, to allow light and oxygen to penetrate to the bottom, and is, finally, protected from all other waste materials, the bacteria will become aerobic, working with oxygen, and will produce no smell: provided the surface area per animal is great enough, evaporation from the surface will equal the addition of water to produce a *status quo*. In contrast, effluent in a cesspool, without oxygen, will have an anaerobic action, producing unpleasant gases.

3. *Production techniques.* The techniques for handling manure and slurry have been discussed above. Though it is not generally relevant to existing techniques in the United Kingdom, methane gas can be produced by mixing a little water with the dung before it enters the digester tank, where the bacteria create a methane and carbon dioxide gas approximately in the ratio of 2 : 1. A decomposed effluent remains, which can be drawn off from the digester as a semi-liquid of about 10 per cent dry matter containing 6 per cent nitrogen, 5 per cent phosphates and 1 per cent potash (4).

4. *Work routines.* Farmyard manure handling will take place at the end of the annual housing period in the spring, when the land is ready to receive the manure. Handling can be carried out with a tractor and fork lifting the manure into a trailer or spreader. Slurry can be scraped from yards into a pit every day or two, either with a tractor and scraper blade or from channels and passage-ways with a powered scraper operated by hand, or with various forms of conveyor belts and chains with scraper (Pt. 2, Ch. 3C, p. 46). The slurry can be converted into a semi-solid or can be handled from the pit as a semi-liquid.

The semi-liquids (about 25–33⅓ per cent dry matter) can be sucked by a vacuum tanker, either from a reservoir under the animals or from an external pit, to be spread on the land only when the land is dry enough to take the tanker (Pt. 2, Ch. 3B, p. 42). In wet districts and on heavy land storage for three months may be required. The advantage of piping the slurry on to the land and

spreading it through a pressurized jet is that the operation can be performed at any time.

Labour requirements for handling slurry have not been established. However, one survey has shown that a tanker system, including cleaning yards into the tank and for emptying it, ranged from about ⅔–5 hr/1000 gal, averaging 2¼ manhr/1000 gal. With a pipeline system, the time range was about 1/10–⅛ hr/1000 gal averaging just over 7 man.min/1000 gal (16).

5. *Design data.* The data for storage requirements is inconclusive, as is shown by the figures quoted below, since insufficient is known concerning the variables in the production of effluent, particularly with regard to feeding, environment and breed.

a. A cow may produce 3 gal of urine per day, young stock averaging 1½ gal (5). However, American research has shown that this varies with heat and water intake, the quantity being related to muscular relaxation, increasing from about ¾ gal at about 2° C (35° F) to 5½ gal at 35° C (95° F), with a corresponding increase in water consumption from 5 to 13¼ gal (7). Similarly, dung produced will be 55 lb/day (5). Other sources quote Aberdeen Angus and Hereford cows producing 46 lb/day (8), and a 1000-lb cow 18,000 lb/yr (9), i.e. between 6½ and 7 ft³/wk, or mature cattle 5 ft³/wk of dung and 2½ ft³/wk of urine and young stock 4 and 2 ft³/wk respectively (10).[1]

b. Pigs will produce ⅓ gal/day of urine and 7 lb/day of dung (5), or 1 gal of sludge/day, i.e. about 1½ ft³/wk (6), though this will be increased with liquid feeding (perhaps to 2–3 gal of sludge/day) or with high-temperature housing, but another source quotes 1½ ft³/wk of dung and ½ ft³/wk of urine (10), for dry feeding.

c. Weight of dung is about 75 lb/ft³ (5), and volume of urine about 6¼ gal/ft³ of storage; therefore, on the basis of the figures quoted, an adult cow may require about 8½ ft³/wk storage tank, and a pig about 1½ ft³/wk with dry feeding.

d. Slurry to be pumpable for organic irrigation must have a dilution of dung and urine to water of 1 : 1 (3), though this may have to be substantially increased in hot weather. Therefore, cattle require 17 ft³/wk storage and pigs 3 ft³/wk.

e. One pound of wheat straw will absorb 2 lb of urine within 24 hr (oat straw, 2½ lb) (11). A ton of straw used as bedding will provide 4–6 T of manure (12). A cubic yard of farmyard manure will weigh 12–16 cwt (13).

f. Effluent discharges from a parlour and dairy are impossible to assess. A guide can be taken (14):

[1] Manure collecting in pits below slats for cows has been given as 21 ft³/cow/month for the lying area, and 31 ft³/cow/month for lying, feeding and collecting areas. (Ref. *c.*).

Washing down parlour and dairy 100 gal/day
Cleaning out bulk tank   100 gal/day

If a surface cooler or turbine churn heads are used, about 3 gal of water per gallon of milk is required, but up to 5 gal of water per gallon on milk if sparge rings are used.

g. The seepage of effluent from ensilaged grass is related directly to the moisture content of the grass brought from the fields. Half the discharge occurs within the first three or four weeks after the silo is filled. Figures for effluent discharge, which have been calculated for tower silos, are given below (1). Results for covered clamp silos probably would show little difference.

% d.m. crop content 17·0 20·2 23·3 26·4 35
Gal effluent/silage   46·3 33·7 20·3 2·3 1·2

At about 30 per cent d.m. content the effluent is slight. The practice of wilting the crop for 6–12 hr after cutting, in fair weather, should do much to enhance the quality of the silage, but the average dry matter content of ensiled grass in this country is 20–25 per cent (15). At 22 per cent the effluent amounts to about 25 gal per ton of silage. Haylage should have little effluent.

h. Rainwater fouled from open yards must be treated as effluent and must be calculated from the maximum rainfall for the district which can occur whilst the effluent is stored.

i. Very little information is available with regard to methane gas. It is claimed that 500 pigs or 60 cows would produce 5000 ft³ of gas at a value of 711 B.t.u./ft³, and 50 T of dry fertilizer (4).

j. Very little information is available with regard to the lagoon area required, though a report from Missouri University quotes 15 ft²/pig, but other areas between 7½ and 30 ft² have worked successfully in American conditions.*

k. Underground dung storage channels should be of rectangular section, with smooth walls and sides and with a longitudinal fall of about 1 : 150 for the slurry to flow towards a sluice or draw-off point without leaving the solids behind.

6. *Equipment.* The equipment for removing manure and slurry from the place of storage, whether tractor and buckrake or vacuum tanker, is described in Part II. No modern national research has been carried out in this country on the equipment for the production and storage of methane gas from slurry, though at least one manufacturer markets equipment including a digester tank about 35 ft × 8½ ft × 5¼ ft high to produce up to 7000 ft³/day of methane gas from 800 pigs or 130 cows

* Lagoons have not proved completely successful. Early estimates suggested that 15 ft²/pig would be needed, more recently 45 ft²/pig has been recommended. But, in Holland, small lagoons with a central rotor agitator have been used.

and equal to nearly 5M B.t.u. Proprietary equipment is available for the mechanical agitation of slurry and water stored for organic irrigation. Timber paddles are required with a diameter slightly less than the cross-section of the tank, spaced and supported at about 12–15-ft centres. They are attached to a spindle driven by a motor powered at about 1 h.p. per paddle. If the slurry contains straw or silage it will be designed to pass through a preliminary chamber, where these will be chopped into short lengths by a cutter pump. Space is required, either above or at the side of the tank, to take the pump which will force the slurry through the pipes to the fields. The pump can be mounted on a trolley or may be fixed on to a base. A tractor-powered auger, 9 in. dia. for handling slurry is available, having a removable cover.

7. *Environment control.* With strawed bedding, or with the use of a pit under livestock, the manure or slurry may heat to temperatures of over 40° C (104° F). The heat is an asset for winter housing. The smell from silage effluent is very offensive, but livestock effluent need not be offensive.

8. *Layouts* and 9. *Siting.* The layouts and siting for deep litter and pit arrangements of storage are discussed in the livestock sections. The tank for organic irrigation is designed normally to have a cross-section of about 10 ft × 10 ft, with lengths in multiples of the agitator paddle unit. The tank is situated in relation to the buildings and yards to give easy and straight lines of drainage of about 1 : 40 falls, and access to the fields for the pipelines. In addition, siting should take into consideration the possibility of the tank smelling. Plastic-lined cesspits can be formed, various polythene sheets being marketed for the purpose.

10. *Services.* Services are usually limited to the requirement of adding water to the organic irrigation tank, the motors being mainly petrol driven.

11. *Costs.* The cost of storage is impossible to assess. Excavation or building up will vary with site conditions and layout. An allowance of £5–£8 per cow might be required for a slurry pit in a cattle unit. An organic irrigation tank might cost £500–£1000, plus another £1000 for agitator, pump and 300 yd.R of 3-in. pipes on to the fields. Charges for drainage of effluent into public sewers have not been established by the autumn of 1962. A cesspit for 200,000 gal, 100 ft × 80 ft, might cost £150 to bulldoze and £200 to line with polythene.

12. *References*
(1) JONES, E. E. & MURDOCH, J. C. 'Polluting character of silo effluent'. *Water and Sanitary Engineer* (July 1954).

(2) FISH H. 'Disposal of farm waste products'. *Agriculture*, p. 60 (May 1962).

(3) WRIGHT RAIN LTD. *Tech. Bulletin.* B213 (January 1961).

(4) FRY, L. J. 'Methane gas power'. *Farmers Weekly*, p. 87 (3rd November 1961).

(5) MINISTRY OF AGRICULTURE. *Farm Buildings Pocketbook*, p. 37 (1960).

(6) VITAMEALO LTD. *Manual of Modern Pig Housing*, p. 33 (1962).

(7) KAMAL, T. H. & JOHNSON, H. D. 'Water consumption in dairy cattle as influenced by environmental temperatures and urine excretion'. *Missouri Agric. Exp. Sta. Journal*, 1958–59 and *J. Dairy Sci*, Vol. 42, No. 5, p. 926 (1959).

(8) JOHNSTONE-WALLACE, D. B. 'Animal behaviour and grazing'. *Agric. Soc. England*, Vol. 114, p. 13 (1953).

(9) ECKLES, C. H. & ANTHONY, E. C. *Dairy Cattle and Milk Production*, p. 536 (1956).

(10) 'Farmstead sewage problems'. *Farmers Weekly*, p. 85 (16th November 1962).

(11) WHISENAND, J. *Agric. Res.* Vol. 14, p. 187 (1918).

(12) WATSON, J. A. S. & MORE, J. A. *Agriculture*, p. 94 (1949).

(13) MOORE, H. I., B.Sc., Ph.D. *Agricultural Notebook*, 14th Ed., p. 583 (1962).

(14) MCGRATH, J. L. & HOWSE, R. E. 'Disposal of farm effluents'. *Agriculture*, p. 110 (June 1962).

(15) WATSON, S. J. & SMITH, A. M. *Silage*, p. 108 (1956).

(16) HALL, W. K. 'Disposal and handling of liquid manure and farm effluents'. *Farm Mechanization*, pp. 40–1 (May 1963).

SELECTED REFERENCES

a. LONG, D. 'Farmstead sewage problems'. *Farmers Weekly* (9th November 1962, 16th November 1962, 23rd November 1962, 30th November 1962, 7th December 1962).

b. 'Disposal of farm waste products'. Report of the sixth winter conference of the Farm Buildings Association (December 1961).

c. LIVINGSTONE, H. R. 'Slatted floors'. *Experimental Farm Buildings Report* No. 3 (1965).

IH. Potatoes

1. *Activity.* The potato crop for 1962 has been estimated to be more than $5\frac{1}{2}$M T, of which over 5M T came from the maincrop. Average yields for early potatoes were 5–6 T/acre and for the maincrop 8–10 T/acre, though higher yields, perhaps of 15 T/acre, may be sometimes obtained. In 1958 the maincrop yielded less than $2\frac{1}{2}$M T, of which 25 per cent was sold off the field and, of the remainder, nearly half was stored in buildings, that is about 850,000 T. The rest was stored in field clamps. It is probable that most of the ware potatoes, that is, other than those used for seed or animal fodder, which are not sold at harvest will be stored in permanent or temporary buildings before the end of this decade. Therefore storage buildings holding up to 3M T might be required.

At present the financial incentive for potato storage (whether in field clamps or in buildings) is that the market price for potatoes tends to rise between mid-October and March by £5/T in a surplus year, but by £11/T in a shortage year (1). The five main reasons in favour of storage in buildings rather than in field clamps have been given in an economic survey of the 1955 and 1956 crops made by the Universities of Nottingham, Leeds and Reading (2):

(1) shortage of skilled labour for building clamps;
(2) shortage of suitable straw for covering clamps;
(3) to avoid loss of production on the clamp site;
(4) to provide better working conditions;
(5) to save labour costs.

Many farmers consider that straw from combine-harvesting is unsuitable for clamp storage and, if a farmer should have to buy straw at £6/T, for example, then the cost per ton for straw used for clamped potatoes would equal 6s./T (3). Moreover, the loss of production from the clamp site averaged 6d./T clamped, but could be as much as 1s. 6d./T. Good working conditions are essential for the modern skilled labour force and the practice of lifting, riddling (i.e. grading) and carting potatoes from field clamps in winter weather is to be discouraged, especially since potatoes are liable to damage if exposed to frost. The highest prices for potatoes are obtained during the severest weather, though this will be a diminishing advantage as more stores are built. With indoor storage, riddling can take place when outdoor work is impractical.

An estimate was made to show that in 1956–7 the average savings in harvesting and handling costs for storing potatoes in buildings could be assessed as (4):

During harvesting	2s. 7d. per ton
During storage	2s. per ton

In addition, 6d./T was saved by having the clamp site in productive use, with 3s./T saved in straw. However, the latter saving was made only if the straw was either purchased or, if it came from the farm, it was sold or put to other effective use. A total saving of about £$\frac{2}{5}$/T had to be balanced against extra costs for providing and maintaining a building and additional equipment, which came to about £$\frac{1}{2}$/T. It was assumed that the extra shrinkage incurred by potatoes in indoor storage was offset by the fact that clamp potatoes had a greater tendency to disease. The conclusion was that, for indoor storage to be economic, the building cost had to be less than £$\frac{1}{4}$/T.

Higher yields and increased labour costs, together with new equipment for handling potatoes and the continual emphasis for providing better working conditions, have made it more advantageous to have storage buildings than in 1956. In the past one expensive item within the cost of providing storage buildings has been the erection of restraining walls to hold the thrust from bulk storage of potatoes and another has been the provision of concrete floors. Such stores tended to cost £6–£12 per ton storage space, but others combining temporary walls and earth floors might have cost less than £4/T storage space. Bulk storage relied on the potatoes being taken from the fields in trailers, which would tip them into a hopper to an adjustable elevator to load the store.

Storage has to be considered in relation to modern experimental work, which has shown that it is practical to harvest and store potatoes in pallet boxes, thus making it possible to use a building with sheeted walls, since the latter do not have to withstand any thrust. Building costs can be reduced substantially by this method. In addition, during 1961–2 research has shown that it is practical to store the boxes out of doors at the farmstead (5). In this experiment the boxes were stacked three high on a concrete apron to a total height of about 10 ft. They were surrounded by straw walls three bales thick, with a plastic sheet to act as a wind barrier between the inner and the two outer bales. Straw was laid on timber poles over the top, and this was covered by a tarpaulin which was taken down the sides for about 5 ft, the tarpaulin being tied (Fig. 26). During the winter the stack was opened each day and a small number of boxes were removed within a few minutes and taken into an adjacent shed for riddling. A tractor with a rear fork-lift attachment is suitable for this work (Part 2, Ch. 3B, p. 49), and can cost under £400 for the fork-lift. However, additional research is required to show whether outdoor box storage will suit not only all climatic conditions but also late storage until March. It may thus be shown within the next year or two that no permanent storage is required other than a concrete apron and a riddling and loading shed.

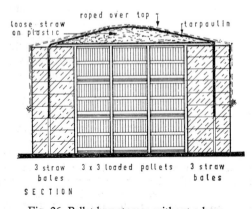

Fig. 26. Pallet box storage without a barn

2. *Managerial requirements*. The storage required will be determined by the methods for lifting and transporting potatoes. Mechanical harvesters are being developed, which will lift potatoes, remove dirt and tare, leave few potatoes in the ground and handle the crop into pallet boxes, whether working on medium or on heavy land. However, it was estimated that, in 1960, only one-tenth of the acreage was mechanically picked. The 1962 International Potato Harvester Demonstration showed that the best machines working on medium loam proved more efficient than hand pickers, except for dirt, tare and damage (6). However, boxes can be used by hand pickers as well as by mechanical harvesters, either by filling $\frac{1}{2}$-T boxes, which can be lifted by foreloader on to trailers to be taken to the store, or by filling $\frac{1}{4}$-T boxes, which can be lifted by foreloader and emptied into 2000-lb boxes on a trailer. Double-handling would be avoided by harvesting direct into 2000-lb boxes.

It is probable that potato handling will be standardized either in $\frac{1}{4}$-T or 2000-lb boxes, the latter being cheaper both to handle and to store, two boxes being carried on a 10-ft platform trailer. Alternatively, the potatoes may be carted in bulk in 2-T loads in tipping trailers, with two trailers alternately being loaded and transported, capable of transporting 44 T/day to a storage point about $\frac{1}{2}$ mile from the field (7). However, storing rates of more than 60 T/day may be required, when a third tractor and trailer would be needed.

Storage should be designed so that potatoes are excluded from light and keep firm, without any wilting, sprouting or loss from disease, for periods of 4–6 months. In addition, the harvesting routine should not be delayed when filling the store and it should be possible to empty the store daily during the winter, if required, without damage to the potatoes, to riddle the potatoes and to load them on to transport for sale. In a few cases the potatoes may be washed, graded and pre-packed on the farm, and on at least one farm they are peeled prior to pre-packing (IIK). Moreover, potatoes, in particular those required for chips and crisps, should have a low sugar-reducing content of less than $\frac{1}{4}$ per cent to prevent discoloration, and this content increases as the temperature is lowered (8). Unfortunately, the tendency to sprout is increased as the temperature is raised, so that the two conditions of good storage cannot be provided by thermal control alone.

3. *Production techniques*. The storage building will be empty for about 6–8 months of the year. For this reason many of the buildings are put to alternative uses during the summer. However, most of the buildings are used casually for implements, fertilizers and other storage purposes, and very few for productive enterprises, though the winning

21 & 22: TRANSIT BULK FERTILIZER STORE

Mr. R. Paterson, Basingstoke, Hants.

Handling fertilizers in bulk can prove to be economic. A natural ground fall, in this case exaggerated by a ramp, can make bulk storage and gravity flow easy. A 20 T bulk lorry tips the fertilizer from the ramp through a hatch into a specialized store of waterproofed concrete blocks. Walls need to be reinforced against lateral pressures and can be lined internally with plastic sheeting. At the lower level can be seen a fertilizer spreader and tractor. The overall height from the lower level is about $12\frac{1}{2}$ ft and from the ramp $3\frac{1}{2}$ ft. External dimensions are about 20 ft $\times$ 11 ft, holding 20–25 T. Since this is a transit store, holding fertilizers for only a day or two, damp is less serious than for long-term storage.

Filling a fertilizer spreader, which may hold up to 2 T, can waste time unless filled from an overhead store. The spreader is backed under the 20 T storage bin, the shutter opened and filled with fertilizer, a task taking only a few minutes. The transit store is sited near the farm road to the fields. The opening for the spreader is about 10 ft wide $\times$ 5 ft deep $\times$ $6\frac{1}{2}$ ft high. The store is filled from the higher ground on the other side. [SEE PAGES 73 & 40] Courtesy of Fisons Fertilizers Ltd.

23: SLURRY TANK

Mr. Maitlaind Mackie, Westertown, Aberdeen

An organic irrigation slurry tank, 10 ft × 70 ft × 10 ft deep and holding 45,000 gal, fitted with 8 wooden paddles mechanically agitated to stir the diluted slurry, which is forced with a piston pump through 1000 yds of 4-in. aluminium irrigation pipes to discharge through a rain-gun on to the land. The pit is emptied in winter every 3 wks. The safety grid over the pit is important. The pit collects the dung from a 150-cow herd with 130 stock and from a battery hen and broiler unit and has operated since 1960. [SEE PAGES 76 & 170] Courtesy of Farm Intelligence Ltd.

24: SLURRY BIN STORAGE

Eyhurst Farm, Kingswood, Surrey

A recent development for handling and storing slurry has been a proprietary auger and bin, the latter being above ground and cheaper to erect than the below-ground tanks. A 120-cow herd, housed in cubicles, produces about 6 yds C of slurry day, which is scraped into a 25 yds C pit covered with 4-in.-dia. steel pipes on steel beams. The slurry is augered by a special 9-in. auger, 20 ft long, driven by a tractor P.T.O. shaft into a 20-ft-dia. steel-plated storage bin which is 10 ft high, providing storage for 110 yds C of slurry. A sluice at the bottom of the bin allows the slurry to flow into the pit, from which it is raised by the auger and discharged, through a second and lower outlet from that used to fill the bin, into a trailer at the rate 1 yd C/min. [SEE PAGE 78] Courtesy of Dairy Farmer.

25 & 26: WARE STORAGE

Copartnership Farms Ltd., Boreham, Chelmsford. Winning design in the Country Landowners' Association's 1962 Farm Buildings Competition for indoor potato storage buildings. Interior and Exterior views.

A concrete portal framed building of 50 ft span, 90 ft long and 16 ft to the eaves, holding 800 T of potatoes stored in bulk 12 ft deep and with space for grading at one end. Auxiliary access is shown on the left-hand side. The floor is of $\frac{1}{2}$-ft-thick woodwool slabs with an internal waterproof render. The top of the potatoes are insulated with loose straw. The roof is uninsulated. Since this building was erected, insulated roofs for ware storage have been considered to be an advantage. There are gable louvres at each end, which can be closed by shutters, for high-level ventilation. A sunken duct in the floor, ventilated from an external 30-in. axial-flow fan, capable of ventilating 400 T at one time, has outlets to the transverse 'A' frames at 6-ft centres, one of which is shown at the edge of the potatoes. Thermostats in the main duct cut off the fan when the air temperature drops to 2° C (36° F). Fluorescent lighting assists loading and grading. An elevator with extension boom is in position. Waste soil, which has to be removed, falls from the potatoes at the griddle to the elevator. The 9-in. brick walls are reinforced and supported by brick piers and are independent of the concrete frame, taking the thrust of the potatoes stacked 12 ft deep. Sliding access doors are at each end of the building giving an opening 14 ft wide × 16 ft high and shuttered gable ventilation is provided above the doors. Side doors give auxiliary access. [SEE PAGE 84] Courtesy of Electrical Development Association.

27: IMPLEMENT AND VEHICLE SHED

A portal framed barn 36 ft long × 30 ft span plus a 10-ft-wide eaves overhang to the front. The two centre stanchions along the front are omitted and the roof is supported on a lattice beam between the two stanchions along the front at the sides of the building. This lattice beam is obscured by the overhang, the latter being cantilevered from the beam. This construction gives a relatively cheap shed providing maximum manoeuvrability for vehicles. [SEE PAGE 89] Courtesy of Croggon & Co. Ltd.

28: SIMPLE IMPLEMENT SHED

Implements can be stored cheaply. Self-supporting curved galvanized sheets in an arc, supported on steel posts to give an open front, can provide a simple implement shelter some 12 ft deep. The supports are at $7\frac{1}{2}$-ft centres or, if a greater opening is required, one post can be omitted if an eaves beam braced with straining wires is used. Though the shed is cheap, being perhaps about £$\frac{1}{5}$/ft^2, the disadvantage of not being able to drive through with a tractor plus implement is obvious. The raised fuel tank can be seen beyond the shed. The wide concrete turning area in front of the shelter is an advantage. [SEE PAGE 89] Courtesy of British Farmer.

entry for a multi-purpose potato store in the Country Landowners Association's National Farm Buildings Competition for 1961-2 was used for potatoes from October to March, for yarded cattle from March to May, for fattening turkeys from May to September and for short-term grain storage in late September.

4. *Work routines.* Handling pallet boxes into and out of storage is simple, if a fork-lift attachment to a tractor is used. It is possible to harvest into 2000-lb boxes and to tip the potatoes from them with a tractor-driven or electrical dumper on to an elevator hopper for bulk storage. Normal bulk storage loading is done by a tipping trailer emptying the potatoes on to an elevator hopper. The process of loading can be fully mechanized, the potatoes being stacked by the elevator, with the exception of the labour required to cover the potatoes with straw after each day's load. High-speed loaders with rates of up to 30 T/hr are available and the rate of loading is important, since the trailer should return to the field as soon as possible.

Unloading can also be mechanized, using an elevator and conveyor. Some machines can have the conveyors placed in ducts below floor level, usually down the centre of the building, the same duct sometimes being used for air ventilation, with the elevator loading directly into trailers or lorries. Alternatively, potatoes can be loaded on to the riddle and potato grader direct from the elevator. Unloading rates of up to 15 T/hr are possible.

Thermometers should be placed both among the potatoes and a few feet above the stack and readings should be taken every day for the first fortnight, thereafter at weekly intervals. Doors and ventilators can be adjusted to suit the temperature requirements. Fumigation may be required to help to suppress sprouting.

An advantage of indoor storage can be that riddling outputs are increased by 50-100 per cent (9). In addition to riddling the potatoes, sacking and weighing may be required as well as loading on to lorries. In some cases the potatoes are washed.

5. *Design data*

a. The density of stored potatoes should be taken at 56 ft³/T. There is no qualification to restrict the length of the store, though good access to both ends is desirable. In addition, one end of the building should include an additional 20 ft for the initial position of the riddle for grading. There is no limit on the width of the store, though this should be designed to suit the elevator, since in a wide building this has to be moved from side to side, which is time-consuming. However, a wide building will reduce the ratio of external walling per ton stored, which

will reduce the structural cost, and this is more important than having the correct width for the elevator. In practice, most stores are 30-45 ft wide. Unless permanent insulation is included in the wall construction, which is desirable, an additional 1½ ft around the perimeter of the potatoes may be required for bales of straw to act as the insulation material.

The angle of repose for potatoes is about 35 degrees, varying with their shape and cleanness. This will increase the length required for the store, so that the stack can slope towards the grading position. A stack 6 ft high will slope for a distance of about 3 yd, holding about ½ T/ft width of store within the slope, and one 12 ft high about 6 yd, holding about 1¾ T/ft width within the slope. The storage capacities per yd.R of the store for the stack 6 ft and 12 ft high are about ⅓ and ⅔ T/ft width of store respectively. Fig. 27 shows the internal layout

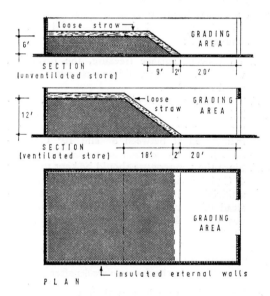

Fig. 27. Bulk storage—angle of repose

of stack, stack slope, insulation and grading position. With box storage, the plan area must suit the size of the boxes used, together with insulation required around them. Storage in 2000-lb boxes will require about 70-75 ft³/T stored.

Storage in bulk can be divided into two main types, depending on the height of the stack. Shallow stores with a maximum height of 6 ft do not require forced-air ventilation, relying instead on natural air circulation from the outside air through ducts under the stack. Deep stores must include artificial ventilation and can be up to 12 ft high, the height depending on the elevator used. The elevator will require a working height of at least 2 ft above the stack, and this is also the space required for loose straw insulation on top of the potatoes after loading. Roof space is required above the straw for ventilation.

b. Potatoes produce heat by respiration, which normally amounts to 150, but can be as much as 250 B.t.u./T/hr at harvest, dropping to about 30–50 B.t.u./T/hr by mid-winter. At a temperature of about 2° C (36° F), 50 B.t.u./T/hr are released, and at about 11° C (52° F), 70 B.t.u./T/hr, which is sufficient to raise the temperature of the potatoes by about $\frac{1}{3}$° and $\frac{1}{2}$° C (0·6° F and 0·8° F)/day respectively (10). Thus, provided the length and breadth of the stack exceed the height, the maximum temperature of the potatoes may exceed the temperature of the store air by rather more than $\frac{1}{2}$° C (about 1° F) for every foot of height (11). The most important source of heat dissipation will be by convection currents rather than by conduction through the walls. The thermal control required can be summarized:

i. To prevent surface freezing, the insulation value of the walls should be designed for U to equal 0·2 or less.

ii. To keep the potatoes in good condition, ventilation should be provided to reduce excess temperature so that the storage temperature is maintained at between 8° and 10° C (46°–50° F).

iii. Since the temperature should be kept to under 4° C (40° F), in order to prevent sprout growth, artificial sprout suppressants can be used instead of thermal control, thereby making it possible to keep the temperature at about 8° C (46° F).

iv. To help heal wounds to the potato skins, the temperature should be kept to about 15° C (60° F) during the first two weeks after storage.

c. Potatoes incure a loss in their weight during storage, which, without forced ventilation, may equal (8):

During October	0·8 per cent per month
November to March	0·5 per cent per month
During April	1·2 per cent per month
May to June	1·5 per cent per month

Therefore, a loss of 3–4 per cent in weight can be expected for normal storage periods of about six months. During periods of forced ventilation these weight losses might be increased by half, although, with continuous ventilation during the first fortnight after storage, a loss of 3 per cent might be incurred for that period. Thus, it would seem that artificially ventilated stacks may lose at least 5 per cent, possibly 8 per cent,

over the winter. However, the depth of storage can be greater than with unventilated stacks. Experiments to show weight losses incurred with box storage, whether indoors or outdoors, are incomplete. One experiment in 1961–2 showed a loss of 8 per cent without ventilation, compared with a loss of 13·2 per cent with bulk storage in similar conditions (12). Another experiment with box storage to about 10 ft and bulk storage to 6 ft, with identical insulation, showed that there was less shrinkage, with the potatoes keeping cooler and better, in the box store (13).

d. The optimum R.H. is between 85 and 95 per cent.

e. U.S. research showed that the lateral and downward pressures of potatoes when stored in bins to 15 ft were 92 and 56 lb/ft² respectively after 3 weeks, being an increase of 10–20 per cent on the pressures incurred immediately after loading (14). The lateral thrust can be taken at about 10 lb/ft² for every foot of storage height.

f. The resistance of the potatoes against air flow depends on the earth present and the degree of sprouting. With clean, unsprouted potatoes it can be only 0·01 in. s.w.g./ft ht, but with soiled potatoes it can be 0·025 in. s.w.g./ft ht, or even 0·1 in. in bad cases.

6. *Equipment*

a. Thermometers should be placed approximately in each 50 T of storage space, preferably at the estimated points of maximum and minimum temperatures, as well as in the roof space, suspended a few feet above the stack.

b. Loading machinery should have a hopper on the elevator the full width of the tipping trailer and include an adequate soil extractor. The elevator should be adjustable and manoeuvrable, with the discharge conveyor able to swivel. The hopper and elevator will need a working space of 20–25 ft from the hopper loading point to the stack by a width of about 8 ft, with the discharge conveyor reaching the sides of the stack. Usually, the elevator is powered by a 2-h.p. motor and an additional 2 h.p. may be required for the soil extractor if independently powered.

c. Manual unloading is laborious, and a tractor and scoop damages the potatoes. Extractor conveyors can be slid along the main underfloor duct, covers to the duct being removed so that the potatoes roll on to the conveyor. The conveyor can load an elevator, which will require about 15–20 ft by 3 ft wide of floor space, and the elevator can load on to either a grader or a lorry, requiring 2-h.p. motors.

d. Potato graders and other equipment require 250–600 ft² of floor space and 1½- or 2-h.p. motors. In addition, a portable radiant heater

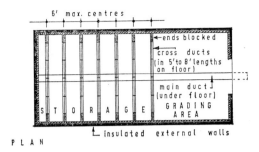

Fig. 28. Bulk storage—ventilation ducts

on a vertical support with a power lead should be used to warm the area around the graders.

e. Electrical power is preferable to diesel to prevent fumes within the storage area.

f. Fumigants can be small portable units, including a drum, and can be connected to the ventilation ducts, using an axial-flow fan giving an air speed of 5 C.F.M./T.

g. Entrance doors should be provided at both ends of the store, 10–14 ft wide by 12 ft high. Similar emergency access doors along the side of the store should be provided when the storage is more than 60–75 ft in length.

h. A main duct from the air intake point should be provided down the length of the store, usually positioned down the centre (Fig. 28). This duct may be either below ground or in the form of a portable unit in short lengths. Cross ducts will be required at right angles from the main duct at 6-ft maximum centres. These can be portable, interlocking units, each between 5 and 8 ft long, to suit the width of the store, and made from timber slats. The ducts must have a minimum open cross-sectional area of 2 in.²/T of potatoes ventilated (Fig. 29). The end of each duct

should be closed and the frictional losses within the ducts should be kept to the minimum.

i. Potatoes stacked above 6 ft high will require a fan for artificial ventilation. The fan should be capable of ventilating against the maximum resistance, but since this seldom occurs, there should be an automatic control against overloading. Ventilation is required both to dry wet potatoes quickly and to dissipate heat developed by respiration. Forced ventilation should be kept to the minimum periods for these conditions, using the maximum air flow rates practicable. The minimum rate should be 40 C.F.M. for each ton to be ventilated at any one time, since this should keep the temperature of the stack to within 1° C (2° F) of that of the ventilating air measured against 1·5 in. s.w.g., the latter requirement being based on 0·5 in. resistance within the ductwork and 1 in. in the stack 12 ft high. Higher rates are used on the Continent, even up to 90 C.F.M., and at 60 C.F.M. will be about 40 per cent more efficient, but must be measured against about 3·5 in. s.w.g., which needs four times as much power, though run for shorter periods. The higher rates are suitable, particularly if a fan with greater air-flow capacities, perhaps for grain drying, is adjacent to the potato store. A fan capable of ventilating one-third of the store at a time should be adequate.

In most cases an aerofoil axial-flow fan with an impeller blade capable of automatic adjustment against overloading may prove suitable and it should include a frost-guard thermostat on the downstream side of the fan, if placed in a duct. The fan may be portable on a trolley or permanently fixed in a duct. If the duct is below floor level it should be extended beyond the building at each end (see 8, below).

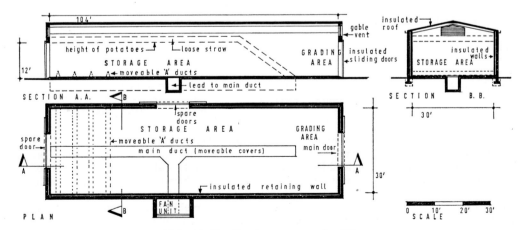

Fig. 29. Ventilated potato store for 500 tons

j. Standard designs for storage boxes for construction with farm labour have been prepared by the N.A.A.S., the 2000-lb box being $43\frac{1}{2}$ in. high. A tipping cage and hopper is required for unloading the boxes on to the grader.

7. *Environment control*

a. On dry, well-drained sites it is possible to have an earth floor, though the latter is not the best surface for handling equipment. To protect the crop against rising damp and to provide a good surface, it is a better policy to have 6 in. of concrete with a damp-proof membrane on hardcore. The floor should be protected against surface water from adjoining land. The walls must be insulated and waterproof, as well as being capable of withstanding the thrust from the potatoes. Many walls have been constructed with 9-in. brickwork, with piers at least at 12-ft centres, even for storage to a height of 12 ft, though much depends on the quality of brickwork. Alternatively, the building can have a steel or concrete frame. Cheap storage can be formed by using 'Nissen-type' huts. The internal surface of the wall should have a bitumen water seal, and, if permanent insulation is provided a clout-nailed layer (including large washers) of 2-in. woodwool or compressed straw slabs, with an internal cement–sand rendering, should be adequate. Some examples of this construction have shown no deterioration even after 15 years of use (15). An alternative insulation can be to have an internal, removable lining of straw bales against the damp-proof membrane.

The top of the potatoes should be insulated with 2 ft of loose straw, which also prevents light from affecting the crop and acts as a medium to hold condensation without wetting the top of the stack.

b. The need for bottom ventilation has been explained above, but the design of the main duct needs careful attention, since it should be waterproofed and should have a slight fall to one end. Moreover, if the air flow is to be restricted to ventilate different parts of the store as required it will be necessary to block some of the secondary ducts. A man has to crawl along the main duct, which should have a minimum cross-section 3 ft wide by $4\frac{1}{2}$ ft deep for this purpose. However, it should be possible to form a series of shutters, manually operated by remote control, without much expense, if the feed holes into the secondary ducts are divided into three sections, so that the fan could ventilate one-third of the store at a time.

c. Top ventilation, above the loose straw insulation on top of the stack, is essential to remove excessive heat and humidity given off by the potatoes.

Ventilation should be provided by closeable openings in each gable allowing between 3 and 5 ft^2/100 T stored. The openings should be louvred against rain penetration. There should be no condensation from an uninsulated roof, but insulation may prevent downward convection currents, causing losses along the sides of the store.

d. Though the need for local heat during grading has been referred to above, good lighting is also essential. Illumination levels at 2 lumens/ft^2 should be provided for general loading and unloading, with 10 lumens/ft^2 as a localized level at the grader, on the average working plane. Rooflights can be included.

8. *Layouts.*

The store size will depend on the maximum tonnage to be stored, the loading and unloading machinery, and the methods of insulation and ventilation. Normal expansion joints should be provided in the walls of stores more than 80 ft long. The building will be in the form of one enclosed, rectangular space, with the exception of any side access and of the fan unit. The main sunken duct, if provided, can be taken to an external point at one side of the main entrance to the building, the duct having an easy bend to facilitate the air flow. The end of the duct can have either a controlled opening to suit a portable fan unit, or the fan can be housed permanently in the duct. In the latter case the fan is usually placed at the end opposite to the convective ventilation intake and is provided with a separate intake. The duct, therefore, normally has to be taken beyond the building at each end, though, if there is only one opening provided, the duct should project beyond the store, so that the fan can be placed between two intake grilles, one acting for convective and one for forced ventilation. Intake grilles should allow not less than 50 per cent more free air than the cross-sectional area of the duct. The top of the duct should be formed with removable concrete covers externally and removable board covers internally.

It is possible to take the main duct to the side of the store, the duct feeding another duct along the centre of the building. Fig. 29 shows a layout for a store to hold 500 T in bulk.

9. *Siting.*

The store should be sited to suit the annual crop rotation, either at the farmstead or to keep the length of the journeys from the fields to the minimum. Access for merchants' lorries is essential and there should therefore be good roads, usually to each end of the store and sometimes, in addition, at the sides to the emergency unloading doors. External box stores should be adjacent to a grading shed. In all cases the store should be sited so that the air intake and ventilation grilles are not restricted by other buildings or obstructions to the natural air flow.

10. *Services.* An electrical supply is, with few exceptions, essential for successful and economic storage and should preferably be 400-volt, three-phase. The electrical installation must be designed to withstand high levels of humidity and severe knocks. Much of the installation can be taken externally round the building under the eaves. Plastic or alloy tube or galvanized heavy gauge conduit may be used internally, and all socket outlets, switches and fuses must be waterproof. Trailing cables, required for the grader, the elevator and the heater, should be armoured with metallic braid. Light fittings should be able to withstand the humidity. Effective earthing can be difficult to provide.

A water supply may be required if the potatoes are to be washed prior to sale. All roof and surface water should be drained clear of the site.

11. *Costs.* The cost of the store will depend on the standard of construction used as well as on the overall size. Ventilation equipment may cost about £1/T storage space and the total cost, including the building with permanent wall insulation and loading and unloading elevators, may be about £8–£12/T bulk storage space. However, a complete range of handling machinery, suitable for stores of more than 500-T capacity, and including a 3-T bulk handling trailer body, an elevator, an unloader and a grader can cost £1500–£2000, say, on average, about £4/T. This sum, plus the ventilation plant and ductwork, might come to a total of about £5/T storage space, which, depreciated over 6–7 years, might give an annual cost of about £1½/T stored. The building, including insulation, designed for loading to 12 ft and including 600 ft² of handling space, so that the total area equalled 6 ft²/T, might cost £6–£7/T storage space. This, depreciated over 10 years, might equal £1/T stored. Smaller stores, with similar construction, would be proportionally more expensive.

Alternatively, indoor box storage might require £500 for a forklift attachment and hopper, equal to £1/T storage space or about £⅓/T stored. Farmmade boxes might cost £3½/T storage space, or £1/T stored, and the building £5/T storage space or £¾/T stored. However, it may be shown that some artificial ventilation is required with box storage, which would increase the cost. External storage would be substantially cheaper.

Cheaper buildings for bulk storage without permanent insulation, possibly of Nissen-hut design, might cost £3–£4/T storage space plus equipment. Not having a concrete floor might save £¾/T storage space. Running costs should be under £¼/T for fuel.

12. *References*

(1) HICKS, N. 'To have or to hold'. *Farmers Weekly,* (19th October 1962).
(2) Economics of Potato Storage, p. 19 (see below).
(3) *Ibid.,* p. 21.
(4) *Ibid.,* p. 44.
(5) SMITH, N. 'Prospects look bright for boxes'. *Practical Power Farming,* pp. 20–1 (August 1962), also: MACKINTOSH, J. M. 'Boxes add brightness'. *Farmers Weekly* (2nd October 1964), pp. ix–xv.
(6) 'Potato harvesters performance'. *Farm Mechanization,* p. 398 (November 1962).
(7) Economics of Potato Storage, p. 34 (see below).
(8) BURTON, W. G. 'Take them out as good as they went in'. *Practical Power Farming,* pp. 30–3 (September 1960).
(9) CULPIN, C. *Farm Mechanization Management,* p. 176 (1959).
(10) BURTON, W. 'Heat production and ventilation of potatoes stored in buildings'. *Agriculture,* pp. 280–3 (September 1962).
(11) BURTON, W., MANN, G. & WAGER, H. 'Storage of ware potatoes in permanent buildings'. *J. Agric. Sci.,* pp. 150–63 (August 1955).
(12) MCCLEAN, S. P. 'Boxes banish bottlenecks'. *Practical Power Farming,* pp. 30–1 (July 1962).
(13) SMITH, N. 'Safe in boxes—inside and out'. *Practical Power Farming,* pp. 6–7 (October 1962).
(14) EDGAR, A. 'Potato storage research results'. *Agric. Engng. St. Joseph,* Mich., p. 549 (October 1951).
(15) COUNTRY LANDOWNERS ASSOCIATION. *National Farm Buildings Competition Report,* p. 2 (1962).

SELECTED REFERENCES

a. BISSET, G. B., DAWSON, E. & BENNETT JONES, R. *The Economics of Potato Storage* (1959).
b. TWISS, P. T. G. Electrical Development Association. *Electricity and Potato Husbandry* (1961).
c. 'Sugar beet and potatoes'. *Farmers Weekly Supplement* (16th May 1958).
d. Agricultural Research Council. *A Bibliography of Farm Buildings Research,* 1945–58. Part II. Buildings for Potato Storage.
e. 'Potatoes'. *Farmers Weekly,* pp. 72–85 (9th August 1963).

IJ. Implements

1. *Activity.* The maintenance of machinery is the basis of successful farm mechanization. A farmer has to rely on the efficiency of his machines and a breakdown may jeopardize the use of fine weather for important fieldwork, such as sowing or harvesting, and may seriously disrupt much of the building work, such as drying, feeding, milking and cleaning. The maintenance of machinery includes two requirements which affect buildings: the machinery must be stored; and it must be serviced and repaired. The latter is studied in IIJ, though implement housing and workshops are usually grouped together.

Simple implements may depreciate slowly if unsheltered, but complex machinery, such as tractors and harvesters, are susceptible to damage not only by rain and snow but by damp, dust and interference. The attitude of farmers to the storage of their implements and machinery probably shows more variation than that for any other farm building. The view may be maintained that implement storage does not contribute directly to farm income, representing an unproductive form of tied capital. Since most farms have a nucleus of outdated buildings, cover of some kind can usually be found for most of the implements in general use, while large machines used for a short season each year can be covered by a tarpaulin when not needed. This view is incompatible with the management of a small, organized and mechanized labour force, for reasons discussed in 3, below, and need not be considered further, since it does not affect the design of buildings.

The storage of implements should reflect the investment made in machinery. British farms are heavily mechanized, and in 1961 over £100M was spent on new machinery and vehicles, excluding expenditure on fixed equipment, which represents an annual investment of about £7/acre of tillage land. There are nearly ½M tractors and over ½M other forms of farm transport in use. In addition, there are some 2–3M field machines of various kinds, as well as barn, grain, milking and conveying equipment in buildings. These estimates may be conservative. As discussed below, the maintenance of this machinery should be carried out with military efficiency.

2. Managerial requirements. It is impossible to assess how much capital per acre should be invested in farm machinery, and difficult to estimate the capital required in relation to farm output. It is therefore difficult to make any estimate of the storage area required, in terms either of farm acreage or of farm output. Denman and Roberts, in a survey of machinery used on farms, showed that, in the main, the total number of machines and implements per acre is in inverse ratio to the size of farm. Though the number is also related to the type of farm, generally the same inverse ratio applies as shown in the abbreviated table of their survey (1); again, Rathbone has assessed the storage requirements in each case, both for a farm having the minimum number of implements for adequate management and for one having full mechanization at an advanced level.

The minimum storage requirement for all farms of more than 100 acres averaged 1000 ft². The survey gave a general assessment that storage required in ft²/100 acres might be:

Rearing, grass dominant, large arable farms	500–1000
Dairying, mixed and heavy arable farms	660–1800
Intensive arable farms	1000–2800

Many farms have a tractor for each worker, whether for fieldwork or livestock building work. However, fully automatic fed and cleaned livestock units are unlikely to need a tractor for the stockman. There is likely to be one tractor for each 80 acres of cultivated land or one for each 50 acres of arable land. Since the tractors should be housed in enclosed buildings, this may influence where the other implements are stored.

No. of machines and implements per 100 acres

Farm Size	Farm A	Farm Size	Farm B	Farm Size	Farm C
304	9·5	590	5·9	1070	7·0
265	4·9	550	11·1	692	8·5
220	14·1	365	11·8	560	17·3
146	18·5	268	10·5	353	17·0
100	22·0	196	16·8	250	18·0
50	28·0	137	21·2	129	25·6
40	30·0	64	37·5	81	37·0

Implement storage required in ft²/100 acres

Farm Size/Acres	A1	A2	B1	B2	C1	C2
200–300	667	1134	837	1287	732	1482
100–200	858	1400	1225	1650	1080	1900
50–100	1253	1847	1387	1657	1557	2307

Farm A: Pasture and miscellaneous farming types.
B: Intermediate types.
C: Arable farming types.

3. *Production techniques*

a. Providing well-planned storage for machinery and implements is difficult, since not only is it necessary to know their number and size, but their frequency in use and their frequency of movement between different buildings and also the combination in which the different machines may be used together. The latter is important, since most of the implements are tractor-operated and only a few machines have independent power. With the exception of the combine harvester, which occasionally may be left overnight in a field, no machinery and few implements should be left out between one day's work and the next. In particular, all tractors should be housed overnight. Therefore, siting the tractor shed is important, and there are two views on siting:

i. The tractors may be dispersed about the farm, being situated either near their most frequent place of use or at random, to suit the worker or the buildings available.

ii. The tractors may be housed together in a special tractor shed, with the exception, perhaps, that a tractor used solely for work in a livestock building may be housed within that layout.

However, since, for the most part, there is a tractor for each man, it is best for each man to be responsible for one particular tractor, maintaining his own vehicle and giving it a daily servicing before leaving the farm each night, a monthly servicing and an annual check. The tractor, after servicing, should be driven into a shed at night, ready for the next day's use, and it is inconvenient if it has to be backed into a shed or if any implements which are in use from one day to the next have to be unhitched.

b. On a mechanized farm of any size it is desirable for all machinery and implements to be housed either in one building or several buildings opening on to one area, with fuel storage and workshop adjacent. Even if there is no full-time mechanic on the farm, it is probable that one man should be storeman-mechanic in addition to his other work, responsible for seeing that all implements and spares are available when required. Therefore, a scattered layout can waste considerable time, no man being fully in control of the farm mechanization. Some of the implements may be housed in open-fronted shelters, but others should be in enclosed, pull-through sheds.

4. *Work routines.* The daily servicing includes re-fuelling, checking the tractor for its running order and completing the log-book. The monthly servicing includes the normal greasing and oiling and, if there is a trained mechanic on the farm, the tractor driver may not have to service his own vehicle.

5. *Design data*

a. The size of the machinery used on a farm should be checked and ample allowance made for an increase in the number and size of machines which may be used in the future. The following chart is an approximate guide giving normal dimensions in feet:

Implement	Length	Width	Height	Area/ft²
i. Transport equipment				
Small tractor, 35 h.p.	$9\frac{1}{2}$	$5\frac{1}{4}$	$5\frac{1}{2}$	50
Medium tractor, 45 h.p.	10	$5\frac{1}{2}$	6	55
Medium tractor, 55 h.p.	$11\frac{1}{4}$	$6\frac{1}{2}$	$7\frac{1}{4}$	68
Large wheel diesel	$12\frac{3}{4}$	$8\frac{1}{4}$	$7\frac{1}{4}$	105
Medium tracklayer	10	6	$6\frac{1}{2}$	60
Large tracklayer	$13\frac{1}{4}$	8	$8\frac{1}{2}$	106
Tractor with cab	—	—	$8\frac{1}{2}$	—
3-T trailer	$13\frac{1}{4}$	6	4	80
3-T tipping trailer	$13\frac{3}{4}$	$6\frac{1}{2}$	4	88
3-T tipping silage trailer	$13\frac{3}{4}$	$6\frac{1}{2}$	9	88
6-T trailer	20	$6\frac{1}{2}$	4	190
6-T tipping trailer	16	7	6	112
Large lorry	25	6	$7\frac{1}{2}$	150
Small lorry	14	6	$5\frac{1}{2}$	84
Small livestock trailer	9	6	$6\frac{1}{2}$	54
Cattle truck (10)	16	7	7	112
Cattle truck (18)	24	7	7	168
Small manure spreader	14	$6\frac{1}{2}$	6	91
Large manure spreader	$17\frac{1}{2}$	7	6	128
Large vacuum tanker	12	5	7	60

Implement	Length	Width	Height	Area/ft²
ii. Field machines				
Medium small combine	22	10	10¾	220
Medium large combine	27	11½	11½	310
Pick-up baler	20	9	8¾	180
Binder	14	8	6	112
Sugar beet harvester (raised)	12	7	13½	84
Sugar beet harvester (lowered)	12	11	9	132
Forage harvester	11	5½	9½	60
Potato harvester (small)	14	10	7	140
Potato planter	5	7½	5	38
Haulm pulverizer	5	6½	3	32
Combine drill (small)	7	10½	4	74
Seed drill	14	9	6½	126
Cultivator	5	9	3¾	45
Fertilizer drill	7	9	3½	63
Fertilizer spinner	4	6	5	24
Fertilizer spreader	4	12	3	48
Crop sprayer	3	7	6	21
Carrot washer	14	7	5½	91
Swathe turner	7	10	3½	70
Mower	4½	7½	4	34
Elevator	14	5½	6½	77
2-furrow mounted plough	6½	2½	3½	16
3-furrow mounted plough	7½	4½	3½	34
Roller or harrow	7½	14	2	105
Foreloader (small)	2½	6	2½	15
Foreloader rake (large)	3½	8	2	28
Root bucket loader	3½	4	2	14
Bale loader	4	8	5	32

b. Most tractors and other equipment weigh up to 2 T, though large tractors and tracklayers and large combines may weigh up to 5 T and loaded transport up to 8 T, with bulk tankers and lorries in excess of that amount. Though a tractor may be able to turn in its own length, power-operated manure spreaders and self-unloading trailers coupled to a tractor may need a turning circle of up to 30 ft. The minimum width of a pull-through shed, capable of housing a tractor and trailer, should be 25 ft, but, if the shed is made 30 ft wide, not only should it be able to house the largest combination of implements or a lorry, but it could house tractors with small implements two deep (Fig. 30). The length of the store should be in multiples of 7½ ft. Some implements, such as drills, are much wider than 7½ ft. In some cases, these can be swivelled, otherwise space must be made for them to suit their dimensions. The clearance height should be 10 ft minimum, 12 ft for preference, but a few machines may need a greater height and it should be noted that, though a height of less than 9 ft may be adequate for a tractor, the exhaust needs good clearance above the pipe before the hot air strikes a roof. The shed should have sliding and lockable doors. An open-fronted shelter about 12 ft deep should be adequate for simple implements.

c. The floor should be of 6-in. concrete, reinforced with mesh, and it should have a small fall to the openings. The latter should open on to a concrete apron, which can be used for washing vehicles and implements. The walls should be of solid construction up to the height of the doors.

d. The shed should be adjacent to the workshop and store (Fig. 30) (IIJ). Petrol tanks should be sited outside the store and below ground (Pt. 1, Ch. 7 *iv*, p. 18). Diesel oil may be stored above ground on a raised platform about 4½ ft high, but not greater than 10 ft above ground, the tank having a 3-in. fall to a drainage point opposite the intake pipe. There should be an inspection ladder to the top of the tank, for taking dipstick readings. The tanks should hold at least a month's supply of fuel, most tractors holding 9–15 gal, with specific fuel consumption (2):

	Lb per b.h.p. hour		
	At full load	At ½ load	At ¼ load
Medium-sized petrol engine	0·65	0·90	1·40
Medium-sized diesel engine	0·47	0·58	0·86

Three sizes generally used for tanks are as follows:

250 gal: $4\frac{3}{4}$ ft $\times$ 3 ft $\times$ 3 ft $\times$ 1 T (full)
400 gal: $4\frac{3}{4}$ ft $\times$ 4 ft $\times$ 4 ft $\times$ 1 T 13 cwt (full)
600 gal: $6\frac{1}{2}$ ft $\times$ 4 ft $\times$ 4 ft $\times$ 2 T 7 cwt (full)

e. Some livestock trucks can be dismounted from a lorry platform, making it possible for the lorry to be used for general purposes. In this case the lorry should be able to back into an open-fronted shelter and the truck should be fastened with chains to the roof construction so that the lorry can drive away, the truck being mounted on trestles for support.

6. *Equipment.* Equipment, such as lifting tackle and an inspection pit, are discussed in IIJ.

7. *Environment control.* No special provision for the environment has to be made, though open sheds should face leeward, north-west or north, depending on the site.

8. *Layouts.* Fig. 30 shows a layout for a four-tractor farm, that is one probably of 200–300 acres, combined with the workshop. This building requires an island site, with access from three, if not all four, sides.

9. *Siting.* The siting of implement and machinery storage will depend on the general farm layout,

but it should be near the main access to the fields, and, for preference, should be near the main record office.

10. *Services.* The shed should be well lit and free from surface water. A pressure tap should be available for washing down on the concrete apron.

11. *Costs.* The building shown for four tractor-lines, 30 ft $\times$ 30 ft, might cost £1200, plus the implement shed with an earth floor at £150, plus the reinforced-concrete apron, complete with water tap and drainage, at about £150, making a total of £1500, but excluding fuel storage and the workshop. This represents about £56 p.a. per tractor, but since this is a general-purpose building, a depreciation period of 20 rather than 10 years might be considered, and the annual cost per tractor might be about £30 p.a. or about 1s. 8d./ft² storage space/p.a.

The depreciation of farm machinery, as opposed to that of the implement sheds, is discussed in the introduction to Part 3 (p. 53), in so far as it affects this study. However, Miss Mathieson has given the subject a detailed analysis, particularly for field implements and machines, suggesting appropriate diminishing balance and straight-line depreciations for normal equipment (3).

12. *References*
  (1) DENMAN, D. R. & ROBERTS, H. 'Provision of implement storage'. A.L.S. Technical Report No. 5, pp. 5–7 (1959).
  (2) CULPIN, C. *Farm Machinery*, p. 35 (1963). CULPIN, C. *Farm Machinery*, 6th Edn., p. 35 (1960).
  (3) MATHIESON, M. C. 'The depreciation of farm machinery'. *The Journal of Agricultural Economics*, pp. 451–60 (June 1963).

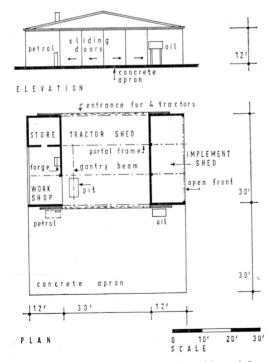

Fig. 30. Tractor and implement shed with workshop

IK. Records and Office

1. *Activity*
a. Recording and filing is a vital part of modern farming and is essential for all farm enterprises. The traditional farm office as part of the farmhouse is seldom adequate or convenient, except on small farms. Occasionally, an outbuilding can be converted successfully for the purpose. The office on a modern farm should be the centre of an efficient administration, reflecting an organized industry. This should be stressed, since few farm offices include modern techniques of business efficiency, normal to other industries. On a large farm, or on one with a large turnover, there will be numerous records to be kept. In addition, the recording office will be a reception area for many different purposes.

b. In most cases recording will take place on the job, but most of the records should be filed in the office. Examples of job recording include such tasks as:

   i. Job time-keeping

   ii. Milk yields weighed in a parlour

   iii. Livestock weighed within a production building

   iv. Rations weighed at a feedroom or at a trough

   v. Servicing, calving or farrowing dates

   vi. Measuring moisture and temperature of grain in store

   vii. Measuring potato wastage and weights in a riddling area.

c. Other recording will be essentially office work, and can include such details as:

   i. Seasonal and weekly time schedules

   ii. Plans for annual rotations and fertilizer use

   iii. Harvesting dates and yields

   iv. Quantities of crops or fodder stored

   v. Livestock pedigree and progeny sheets

   vi. Calculations of output, costs and income

   vii. Budgeting plans

   viii. Diary of routine tasks, such as maintenance, buying and selling

   ix. Feed records.

d. The record area will include the normal office administration files for trade correspondence, legal and financial documents of insurance, wages, taxation and all other business affairs. In a few cases close-circuit television is included, with the monitor set in the office, for observation of the livestock in intensive housing layouts.

e. A reception area will be required for a wide range of visiting personnel, which can include:

   i. Merchants' representatives delivering supplies or collecting sales, including fertilizers, seeds, livestock, produce and feeding-stuffs

   ii. Trade representatives for machinery, agricultural goods and allied concerns

   iii. Ministry officials and other representatives of official groups

   iv. Veterinary surgeons and other professional or technical consultants

   v. Visitors and prospective purchasers of livestock or produce.

It is desirable for all visitors on official business to come by appointment and many of them should be encouraged to come at regular and specified times. However, there will be many visitors who do not arrive by appointment. Correct siting of the office is important.

2. Managerial requirements. The farm office, particularly on medium to large farms, should command the main farm entrance and exit. It should be clearly signposted, since a considerable amount of time can be wasted, if the position of the office is obscure. Sometimes the office can command the farmyard as well as the main approach. However, the modern farm is seldom based on a yard plan, since a linear layout, which suits farm mechanization, is more suitable, and it will usually have a main service road with the various buildings on either side of it. The office may command this service road. In some cases, and possibly more often in the future, the farm buildings may be dispersed. The traditional pattern of the farmstead, with the buildings grouped together for protection, is no longer of such importance.

Staffing the office will vary to suit different farms. The farmer, or his manager, will have to spend many hours every week in the office, particularly on intensive livestock farms. The farm labour may be briefed at the office first thing every morning. The office can have ancillary rooms for the staff. Many farms have part-time, sometimes full-time, secretarial assistance. A few farmers employ recording staff, such as clerks or trained cost-control personnel. Farms of several hundred, or, perhaps, of over one thousand, acres in size may have an office staff of three or four, and large estates may have more.

3. Production techniques

a. Livestock weight recording, as well as that of the rations fed, is an essential part of breeding and of establishing and maintaining low food conversion ratios. For the latter purposes, weights should be recorded when fattening starts and finishes. A farmer may accept that weighing is adequate off the farm when buying the young stock from a breeder and when selling the fattened animal at a slaughterhouse. However, this policy is seldom satisfactory with large fattening units and it is desirable, in any case, to weigh a few weeks before finishing weights are reached. Many farmers may want to weigh more frequently, perhaps at fortnightly intervals. In such cases livestock weighing will take place in the fattening unit. With pigs, a mobile weighing crate is normally used, though a fixed weigher may be preferable in some layouts (IIIE 6*e*, p. 214). Cattle-fattening units also can have either a portable or a fixed weigher (IIIB 4*b*, p. 187). Some farmers may consider that batch instead of individual weighing will give adequate control. For this purpose, a lorry weighbridge will be needed.

b. A weighbridge can be an asset on most medium- or large-sized farms, especially when large quantities of produce, such as grain, vegetables or livestock are sold. In addition, a weighbridge can be useful for checking purchased goods, such as feeding-stuffs and fertilizers, when delivered to the farm. The cost of a weighbridge might be recovered either by the prevention of errors in weights occurring at purchase and sale, or by the time saved in not having to use a public weighbridge, especially when the latter is some distance from the farm. Even a weighbridge at a slaughterhouse or mill can be expensive for a farmer to use, if the lorry is delayed on arrival before being weighed.

c. Staff facilities should be provided for the farm workers. Though these may be limited to the use of a lavatory, some of the principles of industrial staff welfare should be introduced on most large farms. A cloakroom should have the normal facilities, such as a lavatory, a hand-basin, lockers, a table, a mirror and possibly an electric clothes drier. A shower may be justified, especially for such workers as pigmen, though many farmers will consider that such functions should be excluded from the farm, especially if cottages are provided. The cloakroom may be formed as a staffroom, with facilities for sitting to eat sandwiches, especially if the workers come from distant villages.

d. Car parking spaces should be provided for the modern farm worker not living on the farm, as well as for visitors. These should be clear of the main circulation routes.

4. *Work routines.* The work required in recording is considered in the specialized building sections. Systems for keeping records are given in most farm management books. Large fattening units may require elaborate card index systems and various wall progress charts should be provided.

5 and 6. *Design data* and *Equipment**

a. Proprietary weighing platforms are available, some including a crate on top, others requiring the addition of a crate. The platforms are set in a pit, which should be deeper than the minimum dimension given, and should be well drained. Average-sized platforms might be as follows:

Pig weigher: 3 ft × 3 ft × $1\frac{1}{4}$ ft deep
Cattle weigher: $8\frac{1}{2}$ ft × $3\frac{1}{2}$ ft × $1\frac{1}{2}$ ft deep
Lorry weigh-
   bridge: 20 ft × 8 ft × 4 ft deep × 6T

The weighbridge will probably be capable of carrying weights of up to 30 T, even, though the largest farm merchant's vehicle may weigh not more than 20 T with a wheel length of under 17 ft, some bulk tankers have a wheel base of

* In 1964, farm offices in which people are employed for more than 21 hr. came under the control of the Shops, Offices and Railway Act, 1964 requiring certain accommodation standards to be maintained.

about 30 ft. An underground arm connects the platform to the steelyard or dial which is normally about 4 ft to one side of the platform, preferably under cover and controlled from the office. The arm can be extended if required.

b. The office should be not less than 80 ft² in area and offices of 150–200 ft² will be more convenient. Among the equipment should be:

i. A table or desk with drawers, approx. 12 ft²
ii. A wide working surface, possibly with a washable top, approx. 25 ft²
iii. A lockable filing cabinet, 4-draw, approx. 2 ft × $1\frac{1}{2}$ ft (possibly, more than one cabinet)
iv. Two or three chairs, including a typing chair
v. A cupboard with hanging space and with shelves, approx. 6–10 ft²
vi. A map wall, with a large farm map and a district map
vii. Wall progress charts as required
viii. A pin-board and a blackboard
ix. A service counter and hatch to the approach road
x. A bookcase
xi. Possibly a hand-basin
xii. Possibly a safe.

Larger farms will require sufficient space to act as a conference room for five to eight people and large estates may have a general and a private office. A lobby or area for removing boots and washing hands may be required.

c. A staffroom might require 30 ft² for a W.C. pedestal and a hand-basin to 100–150 ft² for a separate W.C. and a cloakroom. Requirements included might be:

i. W.C. approx. $5\frac{3}{4}$ ft × $2\frac{3}{4}$ ft
ii. Hand-basin approx. 2 ft × $1\frac{1}{2}$ ft
iii. Roller towel
iv. A locker per man, approx. $1\frac{3}{4}$ ft × 1 ft each
v. A clothes drier, approx. 2 ft × $1\frac{1}{2}$ ft
vi. A table, and possibly benches
vii. A pinboard
viii. A hot-water heater.

7. *Environment control.* The office and cloakroom should be of domestic type construction, insulated and heated, with natural ventilation and good electric lighting of up to 20 lumens/ft² on the working surfaces. An external light is desirable.

8 and 9. *Layouts* and *Siting.* Fig. 31 indicates the position and siting of an office, in relation to a modern, mechanized farm, though each farm office must be considered in relation to the requirements of individual farms. Fig. 32 shows possible layout for an office, cloakroom and weighbridge.

10. *Services.* Electrical power may be required for heating as well as normal lighting requirements.

11. *Costs.* Fixed weighers for pigs may cost under £200 with a steelyard or £300 with a dial, plus about £150 for a pig-crate, the pit and installation. Cattle weighers may cost about £300 with a steelyard, £400 with a dial, including the crate, plus about £100 for the pit and installation. Lorry weighbridges may cost about £1100–£1200 with a steelyard, under £1300 with a dial, plus £300–£350 for the pit and installation. However, second-hand equipment may be available and considerably cheaper.

A new office and cloakroom is unlikely to cost less than £3/ft² and, with its basic equipment, might cost £5/ft². However, a conversion might be possible, costing perhaps less than £1/ft². Though an expenditure of, say, £400–£1200 may seem an excessive burden to pay for a farm office on a normal farm, this can be judged only in terms of the overall farm turnover and efficiency. An office and cloakroom might be depreciated over 30 years and a capital expenditure of £1000 might be assessed not much more than £1 per week. A few hours wasted every week by an inefficient and misplaced records office would soon cost more than a well-designed office.

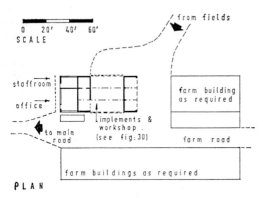

Fig. 31. Linear planning for farm buildings and control office

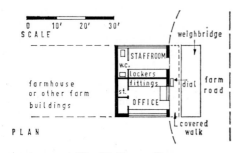

Fig. 32. Farm office

PROCESSING BUILDINGS

Introduction

There are ten specialized buildings which may be required for processing foods or materials on the farm. Six are used in conjunction with the production units in Section III; of these, four are ancillary operations being used to process feeding-stuffs and two are used to process the final product ready for sale. In addition, grain drying and workshops may be required for a livestock enterprise, though both of these units may be needed on non-livestock farms. In fact, workshops to a greater or lesser extent are required on most farms. Of the two other specialized buildings, chitting houses have much in common with some horticultural buildings; and packing sheds for farm produce, though important, since their requirements may control farm practice, may not be built on farms.

Three of the processing buildings are required for grass, though it is debatable whether grass should be processed in the fields and then be stored, as for haylage, or in buildings, as for dried grass, hay and silage. Research during the next few years will probably relate more fully the relative costs of each method to the nutritional value of the processed food. Grain-drying plant is required in corn-growing areas and can be combined with its storage, though the plant may be centralized and not on a farm. Grain used for feeding-stuffs can be stored without drying. On an arable and livestock farm a mill–mix unit may be coupled to the drying–storage plant. Milking plant, which is expensive and needs skilled operation, should be used for as long as possible each day with the maximum throughput, in order to reduce the capital cost per gallon produced. As with storage buildings, the design and cost of modern machinery tend to make centralized buildings for processing cheaper and more efficient than several smaller units. Principles and methods in processing food and materials change rapidly. Processing on the farm should be reduced to the minimum and, where required, the number of operations to obtain the processed material should be as few as possible, and the handling of materials during their processing should be mechanized. It is preferable to process materials, as with grain drying, within the place of storage, or near the production unit, as with milking. Sometimes storage facilities prior to and after the processing operation must be provided.

IIA. Grass Drying

1. *Activity*

a. Drying grass to a low moisture content by means of air heated to high temperatures was popular a decade or more ago. Most of the grass driers installed in the decade after the war are now either disused or are an inefficient method of conserving grass. By 1958 no more than 2 per cent of conserved grass was dried in this manner. Modern techniques of conservation are as hay (IIB), silage (IIC) or haylage (IC). The main disadvantages in dried grass are the high labour and fuel costs incurred. There is little point in giving extensive information on a declining practice. However, it is worth noting the principles of high-temperature drying, not only because a few modern driers have been installed in recent years but because new methods of grass handling could make it an economic proposition in the future. This is a matter for research.

b. Unlike other methods of conservation, the aim of grass drying is to remove almost all the moisture in the cut grass, that is, from the usual average of about 80–85 per cent when cut to about 5–10 per cent. This is in contrast to the normal minimum of 18 per cent for hay, 45 per cent for haylage and 65 per cent for silage. Grass drying, to be successful, must be based on suitable crops cut at the right moment, that is at a very early stage when the grass has its maximum feeding value. Moreover, to be economic, the evaporation of the water in the grass must be correctly planned to use the minimum of fuel and not to burn the grass.

Drying, basically, can be in two stages. Firstly, the water in the outer tissue and on the surface of the grass or clover can be evaporated rapidly. This process, in order to reduce fuel requirements, may be partially achieved by wilting for a few hours in the fields in good drying conditions. In practice, the aim may be to reduce the m.c. to 75 per cent, since this will appreciably reduce the fuel costs, perhaps even by one-quarter, with only a slight loss of protein and starch within the grass. The latter is important since dried grass is of value mainly for

its protein content. Secondly, once the outer evaporation has been completed, moisture has to be removed from the inner cells; the maximum air temperature to prevent scorching of the grass surface is about 175° C (350° F), whereas in the initial stages temperatures of more than 815° C (1500° F) may be used.

c. It is obvious that the equipment and fuel required to obtain high temperatures will be relatively expensive compared to other methods of conservation, even though in some methods the initial drying is completed at the same temperature as the secondary drying, that is, between 150° and 175° C. (330° F–350° F).

In some drying methods the grass is lacerated in the fields so that the drying rate can be almost uniform even when the higher temperatures are used. Most processes are based on drying the grass in batches, either on trays, conveyors or drums. After drying, the grass may be handled loose, milled, cubed or baled. Handling dried grass, particularly when loose, is difficult without loss of nutrients caused by the disintegration of the leaves. Though the cost of the fuel for drying might be justified, the labour requirements and inconvenience in handling the grass can make the method uneconomic.

d. Since new techniques in hay production are based on handling chopped grass mechanically from the fields to the drier and on self-feeding the dried hay directly from the drier (IIB 9, p. 104), it is possible that such methods could be coupled to high-temperature drying. This would be justified only if the value of the fodder was increased above the greater cost of the drying, and this is a matter which could be established only by research.

2. *Managerial requirements*
a. Value of Dried Grass
The aim of grass drying must be to obtain a top-quality fodder, rich in protein and starch, and worth perhaps £25–£30/T dried material, with over 2 T dried grass produced per acre at 20 per cent crude protein content, that is some 800–1000 lb crude protein per acre. In contrast, good hay might have under 14 per cent crude protein. In the past this has not been easy to achieve, so that many studies of drying costs have not been favourable, as shown overleaf in an analysis into grass conservation in the Eastern Counties during 1949 and 1950 (the former being a dry year with $8\frac{3}{4}$ in. rainfall between April and September, the latter more favourable with $14\frac{1}{2}$ in.) (1).

As Culpin has discussed (2), on the basis of these figures grass drying would be uneconomic in that the cost of conserving P.E. and S.E. is respectively double and treble that in the case of hay or silage. But, he pointed out that the grass driers analysed

	Hay		Silage		Dried grass	
	1949	1950	1949	1950	1949	1950
S.E.: Lb/acre	974	926	2944	2590	1804	2265
Cost/T in £	15	14	15	15	40	38
P.E.: Crude protein as per cent d.m.	12·1	14·0	15·7	16·0	17·8	17·3
Lb/acre	169	182	526	450	400	468
Cost/T in £	86	70	83	86	180	186

N.B. dries grass: 2 cuts in 1949: 3 cuts in 1950.

were few in number and generally inefficient in operation, there being also no technical reason why the yield of P.E. should be so low, so that the comparisons are not particularly valuable today. However, it may be useful to quote the cost breakdown for grass drying, taken from the same survey, as a basis of future discussion:

Type of drier	Tray	Con-veyor	Pneu-matic
Cutting and carting to drier	3·0	3·0	3·0
Labour at drier	3·8	2·0	2·6
Fuel and power	5·8	4·6	4·6
Bags, baling	1·4	1·2	1·8
Repairs	0·3	0·7	0·9
Sundries	0·5	0·5	1·9
Overheads	1·8	2·3	5·7
Total £/T	15·6	14·3	20·5

It is possible that a drying cost of £12½–£17½/T might be reduced in a modern installation including mechanical handling and, possibly, self-feeding. For comparison, cutting and carting might be taken as before at £3/T, though many factors might vary this cost. The fuel cost might be about £6½/T dried grass if the grass is wilted to 80 per cent m.c.

For the installation to be effective, a large crop would have to be dried producing, perhaps, 400 T of dried grass p.a. (360 T d.m.), which would be equivalent to a tower silo holding 700–750 T of haylage. Modern methods of handling chopped grass to a tower or clamp or drier would be approximately the same, perhaps with some variation due to different tedding techniques in wilting the grass. If, for example, a new grass-drying installation cost £6000 for equipment and £4000 for a drying barn this would represent about £5/T dried. On this basis, drying would cost £11½/T, that is,

about £13/T d.m., but no further storage costs would be incurred and labour costs might be almost nil for feeding. If the P.E. content was 20 per cent the cost/T of P.E. would be about £58, that is less than one-third of the cost in the survey of 1949/50 and even less than the comparative cost for hay and silage.

b. Fuel Costs

Though electric motors may be used to drive the fans and conveyors, electricity is too expensive for heating the air used for drying. Usually, oil or coke are used. If the grass is wilted to 75 per cent m.c. an efficient installation will require 90 gal of oil/T dried to 10 per cent m.c. on the basis of it evaporating 90 lb of water/gal. However, if the grass is harvested when wet, with an m.c. of 85 per cent, 120 gal will be required. Fuel costs might be expressed as shown in table below.

Thus a drying cost for fuel of about £5½–£7½/T/ dried grass might be incurred in normal conditions, that is, about £6–£8¼/T d.m. This should be compared with a drying cost for hay of £¾–£2/T dried hay (IIB 2c, p. 99), that is, about £1–£2½/T d.m. On average, the fuel cost for dried grass is about £4¾/T d.m. more expensive than that for hay, and the value of the former must be increased by this amount, plus the difference in the capital cost, before drying grass would be justified. The total differences in capital and running costs might be about £8/T d.m.; and, provided there was no extra in the labour costs, it is possible that the dried grass could be worth this amount over the cost of barn-dried hay. This is unlikely to be true for small units drying less than 200 T p.a., except, perhaps, in the case of cheaply made tray driers.

3. Production techniques

a. Low-temperature Driers

Most low-temperature driers dry the grass with

Harvested grass at m.c.	Coke at £10/T		Oil at 1s. 3d./gal	
	75 per cent	85 per cent	75 per cent	85 per cent
Heat produced, b.t.u./lb fuel	11,500	11,500	18,500	18,500
Wastage in pre-heating, per cent	15	15	3	3
Efficiency of furnace, per cent	85	85	90	90
Fuel required/T dried grass	11 cwt	15 cwt	90 gal	120 gal
Fuel Cost/T dried grass	£5½	£7½	£5⅝	£7½

temperatures not exceeding 175° C (350° F). There are two main types.

i. Tray or batch drying which can be in a home-made or in a proprietary unit and can be as a single- or multiple-tray drier is the simplest and, usually, the cheapest method. However, grass has to be loaded into and out of the trays. The drier is loaded to a depth of $2\frac{1}{2}$ ft, partially dried, air being blown through a mesh floor, topped up with more grass and dried again. Sometimes, a third layer can be added. Some units recirculate the air during the later stages of drying, when it is not saturated. Driers of this kind may be also used for grain drying on small farms.

ii. Endless belt conveyors pass the grass through a drying chamber on a perforated bed through which warm air is passed and then recirculated. There can be a self-loading device to pass a uniform quantity of grass through the drier. The drier could be coupled both to an intake hopper or loader and after drying to an auger to take the grass into a store or for processing into cubes or meal. Therefore, such plant could be almost automatic with few labour requirements and fuel conversion can be efficient. Throughputs are about $\frac{1}{4}$ T dried grass/hr, though some will dry $\frac{2}{5}$ T/hr from 80 per cent m.c.

b. High-temperature Driers

High-temperature driers, using air during the initial rapid drying stage at about 600–850° C (1100–1550° F), followed by a longer drying period at 175° C (350° F) may be of the pneumatic tower or rotary drum type. The thermal efficiency of these driers is higher than that of low-temperature driers, especially for wet grass. If the grass is wilted in the field their advantage is reduced. Though throughputs of $\frac{3}{4}$ T dried grass/hr may be obtained with some plant, a man should be in attendance most of the time because of the danger of scorching.

c. Losses during Drying

Losses with a pneumatic-drum high-temperature drier used in the United States for lucerne were smaller than for other methods of conservation in an experiment made over several seasons, though all crops were cut at the hay stage (3):

	D.m. loss	Protein loss
	per cent	
Dried grass	10	18
Barn dried hay	15	21
Haylage	17	17

However, United Kingdom losses for grass drying have been given as low as 5 per cent S.E. and $7\frac{1}{2}$ per cent P.E. (2).

4. *Work routines.* The high labour requirements in loading, running and unloading the driers, especially in the case of tray driers, have been noted. The problems in handling wet or dry grass while loose have been a principal factor in the decline of grass drying.

5. *Design data*

a. M.C. Required

A m.c. of 15 per cent, if uniform, could be satisfactory for baling. In practice, 10 per cent is required to allow for possible unevenness in drying. With milling or cubing, the m.c. should be 5 per cent. Grass should not be baled until several hours after drying. Approximately 15 h.p. is required for milling when the m.c. is 5 per cent. An output of 4 cwt/hr requires an input of 18 cwt/hr of grass at 80 per cent m.c.

b. Space required

Tray driers can be fairly small, perhaps 12 ft × 8 ft in area, though a large multiple drier might require some 25 ft × 25 ft. Belt conveyors may require some 60 ft × 10 ft, and usually have chimneys over their centre to about 12 ft off the floor for removal of the saturated air. A pneumatic drier will be shorter and taller, perhaps 30 ft × 15 ft × 15 ft. Oil or coke furnaces also are required, and might need another 20 ft × 15 ft, plus a chimney.

6. *Equipment.* Usually any type of baler can be used. Mills and pelleters are similar to those for compound feeds, but may be a little larger.

7. *Environment control.* Considerable moisture has to be removed: therefore, an exhaust fan to the exterior is essential. Furnaces need the normal equipment and protection for such plant.

8. *Layouts.* Layouts for modern installations have not been developed. However, it is possible they might be based on a fine-mesh floor over a plenum chamber similar to a hay-drying barn. Alternatively, a belt conveyor drier might auger the dried grass into a self-feed barn.

9. *Siting.* A new unit should be sited in conjunction with a cattle layout so that the dried grass can be fed easily into mangers.

10. *Services.* Electricity is required for the fans and motors. Oil tanks have to be housed externally to the main plant. Furnaces, if enclosed, can be adjacent to the plant.

11. *Costs.* Cost has been discussed above in 2a and 2b. There is little value in commenting further, except in so far as, if mechanized, grass drying may be valuable in the future—provided the value of

the dried product proved sufficiently greater than other methods of conservation to justify the additional expense. It might prove considerably more nutritious than hay, even barn-dried hay, and cheaper than haylage, since the latter requires expensive storage space for an additional two-fifths T of water for each ton d.m. stored. It is claimed that costs as low as £15/T dried grass for collection and drying can be attained by a well-managed plant (2). A small home-made tray drier might cost less than £1000.

12. References

(1) MACKNESS, R. A. 'Economics of green crop conservation'. Cambridge Univ. Farm Econ. *Branch Report No.* 38 (1952).
(2) CULPIN, C. *Farm Management Mechanization*, pp. 117–20 and pp. 137–41 Crosby Lockwood (1959).
(3) 'Relative merits of four methods of harvesting and preserving alfalfa forage for dairy feed'. *U.S.D.A. Circular* 936 (1955).

SELECTED REFERENCES
a. GIBB, J. A. C. *Crop Drying, Barn and Storage Machinery*, Temple Press, pp. 70–81 (1955).
b. CULPIN, C. *Farm Machinery*, pp. 475–87 (1960).

IIB. Hay Drying

1. *Activity.* Hay is the staple part of the winter feed for cattle and sheep. Over four-fifths of the grass conserved is made into hay (IB. 1). Most of the hay made is from grass wilted in the field, and is not dried artificially. In ideal weather conditions field-dried hay is satisfactory. But rain or humidity can detract from the nutritional value of hay produced in this manner, and few parts of the country have good haymaking weather sufficiently often for the loss from rain not to be serious. The cost of a drier may not be excessive and it can be justified, even if in some years it is not used because the weather is satisfactory. This can be true particularly if a special building for drying is not required, drying taking place within the hay store (IB) or within a tunnel of bales. Artificial drying is a modern method of grass conservation, comparable, perhaps, with haylage as a fodder (IC), but the cost of drying must be related to the feeding value. The latter must be enhanced by an amount greater than the cost.

However, barn drying has several secondary advantages. Cutting can start earlier in the season and this is important, since cutting should be between ear emergence and flowering of the grass, when its digestibility is best. Though the m.c. of the crop at this stage may be at least 80 per cent and natural drying may be more difficult, barn drying can complete what would be impossible in the field. Though dairy cows have a higher nutritional requirement than beef, it has been suggested that, even with the latter, the stage of cutting can be very important, since, if cutting is delayed from mid-May to early June, liveweight gain per acre can fall by a third (1). The greatest possible amount of digestive feed in relation to an economical method of production should be conserved from each acre, even if some of the nutritional value has to be sacrificed to obtain bulk in the ration.

Equally important is the fact that with barn drying there is less dependence on the weather and, therefore, farm management can be more flexible in planning haymaking within the farm programme. With barn drying, the average time required for wilting in the field can be reduced from 4–5 days to under 2 days. Moreover, since the hay for barn drying requires less handling and can be handled before the risk of leaf shatter becomes excessive, and since there is less likelihood of leaching in the field, there is a greater chance of obtaining a nutritious and palatable fodder than with field-dried hay.

It is more difficult to decide whether to have hay or haylage or silage than to decide whether to have field-dried or barn-dried hay. Usually, there is a place for both barn-dried hay and silage on a farm, as far as fodder and rationing are concerned. But, on any other consideration, it is preferable to have either all hay or all silage, since capital investment is lower, there being only one set of equipment required, and only one technique has to be learnt (2). Haylage requires so much capital investment that other forms of conservation on the same farm are unlikely to be justified except in exceptional circumstances. Many management factors have to be considered when deciding between the various methods of conservation. The issues are not regional nor ones of unit size alone, even when considering local conditions affecting the grass crop. The problems are equally those of capital investment, continuity of management policy, possible expansion, labour, existing mechanization and buildings, and the level of intensive farming desired. However, it is possible that silage as a production technique is valuable, particularly in the west, whereas hay is cheap to produce in the east, and, as a fodder, is valuable, particularly for dairy cattle, whereas hay is preferable for beef cattle. Much research is still required relating conservation method with nutritional value for the different techniques, together with their overall cost.

Barn drying is one of the methods available for improving the value of the grass crop when conserved as a fodder. For success, the raw material must be good. Expensive conservation is unlikely to be worth while for an inferior crop. However, it

29: GRASS DRYING
British Crop Driers Ltd., Lincs.

Though grass drying is a declining custom on farms, it is still practised commercially. In this case, 5000 T of dried lucerne and grass meal are produced p.a. Bulk handling is essential, and large trailers bring the grass from the fields. The trailers are hoisted by an overhead winch and the grass is tipped on to an inclined conveyor to the drier. [SEE PAGES 95 & 41] Courtesy of Practical Power Farming.

30: HAY DRYING BARN
Auchincruive, Ayr

A pole-barn under construction in 1958, using second-hand timber with walls and roof clad with galvanized corrugated sheets, divided into three bays, each of about 300 ft^2 in floor area. A weld-mesh floor is being laid over timber bearers, with an area of 2 ft around the mesh blanked off with concrete, to form a plenum chamber 2 ft deep. The wall at the right-hand side shows the sheeting finishing 2 ft below the eaves; this detail will be continued around 3 sides to give top-level ventilation. Also shown are the 5-ft-wide openings ready to receive the doors to the chambers. One dividing frame between the chambers has been erected. This will be covered with flat sheets to form a partition. Each bay will hold about 8 T of dried hay: the complete unit being designed to dry 120 T annually. Each bay has its own two-stage axial-flow fan, with a capacity of 16,000 c.f.m. at 2 in. s.w.g., at the rear of the bay with a duct to the plenum chamber. A 36-kW heater in three banks of 12 kW can be fitted to any fan unit by means of a trailing cable. The electrical control panel and meter are housed in a cabinet near the fan units. [SEE PAGE 103] Courtesy of West of Scotland Agricultural College.

31: FILLING A SILAGE CLAMP: SELF-UNLOADING TRAILER
Cut grass can be deposited in a silobarn from a self-unloading trailer, in this case adapted from a manure spreader. The trailer can be loaded in the field, drive over the clamp in the barn, unloading and compacting at the same time, and return to the field without delay and without a man being required to buckrake the grass into the clamp. [SEE PAGES 107 & 42] Courtesy of the Farmers Weekly.

32: RATIONED FEEDING AT A CLAMP
A silage clamp can be used both for self-feeding or for rationed feeding. Though the labour required for cutting the silage may seem excessive, with good quality silage this can be justified since less expensive fodder will be wasted. Silage can be over 9 ft high when rationed, the face being cut in steps and sufficient fodder for a day's feed being dropped to the floor. A manger can be formed with a portable silage barrier. In this case, the barrier is of simple construction using tubular steel and clamp fittings plus some base boards. The silage walls are of mass concrete about 7 ft high, since the settled silage ht. is limited to 6 ft. Additional hay is fed at a yoke at one end of the silo. [SEE PAGE 106] Courtesy of British Farmer.

is not easy to relate d.m. stored per acre harvested, since much depends on the stage of growth when cut, and digestibility is more important than bulk (IB 3). Early cutting could ensure an additional cut/yr. Conversely, early cutting might be coupled with summer or autumn grazing. Yields of d.m. from grassland can be (occasionally) more than 5 T/acre (IC 1d, p. 59).

Hay is likely to remain an important part of farm economy. However, the artificial drying of hay is likely to become a standard part of farm practice when cattle or sheep are kept, except in the cases when haylage takes its place. All-silage farms will probably be in a minority, though even this is uncertain, since silage techniques are changing. Methods of handling hay are changing also and, since labour requirements in traditional haymaking methods were high, new techniques, using less labour, could make hay as economic to handle as silage.

2. Managerial requirements
a. Nutritional Value

Conservation cannot increase the nutritional value in the grass. In fact, after cutting there is bound to be some loss. Drying hay in a barn costs more than wilting in the field. Therefore, it is vital for the nutritional value of the former to be greater than that of the latter. This may not prove to be so, since, if hay is dried in the field in perfect weather conditions, it would appear to be as good as barn-dried hay. However, if rain falls on the cut grass while wilting in the field the value of the hay made from that grass quickly becomes inferior to barn-dried hay as fodder. Naturally, prolonged rain can ruin the cut grass, but even a short shower can have serious effects. Experiments made by the N.I.A.E. and The Grassland Research Institute in 1958 and 1959 have been quoted to show the effect of weather on different methods of hay making (Ref. (a)):

	Silage	Barn-dried hay	Field hay
Percentage loss in conservation	26·0	13·3	22·8
Fodder yield, cwt d.m./acre	30·4	35·7	31·8
Conversion rate, d.m./lb livewt increase	13·1	9·9	13·0
Livewt increase, lb/acre	260	404	275

Such a comparison must take into account the fact that grass is normally cut at a different season for field hay than for silage. But in beef production liveweight increase is one method of judging the nutritional value of different methods of conserving grass. In this particular trial the value of barn drying in relation to acreage used for production was established. In fact, it was assessed that, for beef production, barn-dried hay was worth £3½/T more than field hay, though the cost of drying has to be considered (4).

Similar work has been carried out at the West of Scotland Agricultural College (Ref. (c)). Comparisons were made of the chemical analysis from one sample of above-average-quality field hay with the mean of eight barn-dried samples from 1959 and 1960:

Composition, percentage	Barn dried	Field dried	Difference
Dry matter	84·38	86·2	−1·8
Crude protein	7·66	5·53	+2·13
Crude fibre	25·36	32·24	−6·88
Digestibility, percentage			
Dry matter	63·3	56·6	+6·7
Crude protein	56·6	31·3	+25·3
Crude fibre	63·7	63·4	+0·3
Starch equivalent	36·1	28·0	+8·1
Protein equivalent	4·5	1·7	+2·8

Percentage fall in feeding value during haymaking

Haymaking method	Digestible dry matter		Digestible protein	
	Wet year	Dry year	Wet year	Dry year
Barn dried	5·5	1·6	0·6	0·4
Tripod dried	6·9	1·6	0·8	0·3
Swath dried	13·1	4·4	1·8	2·2

Experiments at the Drayton Experimental Husbandry Farm have also shown that there is no noticable difference between the feeding value of hay wilted in perfect weather and barn-dried hay (Ref. (b)). On this basis, barn drying could not be justified. However, perfect weather cannot be guaranteed to coincide with the correct time for harvesting any particular grass crop. A comparison of different methods of grass conservation used for fattening beef has been made at Drayton from a crop yielding 41·3 cwt/acre (3):

The experiments showed the increase in nutritional value occurring in barn-dried hay. This was reflected in a decrease of 11 per cent in the hay ration for dairy cows, without any apparent reduction in production performance, representing 2 cwt hay/cow/winter; and a net saving in cost, taking into account the cost of barn drying, was assessed at £1/cow/winter.

In heavy rainfall areas, such as Cumberland, barn drying can be exceptionally important, leading to such claims, for example, as that an extra

H

gal/cow can be obtained from bulk fodders, with Friesians averaging 1000 gal, for a capital cost of under £1500 (5). On this basis, the outlay would be justified for about 30 cows, without taking into account the possibility of improved milk quality and easier management with less wastage. An analysis of a good sample of barn and of field hay showed the following percentages:

	Barn dried	Field dried
Moisture content	10·9	11·5
Crude protein	13·4	9·8
Crude fibre	29·1	32·1
Starch equivalent (estimated)	48	43

Many other experiments, both in research and in practice, have been made to show the increased nutritional value to be obtained by drying hay artificially. An assessment has been made to show the S.E. and P.E. obtained with different methods of conservation, assuming that fresh grass is valued at 100 (2):

Crop	S.E.	P.E.
Fresh grass	100·0	100·0
Hay, made with ordinary methods	55·0	67·0
Hay, made with special appliances	66·0	75·0
Hay, barn dried	82·5	87·0
Dried grass	95·0	92·5

'Hay is primarily an energy food so the effect of hay-making method on the loss of starch equivalent from one ton of grass dry matter will be calculated. Because the actual loss of starch equivalent will be influenced by the quality of the original material the following table gives three different qualities, and the lower S.E. losses with barn drying have been equated to a saving in purchased barley costing £20/T or 3d./lb S.E. On the basis of the dry matter loss figures shown, and assuming the made hay in both cases contains 85 per cent dry matter, the original one ton of grass dry matter produces either one ton of barn-dried hay or 0·93 ton of conventionally made hay. On the basis of a drying cost per ton of barn-dried hay of approximately £2, it is not possible to justify more than approximately half the cost of barn drying through a reduction in loss of nutrients.'

Obviously, there has to be some reservation to the belief that in all cases the S.E. value of barn-dried hay will justify the additional costs. But, with a lower cost for drying, and with barley at £30/T

(unlikely, at present), or with a greater saving of S.E. by barn drying, there would be greater benefits. However, only the highest-quality product can be justified if barn drying is undertaken.

A recent experiment has given additional evidence that barn-dried hay can be valuable in beef production, if supplemented by moderate concentrate rations, in that a high rate of gain can be obtained at reasonable cost. The hay, with S.E. between 33 and 39 and P.E. between 2·9 and 3·9, together with the supplements, giving gains of up to 2·66 lb/day, costed less per lb gain than often experienced with silage or field hay rations (6).

It is doubtful whether field-dried hay, except in an exceptional year, could give results as satisfactory as those obtained from barn-dried hay.

b. Moisture Content

The moisture content of grass when cut is normally between 75 and 80 per cent. As the grass lies in the field, the moisture in the air and in the grass will interchange until equilibrium is reached. Equilibrium is constant when the relative humidity of the air and the moisture content of the grass are as follows:

Air, R.H., per cent	95	90	80	77	70	60	50
Hay, M.C., per cent	35	30	21·5	20	16	12·5	10

On a dry day with a good breeze, wilting on the surface of the grass is rapid, and the grass should be tedded to give even drying. On a windless dry day moisture will pass from the grass into the air, but the air above the field will soon become saturated and, without a wind, drying will be slow. Rain or humidity will harm the hay. To hasten drying, the grass can be crimped after cutting. The aim should be to wilt the grass to below 50 per cent m.c. as quickly as possible to reduce activity in the grass cells, which wastes sugar and carbohydrates. However, the m.c. should be further reduced before collection for barn drying, perhaps to 35–45 per cent, otherwise the time and cost involved in the drier becomes excessive. As the m.c. is reduced below 40 per cent, the greater is the danger of leaf shatter, resulting in serious losses of nutrient. The degree of wilting before baling which is practical depends on the period in which the grass can be left after cutting without rainfall occurring. For preference, baling should be on the day after cutting and should seldom be delayed for more than 48 hr. Obviously, the economics of barn

Quality	S.E. of original grass d.m.	Weight of S.E. in lb				Saving cost of barley purchased
		In original grass d.m.	Lost with barn drying	Lost with field drying	Saved by barn drying	
1.	58	1300	455	546	91	23s. 0d.
2.	54	1210	424	508	84	21s. 0d.
3.	50	1120	392	470	78	19s. 6d.

Group	Daily ration in lb				Daily Livewt gain	Food Cost/lb gain
	Barley	Cake	Beet	Hay		
6 steers	4–6	$1\frac{1}{2}$	—	10–11	2·21	$13\frac{3}{4}d.$
3 steers, 3 heifers	1–2	$1\frac{1}{2}$	4	10–11	2·45	$12\frac{3}{4}d.$
6 heifers	$1\frac{1}{2}$	$1\frac{1}{2}$	—	12–14	2·07	$12\frac{3}{4}d.$
6 heifers	—	—	—	12–17	1·6	$12\frac{1}{2}d.$
5 steers, 4 heifers	5	$1\frac{1}{2}$	—	15–16	2·66	$13\frac{3}{4}d.$

drying depend on the successful part wilting of the crop in the field. This can be shown, to some extent, by the weight of water which has to be removed to produce 1 T of hay dried to 20 per cent m.c.:

Hay, m.c.	60	55	50	45	40	35	30	25
Water removed, cwt	20	16	12	9	7	5	3	1

Hay, for storage without serious risk of overheating or deterioration, should have an m.c. of 15–20 per cent. Thus, in normal practice the aim should be to remove about 35–40 per cent of the m.c. in the field and a further 20–30 per cent by the drier.

c. Running Costs

An estimate for the running cost of the drier has to be made when considering the management requirements which might justify drying as part of the farm plan. This is not easy. Various estimates have been made. Drying requirements, and therefore the time required for drying, depend on:

i. M.C. to be reduced: 20–30 per cent normal.

ii. Volume and/or weight of hay to be dried at one time.

iii. Air flow and temperature rise employed.

These factors have to be related to the cost of fuel used. Sixty installations were costed in 1954–6 (7):

	Cold air Plants	Air speed with heater	
		Medium	High/Low
Fixed cost/T	$£1\frac{3}{4}$	$£1\frac{1}{2}$	$£1\frac{5}{8}$
Av. running cost/T	$£\frac{3}{4}$	$£\frac{3}{4}$	£2
High running cost/T	£1	$£2\frac{1}{2}$	£4

It is important that the running cost should be low, and that the efficiency of the plant should be checked. A more recent cost study of an efficient electrical drier has been made by the West of Scotland Agricultural College over 3 yrs (8):

Fuel cost/T dried hay at 0·9d./unit (after 1st December 1960 0·85d./unit)

1959	1960	1961
£1 5s. 4d.	£1 4s. 11d.	£1 6s. 1d.

Thus an approximate allowance of $£1\frac{1}{4}$/T dried hay might be made. However, the costs ranged from about $£\frac{3}{4}$ to $£2\frac{3}{4}$/T, depending on the m.c. of the incoming crop, being increased if the drier was not loaded to full capacity due to an underestimate of the area to be cut. Atmospheric conditions at the time of drying also influenced the final cost. The number of electrical units per ton dried hay varied between about 200 and 750, averaging about 400. Culpin has given the theoretical relative costs of drying with different methods using electricity or coke (oil being about intermediate to these costs), assuming that air leaves the hay at 94 per cent R.H. In general, drying with cold air is cheaper than electrical heating, except in extremely cold and damp conditions. Electricity becomes increasingly costly as the R.H. is raised, being more expensive than coke for warming the air. In the assessment electricity has been taken at 1d./unit and coke at $£9\frac{1}{8}$/T, with 80 per cent efficiency, and calculations have been given on the basis of each cwt of water removed. Thus, hay baled at just over 40 per cent m.c. and dried to 20 per cent requires $\frac{3}{8}$T of water to be removed per ton dried hay. On this basis electrical drying, when the air temperature is about 10° C (50° F) with R.H. at 75 per cent, might cost for fuel about $£1\frac{1}{2}$/T dried hay; but on a warmer, drier day, with a temperature of 20° C (68° F) and R.H. at 60 per cent electricity might cost about £1/T. Such costs should be recovered by improved hay quality (9): Drying costs can vary, therefore, between $£\frac{3}{4}$ and £3/T dried hay, due to choice of fuel and atmospheric conditions. However, in normal conditions, that is, with moderately warm, dry air, an allowance for the electrical heating of the air of $£1\frac{1}{4}$–$£1\frac{1}{2}$/T dried hay should be made. Similarly, in wet conditions, with hay baled at 50 per cent m.c. and dried on a cool, moist day, at least $£2$–$£2\frac{1}{2}$/T should be allowed; whereas naturally well-dried bales of 35 per cent m.c., when harvested on a warm, dry early summer day, might cost rather less than £1/T. Such factors have to be considered when assessing the value of barn drying and, to some extent, the running costs could be averaged for different parts of the country. An assessment for running costs per year might be $£1\frac{1}{2}$/T in the north but only £1/T in the south.

Temp.,	R.H.,	Cost/cwt moisture removed				
		Temperature of drying air				
		Air temp.	+5½° C	+5½° C	+11° C	+11° C
°C	per cent		Elec.	Coke	Elec.	Coke
		s. d.	s. d.	s. d.	s. d.	s. d.
7½	80	2 4	4 9	2 1	4 9	2 0
	90	8 5	5 9	2 6	5 3	2 2
10	60	11	3 2	1 5	3 8	1 6
	70	1 3	3 8	1 7	4 1	1 8
	80	2 1	4 4	1 11	4 6	1 10
	90	7 10	5 5	2 5	5 0	2 1
15½	60	9	2 8	1 2	3 3	1 4
	70	1 1	3 2	1 5	3 8	1 6
	80	1 11	3 11	1 9	4 0	1 8
	90	6 1	4 9	2 2	4 6	1 10
20	60	8	2 5	1 1	3 0	1 3
	70	11	2 11	1 4	3 6	1 5

3. Production techniques

a. Drying in Bulk or Bale

Barn drying of loose hay had the disadvantage that it was laborious; and the method was not popular, until it was shown that drying in the bale was practical, and this method, coupled with the development of the pick-up baler, proved then to be economic. Most hay is now dried in the bale, long hay being restricted principally to small stock farmers. However, there are developments for handling hay as a chopped material. Experiments in drying chopped hay have been made at the Drayton Experimental Husbandry Farm. The method has a number of advantages compared with baled hay (10):

i. After cutting and crimping, the wilted grass can be picked up with a double-chop harvester into a self-unloading trailer, which can unload mechanically with a forage blower direct into a barn for drying.

ii. Compaction of the hay for drying is greater, being about 10 per cent more dense than baled hay; and since there are no gaps, as with bales, drying should be more uniform.

iii. After drying, the chopped hay is held in the drying barn. It can be self-fed to cattle direct from the barn, or it can be augered to mangers, or it could be rationed manually.

iv. In the experiment the hay was wilted in the field to 30 per cent m.c., due to exceptional drying weather, though this had not been intended, and the cost of drying with a mobile drier was only 8s. 7d./T dried hay. The chopped hay was superior to baled hay from the same crop which was dried naturally. Cattle self-fed from the chopped hay, with 2½ lb/head/day of corn, averaged 2·3 lb/day liveweight increase, consuming with the corn 25½ lb d.m./day.

It has yet to be shown whether hay chopped at 40 per cent m.c. will dry and handle satisfactorily. However, due to the low labour requirements in handling chopped hay, this method could prove to be preferable to baled hay. In Germany chopped grass is blown into tower silos, 20–40 ft high and about 24 ft in dia., with a central, vertical shaft used as an air duct and with perforated walls so that the grass can be dried with cool or warm air, producing hay with a compaction of 1½ cwt/yd³. The towers are emptied by a cutter which forces the hay down the central shaft on to a bottom conveyor at 45 lb/min (11).

b. Drying Methods for Baled Hay

It is possible to blow air for drying through baled hay, the bales being stacked on edge, cut side downwards, when the air is blown through a mesh floor from below, or sideways for tunnel drying. Three methods are used. Drying can take place while in store; or the bales can be dried in batches, either on a mesh floor or in a tunnel, the bales having to be double-handled for storage. Bales should preferably be of medium density and, if 2½ ft long by 18 in. × 14 in. × ½ cwt at 45 per cent m.c., are easy to handle. High-density bales are difficult or impossible to dry, and ¾-cwt bales are heavy to handle. Bales must be packed tightly for even drying (12).

i. *Cold-blow storage method.* Bales can be stacked to form 10 layers on a mesh floor, which, including a plenum chamber and eaves ventilation space, requires a total height of 18 ft. To be economical, the maximum number of bales must be dried at a time, though blowing should start as soon as the first layer has been laid, and 3 or 4 layers should be laid during the first day. A further 2–3 layers should be added after 2–3 days, loading continuing in similar stages until the drier is full. Under normal conditions drying may have to continue for about 10 days after loading is complete, though no set programme for loading and drying is essential. The air flow should be 30–45 C.F.M./ft² of floor area at $2\frac{1}{2}$–3 in. s.w.g. Electrical consumption should be between 150 and 240 kW/T dried for normal conditions.

ii. High–low batch method. Bales are stacked and dried in batches on a mesh floor to a depth of 4 layers, though 6 layers are possible, provided any damp bales from the top two layers are re-dried when the drier is unloaded. Therefore, the overall height required is about 9 ft, or 12 ft for 6 layers. After drying the bales can be handled via an elevator into a haybarn (IB). Cold air is blown through the bales for 4–5 days, followed by air warmed to a temperature rise of 4–7° C, with a heater loading 3–5 kW/1000 C.F.M. The air flow should be 45–50 C.F.M./ft² of floor area at 2 in. s.w.g. Electrical consumption may be 180–360 kW/T dried.

iii. Tunnel method. Bales can be stacked to form a tunnel on a concrete or earth floor, either in a barn or in the open. Therefore no special building is required, though adequate space and a headroom of 12 ft is desirable for economical drying. The tunnel must be constructed soundly, and labour requirements are higher than with other methods. Tunnels have side and end walls 3–4 bales high, with a pyramid of bales over the tunnel, supported on hurdles, 3–4 high. Therefore, the height is about 7–10 ft. An air flow of 45 C.F.M./bale or 2000 C.F.M./T dried at $2\frac{1}{2}$ in. s.w.g. is necessary, possibly with air warmed to a temperature rise of 4–7° C for the final stage of drying. The duct should not restrict the air flow, and the cross-sectional area should be:

$$\frac{\text{Max. fan output (C.F.M.)}}{2000} = \text{Area (ft}^2)$$

Under average conditions electrical consumption may be 240–360 kWh/T dried.

c. Drying Methods for Loose Hay

Loose hay can be dried either by the cold-blow storage method or with the high–low batch method. The principles are similar to bale drying, though labour and air-flow requirements are greater. There is insufficient evidence to give the requirements for drying chopped hay.

d. Power

The air flow is governed by the fan (6, below), which can be powered by solid fuel, oil or electricity. Solid fuel, such as coke, is cheap if the boiler and flue are efficient, but requires considerable labour for stoking and is unlikely to be used for any large, modern layouts. Oil usually proves to be more expensive than coke, but cheaper to run than electricity. Diesel engines can be used. However, the installation cost of an oil tank and furnace means that the extra capital cost is not recovered by lower running costs, when compared with electricity, for many years. Electricity is clean and simple in use, requiring little capital cost, if power is available, but moderately high running costs, as stated above. Comparative costs for modern plant are not available. However, the drying capacity at atmospheric air temperature and at various temperature rises has been given (*see also 2c,* above) (13):

Temp., °C	R.H., per cent	Air temp.	$+2\frac{3}{4}$° C	$+5\frac{1}{2}$° C	$+8\frac{1}{3}$° C	$+11$° C	$+14$° C
		Drying capacity per 24 hr of 1000 C.F.M., cwt of water					
$7\frac{1}{2}$	80	0·44	0·98	1·55	2·18	2·82	3·38
	90	0·11	0·70	1·27	1·90	2·53	3·17
10	60	1·23	1·81	2·37	3·00	3·56	4·30
	70	0·34	1·46	2·09	2·72	3·28	4·05
	80	0·49	1·11	1·74	2·37	3·07	3·69
	90	0·13	0·76	1·39	2·02	2·71	3·34
$15\frac{1}{2}$	60	1·44	2·10	2·73	3·35	4·03	4·71
	70	1·01	1·70	2·32	3·00	3·68	4·36
	80	0·57	1·22	1·90	2·65	3·33	4·01
	90	0·14	0·88	1·56	2·31	2·92	3·53
20	60	1·67	2·40	3·07	3·74	4·47	5·07
	70	1·15	1·86	2·53	3·19	4·00	4·80

Method	Floor Area, ft²	Fan, C.F.M.	Fan, h.p.	Heater, kW ★	Total, kW	Hay dried, T
Batch	200	9,000	7½	15	21	6
	300	13,500	12	22	31	9
	400	18,000	15	30	42	12
	500	22,500	22	38	54	15
Tunnel	No. 1	9,000	7½	15	21	5
	No. 2	18,000	15	30	42	10
Storage	200	9,000	7½	—	6	12
	300	13,500	12	—	9	18
	400	18,000	15	—	12	24
	500	22,500	22	—	16	30

★ These heater loadings will give a temperature rise of $2\frac{7}{8}°$ C.

Similarly, a guide for performance and electrical requirements is given above for bale drying (14). At least one proprietary mobile moisture extraction unit is available, including an axial-flow fan powered from a diesel engine, the heat from which can be used to raise the air temperature by 12° C (55° F) for drying. Alternatively, a tractor can be used to drive the fan. One advantage of hay drying is that the plant provided can be used also for drying grain, if required, especially sacked grain.

4. *Work routines*
a. Labour requirements during drying are negligible, especially if electricity or an engine drier are used, though temperature and humidity within the hay should be recorded at intervals. Adjusting the air flow and temperature to suit the condition of the hay will greatly affect the speed and cost of drying.
b. The major task for drying is in loading the bales into the drier or in the construction of a tunnel, together with the unloading of the drier, if batch drying is practised. Though an elevator and conveyor can be used to assist the task, for the most part mechanization is not practical. However, if chopped hay can be blown into the drier, aided by a little manual spreading with a fork to give even consolidation and surface, then the labour requirement will be reduced considerably. Haymaking tends to be concentrated into a 4–6-week period in the months of June and July, possibly with additional periods for second or third cuts later in the year.

5. *Design data*
a. Volume of Hay
The size and capacity of the drier required will depend on the quantity of hay to be dried at any one time, and this depends on the area to be cut, together with the expected yield. A mobile drier might be able to dry 600–800 ft² of floor area × 15 ft ht of hay, producing 20–30 T of dried hay. Many units are much smaller in size, being perhaps only 200–300 ft² of floor area. In some cases a number of compartments can be formed to divide a large haybarn into smaller areas for storage drying at different times. Bales for drying should have a density of 12–13 lb/ft³; a 3-ft-long bale at 45 per cent m.c. weighs about 70 lb, one 2½ ft long about ½ cwt (IB 5). Dry hay may weigh 1 T/400 ft³. Obviously, the size of drier must be related to the size of fan.

b. Floor
Any perforated floor can be used, but welded wire mesh is cheap and satisfactory, being perhaps of a ¼-ft square mesh supported on timber cross-bearers, at, possibly, 4-ft × 2-ft centres, in turn supported on ¾-ft-square block pillars. Strength depends on the depth of loading. The mesh should not cover the complete floor. There should be a solid edge at the sides of the floor 1½–2 ft wide, since, though this will be covered by bales as well as the mesh floor, it prevents air escaping up the walls. Chopped hay requires a smaller mesh.

c. Plenum Chamber
The air space below the mesh floor should be 2–2½ ft above the sub-floor, the latter preferably being of concrete, and the fan should have an air inlet direct into the chamber. Alternatively, the fan can be coupled to a duct running alongside a series of chambers, there being a baffle control capable of sealing the chambers from the duct, so that the fan can ventilate each floor in turn. The cross-sectional area of the duct will depend on the fan size, but normally varies between 2 and 4 ft square.

d. Walls and Roof
All walls must be airtight, but can be of galvanized sheeting on the inside of timber framing. Blockwork is easier than sheeting to make airtight. The internal surfaces should be smooth, preferably with the corners rounded. The walls should be as high as the stacked bales and be open above the bales for 1½–2 ft up to the eaves along at least three sides of the barn, to give an adequate air flow for re-

moving the excess humidity from the drying bales. Provided there is adequate eaves ventilation, any form of roof can be satisfactory. There should be protection from driving rain, and therefore the eaves ventilation strip should be louvred on exposed sites. The openings might be based on 5 ft²/1000 C.F.M. air flow.

e. Doors
Doors must be for the full height of the bales and are usually about 5 ft wide per chamber. They must be rebated to the frame and airtight, flush with the internal chamber walls.

6. Equipment
a. Fan and Motor Unit
The unit can be a mobile diesel moisture-extraction unit, the latter being coupled to the plenum chamber or duct through a fan-shaped portable air-entry duct about 5 ft long. Such units may need refuelling every day. Alternatively, the unit can be electrically operated and permanently housed as an external unit joined to the plenum chamber. The size will depend on the type of unit, being normally about 5 ft long by 3 ft × 3 ft. The unit must be watertight, with an air inlet at the exposed end. Two-stage axial-flow fans are efficient with low h.p. requirements, though a centrifugal fan is quieter to run. The noise level, especially with a high-powered diesel engine, can be severe and, if the unit is run in a confined space, can be a nuisance for at least half a mile. Noise can be reduced by a baffle of bales, provided they do not restrict the air flow. Heaters can be coupled to the fan, metal-sheathed or open-wound heating wires within a metal frame and mesh guard being available. The size of heater may be based on 1 kW raising 1000 C.F.M. of air by rather more than $1\frac{1}{2}°$ C (36° F). The heater loading will probably be banked. For example, a 12/24-kW heater might be used to dry a chamber of 3000 ft³, coupled to a fan providing 16,000 C.F.M. at 2 in. s.w.g. The heater bank can be moved and coupled to different fan units.

b. Gauges
A manometer to measure the static air pressure, against which the air flow is calibrated, is essential. A wet- and dry-bulb hygrometer, to measure the humidity in the stack, is desirable, and this can be coupled to an automatic switch controlling the heater, so that the latter operates only when the humidity rises. The controls should be positioned where they are easy to read, preferably near the fan unit.

7. Environment control.
Hay is dried by controlling its environment. Details have been given with regard to the moisture extraction, with details of

humidity, temperature and air flow, required for drying. The fan must be large enough to suit the volume and moisture content of the hay. There must be an unobstructed air intake for the fan and good high-level ventilation to remove the humid air. Drying needs supervision, but can be semi-automatic. Noise can be a nuisance, unless the unit is sited away from buildings.

8. Layouts.
Fig. 33 shows a typical three-compartment hay-drying barn, with simple construction, each bay holding 3000 ft³ of hay, that is about 8 T dried hay. If 2 T is the expected yield per acre 4 acres would have to be cut for each bay, providing about 6 layers of 70 bales each, these being cut over a period of several days. A unit of this kind might batch dry 100–150 T p.a. (Ref. (c)). Though it is not essential for each compartment to have its own fan and heater unit, this is desirable for the maximum throughput.

Fig. 34 shows a single-compartment barn holding 12,000 ft³ of hay, that is about 30 T dried hay. At the same yield 15 acres would have to be cut over a period of, perhaps, 10 days, if baled at 40 per cent m.c. The compartment might be a storage drier coupled to a mobile drying unit, thus eliminating double handling of the hay. If required, there could be more than one compartment of the same size, still using only one drying unit,

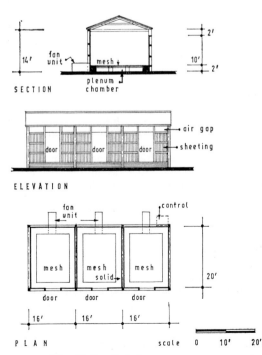

Fig. 33. Small drying compartments

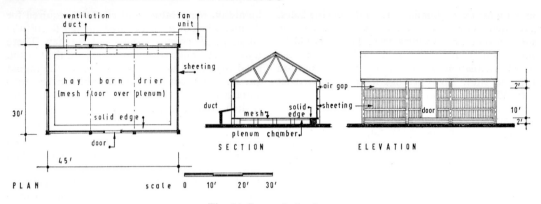

Fig. 34. Large drying barn

provided the cutting period was extended for more than 3 weeks.

9. *Siting.* With batch drying, the drier should be near the haybarn. Both with storage and batch drying, the stored hay should be near the livestock unit requiring hay as fodder. There should be good access from the fields. The fan unit should be sited to obtain a good air inlet, without obstructions from buildings and away from foul-air sources and from livestock and people. The eaves ventilation should be sited to obtain a good through draught.

Fig. 35 shows how a chopped hay drying barn could be sited for self-feeding to cattle (10). Otherwise, with baled hay within a storage drier, the barn could be opened on to a bale conveyor for off-loading direct to the mangers. Alternatively, off-loading can be into a feeding passage for manual distribution.

10. *Services.* With electrical drying, an electrical service will be required, possibly capable of high loading. Otherwise, the services are simple. Rainwater must be taken clear of the building.

11. *Costs.* Many hay driers are installed in existing buildings. A simple drier, as in Fig. 33, using second-hand timber and farm labour, might cost about £700–£800 for the building and £100–£200 for the equipment. If 140 T p.a. of dried hay are made the capital cost might represent £1/T dried. A steel-framed barn, as in Fig. 34, might cost £800 complete, plus another £800 for the mobile drier. The latter unit will probably have several uses besides hay drying. However, if used as a storage drier the building alone represents £4/T dried hay, but there are no other storage costs (IB 11). With tunnel drying there may be no building capital costs. Running costs of £¾–£3/T dried have been discussed above in 2c. All costs, both capital and running, have to be balanced against the improved

value of the hay as a fodder and the reduced drying losses. The latter in many years may show a saving of at least 20 per cent above the value of field-cured hay, perhaps representing £2/T d.m. cut. The value of the actual fodder may show improved fattening or milk-production rates, perhaps worth £1–£4/T. Obviously, drying costs can be recovered in the value of the fodder. In addition, there is greater security in a bad year.

12. *References*

(1) 'Off the grass'. *Farmers Weekly Supplement*, p. 1 (14th September 1962).
(2) MOORE, I. 'Make haymaking less hazardous'. *Practical Power Farming*, pp. 30–1 (March 1962).
(3) Ref. (*b*), p. 8.
(4) Ref. (*b*), p. 8.
(5) 'Beat-the-weather hay'. *Dairy Farmer*, pp. 37–9 (June 1962).
(6) COLDWELL, D., GRIFFITHS, J. R. & YOUNG, W. 'Barn dried hay feeding test'. *Farmers Weekly*, p. 99 (19th April 1963).
(7) 'Barn hay drying'. N.A.A.S. Technical Report No. 10. (1957.)
(8) Ref. (*c*), p. 13.
(9) CULPIN, C. *Farm Mechanization Management*, Crosby Lockwood, p. 144 (1959).
(10) CULPIN, S. 'Handling hay the chopped way' and 'Self-fed hay'. *Dairy Farmer*, p. 55 (December 1962); p. 45 (June 1963).

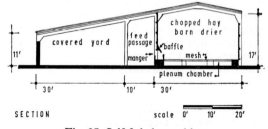

Fig. 35. Self-fed chopped hay

104

(11) ZICHE, J. 'Haytowers in Germany'. *Farmbuildings*, p. 19 (Winter 1963/64).

(12) Ref. (*a*), Ch. VI.

(13) Ref. (*a*), p. 77.

(14) Ref. (*a*), p. 73.

(15) ROWLAND, F. E. *Electricity in Modern Farming*, Land Books, p. 159 (1963).

SELECTED REFERENCES

a. *Farm Electrification Handbook No. 7.* 'Greencrop drying'. Electrical Development Association. (1961.)

b. CULPIN, S. 'Comparisons between barn-dried hay and silage with regard to efficiency of conservation and feeding value'. *Perth Conference Report.* Scottish Branch of the Institution of Agricultural Engineers (March 1962).

c. 'Barn hay drying at Auchincruive'. *West of Scotland Agricultural College Research Bulletin No. 30* (June 1962).

d. 'Green hay'. *R. A. Lister & Co. Publication* 104H (1962).

e. 'Modern haymaking'. *Farmers Weekly Bulletin* (21st April 1961).

f. 'Off the grass'. *Farmers Weekly Bulletin* (14th September 1962).

g. *Electricity and Greencrop Drying.* Electrical Development Association (1959).

IIC. Ensilage

1. *Activity.* The ensilage of green forage crops by fermentation can preserve most of the nutrients within the crop, the carbohydrates being converted into lactic, acetic and butyric acids. Silage can be derived from grass, maize or kale, or from the by-products of arable crops such as oats, tares, rye, root tops or pea haulm. Grass silage is the most common product. Brewers' grains are sometimes mixed in layers with grass. Ensilage requires that forage crops, in order to change their physical state, should be processed within the place of storage required for the silage itself, and the latter can be in the form of a clamp, a pit or a silo, only the last of these being in the nature of a building. Therefore, it could be argued that silos should be classified as one of the storage buildings within Section I, especially since the production of haylage in tower silos (IC) is also a form of ensilage. Though this is true, silage requires mechanical compaction to assist fermentation and there can be a considerable discharge of effluent from the silo. Haylage, in contrast, does not require mechanical compaction and produces little effluent, while the change in the physical state of the crop within the silo is less pronounced.

Grass required for silage can be harvested and transported in a similar manner to that for haylage, except that it may not be wilted in the field to the same extent and, in fact, in most cases it is harvested without wilting. Though silage can be made from grass cut in any lengths, modern forage harvesters can lacerate or chop the grass into lengths of $\frac{1}{2}$–1 in., a process which assists compaction and fermentation in the silo. Good silage will contain 2 per cent of its fresh weight as lactic acid, but almost no butyric and only a little acetic acid. The sugar and moisture contents of the crop largely control the acids produced. Molasses can be added during ensilage, if the sugar content is low.

At harvesting the grass should have a moisture content of 70 per cent, though in the right conditions, using modern forage harvesters, wilting down to 65 per cent m.c. may be the aim (1). However, harvesting at 85 per cent m.c. may be enforced by bad weather and the silage, though poorer in quality, may be palatable.

Silage can be used as fodder for beef and dairy cattle and, to a limited extent, for sheep. As with haylage, it is the dry matter, protein and starch contents of the conserved crop, together with its digestibility, which are important. Four crops may be cut from a field, sometimes yielding more than 5 T d.m./acre, though an annual yield of 2–3 T is more usual, or even less if the field is grazed as well as cut. Probably four times as much hay as silage is made (IB 1), but the relative merits of conserving grass as silage or as hay are debated both by farmers and by scientists, and the methods of conservation and handling are changing so rapidly that no conclusion can be given to the discussion. Good silage is easier to make than good hay, especially in the wetter parts of the country, but the development of barn hay-drying methods may alter this factor, and hay is easier than silage to handle. Some of the factors governing a choice between making silage or hay will be locality, size of crop and system of animal husbandry practised. Dry matter and nutrient losses can be considerable in badly made silage, and the d.m. lost from an uncovered silo can be as much as one-third of the weight harvested, but wilted and well-made silage in a covered and sealed silo should have a loss of under 15 per cent. Estimates of losses are given in IC 1*b* (p. 58).

Grass is normally brought from the fields in self-unloading trailers and emptied usually outside the silo, but sometimes directly into the silo. In a few cases, mainly with small silos which are near the fields (under 300 yd), a tractor and buckrake may transport the grass directly from the field into the silo. In either case the vehicle must return to the field with the minimum delay and the harvesting operation must be planned to keep the number of machines and men required to the minimum (1).

2. *Managerial requirements*

a. Crops can be ensiled in various ways:

　　i. The crop can be cut either when past full flower or at an early stage of growth, when molasses should be added. The quick formation of acids can be assisted by the addition of acids to the crop and bacterial action may be limited by the addition of certain chemicals, the silo being filled and sealed as soon as possible (2).

ii. Heaps or clamps can be made on different sites in the fields each year to suit the cropping and feeding policy, but their compaction with a tractor is dangerous and the nutrient losses from the crop can be considerable. This system may be useful either when stock are outwintered or as an emergency supply of fodder.

iii. A clamp can be formed in a pit, which may include a concrete floor and sloped sides, possibly lined with railway sleepers, but drainage can be difficult unless the pit is formed down a hill slope. Nutrient losses can be severe.

iv. Clamps can be above ground with side walls, the top of the silage, as in the previous methods, being sealed with rolled chalk, lime or earth, or covered with removable galvanized sheeting, plywood or plastic mounted in sections on bearers resting on the walls. Nutrient losses may be considerable.

v. Walled clamps can be erected in a building to form a silobarn, the silage being sealed.

vi. Pea-haulm silage is usually made in clamps or pits, but some is made in walled clamps. It is unsuitable for self-feeding.

Generally, it is only the silobarns and, to a limited extent, the walled clamps which can be classified as farm buildings and their design will not be affected whether chemicals are added to the crop or not.

b. The silo must maintain the food in good condition, with as little loss of nutrients as possible The grass must be compacted by a tractor and excess moisture must be able to drain away at floor level. No water must penetrate into the silo and, to obtain the best silage, oxygen should be excluded. The walls must resist the thrust of the silage and should be designed to facilitate compaction. Materials used should be able to resist the silage acids and a temperature may be generated by fermentation of as much as 50° C (112° F), though this should not normally exceed 35° C (95° F). Filling and emptying the silo should be made as easy as possible. To some extent, the design should be governed by the requirements for the livestock buildings with which it is associated.

3. *Production techniques.* The method for feeding the silage will be fundamental to the design of the silobarn. The merits of self-feeding or of rationed-feeding silage are difficult to assess, especially since methods for mechanically cutting and handling silage have not been perfected. If feeding silage can be mechanized, rationed silage is probably the better method, since it is mainly reduced labour requirements in self-feeding which make the latter desirable.

a. It has been estimated that cutting and carting silage can take four to five times longer than cleaning the silage face with self-feeding methods (IC 1c, p. 59). A man cutting silage with a hay knife, forking it into a trailer, driving the trailer to a manger 50 yd away, moving the trailer after filling a manger length sufficient for 8 cattle and forking a ration of $\frac{3}{4}$ cwt head into the manger would need about $1\frac{1}{2}$ hr/day for 60 cattle, longer if the daily ration is divided into two feeds (3). In contrast, cleaning the slurry from a self-feed silo face and moving an electrified control wire should need less than $\frac{1}{3}$ hr (4). However, using a foreloader could reduce the time required for rationed feeding to under $1\frac{1}{4}$ hr. On this basis, with a four-month housing period, self-feeding might save about 100–125 hr of labour (equal, perhaps, to £100 in running costs) or enabling more cows to be kept for the same labour. Moreover, if a foreloader is used to fill a self-unloading trailer it is possible that the task of rationed feeding could be completed in under $\frac{2}{3}$ hr/day. Similarly, easy-feeding (cutting and placing silage into mangers alongside the silo) saves labour. But the task of cutting silage with a knife is laborious and several machines have been designed in the United States having an auger cutter capable of being manoeuvred up and down the face of the silage and able to load an elevator for filling a self-unloading trailer at rates of as much as 15 cwt/min (5). On this basis it should be possible to ration feed in the same time as is required for cleaning a self-feed silo unit. Research is required to establish the best method of feeding silage and to develop appropriate machinery to mechanize the task.

b. Self-feeding implies, to some extent, ad lib. feeding, though it is possible to restrict the number of hours each day in which self-feeding is allowed, and this will reduce the quantity of silage consumed, particularly by the more timid cows. However, the ration will not be restricted to any specified quantity. Ad lib. feeding, especially with bulk fodder for beef cattle, may be undesirable, since it allows inadequate control over the food conversion ratio and may be wasteful of a valuable fodder. Moreover, if desired, it is possible to feed ad lib. in a manger. A recent experiment at the Bridget's experimental husbandry farm near Winchester showed that, though cows consumed 4 lb d.m./day less when self-feeding compared with ad lib. feeding at a manger, without affecting yields, the butterfat content was reduced by 0·2 per cent—an appreciable amount, which might justify the labour of carting the fodder.

c. In many cases silage is not the only bulk fodder in the ration. If mangers have to be provided for feeding roots, kale or other foods, then no extra cost is incurred in using the mangers for feeding silage. In some cases designing a self-feed silobarn to suit the cattle housing may be inconvenient and it may be simpler to use mangers.

4. *Work routines.* As with the storage buildings, the work requirements are concerned with filling and emptying the walled clamp or silobarn, activities which influence the design of the building in several respects.

a. Most silos are filled by tractor and foreloader, as stated above, the grass being lifted from a heap outside the silo and deposited between the walls of the clamp, load by load. When the floor has been covered, or partly covered, the tractor has to drive on top of the grass to form additional layers and, as the height of the clamp is increased, a ramp of grass has to be formed to take the tractor. The tractor has to manoeuvre on top of the grass to aid compaction and its wheels should be taken to about 1 in. from the side walls. After the silo is filled the ramp can be cut away, the grass being formed with a vertical end and the top of the clamp being sealed. The top of the clamp can be used to store straw or house cattle (IIIA and IIIB). There are other methods for filling the silo, such as using a self-unloading trailer which either tips the grass into the silo from the sides and ends, the grass being spread by tractor or by hand, or drives on to the clamp to deposit the grass. Chopped grass can be blown into the silo, as with a tower, but compaction with a tractor is desirable. Filling seldom starts before late April and finishes by November, though May and June tend to be the principal time for harvesting.

b. Emptying the silo depends on whether the silage is self-fed or rationed, as discussed above and, in more detail, in the relevant sections on animal husbandry.

5. *Design data*

a. The average density of silage is not easy to assess, since it varies to some extent with the length of cut, the moisture content, the overall silage depth and the degree of compaction. Usually densities can be taken as:

Long grass: 45 lb/ft³ or 50 ft³/T
Lacerated grass: 56 lb/ft³ or 40 ft³/T

Densities measured from sample cores taken from silos in the North of England confirm these averages to some extent (6) (see table below). On this basis the d.m. density with lacerated grass silage varies between 13 and 16 lb/ft³. Pea-haulm silage may compact to about 11 cwt/yd³.

b. The compacted depth should not be greater than 6 ft if the silage is self-fed, though this can be increased, provided that the silage above 6 ft is cut and dropped behind a feeding barrier along the face of the silage or carted to other stock. The compacted depth is seldom taken above 9 ft, though there is no limitation on the height possible, except the practical difficulty of filling and compacting. Since the depth may be increased by at least 3 ft during compaction and the tractor needs a height of about 6 ft, the overall working height from the floor to obtain a settled depth of 6 ft is normally considered to be at least 15 ft.

c. With self-feeding and with unrestricted access, the width of the silage face for feeding is normally taken to be 6 in./cow, or perhaps 5 in./cow for small breeds, with possibly 9 in./bullock for beef fattening. Any width greater than about 9 in./beast tends to waste fodder, due to lazy eating, whereby some food is dropped and trampled underfoot. With rationed feeding, any width of silo is practical, though, if a buckrake is used to fill a trailer, widths less than 25 ft may prove cramped for working in order to allow the tractor to back and turn, and widths greater than 30 ft may be preferable. It is desirable for the buckrake and the silage widths to be related, so that the latter is a multiple of the former plus about 2 ft in order to assist filling. Each load may be about 50–70 ft³, which may compact to about half its volume. There is no limit to the

Type of silage	Cwt/yd³	Lb/ft³	Per cent d.m.	Cwt d.m./yd³	No. of cores
Long:					
Wet	12·0	50	22·8	2·7	22
Dry	11·1	46	29·9	3·3	14
Average	11·7	49	25·6	3·0	36
Lacerated:					
Wet	13·6	56	22·6	3·1	32
Dry	13·0	54	29·9	3·9	7
Average	13·5	56	23·9	3·2	39

width or length of silage in a clamp, but a square rather than a long oblong plan should be cheaper to build and should cause less wastage of fodder. However, widths greater than 50 ft are difficult to fill, unless a large quantity is made at one time, and most silage faces are under 40 ft wide. If silage making is interrupted due to bad weather, wide silos cause greater wastage of silage.

d. The quantity of silage required will depend on the ration, the number of animals and the period of feeding. Ad lib. feeding should be based on a maximum consumption of 3 lb d.m./cwt liveweight/day, further details of which are given in IE 2, but an allowance for storage should be made to include for d.m. losses within the silage.

e. With self-feeding the floor should have a fall towards the silage face of 1 : 30, with a cross-fall to one or both sides of about 1 : 60. The cross-fall should be checked a few feet within the silo to form a small V channel, which helps to prevent effluent seeping through the walls (Fig. 36). With rationed silage, a fall to one end of 1 : 40 should be sufficient, or cross-falls to a sunken channel at the centre or side, the channel, having a longitudinal fall, may save hardcore fill to the floor. Loose land-drains can be laid in the drainage channels. The floor should be 6 in. concrete on hardcore or slatted (10).

f. Effluent discharge quantities are discussed in IG 5g, p. 78.

g. The height of the silo wall should at least equal the settled depth of silage on either side and there should be guard rails at 3 ft and 6 ft above the wall to prevent the tractor falling over the edge during compaction. In order to aid compaction, the wall should slope outwards at 1 : 8 or 10 degrees, though this is less essential with well-cut grass than with long grass. The tractor wheel during compaction will be beyond the centre of the wall's gravity and therefore considerable stresses occur in the wall, but since inadequate research has been carried out to

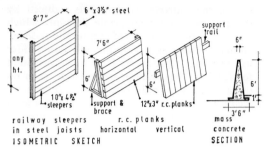

Fig. 37. Silo walls

establish the turning moments, silo walls are erected empirically. U.S. research to establish the moments in a vertical silo wall 6 ft high during compaction with a light tractor established that (7):

i. Maximum unit lateral pressure (without tractor) occurs temporarily 1–2 ft below the surface during filling at 150 lb/ft².

ii. After filling, lateral pressures from 2 to 6 ft occur at 100 lb/ft².

iii. Maximum pressure during filling occurs $4\frac{3}{4}$ ft above floor level at 190 lb/ft², and minimum pressure at 1 ft at 135 lb/ft².

iv. To calculate the overturning moment caused by the tractor:

$$Y = AX^b$$
where Y = moment in ft lb/ft run;
X = depth of silage in ft;
A = 61·019 for chopped grass;
51·261 for unchopped grass;
b = 1·774 for chopped grass;
1·823 for unchopped grass.

However, other U.S. research showed that the maximum pressure on a vertical wall was only 60 lb/ft² and on a sloped wall 73 lb/ft² (8).

A number of proprietary concrete, timber or steel walls are available:

v. Concrete units for walls are mainly densely vibrated r.c. planks, laid vertically or horizontally, depending on manufacture, and normally requiring support at 7½-ft centres; the techniques of fixing vertical planks against a supporting rail vary. The planks are normally 1½–2 ft wide, weighing between 1 and 2 cwt each, and should be erected in a slot in the concrete floor, perhaps 1 ft deep; they are designed to slope outwards. In most cases the walls are supported by a barn frame at 15-ft centres with intermediate braces, and their maximum heights seldom exceed 6 ft. Some walls have projecting external braces up to 4 ft from the

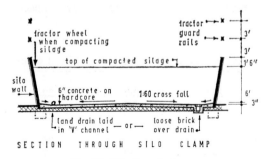

Fig. 36. Silo floor drainage

wall and some panels are thickened at the base into a pedestal to make the wall self-supporting to a height of 5 ft, with the panels weighing up to 3 cwt each (Fig. 37).

vi. Plywood units formed in panels usually 4 ft long by 6 ft high, requiring substantial external bracing, are available, though they can be supported on rails similar to the concrete planks. Similarly, steel panels sometimes $2\frac{2}{3}$ ft $\times$ $5\frac{2}{3}$ ft $\times \frac{1}{8}$ in. $\times$ 90 lb, including braces, are available.

Purpose-made walling can be of many forms, including mass concrete, reinforced concrete, concrete block and railway sleepers:

vii. Mass concrete, reinforced concrete and concrete block walls tend to be expensive, unless erected by farm labour, and their designs and specifications are given in detail in the Cement and Concrete Association's publication *Farm Surface Silos.* Since good workmanship is essential, it is undesirable to abbreviate the information given (Fig. 37).

viii. Second-hand railway sleepers usually provide the cheapest form of walling. They can be laid horizontally in the webs of steelwork and the latter can be inclined outwards, if required and if given substantial footings. Alternatively, they can be laid vertically against a rail.

The number and type of walls required depend on several factors other than cost:

ix. Two parallel walls are the minimum, but in some cases it may be desirable for one wall to be removable, so that it can be opened to provide access either for cutting and placing the silage into mangers alongside the buildings or for self-feeding.

x. It may be undesirable to have braces projecting from the walls, especially if livestock housing or access roads are adjacent.

xi. A wall at the rear of the silo may be desirable, though it adds to the expense. If the silo is filled entirely from one end the back wall assists compaction and sealing the silage, but a grass ramp may be desired at both ends, the tractor entering and leaving the clamp at different ends. Alternatively, if the ground levels are convenient, one end of the silo can be partly below ground level and partly enclosed by a ramp, so that the grass can be emptied over a retaining wall (Fig. 38).

Where the walls are designed to transmit part of their load on to the structural frame of a building, it should be noted that the frame may have to withstand a lateral pressure for which it has not been designed.

h. If the grass is unloaded by a trailer outside the silo and is lifted by foreloader, there should be a concreted area outside the filling end of the silo at a minimum width of 15 ft and preferably 25 ft.

i. The acids caused by fermentation will damage normal building materials, such as concrete and steel.

6. *Equipment.* With self-fed silage the cattle should be held by a barrier to a distance of $1\frac{1}{2}$–2 ft from the silage face, in order to restrict spoilage. Various types of barrier are available, including free-standing yokes, rails with spikes which can be driven into the silage or electrified rails hanging from an overhead cradle supported on the silo walls. The barrier should not be difficult to move, since this will have to be done daily as the silage is eaten (Fig. 39).

7. *Environment control*

a. Walls made from planks or panels are not fully impervious to moisture or air. Pressures on the wall tend to increase the gaps. Therefore

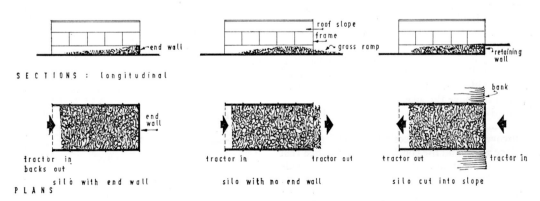

Fig. 38. Filling a silo barn with a tractor

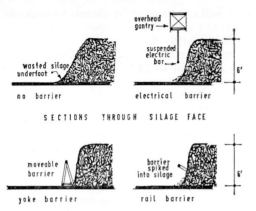

Fig. 39. Types of self-feeding barrier

and a special concrete varnish gave good results. U.S. practice has recognized the need for concrete surface protection. Pea-haulm, beet-top and wet grass silage, in particular, cause damage. However, few silos receive protection, the opinion being that good concrete will give a reasonable life without protection, though acid penetration could cause reinforcement to corrode, if near the surface, and it would be possible for sudden failure to occur during compaction.

8. *Layouts.* Fig. 40 shows a typical silobarn, in which a portal frame provides unrestricted headroom and which has side walls formed from sleepers set on end at 80 degrees against a rail, with intermediate supports at mid-bay spacings. The barn, with an overall span of 30 ft and a length of 90 ft, has an effective silage face of 26 ft, since the base

especially with vertical and/or sleeper walls, silage against the walls will be of poorer quality and wastage may be visible even up to 1 ft from the wall. In addition, the top foot and end 2 ft of the silage may be of poor quality, due to poor compaction, and the bottom half foot may be discoloured, due to poor drainage. In such conditions, a silo 90 ft × 30 ft × 6 ft high could have over one-third of its material poor in quality. Spoilage at the sides can be reduced if the walls are lined with impervious sheets, perhaps of 6-mm plastic or of building paper, and, as has been stated, d.m. losses can be reduced to under 15 per cent. All unroofed silage should have a plastic sheet cover in addition to the sealing material.

b. Silos, particularly with certain types of self-feed layout, may be totally enclosed within a barn, and others may have a lean-to enclosure on one or both sides. External ends or sides, which do not have to be open to provide access, should be sheeted to exclude rain, since excessive spoilage can occur in the silage, due to moisture penetration. Galvanized sheeting or timber boarding are preferable to asbestos-cement, since the latter is liable to fracture, due to blows during filling.

c. With unrestricted self-feeding, low-intensity lighting is desirable at all times to encourage night feeding. Therefore, a lighting point should be provided, from which a lead-light can be taken to above the silage face.

d. The Swedish State Research Institute for Farm Buildings carried out tests over four years to discover means of protecting concrete silos from silage acids, and the conclusion was reached that a surface coating to the concrete must be made immediately after erection, the concrete being of good quality. Coatings from proprietary chlorinated-rubber paints, special plastic solutions

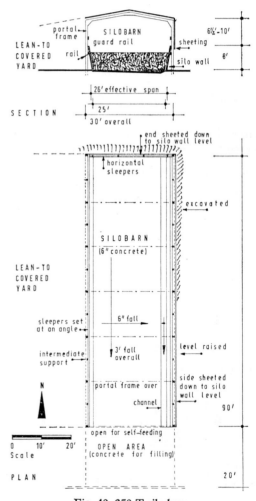

Fig. 40. 350 T silo barn

of the side walls are inset $2\frac{1}{2}$ ft from the edge of the frame. With a settled depth of silage at 6 ft the silobarn will hold about 350 T of lacerated grass silage, which might equal about 85 T of dry matter. One end wall is shown formed from sleepers set horizontally in steel stanchions. One end and one side wall are sheeted down to the silo wall, the other side being enclosed by a lean-to; and the south end opens directly on to a concreted area for filling, 20 ft wide. The silo floor has a cross-fall of $\frac{1}{2}$ ft and a longitudinal fall to the south of 3 ft, therefore the barn stanchions will vary in height from 18 ft at the S.E. to $14\frac{1}{2}$ ft at the N.W. Unless it proved possible to use a site with a natural fall of 1 : 30 towards the south, the required levels would have to be formed on a cut-and-fill basis, ramps being formed externally around the floor where it is above ground level. Only one guard rail above the side walls should be required, since the top of the sleepers project above the silage.

In contrast, Fig. 41 shows another silobarn, with the same storage capacity, but having a span 40 ft × 60 ft. In this case all the three silo walls are formed from sleepers set horizontally in the webs of the steel, with intermediate supports at mid-span, and there are two rails above the walls at the side. The effective silage face is about 39 ft. If the barn has a lean-to on each side sheeting will be needed only at the north gable. The floor has a crossfall of $\frac{1}{2}$ ft to the centre from both sides and a longitudinal fall to the south of 2 ft, the stanchion heights varying from 18 to 16 ft.

Though both examples provide storage for the same quantity of silage, the cost per ton of d.m. storage space will be different. It is possible to assess the cost on a comparative basis:

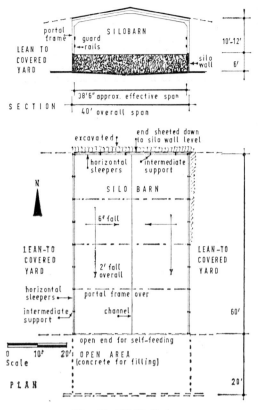

Fig. 41. 350 T silo barn

This comparison, which excludes such factors as the drainage of effluent and the cost of sealing the silage, illustrates that the shape of the silo, its relationship to other parts of the building and the

	Fig. 40	Fig. 41
Frame, foundations, roof, rooflights, rainwater goods at $£\frac{1}{3}$/ft²	900	800
Excavation at S. end to form levels at $1s$./ft²	60	60
Earth ramp to floor at N. end at $£\frac{1}{4}$/ft.R	20	20
Hardcore fill to form levels at N. end at $£1\frac{1}{4}$/yd³	60	40
6 in. concrete on hardcore laid to falls at $£1\frac{1}{2}$/yd²	430	390
4 in. concrete on hardcore laid to falls at $£1$/yd²	70	80
Intermediate stanchions at end and sides at $£10$ each	160	130
Rail to support sleepers at $£\frac{5}{8}$/ft.R	115	—
Sleepers, cut and fitted at $£\frac{3}{4}$ each	180	130
Guard rails at $£\frac{1}{2}$/ft.R	90	120
Side sheeting at $£15$/bay	90	—
Gable sheeting	50	70
Electricity, excluding supply	20	20
Rainwater drainage	30	30
Total cost	£2275	£1890
Cost per ton storage space	£ $6\frac{1}{2}$	£ $5\frac{1}{2}$
Cost per ton d.m. storage space	£ 27	£ 22
Annual building cost per ton d.m. stored	£ 4	£ $3\frac{1}{4}$

type of construction for the silo walls will influence the cost. Such factors have to be taken into consideration when designing a layout. Fig. 40 would require a buckrake 8 ft wide for ease of filling, but this would be difficult to use in Fig. 41, and it would be better to have a foreloader made $7\frac{1}{2}$ ft wide.

9. *Siting*. Siting a clamp or silobarn will depend on the policy of herd management (IIIA and IIIB). In order to economize on cut-and-fill and hardcore, the selection of a site is important, since a natural ground slope can be used to assist the required falls for drainage. In addition, the method for removing the silage effluent from the site, since it cannot be drained into a watercourse, may influence the site selection.

10. *Services*. Electric lighting is desirable, though not essential, and an electrical supply may be required for a self-feed barrier. However, it is possible that electrically powered equipment for cutting silage, prior to rationing it, may be developed in the future. The silage effluent has to be treated as a trade effluent (IG 1*a* and 1*b*, p. 75), and is particularly potent, being able to kill trees, shrubs, grass and fishes if undiluted. It must be drained into a tank, for removal by vacuum tanker or pipeline, or be allowed to drain into waste land away from any natural watercourses or land-drainage. The effluent has been known to block 12-in.-dia. drainage pipes by bacterial growth, and no drainage pipe should be less than 9 in. in diameter and should be capable of being rodded. Quantities of effluent produced are given in IG 5*g*, p. 78. The effluent should not be allowed to drain across the open concrete area, but should be channelled towards the tank or slurry pit.

11. *Costs*. The cost of forming silo floors is likely to be greater than that for normal concrete floors, due to the formation of the required falls, profiles and slots at the base of the silo walls, in addition to any hardcore fill required. The cost of walling can vary, that shown in Fig. 40 being on average about 2 guineas/ft.R 8 ft high, and that in Fig. 41 a little over $£1\frac{1}{2}$/ft.R 6 ft high. Most proprietary concrete, timber or steel panel walls, 6 ft high, cost $£2\frac{1}{4}$–$2\frac{1}{2}$/ft.R; mass concrete walls, excluding labour, about 2 guineas/ft.R and reinforced-concrete-block walls, excluding labour, about $£1\frac{1}{2}$–$£1\frac{3}{4}$. Sealing the walls with waterproof sheeting might add about $£\frac{3}{8}$/ft.R to the cost. Free-standing self-feed silage barriers may cost about $£1\frac{1}{2}$–$£2$/ft.R, simple spike barriers or suspended electrified rails $£1$–$£1\frac{1}{4}$/ft.R, and perhaps $£2$/ft.R for more elaborate designs.

Examples have been given of silos costing approximately between $£5\frac{1}{2}$ and $£6\frac{1}{2}$/T of storage space, which can be taken as normal for most silo-barns, though, with the inclusion of an effluent pit and other features such as a self-feed barrier, the cost can be up to $£8$/T of storage space. Small, simple silobarns might cost under $£5$/T storage space, but an uncovered, walled clamp, with braced silo walls, could cost less than $£4$/T of storage space. If the building should cost a little over $£6\frac{1}{2}$/T storage space, being perhaps equal to $£28$/T d.m. storage space, or $£4\frac{1}{4}$/T d.m. stored, and, if sealing the walls cost $£\frac{1}{8}$/T d.m./p.a., sealing the top adding possibly another $£\frac{1}{8}$/T d.m./p.a., the total annual building cost might be considered to be $£4\frac{1}{2}$/T d.m. stored, excluding the cost of filling and emptying. In contrast, a tower silo of equal volume might hold 100 T of d.m. costing $£18$/T d.m. storage space, or $£2\frac{3}{4}$/T d.m. stored, plus a blower and unloader costing $£9$/T d.m. storage space, or about $£2\frac{1}{4}$/T d.m. stored, giving a total cost of about $£5$/T d.m. stored, excluding filling and emptying, but including for the equipment for mechanical loading and unloading. The two costs, on this basis, could be considered to be almost comparable (IC 11, p. 62).

12. *References*
 (1) CULPIN, C. *Farm Mechanization Management*, pp. 131–3 (1959).
 (2) MOORE, I. *Agricultural Notebook*, pp. 163–5 (1962).
 (3) BELSHAW, D. G. R. & SCOTT, A. H. *Technical Report (Work Study) No. 1. Work Routines and Work Elements for Yard and Parlour and Cowshed Systems*, pp. 19–20 (1962).
 (4) NIX, BELSHAW & WELLER. Univ. of Cambridge. *Farm Econ. Branch Rep. 58. The Yard and Parlour*, p. 50 (1962).
 (5) JONES, P. 'Silage on the move'. *Farmers Weekly*, p. iii (19th January 1962).
 (6) ADDISON, J., JOCE, E. H. & TRINDER, N. Personal communication.
 (7) ESMAY, M. L., BROOKER, D. B. & MCKIBBEN, J. S. *Univ. of Missouri Research Bull. 660. Ground Horizontal Silos Design Data.* (March 1958.)
 (8) YOUNG, H. 'Pressure on walls in bunker silos'. *S. Dak. Fm. Home. Res.*, pp. 16–18 (August 1957).
 (9) GERHOLM, T., HENRIKSSON, R. & PETERSON, O. *S.R.I., Sweden. 1957. Protective Measures for Concrete in Silos containing Silage.*
(10) LIVINGSTONE, H. R. 'Slatted Floors', Experimental Farm Buildings Report No. 3 (1963), p. 11.

SELECTED REFERENCES
a. FORSYTH, R. J. W. of Scotland Agricultural College *Bull.* 155 (1961). *Silos.*
b. HENDRIX, A. T. & CALMONT, J. R. *S.R.I., Sweden.* Symposium on Modern Construction Technique in Agriculture. 'Harvesting, storing and feeding silage'. (June 1962.)

33: GRAIN INTAKE AREA FOR DRYING AND STORING
Hampshire Farm Institute, Winchester

A proprietary drying and storage unit includes metal panel rectangular bins, supporting overhead catwalk and roof and extension housing equipment and intake pit for wet grain, near large sliding doors at one end of the building, filled from a bulk tanker or trailer. The pit has removable, extension sides. Connected by its boot to the bottom of the pit, is the elevator with a double 10-T/hr leg and wood casing, which lifts grain to a pre-cleaner at its side or to a top 10-T/hr conveyor for filling the bins. A catladder gives access to catwalk and top conveyor. Behind the elevator is the fan unit, which draws air from the intake area, but has a dust extractor to the exterior. The plant is electrically operated throughout, though it is possible to dry the grain from a mobile moisture-extraction unit external to the building and coupled to the ventilated duct. The latter is central and below the bins, ventilating through a plenum chamber and mesh floor, and includes a 20-T/hr bottom conveyor which can return the grain from the bins to the intake pit. The size and capacity of the store can vary within a standard range of models, normally between 100 and 300 T. [SEE PAGE 118] Courtesy of Practical Power Farming.

34: RADIAL LAYOUT OF GRAIN DRYING/STORAGE BINS WITH BULK HANDLING
Mr. N. J. M. Anderson, Hamptworth Estate, Salisbury. See also Fig. 46, p. 122

Proprietary equipment includes six 60-T wheat (55-T barley) corrugated galvanized-steel grain-storage bins with individual roofs set in a semicircle on a raised concrete plinth foundation, formed from 3-ft-deep hollow concrete block foundation walls infilled with hardcore and capped with reinforced concrete to $\frac{1}{2}$ ft above ground level. 18-ft-dia. bins are around a handling area with reception pit, holding 6 T of wet grain from which it is augered to a pre-cleaner in a timber structure, rated at 4 T/hr, then to a central pit from which a 40-ft auger, powered by a 5-h.p. motor, can deliver it into any bin. The auger, mounted on a wheeled tripod, can be moved by hand. Bins have a ventilated floor: pairs of bins are coupled to an electric heater and fan unit, operating for either or both bins at one time. Centrifugal fans are driven by 15-h.p. motors with incoming air drawn over a bank of heaters of 36 kW, giving a temperature rise of about 5° C (10° F), then through a plenum chamber under the bin floors. Drying rates normally can be $\frac{1}{2}$–1% m.c. per 24 hrs for 60 T, though with grain incoming at over 22% m.c. less grain should be dried at one time. For unloading, an auger is placed through the circular hatch at the base of the bin, into a duct beneath its floor to a central sump into which most grain can empty by gravity, the remainder being removed by a sweep auger. Grain can be augered back to the central pit, from which it can be re-circulated, emptied into a despatch tanker or conveyed to a mill/mix unit via a pipe shown mounted on a timber tower which connects to the 40-ft auger. [SEE PAGES 118 & 45] Courtesy of Practical Power Farming.

35: GRAIN DRYING CONTROL PANEL

Mr. N. J. M. Anderson, Hamptworth Estate, Salisbury

The electrical controls for grain drying and handling in storage should be centralized. Considerable space may be required—in this case a wall area of about 8 ft × 8 ft for a 350-T grain installation, operating the heaters, fans and motors. A humidistat in the air-ducts measures the air humidity and automatically switches the heater on or off to prevent over-drying and to reduce electrical consumption. It is important that emergency cut-outs operate for each motor and piece of equipment as well as for the complete installation, safe-guarding all eventualities. The fuseboxes, meters, controls and recording equipment should be set out by experts, each item being clearly labelled. [SEE PAGE 115] See also Photo 34. Courtesy of Practical Power Farming.

36: MILL-MIX UNIT

Many different types of machine are available for milling and for mixing and, in some cases, the two functions may be combined in one machine. In this case, they are separate. A self-supporting bulk hopper, mounted on a steel angle frame, discharges into a small feed hopper of the mill. The ground meal is blown by the mill up the 2-in.-dia. pipe to discharge into the top of the mixer, from which, after mixing, the compound can be emptied into a barrow or sack. The unit does not take up much space, though allowing for storage and for working even a small unit may need as much as one bay of a barn or about 300 ft². Dust, even with modern filters, can be a nuisance. [SEE PAGE 128] Courtesy of British Farmer.

c. WATSON, S. J. & SMITH, A. M. *Silage* (1956).

d. *A.R.C. Bibl. of Fm. Blds. Res.* Part vl B (1945–58).

e. 'Grass conservation and handling'. *Farmers Weekly Supplement* (3rd April 1958).

f. 'Off the grass'. *Farmers Weekly Supplement* (14th September 1962).

IID. Grain Drying

1. *Activity*

a. Most of the grain stored on the farm, with the exception of that stored in hermetically sealed containers, is dried either prior to or during storage (ID 1*a*, p. 62). In either case there are several different techniques used for drying the grain, and equipment is available either in the form of a 'package deal', inclusive of the building, or as specialized plant to be used within a barn. The layout required for predried or *in situ* dried grain is dissimilar.

b. Investment in drying plant became general about a decade ago, there being an increase of driers from 2000 in 1952 to 20,000 in 1962, representing, perhaps, an investment (with storage) of £80M, and it has been forecast that there will be 30,000 driers by 1970 (1). However, it has been suggested that in the past many layouts were badly planned, there being inadequate pre-cleaners, poor off-loading arrangements, limited space and restricted drying capacity (1). Recently, there have been many developments in grain driers, as reported by *Farm Mechanization* (2):

'Increased throughput is the aim with many of the latest continuous flow models, which are larger in size and make more efficient use of heat and air. Efforts are also being made to convey the exhaust air, laden with dust and moisture, away from the operating area, and to simplify the cleaning-out of driers. More multi-purpose drying units have also appeared . . . the fan and heater sections being adaptable for the ventilation of hay and potatoes and capable of delivering larger volumes of air.'

Equally important to recent improvements in the design of driers and of *in situ* drying in storage bins has been the development of the drying of grain in bulk during storage on a barn floor by means of ventilation ducts. The latter method has the advantages that it requires less capital than the provision of *in situ* drying bins and that the barn can be used for other purposes after the grain has been removed. The main disadvantage lies in handling the grain on and off the floor, but augers can be used without much labour being required. Keeping varieties of grain separate can be difficult, though large plastic sheets can be used.

c. In the past the normal method for keeping grain in condition has been to remove excess moisture in the grain, when harvested, to prescribed moisture contents, depending on the period of storage (ID 2*a*, p. 63), by blowing warm air through it. In general, higher air temperatures are used for predrying than for *in situ* drying. However, it is possible to store grain for long periods with a higher m.c. than 14 per cent, which is the normal requirement for safe storage until after April. Wet-grain storage in hermetically sealed containers has been discussed (ID 2*b*, p. 64), but it is possible, as practised on the Continent, to store wet grain in bulk, provided the grain is cooled. Though the equipment for the cold storage of grain is expensive at present, the technique may be developed in this country and become cheaper. The principles of cold storage are discussed below. It has several advantages over warm air-dried grain; in particular, bacterial activity in the grain can be controlled and insect attack checked, both of which can occur, even with good supervision, using conventional methods. Moreover, if the grain is cooled and stored at about 18 per cent m.c., it can be rolled immediately when taken from the storage for feeding to livestock, whereas warm air-dried grain, having been dried to a lower m.c., has to be moistened before rolling.

d. Though grain will normally be dried and stored on the farm where it is grown, it may be dried by a contractor or by a syndicate. In these cases bin storage will be used rather than floor storage, since the different owners will require their grain to be kept separate. Drying may be *in situ* or prior to storage. However, it is important to appreciate that, with modern installations, drying and storage needs little labour or attendance. For example, one unit for 1700 T can be managed by one man, 20 T/hr being delivered for drying during harvesting (3).

e. It is obvious from the above that the technique and equipment for drying grain has been revolutionized in recent years, and it is probable that further improvements will be made in the future. The machinery census in September 1962, based on a one-third sample, gave the statistics for the different types of drier as follows:

Platform in-sack driers	4190 (in 1961: 4140)
Tray or batch driers	2510 (in 1961: 1950)
Continuous flow driers	7260 (in 1961: 6100)
Ventilated silo, bin, etc.	5750 (in 1961: 5170)

It is possible that floor drying, either with warm or cool air, with the grain stored in bulk, will become more general for new installations on normal farms, though bin storage will remain the most practical method when several varieties of grain are held or when ease in handling the grain is of paramount importance.

2. *Managerial requirements*

a. Grain-intake for Drying

The variations in harvesting and in handling the grain from the field have been discussed, it being stressed that the vehicles should not be delayed before returning to the fields (ID 1*b*, p. 63). Unless otherwise stated, it is assumed in this section that grain is handled and dried in bulk and not in sacks, the latter being primarily suitable for farms producing less than, perhaps, 60 T p.a. of grain or seed, though even at, for example, 100 T p.a. the method can prove economic if labour is available for handling the sacks, which may be the case, especially on farms with a substantial acreage of roots in addition to corn. With all but the smallest layouts, the plant and the intake point should be designed for handling grain at rates of at least 20 T/hr, though this should be related to the maximum harvesting rate. However, the intake pit may be only sufficient in size to hold one trailer load, that is about 4 T, provided there is a high-speed elevator for removing the grain to the pre-cleaner or to a temporary holding bin. There should be sufficient pre-drying storage for about half the daily combine output. It should be possible for the grain to by-pass the cleaner and the drier from the intake pit.

b. Pre-cleaners

Though, in the future, grain may be cleaned on the combine sufficiently well for it to be ready for drying, it is usual to include a pre-cleaner between intake pit and drier, usually positioned close to the elevator from the intake pit. The cleaner should remove the worst of the dirt from the grain, but, if full cleaning is required (such as for seed), this should occur after drying. The latter may not remove the necessity for a pre-cleaner, being essential anyway for ventilated bin drying. With in-bin drying the pre-cleaner should have the same capacity as the combine, but, with a continuous or batch drier, its capacity should be rated with the drier. The cleaner must be accessible for sieves to be changed and for dirt to be removed, though most of the latter will be blown direct to the outside, as discussed below. The output of the grader is governed mainly by the screen size, the oscillation and the screen angle, but the cleaner should be mounted securely to be effective.

c. Pre- or *in situ* Drying

Drying grain prior to storage can be by a continuous or flow drier, in which the grain either moves horizontally over a bed or flows downwards in a tower, or by a batch drier, in which the grain is held in a tray or tower or small radial-flow silo until dry, when the drier is emptied for another batch to be dried. Obviously, a batch drier requires more attendance than a continuous drier, and is suitable for smaller amounts of grain or when harvesting is spread over a long period, due to there being several varieties of corn. The continuous-flow driers can handle and dry grain rapidly, due to the use of high temperatures, and can be coupled to any type of storage. However, though flexible in this respect, they can seldom dry more than 10 T/hr with a reduction of 5 per cent in m.c., though most driers are limited to under 6 T/hr. Therefore, with a high combining rate of over 20 T/hr (i.e. at least four combines and good conditions), at least two driers would be required, which is expensive compared with *in situ* drying plant, though the grain can be partially dried, being then redried overnight. Similarly, with large tonnages, there may be difficulties in a wet year (though this will slow the rate of combining), when the grain is harvested at over 24 per cent m.c., though the driers can handle very wet grain without damage. Continuous-flow drying is suitable for contract work, economic when storage already exists and applicable, particularly, when harvesting rates are relatively low, i.e. less than 6 T/hr per drier. Though the matter is not clear-cut and much depends on personal preference, flow driers are likely to be less suitable than ventilated bins on a large grain farm. They require more attendance during harvest than ventilated bins and, when bin storage is required in any case, it may be more desirable to dry the grain *in situ*. With the recent development of successful and economic bulk drying and storage, there is less justification either for continuous-flow drying or for ventilated-bin storage, especially if low capital cost is of importance.

d. Sack Drying

Sack drying, suitable for low tonnages and for seed, is a form of batch drying, the sacks being placed on a perforated bed through which warm air is forced. Each sack has to be handled from the trailer on to the drier and, after drying, from the platform or bed into the store, unless the sacks are emptied for bulk drying and handling. The justification for their use has been the low capital cost required compared with other forms of drying, but, since bulk floor drying is suitable even for small amounts of grain, there may be less demand for new platform installations in the future, except for seed drying. Sacks can be dried in a tunnel, like baled hay (IIB 3*b iii*, p. 101).

3. *Production techniques*

a. Continuous-flow Driers

The grain flows over a tray (which may be inclined) or down a tower, usually in bands $2\frac{1}{2}$–5 ft wide and up to $\frac{1}{2}$ ft thick. The m.c. is first reduced by passing heated air through the grain, after which cooler air reduces the temperature, so that the grain is safe to store, usually to not more than 5° C (10° F) above day temperatures, Some flow driers are in the form of a cylinder or drum. N.I.A.E. test reports have indicated that a good drier will remove 5 per cent m.c. at 1 T/hr using 4000 ft³ of air heated to 82°–105° C (180°–220° F). Most driers are rated between ½ and 10 T/hr when removing 5 per cent m.c. at 65° C (150° F), but manufacturer's ratings are not always obtained in practice. Oil-fired heating is considerably cheaper than electrical and less laborious than solid fuel, the latter being popular in the past. About 5–8 h.p./T rated output may be required, with a maximum capacity of 60 h.p. The driers should be fitted with accurate thermometers to prevent overheating. Automation is possible, though desirable only if one man fewer is required in attendance. Each item of the plant should cut-out the complete drier if failure should occur, with a fuel cut-out should the flame fail; and the plant should be switched into operation from a central switch control, though it should be possible to switch off from any position. The horizontal and inclined, cascade driers are more easily accessible for maintenance, some plant being suitable for grass drying. The vertical driers give less trouble from dust and fumes, save floor space, if height is available, and can discharge the grain near the intake point. They require an elevator for loading, but this can also be used to elevate the dried grain into storage.

b. Tray Driers

Tray driers for batch drying can be adapted for continuous drying by having a wet-grain pit, a wet-grain hopper above the drier and a slope of 18–20 degrees to incline the tray so that it self-empties into a dry-grain pit, both pits being emptied by an elevator. Capacities of trays usually are from 1 to 3 T with a depth of grain from 1¼ to 2½ ft, through which air about 15° C (25°–30° F) above ambient temperature is forced at a rate of 50–70 ft³/ft² of tray area against 2½–3 in. s.w.g. back pressure, requiring an electrical heater loading of 20–50 kW. Some driers operate between 9000 C.F.M. at 20° C (35° F) above ambient and 20,000 C.F.M. at 5° C (10° F). Some driers are horizontal when drying, but capable of being tipped for emptying, others are of hopper type with a 45-degree floor, but filled to a depth of 4½ ft. Drying times vary, but with a grain depth of 2 ft and an m.c. reduction from 20 to 14 per cent, drying rates may be (4):

Air flow C.F.M./ft² floor area	Drying time (hr)		
	38° C (100° F)	49° C (120° F)	60° C (140° F)
30	11	7¾	6
40	8¼	5¾	4½
50	6½	4¾	3¾
60	5½	4	3

As the depth of grain in the tray and the air flow are increased, so is the resistance of the grain. A fan has to be chosen suitable for the different resistances and air flow, as indicated in the chart below, showing resistance in in. s.w.g. (5):

Grain	Depth,	Rate of air flow C.F.M./ft² floor area			
	ft	30	40	50	60
Wheat and	1	0·8	1·1	1·5	2·0
barley	1½	1·1	1·6	2·2	3·0
	2	1·5	2·2	3·0	4·0
Oats	1	1·1	1·7	2·3	3·0
	1½	1·6	2·5	3·4	4·5
	2	2·2	3·3	4·6	6·0

c. Ventilated Silos: Floor Ventilated, in situ Drying

Bins may be cylindrical or square, but drying is a slow process, with depths generally not greater than 12 ft, though 15 ft has proved satisfactory. The top of the grain must be level. Air is blown through a mesh floor and, to dry the grain to 14 per cent m.c., the humidity of the ventilating air should not exceed 65 per cent. Therefore in most circumstances the air must be heated to reduce its humidity, and drying may be extended over two weeks without overheating or deterioration in the grain. This period may be extended if the grain is turned into another silo. Generally temperature rises of about 3°–5° C (6°–10° F) are required to reduce the humidity of the air intake with air speeds of 15–20 C.F.M./ft² floor area and up to 5–7 in. s.w.g., giving an average rate of drying of ½ per cent m.c./24 hr with grain 10 ft deep, but rates of up to 1½ per cent m.c./T/hr may be obtained, if dried in shallow layers or with bigger fans. At average rates it will take up to two weeks to dry from 21 per cent m.c. There may be a risk of deterioration in the upper layers of the grain and of overheating in the lower layers if the grain is wetter than about 21 per cent m.c. on harvesting, unless dried in shallow layers of about 3–5 ft or turned during drying. Electric-heater loadings of 3–5 kW are adequate for 15-T silos, consumption averaging about 18 units per T grain for 1 per cent m.c. removed, less being required on warm, dry days, with about 270,000 ft³ of warmed air being required to remove 1 per cent m.c./T. The fan should be a two-stage axial-flow type, with a non-overloading cut-out. For silos grouped together, the overall kW loading, with each silo of 100 ft² floor area, may increase from 21 kW for 6 silos by 6 kW per each additional pair of silos in the group. Though all the silos should be capable of ventilation, the overall fan capacity of 20 C.F.M./ft² floor area need not be capable of blowing more than two-thirds of the total storage capacity at one time. There should always be at least one extra bin in addition to those required for the maximum storage requirements, so that the grain may be turned from one bin into another.

d. Ventilated Silos: Radial-flow Ventilation

Radial-flow silos are cylindrical in shape, with perforated walls of expanded metal or of hessian on steel mesh. They are formed with an inner cylinder, which is a vertical air duct, and with the grain held between the inner and an outer cylinder. The air is forced radially from the duct through the grain. Diameters of radial-flow silos vary mainly between a duct of $1\frac{1}{2}$ ft in a bin of $7\frac{1}{2}$ ft and of 2 ft in a bin of 10 ft, though a few silos have an overall diameter of 12–15 ft. The bin heights mainly vary between 10 and 12 ft. The airpath through the grain is considerably less than with vertical, floor-ventilated silos, usually being 3–4 ft, compared with 10 ft. Therefore, lower fan pressures, which need less horse-power, can be used for the same reduction in m.c. in less time. A reduction of 1 per cent/24 hr can be obtained with an air flow of 220 C.F.M./T for a temperature rise of 5° C (10° F), consumption averaging about 14 units per T grain for 1 per cent m.c. removed. The drying rate can be raised to $1\frac{1}{2}$ per cent/24 hr by a reduction in the R.H. of the drying air to 50 per cent without undue risk of uneven drying. Usually, the air enters the vertical duct from the bottom, the top being closed by a bung. The grain should be coned at the top to maintain the same distance for the air flow at all points. Obviously, more silos, requiring a greater floor area, are required for the same tonnage compared with floor-ventilated silos. However, the silos are easy to erect and to dismount. Thus, the barn can be used for other purposes when grain is not held. Alternatively, slotted timber radial bins can be obtained with diameters up to 13 ft, with central ducts of up to $6\frac{1}{2}$ in. and with heights of 10–20 ft, holding up to 60 T for the largest size bin. High-pressure air is blown through the top of the duct from a mobile blower, which can be used for more than one bin, and which heats the air by compression, with heaters of 5–13 kW. Moisture extraction rates are greater than with low-pressure radial bins.

e. Bulk Floor Drying

Grain for bulk drying should not be more than 7 ft deep (though depths of 10 ft have proved satisfactory) and should be level at the top. Widths of about 30 ft are the most satisfactory and economic, though with a central duct 60 ft overall is possible. The building must have damp-proof floor and walls, the latter also being strong enough to take the thrust of the grain. Air is blown through a longitudinal duct, large enough to give access for a man, into small lateral ducts of up to 30 ft in length and reaching to the edges of the store. The lateral ducts should be of welded steel mesh or timber framing covered with hessian and have their ends to the longitudinal duct and to the perimeter wall blocked off for a distance of $1\frac{1}{2}$ ft, to prevent air passing through the hessian at that point. The lateral ducts should be at not more than $3\frac{1}{2}$ ft centres and have a U-shaped cross-section of $\frac{3}{4}$ ft × $\frac{3}{4}$ ft, which may be increased up to $1\frac{1}{2}$ ft × $1\frac{1}{2}$ ft for larger installations. Air flow should be about 10 C.F.M./ft² of floor area, with a maximum temperature rise of 5° C (10° F), though not all the floor need be ventilated at one time. It should be possible to close the lateral ducts from the longitudinal duct. The total air flow possible should be at least 80 C.F.M./T for about three-quarters of the total store capacity. The dimension of the lateral duct must allow the required air flow, according to the tonnage of grain ventilated from it. Thus, a 30-ft lateral duct at 3-ft centres ventilating grain to a depth of 7 ft should be able to ventilate 13 T and to carry 1040 C.F.M., with a cross-section of $\frac{2}{3}$ ft². The ducts, both longitudinal and lateral, can be below floor level. Though this allows access into the barn for a tractor and trailer, they are expensive to construct. Therefore, it is usual for the lateral ducts to be above the floor and to be constructed to be removable. The main duct may be placed in either position, depending on whether it is desirable to clear the barn floor completely for other purposes. An auger can be used for unloading the store, the lateral ducts, when exposed, being removed in turn.

f. Cool-air Drying

Wet grain can be stored in ventilated bins or in bulk on the floor, provided cool air is blown through it, the layouts being similar to warm-air drying (6), though depths of 15–20 ft have proved satisfactory. The temperature of the incoming grain is reduced quickly by about 5°–8° C (10°–15° F) to under 10° C (50° F), which neutralizes bacterial action. Within 2 weeks, the temperature is reduced to about $7\frac{1}{2}$° C (45° F), which is safe for prolonged storage, depending to some extent on the m.c., and further cold air will be blown through the grain every 4–8 weeks to keep it in condition. Safe storage temperatures for grain with various m.c. are given below:

Temperature	M.c.
5° C (41° F)	22 per cent
10° C (50° F)	18 per cent
15° C (59° F)	16 per cent

Usually, the cooled air is drier than the atmosphere, and this may reduce the m.c. of the grain by 3–4 per cent over long storage periods. If barley is stored at 18 per cent m.c. it can be rolled for livestock rations without further treatment (1c, above). The refrigeration equipment is expensive, costing perhaps £2000–£4000. However, running costs are low, about 30 C.F.M./T air flow being required during the cold-air blows, with an electrical consumption of only about 5 units/T over 3 days.

g. Sack Driers

Sacks are laid on platforms about 2 ft above the ground, forming a plenum chamber. The platform can be formed from precast concrete blocks having an opening about 2 ft × 1 ft for each sack, with a mesh to hold the sack, or from a wire mesh. Warm air is blown through the plenum to reduce the grain mc. at a rate of 0·6–0·7 per cent/hr, that is by 6–7 per cent/12 hr, so that the sacks can be dried and removed from the platform twice per day. A temperature rise of about 14° C (25° F) is required to obtain the m.c. reduction with an air flow per sack of 60 C.F.M., which requires a heater loading of $\frac{1}{2}$ kW. If the air flow is increased to 100–130 C.F.M. the m.c. reduction will be about 1 per cent/hr. Some plants will give a reduction of 3 per cent/hr.

h. Tunnel Drying

The sacks are built into a tunnel about 8 ft high, that is about 6 sacks high each side in an inverted V 2 ft wide at the bottom with 2 sacks across the top, built directly off a barn floor. One end of the tunnel is closed by sacks, the other butts against a wall with an opening about 2 ft² forming a duct to the fan. About 20–60 T can be dried at a time, possibly in several short tunnels connected to one fan duct with an opening to each tunnel. Drying rates are slow, being only about 2 per cent m.c. reduction per 24 hr, with an air flow of about 300 C.F.M./T against 1·5 in. s.w.g. and with the air heated to 5°–8° C (10°–15° F) above ambient temperature.

4. *Work routines*
a. Grain Intake

The work requirements in drying grain depend on the degree of automation provided in the layout. As previously mentioned (1d, above), one man can handle an intake rate of 20 T/hr to a total of nearly 2000 T spread over several days of harvesting. Each tanker load should be emptied directly into an intake pit with an elevator capable of removing the grain before the next load. Thus, handling the grain to the pre-cleaner and drier should be by switch control, only occasional sweeping of split grain at the pit being required. Alternatively, with floor drying, the tanker can either empty the grain directly in the barn, in which case labour is required to auger the grain to a uniform height, to assemble the lateral ducts as the barn is filled and to place barriers to separate different varieties of corn, or it can empty the grain into a

pit, from which it is elevated to a pre-cleaner and conveyed overhead into the barn. In the latter case the work requirements are similar, though the ducts can be assembled prior to harvesting. If the grain is combined into sacks the latter have to be manhandled on to a platform or to form a tunnel, unless the sacks are emptied into a pit for bulk drying and handling.

b. Pre-cleaning

Pre-cleaning is automatic, but the cleaner needs maintenance, so that cleanings can be removed and sieves changed. Some cleaners have dust-collecting socks, which have to be removed, but layouts may include for the chaff and dust to be blown to the exterior, only the heavier dirt having to be removed by hand.

c. Moisture Content

The m.c. has to be recorded both prior to and during the drying process. Meters are used for this purpose, either recording the m.c. *in situ* or of a sample of grain, the latter sometimes being ground for the purpose. The meters for *in situ* recording may be in the form of a manually placed probe or, in the case of bin drying, permanently suspended in the grain, readings being recorded on a dial or on a graph-drum (*see* 6, below). Once dried, the grain should be checked occasionally.

d. Heater and Fan

The R.H. of the drying air must be recorded, controlled and varied to suit atmospheric conditions and the m.c. of the grain. Similarly, the air flow must be controlled and varied. Usually, control is required either once or twice per day, but some equipment, permitting finer control, though automatically adjusting to variations in R.H. and temperature, needs regular supervision of the controls. Ducts may have to be opened or shut to different parts of the grain.

e. Conveying Grain

Augers, elevators and conveyors can be used for moving grain (Part 2). Sacks, generally, have to be manhandled, though inclined elevators or monorails may be used.

f. Maintenance

After grain has been removed from a drier, bin or barn, all equipment and surfaces should be cleaned and serviced.

g. Removing Grain

With bulk drying and storage on the floor, grain may be removed from the barn by an auger or tractor and scoop (ID 4b iii, p. 66). Floor-ventilated bins cannot have a self-emptying floor, though all but the last few tons can be emptied through an opening at the bottom of the bin wall, the remainder being shovelled direct on to a conveyor. Alternatively, an auger can be used, either sub-floor or inclined in the bin. Most modern batch driers are self-emptying. In some cases, after drying, grain is sacked.

5. *Design data*
a. Dimensions of Plant

Some dimensions relating to grain drying have been given under storage (ID 5, p. 66) or under the description of drying techniques (3, above). With regard to drying plant, there are so many proprietary items of equipment that it is difficult to give data concerning their dimensions. A survey published in the *Farmers Weekly* in 1962 gave dimensions and other data, including prices ex-works, of numerous proprietary continuous-flow, batch and radial driers (Ref. *d*).

b. Intake Pits

Normally, a layout will be designed so that the tanker or lorry does not drive over the pit though some layouts are designed specially so that a tractor and trailer can drive over an intake grid, but discharges directly into it from the entrance to the drying area. The pit, to hold about 4 T, should be about 200–250 ft³ in capacity, with a dwarf wall 2 ft high, including removable boards towards the entrance, and with its floor sloping a further 2 ft towards the boot of the elevator. The latter may require a further depth of 2–4 ft. There should be a level concrete area around the pit (Fig. 42). The intake area may be divided into two to allow more than one variety of grain to be held. The pit must be dry and, on wet sites, it may have

to be waterproofed, though with heavy grade plastic sheets this need not be expensive.

c. Pre-cleaners and Cleaner-graders

Pre-cleaners are relatively small pieces of equipment for small throughputs, being perhaps 4 ft × 2½ ft × 4 ft in size. However, pre-cleaners with throughputs of 20 T/hr, which are required for the maximum normal harvesting rates, and cleaner-graders, which can be used after drying to present top-class grain for sale, are considerably larger. Dimensions might be 8 ft × 5 ft × 6 ft, or even more. Usually, the cleaners will be mounted on a raised frame, perhaps 6–9 ft above the intake pit and with the grain passing through it from the elevator. Since access for maintenance is needed around the cleaner, in any large layout it will be mounted on a raised floor or cat-walk, and weights of ½–¾ T may have to be carried. A duct (about 1 ft²) may be taken from the top of the cleaner to the leeward side of the building, terminating with a grill and hood, in order to remove dust. Motors, depending on throughput, may be 1–4 h.p.

d. Continuous-flow Driers

Vertical models vary considerably in size according to make, but typical dimensions may be:

1–5 T/hr	5–10 T/hr
10 ft × 14 ft × 14 ft	21 ft × 15 ft × 22 ft
or	or
6 ft × 20 ft × 14 ft	25 ft × 10 ft × 22 ft

On smaller models, motors of about 3 h.p. for the drying unit and 3 h.p. for the main fan may be required, but these might be 30 h.p. and 15 h.p. respectively on larger models. Horizontal models can require considerable floor space. One model, in which the grain is agitated along a drying trough, can be obtained with 10-h.p. or 20-h.p. motors, with dimensions as follows:

$$2 \ \text{T/hr: } 23 \text{ ft} \times 8 \text{ ft} \times 6\tfrac{3}{4} \text{ ft}$$
$$3\tfrac{1}{2} \ \text{T/hr: } 31 \text{ ft} \times 9\tfrac{3}{4} \text{ ft} \times 7\tfrac{1}{2} \text{ ft}$$

However, one model, which can be used for drying grass as well as grain, with an output of 3 T grain/hr measures 103 ft × 7 ft × 11½ ft. Some models are inclined at about 35 degrees.

e. Batch Driers

Some models are in the form of small vertical bins and, for example, a 2-bin model, holding a total of 6 T, might measure 10 ft × 6 ft × 10 ft, plus the fan and heater, which might be 8 ft × 5 ft × 6 ft. Small tipping trays for 1–1½ T might measure 12 ft × 5½ ft × 10 ft when tipped, whereas a 2-T model might be 16½ ft × 6 ft × 7 ft.

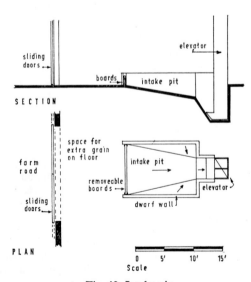

SECTION

sliding doors

boards

intake pit

elevator

PLAN

farm road

sliding doors

space for extra grain on floor

intake pit

removeable boards

dwarf wall

elevator

0   5'   10'   15'

Scale

Fig. 42. Intake pit

Application	Air flow C.F.M.	s.w.g., in.	H.p.	Type of fan
Platform	1200–1800	0·25–0·5	0·1–0·7	Propeller
	3000–6000	0·5–2·0	2–4	Axial-flow, centrifugal
Tunnel	6000–12,000	1·5–3·0	3–12	Axial flow, centrifugal
Tray	3000–6000	1·0–3·0	3–6	Axial flow, centrifugal
Ventilated silo, vertical flow	3000–10,000	4·0–8·0	5–15	2-Stage axial flow, centrifugal
Ventilated silo, radial flow	3000–12,000	1·5–4·0	1·5–13	1- or 2-stage axial flow, centrifugal

Air for the fan should be from an external intake.

Ref. (9)

f. Sack Driers

The overall size of the platform will depend on the number of sacks to be dried at one time, but a 48-sack layout might measure $22\frac{1}{4}$ ft $\times$ $11\frac{3}{4}$ ft (12 × 4 sacks), plus a fan and drier space of $7\frac{1}{2}$ ft $\times$ $11\frac{3}{4}$ ft. The overall height might be 8–12 ft, allowing for a 2-ft plenum chamber.

g. Overall Heights

In most cases the elevator will determine the overall height of the plant. With tower driers or bin storage, an overall building height around the elevator of 25–30 ft may be required, and in one package-deal drying and storage unit the top of the elevator is external to the intake and pre-cleaner unit at about 40 ft (Fig. 43). Discharge points for loading on to bulk grain tankers have been given in Fig. 43. In some layouts two elevators are required.

h. Extracted Moisture

Approximately 28 lb of water has to be extracted for a reduction of 1 per cent in the m.c. of 1 T of wet grain. To extract 8 per cent of moisture, in order to lower the m.c. from 22 to 14 per cent, means that nearly $22\frac{1}{2}$ gal of water/T dried grain must be removed, that is about $3\frac{1}{2}$ ft³. It is obvious that this moisture will condense, unless removed from the building, should the ambient temperature drop.

i. Safe Drying Temperatures

Grain is damaged by high temperatures, which, though many factors are involved, have been given as (7):

Grain and purpose	Max. temp.
Feeding grain	82° C (180° F)
Wheat for milling	66° C (150° F)
Malting barley and seed corn	
Up to 24 per cent m.c.	49° C (120° F)
Above 24 per cent m.c.	44° C (110° F)

The m.c. of the grain affects the safe drying temperature, lower temperatures being essential as the m.c. is increased, if germination of seed-grain or malting barley is not to be damaged (8):

M.c. per cent	18	20	22	24	26	28	30
Max. temp. ° C	67	61	57	53	49	46	44
° F	152	142	134	127	120	114	110

6. *Equipment*

a. Fans

Types of fan suitable for various methods of grain drying have been given in the table above (9).

b. Moisture Measurement

Samples of ground grain can be measured in a portable meter by passing a direct-current electrical potential through it. Probes, with a hair hygrometer, can be plunged into grain to measure the m.c. of grain *in situ*, but lengths are usually 40 in. Similarly, hair hygrometers or wet- and dry-bulb hygrometers can be used to measure the R.H. The former can be coupled to a hygrograph for recording the R.H. or can take readings in the ducts of driers.

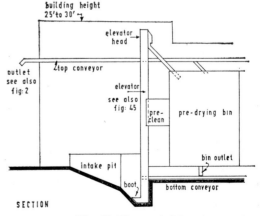

Fig. 43. Elevator height

c. Air Pressure and Air Flow

Manometers and flowmeters can be used for measuring the air pressure and flow, both of which need accurate control. About 12,000 ft³ of air at 60 per cent R.H. will evaporate 1 lb of water. Therefore, 336,000 ft³ of air are required to remove 1 per cent of the m.c./T of wet grain (5*h*, above).

d. Automation

With ventilated bin drying, much of the drying and handling of the grain can be automatic, controlled by pre-set switches and requiring no more than supervision of the control panels. Other systems of drying need greater supervision. Safety cut-offs and control switches have been referred to above. Thermostats can be used for automatic temperature control.

e. Heaters

Heaters can be electrical, based on 1 kW being capable of raising 1000 C.F.M. of air by $1\frac{2}{3}$°C (3°F), usually assembled in banks of 3 kW, so that 7 loadings can be obtained by a 21-kW heater banked at 3-, 6- and 12-kW loadings. However, all electric heating is usually economic only for small drying units. The moisture can be removed by coupling a mobile moisture extraction unit, driven by an air-cooled diesel engine with an axial-flow fan, either to the ducts for bin, tunnel or bulk drying or to the plenum chamber for sack drying. The unit is kept external to the drying building, and one proprietary unit measures about 9 ft × $5\frac{1}{2}$ ft × 6 ft. Alternatively, a direct or indirect oil-fired heater can be used. Oil consumption varies with different driers, but may be in the region of 2–3 gal/150–200 lb water removed/hr. A heater may require about 50–100 ft² of floor space, plus space for oil storage (the latter should be external to the building). Since, when the heater is maintained, there should be no soot or smoke from the heater, there should be no contamination. Therefore the heater is often adjacent to the drying plant and need not be in a separate compartment. Exhaust from the heater can be ducted to the exterior. In many small layouts, especially with batch driers, the equipment is housed within a semi-open building. Obviously, all other factors being equal, there are advantages in keeping the heater and fan away from the grain.

f. Ducts

With some ventilated bins the ducts are formed with the bins; in other cases ducts are formed with the building. Main ducts are usually formed to take a man, that is about 3 ft × 5 ft high minimum, so that the flow of air to individual silos can be controlled from the main duct. They must be watertight. Small above-ground ducts may be formed

in timber, larger ones usually being in brick. Lateral ducts for bulk drying can be obtained as proprietary units, usually about 6 ft long.

7. Environment control. Reference has been made above to certain aspects of environment control, that is, to the removal of dust and moisture. Some machines have dust control included in the equipment. But dust can be a problem with conveying equipment and at the intake and discharge areas. High-temperature grain driers can cause a nuisance from heat and dust. There should be high-level cross-ventilation with louvres, controlled with shutters, above all driers. Some driers discharge their heat and dust to the exterior through a duct, others can be controlled by means of a hood, usually with an extractor fan, but this should be designed or authorized by the manufacturer of the drier. Other environmental factors have been discussed under storage (ID 7, p. 66). The control of the temperature and humidity of the grain during drying, together with that of the air used for drying, is vital, but should be part of the drying equipment provided by a manufacturer. Automatic and manual cut-off controls are essential. Pits and ducts below ground must be watertight, and all drying equipment must be protected from the weather. Obviously, in humid weather it is less easy or cheap to dry grain with an air intake from the atmosphere than on warm, dry days. All controls and those parts of the equipment requiring supervision or maintenance should have good electric lighting, that is 15–20 lumen/ft², with a general lighting intensity throughout of 5 lumen/ft². Due to the presence of moisture and of dust, access for maintenance of the fittings is essential.

8. Layouts. The layout of the drier will depend on the method of storage (ID 8, p. 66), especially with bin or bulk drying/storage plant, when they are integral with each other. Ventilated bins with floor ventilation are usually double-banked around a central, below-floor duct, which can be used both for the air flow and for the bottom conveyor for emptying the bins. Alternatively, the air duct may be longitudinally under the centre of a row of bins,

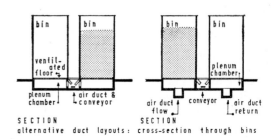

Fig. 44. Ventilated floor bins and duct positions

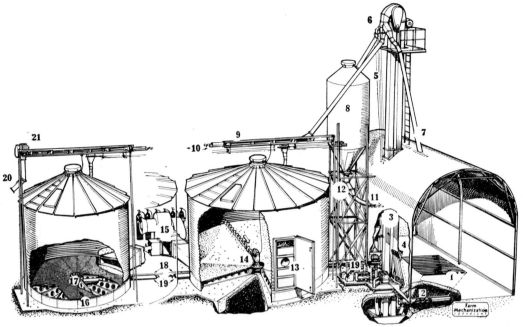

Courtesy of *Farm Mechanization*. Drawn by *C. Hurford*.

1. Intake pit.
2. Pit auger.
3. Bucket elevator.
4. Valve control levers.
5. Valve control cables.
6. Three-way outlet valve.
7. Bulk loading point (through roof).
8. Holding tank (6 T).
9. Gantry carrying electrical services, valve control cables and top auger conveyor.
10. Top auger conveyor.
11. Spout to cleaner.
12. Discharge spout from holding tank.
13. Bin door with hatch for taking samples.
14. Sweep auger for emptying bin.
15. Propane-heated dryer unit.
16. Perforated drying floor.
17. Locating pin for sweep auger.
18. Cables to bin unloading valves.
19. Bottom auger conveyor.
20. Overflow and alternative bulk loading point.
21. Top auger motor.

Fig. 45. Sketch diagram of proprietary grain drying/storage bins with bulk handling. Bins shown with 14 ft and 18 ft dia. Handling rate—20 T/hr.

the conveyor being centrally between two rows or banks of bins (Fig. 44). In such cases the bins are usually either within a barn or support their own roof. Radial-flow bins should be placed about 1 ft apart. However, with some proprietary, circular bins, each bin is self-contained with its own roof, filled from an overhead conveyor from a central intake and pre-cleaner unit and emptied by a bottom sweep-auger. These bins can have a perforated floor and can be coupled to a fan and heater unit, one unit normally drying two bins simultaneously at $\frac{1}{2}$ per cent/m.c./day (Fig. 45). Alternatively, circular drying/storage bins can be grouped in a circle, each being filled and emptied by auger from a central pit which, in turn, can be filled and emptied by bulk tanker (Fig. 46). Floor drying can take place within most dry barns, though the main duct may be below floor level. A unit for 1000 T is shown in Fig. 47. Layouts for continuous-flow or batch driers are more flexible in that they need not be coupled directly with the storage plant, though

there is usually a direct relationship between intake, elevator and pre-cleaner, drier, elevator (usually combined with intake elevator), conveyor and storage. In most layouts where an inclined, vertical or batch drier is used, an area of 400–600 ft² is adequate, with sufficient height for the drier or elevator. Horizontal-flow driers might need double the floor area, but much less height.

9. *Siting.* Siting is discussed in relation to storage (ID 9, p. 68).

10. *Services.* Reference has been made above to the need for electrical power, in some cases with very heavy loading requirements. Obviously, the electrical installation needs especial care, both with regard to damp and dust as well as to safety and maintenance. Power is required for the conveying equipment, the cleaner, the heater and fan, though the latter can be driven by a diesel engine. Oil storage, probably a 500-gal tank, will be required, if an oil-fired heater is used. Dust, heat and

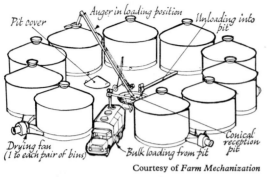

Auger in loading position
Pit cover
Unloading into pit
Drying fan (1 to each pair of bins)
Bulk loading from pit
Conical reception pit

Courtesy of *Farm Mechanization*

Fig. 46. Radial layout of drying/storage bins with bulk handling

moisture extractors are required. These can be blown automatically from the cleaner or heater to the outside air, but gable ventilation, preferably with a fan, is desirable.

11. Costs. A detailed study of the economics of grain driers and drying was made from a survey of installations in 1956, and some comparative costs are given in one of the tables below (10). However, it was pointed out that the cost/T was dependent on the throughput of the drier . . . 'thus, while the annual fixed costs of the continuous drier were four times those of the sack driers the fact they dried four times as much grain made their fixed costs almost identical'. Therefore, a comparison of costs for new installations in 1956, in relation to throughput, was also given on the basis of driers with the capital costs given below (10). Since capital and running costs can be justified

only in relation to throughput, a further table showed the minimum throughput at which it was economic to instal a plant, assuming the alternative to be a contractor drying the corn and charging £2¼/T, including transport (10):

		T p.a.
Continuous drier	2½ T/hr	155
	1 T/hr	95
Ventilated bin	200 T (electric)	50
	100 T (electric)	35
Sack drier	60 hole (oil-fired)	35
	20 hole (electric)	12

A more recent survey in 1962 gave the following analysis of costs in relation to throughput, and, by omissions, showed when the size of drier was inappropriate for a particular throughput (Ref. (d)):

Costs of drying and storing (ID 11, p. 68) have to be related to the expectation that the price/T that a farmer will obtain by selling in the spring or summer will be higher than after harvest. With regard to storage, present guarantee arrangements assure the farmer that he will receive an extra £4¼ and £5/T from storing wheat until March/April and May/June respectively, although the average market price increase is only in the order of £2½/T. The average market price increase for barley is about £2/T, although occasionally it is much higher; a subsidy differential introduced a few years ago raised this by £2¼/T for storing until 1st March onwards, assuming the market price is not affected.

Interest on stored grain (at 6 per cent for 8 months), loss of weight through additional drying

Average total costs of drying/T (Wheat: 4 per cent m.c.r.)

	Continuous driers £ s. d.	Ventilated bins £ s. d.	Sack driers £ s. d.
Fixed costs	14 6	9 0	14 4
Variable costs	6 6	8 1	8 6
Total costs	1 1 0	17 1	1 2 10
Av. throughput (T p.a.)	438	211	107

Av. throughput: T p.a.
(costing/T to nearest £¼ at 4 per cent m.c.r.)

	Capital cost	10	20	50	100	200	400
Continuous drier 2½ T/hr	£2250	30½	15¼	6¼	3¼	1¾	1
1 T/hr	£1250	17¼	8¾	3¾	2¼	1¼	¾
Ventilated bin for 200 T (electric)	£675	9½	5	2¼	1¼	¾	—
100 T (electric)	£475	6¾	3¾	1¾	1	—	—
Sack drier for 60 hole (oil)	£500	7	3½	1¾	1	¾	—
20 hole (electric)	£150	2¾	1¾	1	—	—	—

Type and size of drier	Capital cost £	Depreciation and interest p.a. £	Total cost to nearest £¼/T (6 per cent m.c.r.)				
			Av. throughput/T p.a.				
			20	50	100	200	400
Continuous driers							
1–1½ T/hr	1250	170	—	4	2¼	1½	—
1½–2 T/hr	1750	240	—	—	2¾	1¾	1
2½–3 T/hr	2500	340	—	—	3¾	2¼	1¼
Ventilated bins *							
100 T (electric)	500	70	4¼	2	1¼	—	—
200 T (electric)	750	100	—	2½	1¾	1	—
Tray driers							
1–1½ T (electric)	400	55	3¾	2	1½	—	—
3–5 T (oil)	750	100	—	2½	1½	1	—
Sack driers							
20 hole (electric)	150	20	2¾	1¼	—	—	—
60 hole (oil)	500	70	—	1¾	1	¾	—

* Costs of bins not included (Average cost bin storage: £18/T). These costs can be compared with a contractor's charge (including transport one way) of £2¼/T approximate.

and the cost of additional drying and handling can amount together to £1½–£1¾/T. Depreciation and interest on the plant (with a capital cost after grant of £10/T) can amount to £1½/T. The extent of these costs is one reason why bulk storage on a barn floor has received considerable attention. Thus, the costs for various driers and storage might be (Ref. (*e*)):

Ventilated bin for 100–200 T p.a.: Cost £15–£25/T plus £¼–£½ T p.a. for power and fuel.

Sack drier for 100 T p.a.: Cost £3–£5/T plus £¼–£½ T p.a. for oil.

On average, bin storage, after grants, will cost £10–£15/T storage space.

A ventilated floor store in a general-purpose building for 400 T might cost £9–£10/T storage space, or a continuous drier with floor storage £12–£13/T storage space with similar running costs. Thus, one 120-ft × 60-ft × 14-ft to eaves framed building, (11) (Fig. 47) capable of drying and storing 100 T, based on Ministry of Agriculture standard costs, might cost only about £4½/T storage space for the building, plus about £1½/T for the ducts, fan, heater, etc., but usually costs of up to £10/T storage space are more realistic.

12. *References*

(1) CLARK, R. G. 'Trends in grain drying and storage techniques'. *Scottish Institute of Agriculture Engineers. Report April 1963.*
(2) 'Grain drying and storage'. *Farm Mechanization*, p. 17 (January 1963).
(3) JONES, P. 'One man grain outfit handles 1700 tons'. *Farmers Weekly*, p. 41 (23rd November 1962).
(4) Ref. (*d*), p. 57.
(5) Ref. (*a*), p. 41.
(6) LEONARD, D. 'Cool grain store'. *Farmers Weekly*, pp. 68–9 (16th August 1963).
(7) Ref. (*a*), p. 20.
(8) Ref. (*a*), p. 22.
(9) Ref. (*b*), p. 121.
(10) Ref. (*c*), Ch. V.
(11) HOPE, H. 'Simple system dries grain cheaply'. *Farmers Weekly*, p. 111 (1st March 1963).

SELECTED REFERENCES
a. 'Farm grain drying and storage'. *Ministry of Agriculture Bulletin No. 149.* 1959.
b. ROWLAND, F. E. *Electricity in modern farming.* Ch. 7. *Land Books* (1963).
c. 'Drying and storing grain on the farm'. *Farm Economics Branch*, School of Agriculture, Cambridge University (1956).

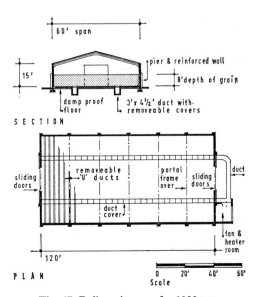

Fig. 47. Bulk grain store for 1000 tons

d. 'Grain drying and storage'. *Farmers Weekly*, pp. 53–76 (28th December 1962).

e. 'Building for grain'. *Report of Farm Buildings Conference. Farmers Weekly*, pp. 84–6 (12th October 1962).

f. *A Bibliography of Farm Buildings Research 1945–1958* Pt. V. 'Buildings for the drying and storage of grain'. Agricultural Research Council (1961): also 1958–61 (1964).

g. *Farm Electrification Handbook No. 5. Grain Drying.* Electrical Development Association (1961).

h. *Top Quality Grain.* R. A. Lister & Co. Ltd. (1962).

IIE. Milling and Mixing

1. *Activity*

a. Grain has to be processed and usually, in addition, mixed with certain additives, before it is suitable as a ration for livestock. Milling and mixing can be carried out by merchants, 8M T of compounded foods being prepared annually (IE 3). If a farmer purchases his fodder it need only be stored on the farm, without further processing, prior to its conversion into flesh or dairy produce (IE). However, approximately one-third (principally barley and oats) of the 9–10M T of cereal grown in this country (ID 1, p. 63) is processed on the farm for the same purpose, milling and mixing taking place at some point between the grain store (ID) and any of the livestock production units (Section III). Sometimes grain is grown, dried, stored, processed and converted all on one farm, or perhaps under a centralized management for a group of farms. This kind of integration in the production of food can lead to considerable economy. Alternatively, grain can be bought, either at harvest or after drying, in order to be processed on a farm prior to its being fed to livestock.

b. It is not the intention, in this section, to examine the efficiency of the many types of milling and mixing machinery available, since this has been done in various standard works in some detail (Refs. (*a*) and (*b*)). Farm processing of grain into fodder must be designed to produce a ration of equal standard to that which can be bought, and the correct milling, mixing and balancing of rations for livestock is of paramount importance. This is not considered here, information being available in several publications, including the Ministry's standard bulletin (Ref. (*c*)). An automatic unit should leave little to the diligence of the operator, except the setting of the controls and the maintenance of the plant. In a complex layout the machinery should, in any case, be serviced by a mechanic. In some semi-automatic units, perhaps excluding an automatic weigher, the stockman may be responsible for the production of the correct mix.

c. It is generally acknowledged that the purchase, maintenance and running of a mill–mix unit is not justified for a throughput of less than about 60 T of food a year, even when grain is grown on a farm. Thus, any farmer requiring less than 1 T/week should buy the food from a merchant. Small mill–mix units, including bulk handling methods, specially designed for farm use, with throughputs of perhaps 250–500 T p.a. have been claimed to save a farmer £3–£5/T compared with the purchase of merchants' compounds. Merchants tend to believe that farm processing of small amounts of grain is inefficient and that large centralized compounding plant gives better results.

d. Since, with electrical power, processing can be automatic and, in large units, almost automated, with time switches for starting and stopping, labour requirements can be almost non-existent. The processing of grain into fodder can therefore be included within intensive livestock production units without making demands on the stockman's time. But processing can be time-consuming if the plant layout is inefficient or if the grain and meal have to be handled in sacks rather than in bulk.

e. Some large livestock production units, which usually include pigmeat as a principal enterprise, may have a mill–mix unit with a throughput as high as 50–75 T/week, in which case the machinery used may be based on small provender-mill plant rather than on normal farm machinery. This could require, and justify, one full-time operator.

f. The compound meal can be fed manually or mechanically to livestock. Alternatively, the meal can be pelleted or cubed prior to feeding. This is an additional process which may both save wastage of food and give better conversion ratios. In some cases the meal may be added to bulk fodders prior to feeding. Generally, processed grain will have to be stored temporarily prior to feeding.

g. Most compounds include a proportion of minerals, antibiotics and other substances, totalling possibly 15 per cent of the mix. These constituents are expensive and may include many ingredients required in very small amounts. Accuracy is important to obtain a balanced mix and great attention to detail is essential in weighing each constituent before mixing. Alternatively, the ingredients can be purchased pre-mixed, ready to be added and mixed with the main cereals. This policy eases the difficulties of the farm operative, but to some extent reduces the financial advantage of mixing on the farm.

2. Managerial requirements

a. Power for Plant

Like most barn machines, mill–mix plant can be powered by a tractor or by a petrol engine housed in a separate shed away from the fodder. However, electrical power is now available on most farms and it is to be assumed, in this section, that electricity will be used. Similarly, it will be assumed that mechanical handling generally is available both for the grain and for the ensuing fodder, even though sacks are used on many farms, especially those having small fodder requirements. The financial advantage of farm milling and mixing can be dissipated by double-handling and the operation should be mechanized as much as possible.

b. Cubing and Pelleting

Until recently, cubing was not considered to be economic on a farm, since the machines available were large and expensive. However, several small cubers are marketed today. Meal can be wasteful in use, since it is liable both to be blown away and to be dropped and trodden underfoot by livestock. Moreover, cubes can be mechanically handled more easily and can also be eaten more quickly by cattle than meal, a factor which can be important when feeding in a parlour (IIF 2b, p. 135). Similarly, with floor feeding in pig production, cubes are desirable, in order to save waste (IIIE 3d, p. 208). Cubes may improve the food conversion rate in fattening. Recently, Laird and Robertson have shown, at the West of Scotland Agricultural College, that baconers fed with cubes increased their daily liveweight gain by 7 per cent and their food conversion ratio by 5 per cent, the latter being approximately equal to 0·2 in the conversion rate. This has been expressed as (1):

Improvement in food conversion rate/ baconer	0·2
Food saved/baconer	$\frac{1}{4}$ cwt
Food saved/T consumed	1 cwt
Financial saving/T consumed at £30/T	£1$\frac{1}{2}$
Cost of cubing/T	£$\frac{1}{4}$
Net saving by cubing/T	£1$\frac{1}{4}$

It is undesirable to pellet meal for barley-fed beef fattening, since rolled barley should be used.

c. Accuracy Required

Grain is milled to improve its digestibility. But the texture and size of the milled particle required will vary with the type and age of livestock to which it is fed. Generally, this can be summarized:

Mixing is required to obtain a uniform and blended consistency, to ensure that each animal receives an accurate ration of each constituent. Mixing improves palatability. However, it has been considered that an inaccuracy of up to 10 per cent in the mix could be acceptable for cows, but ±1 per cent should be the aim for pigs and poultry (2). A perfect mix is unobtainable.

d. Moisture Content

Though grain with any level of m.c. can be milled, the accepted limits at rated throughputs and for safe storage of the meal are (2):

Hammer milling	16 per cent
Roller crushing	17 per cent

Particular attention must be given to the m.c. of barley fed for fattening beef, 17–18 per cent being the optimum for rolling. At an m.c. of 14 per cent, rolling is impractical for this purpose. However, barley stored at 24 per cent m.c., in hermetically sealed towers, can be used, but should not be stored for long after being rolled. A pelleter used in the United States for whole grain operates with the latter at 16–18 per cent m.c., though 12 per cent is possible. A little over 2$\frac{1}{2}$ gal of water has to be added to each ton of barley to raise the m.c. by 1 per cent, or 8$\frac{1}{4}$ gal/T from 15 to 18 per cent m.c., and this should be done 24–36 hr prior to rolling, but not in the storage bin, due to the swelling of the grain. Water can be added into an open conveyor by a spray.

3. Production techniques

a. Sequence of Operations

The sequence of operations can be varied, but may be based on the following (3):

  i. Whole grain stored in bulk, in bins or on floor.

  ii. Conveyed mechanically into hopper over mill. (Direct feed from store into mill is possible, the mill automatically being switched off from the mixer after sufficient meal has been prepared—but this system is seldom used.) In order to avoid blockages in the mill, clean grain with a low moisture content should be used, and there should be a wire $\frac{3}{4}$-in. mesh screen over the hopper. Alternatively, the grain can be fed to the mill over a sieve shaker with a magnetic trap. The hopper can be graduated, preferably if it is tall and narrow, and possibly with a transparent graduation strip. But volume measurements cannot be

Class of stock	Meal	Mill	Screen
Young pigs and poultry	Fine	Hammer	$\frac{1}{16}$ in.
Adult pigs and poultry	Medium	Hammer	$\frac{1}{8}$ in.
Calves and most cattle	Coarse	Roller	—
Cows (usually for cubes)	Coarse	Hammer	$\frac{1}{4}$ in.
Stores and sheep (sometimes)	Very coarse	Plate	$\frac{1}{2}$ in.
Sheep (sometimes)	Coarse	Roller	—

very accurate, due to variations in the grain, though they may be adequate, since it is the weight of the meal prior to mixing which is more important. If more than one grain is to be milled they should be pre-mixed or, if stored in separate bins, the latter should have chutes with graduated openings feeding the mill hopper simultaneously or, if milled consecutively, the mill should have a load-control device.

iii. The milling chamber is filled by suction, with either a vertical, horizontal or upward feed, but the rate of flow must be controlled for the motor to run at full capacity.

iv. Hammer-mills include a fan, or one can be coupled to a roller mill, which conveys the meal from the mill into a store, through ducting $1\frac{1}{2}$–3 in. in diameter. The store is usually a bin, with a balloon top acting as a fabric filter, allowing air to escape with the minimum of dust, 40 ft² being recommended for 3-h.p. mills, and 80 ft² for 5-h.p. The mill must have an automatic control to shut off the motor when grinding is complete.

v. The store, to which the meal is blown, can be the mixer, the latter being capable of taking all the ingredients required for one mix. The balancing ration, or straights, which have to be added to the cereal, may be stored in sacks, usually amounting to 10–30 per cent of the total ration. The sacks can be weighed, if required, and manually emptied into the mixer. Alternatively, the balancers can be stored in bulk, being metered or batch weighed into the mixer. However, if the meal has to be weighed prior to mixing, then a temporary storage bin will be required, so that the meal can be batch weighed before being released into the mixer.

vi. After mixing, meal can be elevated into a weighing bin and this may be a better time for weighing than before mixing (provided the weight of the balancers is known). Weighing at this stage can act as a final check or for rationing out to individual livestock units, pens or animals.

vii. Alternatively, after mixing the meal may be elevated into a hopper above a cuber or may be fed direct into the cuber, though the latter may not prove to be economical. Molasses may be added prior to cubing. After cubing, weighing may be required.

viii. The meal or cubes may be stored temporarily before use, usually in a self-feed hopper, or they may be bagged-off or emptied into a barrow directly from the machine, or they can be mechanically conveyed or blown to the point of use.

b. Separate or Combined Machines

Though separate machines are available for milling, mixing and cubing, hammer mills and mixers are usually combined, being cheaper and more compact than separate machines and having special equipment for the handling of grain and meal and for the control of dust. Some large combined machines can proportion and mix automatically up to four types of grain or ingredients. Similarly, large plant is available which will mill, mix and cube a ration automatically. Another unit will either mill or crush grain, mix the meal, store it and deliver it on to a feed auger for cattle, so that a pre-mixed and balanced ration can be prepared and fed by a switch control.

c. Throughputs

Many different throughputs can be obtained by selecting from the vast range of machines available for farmers. A high throughput/hr is not necessary, unless a tractor is used for power or if the plant requires supervision. Generally, the plant may be operated five days per week by the stockman, but it should be able to provide sufficient food during that time for the two days when the stockman is absent. With a fully automatic unit, it can be operated during the off-peak electrical rates. The plant should be able to keep its throughput constant during the hours of use, having an automatic cut-off. A mill is seldom accurate for a throughput of less than $\frac{1}{2}$ cwt/hr, but small provender plant may handle 2 T/hr or even 4 T/hr for coarse grinding. Obviously, throughput depends not only on the motor but on the fineness of meal required. Hammermills require about 1 h.p. for each cwt/hr of capacity. Outputs of mixers depend not only on their holding capacity and power but on the accuracy of mix required. But, a 1-T mixer might need 10–15 min, plus about 10 min each for filling and emptying. A small cuber or pelleter might handle up to $\frac{1}{4}$ T/hr.

Approximate output for different hammermills (4), and performance data for efficient operation of mixers (5), have been given as shown in the tables opposite.

d. Horizontal or Vertical Plant

There is some confusion as to whether grain should be processed by a series of vertical lifts, followed by gravity feeding into the processing plant, or by an horizontal operation. In a multi-floored building it would seem desirable to lift the grain once to a storage point on the top floor, from whence it could descend by gravity into a mill, then into a mixer, then into a weigher, then into a cuber, a total of five levels being required. Few multi-floored buildings exist which could be converted for this purpose, and a new building of this kind would be too expensive. However, it would

Mill h.p.	Wheat	Maize	Beans	Output in cwt/hr Barley			Oats		
	C	M	F	C	M	F	C	M	F
¾–1	1·3	0·9	0·8	1·0	0·5	0·4	0·8	0·5	0·4
1½	2·2	1·5	1·0	1·8	1·5	0·8	1·5	1·0	0·5
3	5·0	3·5	2·2	5·0	2·5	1·5	4·5	2·0	1·0
5	6·0	4·0	3·0	6·0	3·5	2·2	6·0	3·2	1·5
10	12·0	8·0	5·0	12·0	7·0	4·0	12·0	6·5	3·0

C. F. M.: Coarse-, medium- and fine-ground meal

Mixer capacity	Motor h.p.	Maximum time required in min			Total time min
		filling	mixing	emptying	
5 cwt	2–3	2–2½	5	2½	9½–10
10 cwt	3–4	4–5	5–10	5	14–20
20 cwt	4–5	8–10	10–15	10	28–35

be possible to construct steel caging with catwalks, within an existing barn about 30 ft high, although the mill vibration must be considered. Alternatively, it would seem desirable to process the grain horizontally on a conveyor-belt principle, but no plant of this kind is available. As it is, some two-storied buildings can be converted economically, so that the upper floor is used for storing the grain and meal, the lower floor being used for the processing operations, with the mill, mixer and cuber being gravity fed from the upper floor, the feed being returned to the upper floor after each operation. Otherwise, storage hoppers are required, taking the place of the upper floor. Considerable power is required in handling the grain and meal in this manner; though, at present, this method is accepted practice.

4. Work routines

a. Food preparation for livestock may be carried out once a week or every day. Generally, it may be considered undesirable to keep ground cereals for longer than a week and, if the moisture content is above the normal minimum level for storage, for perhaps only a day or two. Much will depend on the size of livestock unit for which the meal is required and on the degree of automation employed. Layouts requiring both manual handling of the materials and super-

vision during processing may be treated as wet-day operations. But manual labour in food preparation is not desirable, not only because of the physical strain incurred in handling sacks of grain and meal but because it would be unproductive labour better employed in increasing the throughput of the production units. If 2 hr of labour are wasted in food preparation each week this would be worth saving with a capital investment in mechanical-handling equipment of up to about £300, even allowing for running costs, provided the labour could be employed for productive purposes.

b. The table below gives the number of hours required to grind 1 T of grain in a hammermill. For example, feed preparation for 800 baconers (IIIE 8c) might be based on a ration including 1¼ T of barley/day. If a 5-h.p. mill was used to obtain a medium meal, then about 7 hr/day would be required, plus mixing and possibly cubing. The operation could be carried out in the working day or, conversely, with automatic controls during the cheap electrical rates at night.

Some automatic plant can be set to prepare food for different livestock without attention. For example, one machine can select from four ingredients, a dial being set for particular rations, the measuring, milling and mixing being

Mill h.p.	Wheat	Maize	Beans	Time in hr/T Barley			Oats		
	C	M	F	C	M	F	C	M	F
¾–1	15·6	22·4	24·8	20·0	40·0	50·0	25·2	40·0	50·0
1½	9·2	13·2	20·0	11·2	13·2	25·2	13·2	20·0	40·0
3	4·0	5·6	9·2	4·0	8·0	13·2	4·4	10·0	20·0
5	3·2	4·8	6·8	3·2	5·6	9·2	3·2	6·4	13·2
10	1·6	2·4	4·0	1·6	2·8	5·2	1·6	3·2	6·8

C. M. F.: Coarse-, medium- and fine-ground meal

continuous and automatic, perhaps supplying weaners, finishers and a milking parlour. Therefore, one plant can be used for several livestock units, provided the machinery is powered for the operation.

5. *Design data*

a. Densities for meal and grain have been given:

Grain	Part 2, Ch. IB, p. 34
Meal	Part 2, Ch. IB, p. 34

b. The sizes of machinery available vary considerably between different manufacturers or for different capacities. A few examples can be given of typical plant dimensions:

  i. *Hammermills (up to 6 h.p.).* Generally small machines of about 4–8 ft², (perhaps, $2\frac{1}{2}$ ft × $2\frac{1}{2}$ ft, or 5 ft × $1\frac{3}{4}$ ft), weighing about $1\frac{1}{2}$–3 cwt when empty, and between $1\frac{1}{2}$ and 5 ft high, filled from the top, in which the meal is blown by the fan for normal distances between 20 and 60 ft. Some mills include an overhead hopper, and may be 7–10 ft high, weighing 5–$7\frac{1}{2}$ cwt, and others can have a hopper at floor level for side delivery into the mill, being, perhaps, 4 ft × 5 ft × 4 ft.

  ii. *Hammermills (6–20 h.p.).* About 10–25 ft², (perhaps, 2 ft × $5\frac{1}{2}$ ft, or $5\frac{1}{2}$ ft × $4\frac{1}{2}$ ft), weighing $2\frac{1}{2}$–$5\frac{1}{2}$ cwt when empty, and between 2 and 10 ft in ht, the taller mills including a collector or cyclone and sometimes a hopper holding $\frac{1}{4}$–$1\frac{1}{2}$ T.

  iii. *Hammermills (above 20 h.p.; max. 60 h.p.).* About 10–60 ft², (perhaps, $3\frac{1}{2}$ ft × 3 ft, or 7 ft × 8 ft), weighing 3–15 cwt when empty, and between 3 and 15 ft in ht, the taller mills including a collector or cyclone.

  iv. *Grinding and Crushing Mills ($1\frac{1}{2}$–60 h.p.).* About 8–20 ft², weighing 4–25 cwt, and between 3 and $5\frac{1}{2}$ ft in ht. Generally, filled from top and emptied near ground.

  v. *Mixers (horizontal: $7\frac{1}{2}$–30 h.p.).* About 20–90 ft², with lengths between 7–17 ft, weighing $1\frac{1}{2}$–5 T when empty, and between 5 and 9 ft in ht, allowing for batch mixing.

  vi. *Vertical Mixers (bottom filling and bottom emptying: 1–6 h.p.).* About 15–50 ft², weighing 6–20 cwt, and between 6 and 12 ft in ht, though some models can have about 3 ft below ground, and holding between $\frac{1}{4}$ and 1 T, filling and emptying being $2\frac{1}{2}$–3 ft from floor.

  vii. *Vertical Mixers (top filling, and bottom emptying: 2–15 h.p.).* Generally cylindrical, with dia. 3–7 ft, and 7–20 ft in ht, holding between $\frac{1}{4}$ and 4 T.

  viii. *Combined Mill and Mixer (up to 6 h.p.).* Generally include hopper and mill and a cylindrical mixer, supported on a steel frame, about 25–50 ft² (perhaps, 8 ft × 4 ft, or 9 ft × 5 ft), weighing $\frac{1}{2}$–$2\frac{1}{2}$ T when empty, and holding $\frac{1}{2}$–1 T.

  ix. *Cubers and Pelleters (up to 6 h.p.).* Generally, small machines, perhaps 2 ft × 4 ft × 2 ft, or 4 ft × 3 ft × 6 ft, the latter including a filling hopper.

c. Vibration

Plant, particularly mills, vibrate during operation. Therefore, plant should be mounted on a firm base, many mills having to be bolted on to a concrete floor. For this reason it may be impractical to have the mill anywhere except on the ground floor, and the idea of a vertical flow (3d, above) might have to be abandoned.

d. Dust

Processing grain will produce dust, open mills being particularly troublesome, though if the meal is blown into a storage bin this can be fitted with a fabric lid on the basis of a minimum 10 ft²/h.p. (or as above, 3a, iv). A cyclone is essential for the larger mills. Some combined mill-mixers are fitted both with a cyclone and dust filter bags.

e. Meal

The angle of flow in handling meal by gravity, with the problem of doming and funnelling, must be considered, particularly when sacking-off from a meal bin (Pt 2, Ch. 3A, p. 39).

6. *Equipment.* This section is entirely about equipment. However, some comment is required concerning the use for the different machines.

a. Hammermills

A number of steel hammers rotate at high speed, pulverizing the grain being fed into the mill; and the size of meal particle produced is controlled by a perforated screen adjacent to the hammers, with the holes usually graded between $\frac{1}{16}$ and $\frac{1}{4}$ in.

b. Rollermills

Two steel rollers crush or bruise the grain passing through the mill, making the grain digestible for cattle or sheep. Power requirements for crushing are low and the operation can be automatic.

c. Platemills

Useful for coarse grinding or kibbling grain, being cheap and efficient on small farms, the grain passing between steel plates with corrugations.

d. Root Cutters

Small machines are available which will cut or chop roots, being perhaps 8 ft × 3 ft × 5 ft and having low throughputs. However, though these machines are not used for intensive livestock units, other

37: COLLECTING YARD

Mr. J. S. Latham, Flash Farm, Newark, Notts.

The benefit of a covered collecting yard, as seen on the right, is that the cows enter the parlour warm and relaxed even in winter. However, they generate heat and humidity, and therefore ventilation is essential. In this case, the yard is open to the south and there are removable panels to the north. A 4-in. pipe is visible which is used to flush out the yard with water. Beyond the parlour is a double door to a feed room. Concentrates are delivered in bulk, being tipped into a pit and being augered into a high-level store which fills two mobile feed hoppers. Beyond, on the left, is the motor room, dairy and shippon with the parlour, out of sight, to the right. Above the collecting yard, the top of the silobarn can be seen. [SEE PAGE 143] See also Photo 42. Courtesy of the Council of Industrial Design.

38: PORTABLE BAIL

Not all farm buildings are fixtures. Even a modern milking parlour, as a bail, can be portable: some include a food store and dairy. This two-level bail is a 5-unit/10-stall herringbone with slatted timber cow entrance ramps and a milk pipeline mounted for demonstration. Bails make it possible to have a flexible management policy, being used in the fields during summer and, if necessary, within the farmstead in the winter. [SEE PAGE 143] Courtesy of Hosier Equipment Ltd.

39: TANDEM MILKING PARLOUR

Icombe Proper Estates, Stow-on-the-Wold, Glos.

A 6-stall/6-unit tandem parlour is satisfactory for large commercial herds, though it is generally a 2-man parlour. The herd, seen beyond the glazed door in the collecting yard, enter the parlour through sliding doors, the gear to which is set at an angle on the end wall, the cowman pulling a cord to let a cow in and, on releasing it, the door slides shut. The cows stand in tubular framed stalls: ratchet arms above their backs can be operated by the cowman from the pit to let the cows in and out of each stall from the walk-through passages. Milk is extracted from the cows into recording jars on the stalls above which are recording dials. In the centre of the pit is a stand where the cowman records the yields. Since this is a 2-man unit, the pit is wide. The milk is lifted by vacuum from the jars via the glass pipeline to the dairy. Under the milk line is the vacuum pipeline. Feed is placed in the mangers, by turning a ratchet, from the shaft, which is filled from a feed loft above the parlour. Water for washing the cows is available at each stall. Walls and ceiling are impervious for ease in cleaning, and fluorescent lighting is essential. [SEE PAGE 142] Courtesy of Farmer and Stockbreeder.

40: HERRINGBONE PARLOUR

Various types of herringbone parlour are available, largely depending on differences in fittings between manufacturers. The design of the rump bar and mangers shown conform to recommendations made in 1963 by the Ministry of Agriculture. There is a grilled drainage channel against the kerb to the pit. The pit is narrow, since the milk jars are above the cowman's head. Pull cords are used to turn the ratchet releasing concentrates into the mangers. The concentrate holders and mangers are wall mounted. The rump bar, jars and milking equipment are floor mounted, supports being taken into the kerb. At the far end is a blackboard for records. The wall surfaces are impervious. There are no windows and artificial fluorescent lighting is used. [SEE PAGE 142] Courtesy of Gascoignes (Reading) Ltd.

41 : BULK MILK STORAGE
Mr. E. Moffitt, Peepy Farm, Northumberland

A wide range of bulk storage tanks of different size and design are available from several manufacturers. All tanks must conform to certain prescribed standards. The tank shown with a stainless-steel exterior will hold 500 gal. Milk is piped from the parlour to a vacuum releaser above the tank. Access around the tank for cleaning its interior is desirable. In this case the dairy is 18 ft × 18 ft in area, which, being a conversion, gives more space than necessary. A granolithic floor has been used for easy maintenance, and this can be laid to a fall, since the legs of the tank are adjustable for calibration. Similarly, the walls have an impervious dado for cleanliness. Also installed in the dairy is a trough and tank, holding a cleansing fuid, which can be filled and coupled to the milk pipeline on the wall above for recirculation cleaning under pressure. The clusters can be cleaned in the trough, being coupled to the piping. Fluorescent lighting is desirable. [SEE PAGE 143] Courtesy of the Farmers Weekly.

42 : PARLOUR UNIT
Mr. J. S. Latham, Flash Farm, Newark, Notts.

A parlour unit can be a complex of specialized rooms. In this case, viewed from the S.W., high-level clerestory windows light and ventilate under an insulated roof a 16-stall/8-unit herringbone parlour. In the foreground, below the clerestory windows, is a 6-standing shippon which can be used as a shedding box from the parlour. At the near end of the building is a door to the shippon and, beyond it, the two exit doors from the parlour by which the cows return to their yards. At the side of the building is a double sliding door to the dairy, which includes a bulk tank. Within the higher part of the building is a dairy work space and office window, the motor-room, with a ventilation grille to the condenser and a box housing an emergency coupling shaft for a PTO drive to the motors, and a feed room. Behind this area, in line with the parlour, is a pre-feed area linked to a covered collecting yard open to the south and visible at the right. In the left background is a 40-ft-span silobarn with a 30-ft-span covered yard lean-to. Between the silo and the parlour unit is an open exercise yard. [SEE PAGE 146] See also Photo 37. Courtesy of the Council of Industrial Design.

43: LAYOUT FOR SHEEP HANDLING AND DIPPING

Mr. J. W. Mason, Howgill, Westmorland

In this simple layout one man can handle 200 ewes. On the left is a 5-ft-wide handling pen against a barn wall and on the right a hogg house. In the foreground is a circular catching pen with two 6½-ft-long gates hung from a central post. Sheep can be directed into or out of the catching pen either via the handling pen or via a 17-in.-wide race on the right which connects with the hogg house, or, alternatively, with two draining pens at the far end of the layout. For dipping, they can pass from the catching pen through a 2-ft-wide tub in the centre of the layout into the draining pens. Walls are of concrete block 4 ft high, except for the 3-ft-high wall to the race. The layout requires a total space of only 40 ft × 18 ft. [SEE PAGE 154] Courtesy of the Farmers Weekly.

44: SHEARING SHED

Capt. G. Bennett-Evans, Plynlimon, Wales

Much shearing is done by hand, though electric shearers are becoming more widely used for large flocks. Shearing can be done in the open or in rough shelters. Sheds, usually, when available for shearing are of simple construction. The steel barn, in this case, houses the holding pens, catching pens and shearing board. The sheep are divided into three holding groups, each leading via a guillotine gate into a pair of catching pens. The floors are slatted. The sheep are caught ready for the line of shearers around the catching pens. The shearing-floor area is close boarded and smooth. After being shorn, the sheep are sent out through a pop-hole in the external wall between each pair of shearers to a counting-out pen. [SEE PAGE 154] Courtesy of Farmer and Stock-breeder.

forms of cutter are available. It is possible, for example, to have storage hoppers for potatoes or other roots, raised on legs above a side-unloading trailer and with an electrically powered chopper at the base of the hoppers. If a potato elevator is used to fill the hoppers the latter can be quite small, but can maintain a high throughput.

e. Horizontal Mixers

These can be used either for wet or dry fodder, but they cost about twice as much as vertical mixers for the same output, though they require much less headroom.

f. Vertical Mixers

Generally used for all modern dry mixing, frequently in conjunction with a hammermill. For example, some units may have a 3-h.p. mill combined with a 10-cwt vertical 3-h.p. mixer, or a 5-h.p. mill with a 1-T 4-h.p. mixer. The gross capacity of the mixer cannot be utilized, about 10 per cent being required for movement in the mix. Two main types of mixer are available, those that are filled at the top and emptied at the bottom, and those that are both filled and emptied from the bottom.

g. Mobile Mill-mixers

A few mobile mill-mixing machines are available, either for meal delivered by a merchant or for internal farm use. A hammermill with a 2-T mixer, complete with a swinging auger for discharging the meal into troughs, might cost £800–£1000, being mounted on a wheeled platform.

7. *Environment control.* The need for controlled dust extraction has been stated and some methods may include air-release socks. In addition, automatic cut-off controls and good electric lighting are essential, together with clear labelling of all controls and protection of working parts. An illumination of 15 lumens/ft² on the working parts and controls is desirable.

8. *Layouts.* The layout of processing plant has to be related to the storage of grain and to the production buildings for which the meal is required. The flow-line of grain and meal should be kept to the minimum, though, if required, conveyors of several hundred feet can be used or, alternatively, the meal may be taken from the mixer to the livestock by a trailer. The layout of the plant itself, in most cases, is simple, requiring perhaps a minimum of 100 ft² or a maximum of 500 ft², though provender mills for large livestock units may require considerable space.

  i. Fig. 48 shows a layout suitable, perhaps, for a throughput of 5–10 T/week.

  ii. Fig. 49 shows a layout for milling and adding

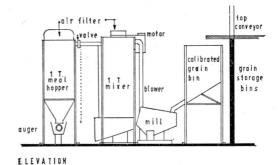

ELEVATION

PLAN   0   5'   10'   15'
Approximate Scale

Fig. 48. Mill/mix unit for 250–500 T.p.a.

meal with concentrates to a chopped-root bulk food.

  iii. Fig. 50 shows a layout for processing set between grain storage bins for high throughputs of meal. The bins empty various types of grain through a meter, set at a predetermined flow by a graduated metal slide, on to a chain and flight conveyor (the latter operating the meters from the top chain). Over the conveyors, at one end

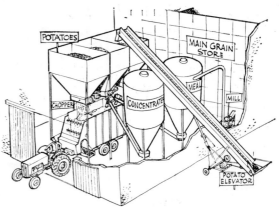

Courtesy of *Farm Mechanization*

Fig. 49. Bulk food storage of meal, concentrates and roots with chopper for large beef unit. Court Lodge, Appledore, Kent.

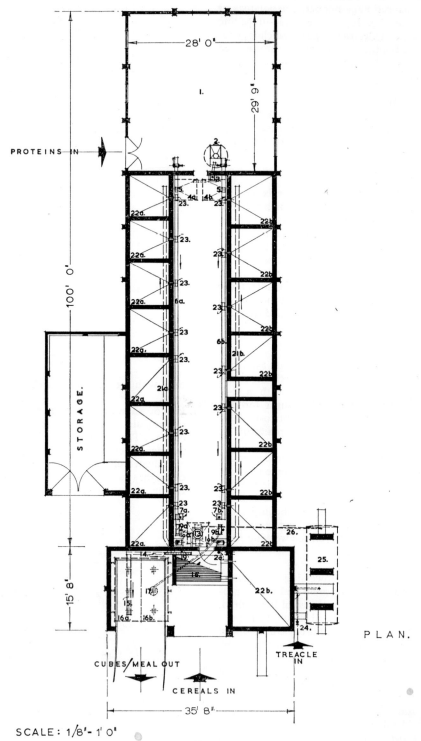

PLAN.

SCALE: 1/8"-1'0"

Fig. 50.

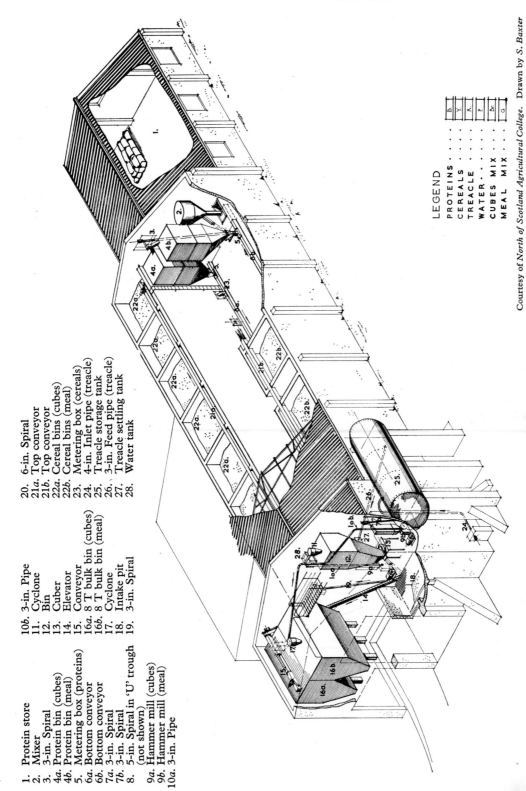

1. Protein store
2. Mixer
3. 3-in. Spiral
4a. Protein bin (cubes)
4b. Protein bin (meal)
5. Metering box (proteins)
6a. Bottom conveyor
6b. Bottom conveyor
7a. 3-in. Spiral
7b. 3-in. Spiral
8. 5-in. Spiral in 'U' trough (not shown)
9a. Hammer mill (cubes)
9b. Hammer mill (meal)
10a. 3-in. Pipe

10b. 3-in. Pipe
11. Cyclone
12. Bin
13. Cuber
14. Elevator
15. Conveyor
16a. 8 T bulk bin (cubes)
16b. 8 T bulk bin (meal)
17. Cyclone
18. Intake pit
19. 3-in. Spiral

20. 6-in. Spiral
21a. Top conveyor
21b. Top conveyor
22a. Cereal bins (cubes)
22b. Cereal bins (meal)
23. Metering box (cereals)
24. 4-in. Inlet pipe (treacle)
25. Treacle storage tank
26. 3-in. Feed pipe (treacle)
27. Treacle settling tank
28. Water tank

LEGEND

PROTEINS · · · ·	P
CEREALS · · · ·	Y
TREACLE · · · ·	K
WATER · · · ·	B
CUBES MIX · · ·	B
MEAL MIX · · · ·	G

Courtesy of North of Scotland Agricultural College. Drawn by S. Baxter

Fig. 50. Plan and isometric diagram of food storage and processing plant for a large pig unit. Muir of Pert Farms Ltd., Tealing, Angus.

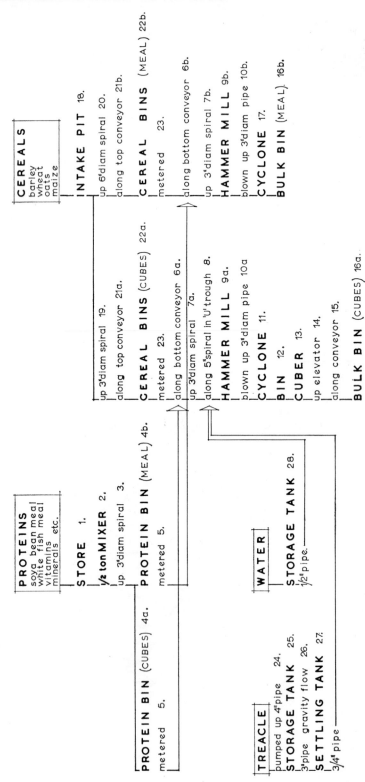

Fig. 51. Flow diagram of materials passing through the food storage and processing plant shown in Fig. 50. Reference numbers relate to plan and isometric diagram. Muir of Pert Farms Ltd., Tealing, Angus.

Courtesy of North of Scotland Agricultural College. Drawn by S. Baxter

of the processing room, are storage bins for pre-mixed concentrates, which can be metered automatically from the bins to the conveyor. Each flow-line operates separately, feeding a hammermill producing 6–8 cwt/hr of meal, one flow of meal passing through a cuber, having molasses added through a controlled drip-feed from an external elevated storage tank. The meal or cubes are elevated into a storage bin for loading on to trailers. In this manner mixing after milling is omitted.

iv. Fig. 51 shows the flow diagram for the ingredients used to form various pig meals in relation to the layout in Fig. 50.

9. *Siting*. The processing plant should be adjacent to the grain store, and if possible within 100–300 ft of the livestock units, unless a trailer is used for conveyance, when distances of $\frac{1}{4}$–$\frac{1}{2}$ mile may be satisfactory, providing there is a good road.

10. *Services*. Electrical power for food processing for large production units is essential. Most plant can have either single- or three-phase motors, though the latter are preferable. Water is seldom required, unless the moisture content of the grain has to be increased prior to milling. Fluorescent lighting is desirable, except in fully automatic layouts, when tungsten bulbs are adequate. Some natural ventilation may be desirable in addition to door openings, but in many cases this need not be provided with efficient plant. The plant room must be kept dry, all external water being excluded. Petrol or tractor engines, if used for power, must be housed separately.

11. *Costs*

a. Costs depend on whether a new or a converted building is used, the latter frequently being the case, and on the cost of machinery. Obviously, machinery prices not only vary between manufacturers but also because of power and operational differences in the plant. However, small crushing or hammermills up to 5 h.p. will generally cost under £150, larger hammermills of up to 20 h.p. between £300 and £500 and heavy plant of 50–60 h.p. £400–£1000. Similarly, most small mixers may cost £100–£150, with some larger or more expensive mixers costing up to £300. Combined mill-mixers for normal farm use, of 3–5 h.p. capacity, may cost £300–£500, which may also be the price range for small cubers or pelleters. Equipment for a provender plant producing 50–75 T/week, with automatic control for one-man operation, might cost £25,000–£35,000, including some storage.

b. A capital outlay on processing plant of £500 might be assessed as equal to a depreciated cost of £100 p.a. Obviously, the maintenance cost for the mill will be higher, replacements being required perhaps for every 200–500 T milled, being equal on average to £$\frac{1}{3}$/T. Electricity and labour costs will vary, but should not be much more than £$\frac{1}{3}$/T. Thus, on a throughput of 500 T p.a., the overall cost of production might be assessed as £$\frac{3}{4}$–£1/T. Large, fully automated plant might have an overall cost of up to £$2\frac{1}{2}$/T. Cubing may be assessed at about £$\frac{3}{4}$/T, though this has been assessed as low as £$\frac{1}{4}$/T (2b, above). These running costs should make it cheaper to mill and mix on the farm rather than to buy compounded food.

c. It is difficult to give building costs, which in a conversion would be negligible. But an extra bay to a grain-storage barn, allowing perhaps 500 ft² for processing, which should give ample space, might cost about £1/ft². On a throughput of 500 T p.a., this might equal £$\frac{1}{8}$/T. Therefore, the total cost of milling, mixing and cubing on the farm, in order to produce 10 T/week, should not be in excess of £2/T.

12. *References*

(1) BROWN, G. 'It pays to feed cubes'. *Pig Farming*, p. 47 (June 1963).
(2) 'Farmers Weekly Conference Report'. *Farm Building Association Journal*, p. 9 (December 1962).
(3) HEBBLETHWAITE, P. 'Installing milling and mixing equipment on the farm'. *Pig Farming*, pp. 50–7 (November 1961).
(4) Ref. (*d*), p. 100.
(5) Ref. (*d*), p. 109.

SELECTED REFERENCES

a. CULPIN, C. Farm Machinery, Crosby Lockwood, pp. 396–413 (1960).
b. 'Milling and mixing'. *Farm Electrification Handbook No. 6*, Electrical Development Association (1961).
c. 'Rations for livestock'. *Ministry of Agriculture Bulletin* 48, 15th Edn. (1961).
d. ROWLAND, F. E. *Electricity in Modern Farming*, Land Books, pp. 93–112 (1963).
e. 'Hammer mills'. *Ministry of Agriculture Farm Machinery Leaflet No. 20* (1957).
f. Agricultural Research Council. Bibliography of Farm Buildings Research. Pt. VI. Buildings for the processing and storage of fodder 1945–58 and 1958–61 (1961 and 1964).

IIF. Milking

1. *Activity*

a. The extraction of milk from dairy cows completes those activities required for milk production described in IIIA. Milk accounts for almost one-quarter of agricultural output. Although the total number of producers in England and Wales has decreased, by 40,000 in the ten years from 1955, there being 102,912 producers in September 1962, milk production has continued to increase since there are larger herds with higher average yields. In the same period, based on figures published by the Milk Marketing Board, the average herd size has risen from 17 to 23 and the average yield per cow has increased by about 40 gal to 780 gal. However, these figures include numerous small herds and, excluding those with less than 20 cows (which seldom justify new buildings), herds average 40–50 cows with yields of 800–900 gal. Moreover, the total sale of milk from farms increased by over 600M gal to nearly 2500M gal, of which about two-thirds was used for liquid consumption, the remainder being sold for manufacturing processes. (However, production fell by 28 per cent between 1955 and 1964.) In addition to the milk sold off farms, a small quantity is used on the farm for calf-feeding or for cheese and butter production.

b. Milking and the buildings for it are governed by the Milk and Dairies Regulations (Pt. 1, Ch. 7V, p. 18). Milk extraction should be designed to fulfil three basic requirements:

 i. The quality and quantity of milk produced should not be affected adversely by the milking system.

 ii. The herd should be maintained in health, without faulty, inadequate or excessive milking, and the cowman should be able to inspect each cow briefly during milking.

 iii. The herd should be milked with the minimum of labour (subject to the above) and within a reasonable time. Due to fatigue developing, no man should have to milk for longer than 2 hr at a session, and milking should be designed for an average session during the period of the peak yields of $1\frac{3}{4}$ hr $\pm\frac{1}{4}$ hr. Rates for milking/man are discussed below.

c. There are three basic layouts or systems for milking:

 i. The herd can be milked in its sleeping quarters (i.e. in a shippon or cowshed), the cowman taking the milking equipment to each cow in turn, and requiring a large central work area (IIIB). Even with modern equipment for milking, work routines are more arduous than with the other systems. Unless mechanized, feeding and cleaning can be time consuming.

 ii. The herd can be milked with fixed equipment in special stalls (i.e. in a parlour), only a few stalls being required, with the cowman working from a small work area, the cows entering and leaving the stalls for milking.

 iii. The herd can be milked in a mobile unit, including stalls and equipment (i.e. in a bail), which can be sited as required, possibly being taken into different fields during the summer to suit the grazing policy and into the farmstead during the winter.

d. A number of subsidiary activities are associated with that of milking and these require special equipment or separate areas for their performance, depending on managerial policy and the milking equipment or building used:

 i. The herd has to be collected from its feeding or sleeping quarters into a special area prior to milking and may have to be held after milking (except with a cowshed).

 ii. Concentrated foods may be fed either in a special area (in the case of a parlour) between the collecting and milking areas or during milking (see 2b).

 iii. The extracted milk has to be cooled (Pt. 1, Ch. 7V, p. 18) and temporarily stored prior to collection.

 iv. The milking equipment has to be cleaned after use.

 v. Concentrates have to be stored, conveyed and rationed into mangers.

 vi. The motors required for the milking machinery have to be housed separately and it should be possible to connect them to a tractor as an emergency source of power.

 vii. Any cow examined during milking and seeming to require further attention should be released into a special holding box (in the case of a parlour).

 viii. Milk yields may have to be recorded, either for farm or national purposes.

e. The areas required for milking and for the subsidiary activities may be summarized:

 i. Milking Area: the work routines and special tasks for milking are discussed below.

 ii. Dairy: to cool and store milk, to clean equipment and to complete records.

 iii. Motor-room.

 iv. Feed store.

In addition, any milking area in the form of a parlour will require this accommodation:

 v. Collecting Yard.

 vi. Holding Box.

 vii. Exit Yard (optional).

2. *Managerial Requirements*. Many factors have to be considered when selecting a layout and milking system to suit a herd.

a. Milk Yield

The recognized lactation period for National Milk Records for a cow is 305 days. This will be the normal milking period assuming one calf/cow p.a., though some cows may be milked for longer even if the yield is very low. It is possible that more than one calving p.a. may be obtained in the future. The total yield from the herd during the year divided by the average number of cows in the herd gives the herd yield. Most herd yields average between 600 and 1200 gal (700–1000 gal is the normal range of yields, with 600–800 gal for Channel Island breeds), though a few cows have yielded over 2000 gal/lactation, 1500 gal is considered to be a very high yield. The peak yield occurs early in the lactation, declining towards the end, and to estimate the peak yield approximately the total yield can be divided by 200. Thus, a 1000-gal cow will have a peak yield of approx. 5 gal/day. Ideally, cows should be milked at 12-hourly intervals, but to give a shorter working day the intervals may be taken as about 14 and 10 hr, in which case approximately three-fifths of the daily yield will be given at the morning milking. The 1000-gal cow should give a maximum yield of 3 gal at any one milking. Milking can take place at 16- and 8-hourly intervals, apparently with little adverse effect or depression in the total yield. Milking can take place three times a day, especially if a herd includes a few high-yielding cows which can be milked separately at midday, so that they will not require longer than the other cows at the two main milkings. Yields should be increased slightly if the cows are milked three times a day. The calving policy can affect the herd peak yield. If most of the calvings are concentrated into a short period, perhaps of two or three months either in the spring or the autumn, most of the cows will give their peak yield at the same time. In this case the herd peak yield will be considerably greater than if calvings occur regularly throughout the year. However, it is difficult to get even three-quarters of the herd calving within 8–12 wks. For example, a herd of 60 cows, with yields varying between 900 and 1100 gal/cow, and averaging 1000 gal/cow, calving at a rate of about 5 per month should have a fairly constant morning yield (except for the spring flush) of about 120 gal, whereas with a concentrated calving period this might be 160–180 gal for about 3–4 months. Thus, the calving policy, as well as the number of cows and the amount of their yields, will affect the time required for milking.

b. Feeding of Concentrates

Food to maintain cows should be obtained either from grazing or from winter bulk foods, such as kale, silage or hay (IIIA). These should be sufficiently nutritious to provide not only maintenance but also part of the milk yield, with good silage sometimes providing maintenance and up to 2–3 gal/day. There can be many variations to the maintenance and production levels derived from bulk foods, but concentrates have to be fed for any milk yielded in excess. Concentrates are normally fed immediately prior to or during milking. However, it is possible that a different policy might be adopted in the future. For example, with wet grain storage, it might prove economical to feed grain plus additives on an *ad-lib.* basis, provided yields were high, thus reducing the labour required in feeding rationed concentrates in the parlour as well as bulk foods elsewhere. Concentrates are normally fed at $3\frac{1}{2}$–4 lb per extra gallon of milk, depending on the overall feeding policy, though these rates may be exceeded to obtain the marginal extra gallons from high yielding cows. A 1000-gal cow, giving $1\frac{1}{2}$ gal from bulk foods, and being fed 4 lb/excess gal, will need 7 lb of concentrates per milking during her peak yield period.

In order that the milking routine may not be delayed while a cow eats her concentrates, the appropriate ration should be consumed before the extraction of the milk is completed. Roberts (1) showed that average eating rates were:

Meal: 0·56 lb/min or 1·8 min/lb
Cubes: 0·77 lb/min or 1·3 min/lb

U.S. research showed that the addition of 1 lb water/lb of meal concentrates increased the consumption rate to 1·05 lb/min (2), but the addition of water is seldom practised. Therefore, 7 lb of cubes should be consumed in about 9 min, or 7 lb of meal in about $12\frac{1}{2}$ min. If this ration is fed as cubes during the 1000-gal cow's peak yield of 30 lb of milk in the morning session, then an extraction rate of $3\frac{1}{3}$ lb/min is required. But, if fed as meal, the extraction rate may be about $2\frac{1}{2}$ lb/min. However, the afternoon yield will drop to 20 lb and the extraction rate could be as low as about $2\frac{1}{4}$ and $1\frac{3}{4}$ lb/min respectively. Since, as shown below, extraction rates can be higher than these amounts, milking may be delayed in order to allow the cows to finish eating. However, if $2\frac{1}{2}$ gal is obtained from bulk foods, only 4 lb of concentrates/milking have to be fed and milking and eating times are more consistent.

c. Milk Extraction Rates (3)

Due to physiological differences, not all cows will yield their milk at the same rate. Moreover, the maximum rate tends to increase with the cow's age, but to decline towards the end of each lactation. Thus, it is impossible to establish a standard rate for extraction, which, in any case, also depends on the milking equipment, including the pulsation ratio between expansion and contraction in the cluster linings, the design of the linings, the vacuum pressure and the rate of the pulsations. However, an approximate guide for normal extraction times can be obtained from the formula: (Ref. e).

$$\text{Milking out time} = 2 + \frac{\text{Yield in lb}}{6} \text{ Min}$$

Most vacuum lines will be installed with a vacuum pressure of 15 in. mercury gauge, but some, to increase the extraction rate, may be set as high as 18 in., though this might cause discomfort or damage to the cow, unless the pressure is reduced between the line and the cows. It is easier to maintain the vacuum when milking into a recorder jar than direct into a pipe-line. With a recorder jar a 15-in. vacuum pressure may drop to about 12 in. at the teat cup, but in a pipe-line to 9 in. Since, usually, 1 in. of pressure is reduced for every foot of height the milk has to be raised, the layout of the plant also affects the pressure. Obviously, the vacuum pressure at the teat cup will affect the extraction rate. Most modern installations will have a pulsation ratio of expansion to contraction in the liners of 3 : 1 or 4 : 1, unless the speed of milking is unimportant; then a ratio of 1 : 1 may be used, which gives the cows longer to eat their food and to be milked. Dodd and Clough (4) showed that with a 1 : 1 ratio, 15 in. mercury gauge and 60 pulsations/min:

Av. true milking rate in min =
$$1{\cdot}93 + 0{\cdot}064 + \text{Av. yield in lb}$$

Thus, a herd averaging 10 lb/milking (1 gal = 10 lb) would require about $2\frac{1}{2}$ min, 20 lb/milking $3\frac{1}{4}$ min and 30 lb/milking nearly 4 min. However, the real milking time will vary, due to the factors given above and also according to whether machine stripping is practised, to obtain the last part, perhaps 3 per cent, of the yield. If the pulsation ratio is increased to 3 : 1 the extraction rate may be increased by 35–40 per cent, if to 4 : 1 by 45 per cent (5). Similarly, doubling the pulsation rate might increase the extraction rate by about 15 per cent. But the average extraction rate obtained in

practice might be taken to be 4–5 lb/min, with a wide ratio, even though for short periods with some cows 12 lb/min may be obtained. Dodd and Clough (5) in an experiment showed that the average yields and milking times from the same cows, when milked at 12-hr intervals at 60 pulsations/min, were as given in the table below. Machine stripping to obtain perhaps no more than 3 per cent of the yield may increase the milking time by about $\frac{1}{2}$ min and a wide ratio may reduce the time by $\frac{1}{2}$–$\frac{3}{4}$ min. This can be important when considering the work routines (4, below).

3. Production Techniques
a. Number of Milking Units Required
The average extraction rate for a milking unit guaranteed or suggested as being normal by a manufacturer can form the basis for deciding how many units are required in a parlour, provided that the work routine is such as to give a specified machine idle time and that the cowman can cope with the total number of units without over or under milking the cows. To prevent over or under milking, the machine cycle time should equal the work routine time multiplied by the number of units (see 4, below). The machine cycle time equals the average milk flow time, plus machine stripping time if practised, plus the machine idle time. The latter will depend for its duration on several factors, the chief of which being whether there is one unit per stall or one unit per two stalls (see 3b, below). If the latter case is taken, then it is possible that not more than 5 per cent of the total time required for milking need be idle, since the unit should be placed on the cow in the second stall as soon as it is removed from the cow in the first stall, and vice versa. But if each stall has a unit, then the machine idle time may represent 10–20 per cent of the total time required for milking, depending on the yield. This means that each unit can handle less milk in $1\frac{3}{4}$ hr than if there is one unit per two stalls and, therefore, more units would be required for the same yield.

If the average extraction rate is taken as $4\frac{1}{2}$ lb/min, then the milk extracted per unit would equal 25 gal/hr if machine idle time equals about 5 per

	Pulsation Ratio	
	4 : 1	1 : 1
Yield in lb before machine stripping	21·8	21·2
Additional yield from machine stripping in lb	0·7	0·7
Total Yield in lb	22·5	21·9
Milking time in min prior to stripping	4·5	5·1
Machine stripping time in min	0·5	0·6
Total milking time in min	5·0	5·7
Extraction rate without stripping, lb/min	4·85	4·15
Extraction rate including stripping, lb/min	4·5	3·84

cent when there are 2 stalls/unit. Thus, a peak yield per session of 120 gal would require a total extraction of 70 gal/hr from 3 units to give a milking session of about $1\frac{3}{4}$ hr. A yield of 180 gal would require an extraction rate of about 100 gal/hr from 4 units. However, if only 20 gal/hr/unit were to be taken as the average extraction rate recommended by a manufacturer, than an additional unit would be required in each case. A rate of 20 gal/hr could indicate either a flow rate of about $3\frac{1}{4}$ lb/min with 5 per cent idle time or one of about 4 lb/min with 15 per cent idle time, that is with 1 stall per unit.

In a cowshed, especially if the milk is extracted into a bucket rather than a pipe-line, the machine idle time will be greater than in a parlour, therefore the total extraction rate per hour will be less or, possibly, fewer units will be able to be managed by the cowman.

Scott has given the basis for calculating the theoretical number of units required, assuming standard work methods are accepted and are completed within standard times, as follows (Ref. *e*, p. 42):

i. Two stall/unit parlours (Tandem, Chute, Herringbone, Abreast)—

$$\text{Number of units} = 0.4 + \frac{\text{Milk Flow Time}}{\text{Work Routine Time}}$$

ii. One stall/unit parlours (Tandem)—

$$\text{Number of units} = 1 + \frac{\text{Milk Flow Time}}{\text{Work Routine Time}}$$

iii. One stall/unit parlours (Chute or Herringbone)—

$$\text{Number of units} = 1.6 + \frac{\text{Milk Flow Time}}{\text{Work Routine Time}}$$

Scott summarized these calculations to show the theoretical number of units required in relation to Milk Flow Time and Work Routine Time (Fig. 52).

b. Number of Stalls Required per Milking Unit
It is difficult to establish whether it is better to have one or two stalls per unit. In either case the cowman must be able to complete his work routine without over or under milking and the cow must have time to eat her concentrates. As Scott (Ref. *e*, p. 45) has said:

'In the past maximum machine utilisation has been considered of great importance. A system which includes a milking unit serving two stalls appears to meet this requirement with the added attraction that more time is allowed for the consumption of concentrates because the cow stands in the parlour whilst another is being milked. However, despite the operation of a simplified work method a much higher standard

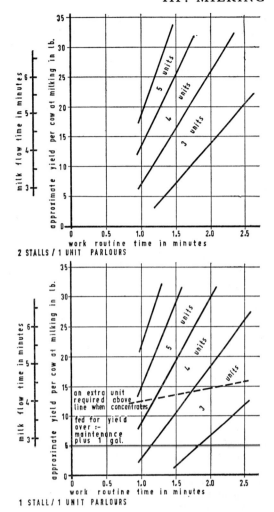

Fig. 52. Number of units suitable for one man in different types of parlour (Ref. *e*)

of skill is required to meet the needs of the individual cow than in the case when each stall is equipped with a separate milking unit. It is suggested that an extra unit in the latter type of parlour can be more economical, meets the needs of the cow more satisfactorily, makes work easier, reduces the opportunities for wasteful feeding and, in some circumstances, could assist in the control of disease. Milking machine utilisation is of a low order but this need not be regarded as a disadvantage.'

This is a fair summary. At first appraisal, sharing a unit between two stalls may appear to save some capital cost, since the difference in cost between having a unit to each stall or one between two stalls may be about £40–£70 for the unit and milking equipment. Moreover, a shared unit may not only make it possible to reduce machine idle time but also, except in the case of a low-yielding herd, make it possible to balance the work routine time with the machine cycle time, which is desirable provided the cows have time to eat their concentrates. But, as suggested above (3a), because a 1 unit/1 stall parlour takes longer for milking, an extra unit may be required to complete milking within a fixed time. Therefore, a parlour to cope with a peak yield of 120 gal per session might need either a 4 unit/4 stall or a 3 unit/6 stall parlour. In this case the former parlour would be the cheaper, since a much smaller building would be required.

Formerly it was considered that a cowman could not cope with more than 4 units and, for preference, not more than 3 units. For example, in a 3 unit/3 stall parlour the work routine time might equal $1\frac{1}{2}$ min, giving a work cycle time of $4\frac{1}{2}$ min for the 3 units. Allowing a maximum extraction rate of 25 gal/hr, and a machine idle time of about 1 min/unit within each work cycle, a cow could only give about 16 lb of milk, which would mean a herd average of about 600 gal. Even with a fourth unit, the herd average could only be about 800 gal. Therefore, generally the 1 unit/1 stall parlours were considered suitable for low-yielding herds and, since with high yielders the cowman would have too much idle time if the cows had sufficient time to eat their concentrates, the 1 unit/2 stall parlours proved popular for commercial herds. But, as Scott (Ref. e, page 21) has suggested, this assumption needs qualification, since, except for the lower machine utilization, the 1 unit/1 stall tandem or chute parlour has advantages compared with their 1 unit/2 stall counterparts:

i. The work routine is simpler, demanding less skill and concentration, giving less risk of mistakes and more satisfactory for a relief milker.
ii. Stimulus time is constant throughout the herd.
iii. All cows can be allowed to feed irrespective of the relationship between yield and milk flow time (tandems).
iv. Generally smaller parlours are required: a 6 unit/6 stall rather than a 4 unit/8 stall or a 4 unit/4 stall rather than a 3 unit/6 stall.
v. A 6 unit/6 stall chute parlour is satisfactory for one operator and allows for batch milking and has an average work routine time of 1·43 min/cow, which is approximately the same as in a 6 unit/6 stall tandem parlour, and preferably coupled to a herd having a milk-flow-time average of 6·4 min. Thus, this type of parlour should be suitable when the herd averages about 1000 gal, and one man should be able to milk 80 cows at the peak lactation period in under 2 hr. Alternatively, a higher herd average, provided calving was spread over most of the year, could be acceptable if the work routine included some idle time.

c. Single or Batch Stalls

Each stall or standing area may be designed to hold one cow or a batch of cows. In the former case the cows can be let in and out of each stall individually, whereas in the latter layout no cow can leave the parlour until the slowest cow has finished being milked. Batch parlours, which include the chute and the herringbone, are cheaper, since the building can be smaller and the stallwork has fewer gates and fittings. They can be suitable either for small herds having a wide range of yields about the average, should the milking time be considered unimportant, or, in cases when all the cows in the herd calve theoretically within about 2–3 months, have a yield $\pm$ about 100 gal of the average yield and a similar extraction rate, all other cows being culled from the herd. In practice, it is not easy to obtain these conditions. Therefore, batch parlours can seldom attain their theoretical maximum efficiency when operated. Batch parlours are chosen for most large commercial herds, since the throughput of cows and gallons can be considerably greater than in individual stall parlours, since the work routine in them is simpler, even though it is probable that in many cases more over milking occurs than is desirable on account of differences in yield and extraction rate, however much an attempt is made to attain uniformity.

d. Milk Conveyance

Milk has to be conveyed from the cluster to the place for cooling and for temporary storage. Until a method was devised for cleaning a pipe-line *in situ* by recirculating hot water and a cleansing fluid, most milk had to be double handled into storage. Some early forms of pipe-line existed, but these were not used widely because of the amount of work involved in keeping them clean. The milk was extracted from the cow either into a bucket or a churn adjacent to the cow, which meant that the churn had to be carried or wheeled to the dairy for cooling. This additional task reduced the throughput per man-hour. Milking into special buckets is still relevant for sick cows or for those confined from the herd or, occasionally, if the vacuum or milk-line is in disrepair. Normal practice for new installations is to milk from the cow into a pipe-line, which conveys the milk direct to the dairy. Since milk recording at intervals is obligatory for those farmers operating the National Milk Records Scheme, and daily or weekly recording in any case may be considered desirable, the milk from each cow may pass into a glass recording jar adjacent to or above the work point before passing into the pipe-line. The recording jar may possibly be superseded by a flow-meter within the pipe-line.

Most pipe-lines are 1 in. in dia, constructed either of glass or stainless steel, but larger herds batch milked may create a restriction, since if 8 units extract at 6 lb/min, the pipe-line must be able to convey 48 lb/min. (In practice, an average rate of $4\frac{1}{2}$ lb/min may be more likely.) It is possible that a $1\frac{1}{2}$-in. pipe-line may be developed. Installations may be based on a 2- or a 3-pipe layout. In the former case there is a vacuum and a milk pipe, both of which are used for circulation cleaning, but it is more usual to have a separate pipe to return the rinse from the milk-line back to the dairy rather than to take it through the vacuum line (see 5, 6 and 8 below).

e. Milk Cooling

To reduce double-handling, it is best for the milk to be extracted from the cow and conveyed by a pipe-line to a refrigerated bulk tank, the latter being coupled to a bulk tanker, sent from the commercial dairy, which collects the milk under vacuum. By the end of 1962, 1500 bulk tanks had been installed on farms, representing about 8 per cent of milk producers and 4 per cent of total production, and these were operated within 47 bulk collection schemes. By the spring of 1964, $7\frac{1}{2}$ per cent of all milk sold off farms was bulk handled from 2565 tanks within 70 bulk collection schemes in England and Wales and 700 new tanks are being installed each year. The cost of installing a bulk tank on a farm can vary between about £4 and £8 per gal storage space, but most collection schemes are designed to give a financial incentive to the farmer to own a bulk tank, which, over a number of years, will help to repay the capital cost of installation. Though a bulk tank is desirable for a farmer, if he wishes to save as much work as possible (provided he has access for a tanker), the financial drawbacks are encountered mainly by the commercial dairies in the organization of collection and of handling and processing plant. However, the initial cost of a tank to a farmer is high and, if he does not aim to attain the maximum throughput/man, the saving in real labour costs may not be great. Most milk probably will be collected by tanker within another decade. In the meantime the milk has to be released from the pipe-line vacuum, either over a surface cooler into churns for storage or into churns for cooling and storage. The churns have to be man-handled on to the collection lorry and empty churns lifted from the lorry into the dairy.

f. Collection and Exit Yards

A collecting yard may be considered an unnecessary expense, but the Milk Regulations require that the access to the milking house should be kept free from any accumulation of dung. Usually, the collecting area is cleaned either once a day or after each milking. This area may be part of the normal exercise yard which is wired off prior to milking. However, in a layout of any size or efficiency it is probable that the collecting area will be designed as a special yard for that purpose, since a dual-purpose yard may restrict the layout and management. In any case, it is desirable that cover, free from draught, should be provided during collection, since some cows may have to wait at least $1\frac{1}{2}$ hr before being milked, and milking is easier and quicker if the cows enter a parlour warm and dry. After milking it may be possible to allow the cows to make their own way back to the fields or yards, but if this policy is unsafe, an exit yard will be required to hold the cows until they can be conducted as a herd.

g. Feeding Position

Though feeding usually takes place during milking, a few farmers prefer to pre-feed, especially with batch milking. The cows are fed at mangers or yokes between the collecting area and the parlour. The two main disadvantages are that additional space and equipment are required, causing additional expense, and that the system should be based on a two-man work routine.

4. *Work routines.* Work routines for milking are complex, depending for efficiency on several interrelated factors, some of which are discussed above. It is impossible to give more than a superficial survey without a full, detailed study being made. Several detailed reports on milking routines have been published (12, below).

a. Milking Routines

To obtain a balanced milking routine it is necessary to co-ordinate the machine cycle time, the work routine time and the milking out/food consumption times in relation to the number of units being operated per man, and to keep the overall time for milking the herd within $1\frac{3}{4}$ hr $\pm\frac{1}{4}$ hr. The milking rate per man hour for 40 cows has been given (6):

Method		Short routine	Medium routine
Parlour:	Pipe-line	45	30
	In-churn	40	27
Cowshed:	Pipe-line	40	27
	Bucket plant	28	20

This table indicates the relative efficiency of the different buildings and equipment, but it is not related directly to yield, since it assumes the number of units used have been related to yield. It should be possible for one man, without undue strain, to milk up to 90–100 cows per session, i.e. about 55 per hr, with medium to high yields, in a modern herringbone batch parlour, though in a tandem or chute parlour a total of 70–80 cows/man is considered efficient within $1\frac{3}{4}$ hr. However, such standards assume an exceptionally high standard of management and building design.

i. Machine cycle time: the milking unit cannot be used the whole time and the machine cycle time has to include the machine off time. The latter in a 1 stall/1 unit parlour includes the time taken for a cow to leave the stall, for another to enter, for the udder to be washed and for the unit to be handled, and can average about 1 min/cycle, but in a 2 stall/1 unit parlour the machine off time should occur only during the transition of the unit from one stall to its counterpart, taking about 0·11 min/cycle (7).

ii. Work routine time: the routine will depend on the milking layout and equipment, but should include, for example, in a 2 stall/1 unit tandem parlour (7):

	Min*
Wash cow Stall B	0·42
Use strip cup	0·15
Move to adjacent stall A, pull open parlour door, open rear gate to stall, shut parlour door, let next cow in	0·13
Machine strip cow	0·40
Remove unit, cross to B	0·05
Apply unit	0·11
Move to stall A	0·02
Open front gate, issue feed, close front gate, close rear gate	0·15
Move to next unit	0·02
	1·45

* Average times with a skilled operator.

The routine has to include for letting the cows into the out of the stall and the parlour, washing the udder, using a strip cup (to test the foremilk), issuing feed, handling the unit and machine stripping (the latter not always being practised), and should average about 1½ min/cow, with 1 and 2 min being the short and long cycle limits. Recording will increase the cycle, but will probably be required not more than once a week. In a 1 stall/1 unit parlour the work routine time will be about the same, and the average time within a cowshed with pipeline milking should also be little different. The average and standard work routine times may be summarized:

	Min Standard time
1 stall/1 unit chute parlour	1·43
2 stall/1 unit chute parlour	1·36
1 stall/1 unit tandem parlour	1·46
2 stall/1 unit tandem parlour	1·45
Cowshed with pipe-line	1·51
Cowshed with buckets	1·76

Similar standard times are not available for the batch herringbone parlours, since the number

of cows in each batch affect the work routine time. Scott has given the work routine time for a 6-cow-batch herringbone as 1·04 min/cow, rising to 1·09 min/cow for a 4-cow batch. Both the machine cycle and work routine times, as well as the milking out/food consumption rates, should be discussed with a manufacturer, when designing a parlour. It is important for the work routine to be carried out with a steady rhythm, and therefore the parlour should be planned so that the cowman has no unnecessary interruptions to his milking. It should be unnecessary to leave the parlour work area during milking, either to handle cows or to inspect the milk in the dairy.

b. Cleaning of Equipment (Ref. *h*)

After each milking the pipe-line has to be cleaned by recirculated water and chemicals, both hot and cold water being required in most systems, the former being at about 85° C (185° F). The time taken for cleaning is about 13 min for a 3-unit parlour in the morning and 10 min in the evening (6). Recirculation affects the dairy layout. The interior of a bulk tank has to be cleaned after collection, with three rinses taking about 20–30 min. Cleaning equipment may take 1¼ hr/day, full details of which are given in the Cambridge Report 58 (6). In addition, the parlour and approaches have to be cleaned at least once a day, taking another 10–15 min, and for this purpose a high-pressure hose is desirable.

c. Handling Feed

Handling concentrates can be mechanized, and this may be desirable when high throughputs are required, but generally quantities handled are relatively small. Unless they are mixed on the farm, the concentrates should be delivered in an economic quantity, which might be on a monthly basis, and these can be conveyed mechanically or manually in bags into a store from the lorry. It is possible to manhandle the feed from the store every day to a local storage point adjacent to each stall. However, with a large herd this would be time consuming, and it is possible to deliver the feed to each cow either by gravity from an overhead store or by conveyor. Occasionally, each cow may be fed a premixed and weighed ration. In such cases rations are prepared in individual buckets in the feedroom and are conveyed to the parlour pit prior to milking.

5. *Design data*

a. The Stall

The size of the milking stall may be varied to suit the breed, at about 7¼ ft × 2¾ ft for small breeds, or standardized to suit any breed at about 8 ft × 2¾ ft. The stall may be divided into a standing area of about $5\frac{1}{2}$ ft $\times$ $2\frac{3}{4}$ ft, plus a manger under the cow's head. A few cows may have a girth of nearly 3 ft, and therefore, though the floor area may be restricted, there should be at least 3 ft of width available per cow. The back legs may be inset at least 1 ft from the rump, and the latter may therefore project over the work area. There are three main stall types, discussed in greater detail in 5d, below (Fig. 53):

i. Individual Parlour Stalls: the tandem stall with side entry and exit, and the abreast or walk-through stall.
ii. Batch Parlour Stalls: the herringbone stall with side entry and exit, and the chute or walk-through stall.
iii. Cowshed Stalls: also used for sleeping.

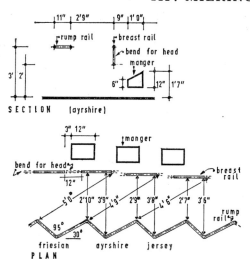

Fig. 54. Dimensions for herringbone rails and mangers to suit different breeds (Ref. 8)

In a herringbone parlour the size of stall in relation to breed is more critical than in the other parlour types, as is the position of the manger. Research at the Ministry of Agriculture's Bridget's Experimental Farm has indicated various dimensions which hold the cow firmly, but allowing a relaxed and comfortable position (Fig. 54) (8).

Normally, the size of stall and the fixing positions for the stallwork are governed by the standards of individual manufacturers, but tandems may need as many as 4 floor fixings per stall, chutes only 1 and herringbones only 4 per parlour, irrespective of the number of cows held in the batch, provided there is some strutting from the ceiling. Floor fixings are an obstruction to cleaning. Floors should have a drainage profile. Tubular steel stallwork may be approximately $3\frac{1}{2}$ ft high, but the mangers and gates may need about $5\frac{1}{2}$ ft and the remote-control gear for the gates in a tandem parlour $6\frac{1}{2}$ ft. In theory, with the exception of the latter stallwork, the stalls could have only $5\frac{1}{4}$ ft clearance to the ceiling for the cows, though normally there are other factors, such as clearance for a man to walk through the stall area.

b. The Work Area

The floor of the work area should be $2\frac{1}{2}$ ft below the cows' stall, and the overall height can seldom be less than 9 ft, in order that recording jars can be suspended from the ceiling over the man's head, though, if clearance has to be restricted to under 9 ft, the jars can be lower, providing the work area width is increased. For ease in recording, many farmers prefer to have the jars at eye level, and this means that a pit 4–5 ft wider is desirable. The width of the work area, with stalls on each side, is seldom less than 4 ft, though, if necessary, $3\frac{1}{2}$ ft

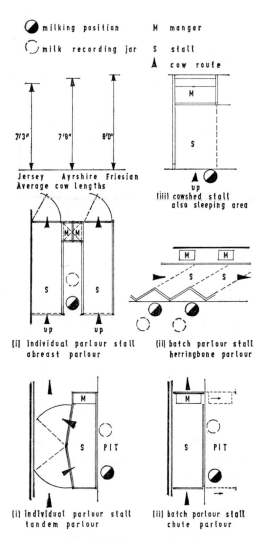

Fig. 53. Basic types of stall

or even 3 ft can be made to work except in the case of eye-level recording jars.

A small writing stand, perhaps coupled to part of the stallwork, should be provided for the cowman to be able to record the yields quickly and easily on a chart. Some farmers record the yields verbally on to tape, operated by a pull-cord, and this saves time and is worth the expense with a commercial herd.

c. Cow Circulation

The individual parlour stalls need a passageway for the cows, 3 ft wide including a rubrail set $\frac{1}{4}$ ft from the wall and about 3 ft from the floor. If the cows have to enter or leave the parlour at right angles to the stalls an end passage width of $3\frac{1}{4}$ ft should be allowed, which in some layouts might increase the length of the parlour by 7 ft.

d. Basic Parlour Types (Fig. 55) (see 3b and 3c, above)

i. Individual Stall Parlours: 1 stall/1' unit—suitable for the smaller herd with yields below the national average, with either 3 or 4 units, or for commercial herds with high yields with 5 or 6 units and expert milking with up to 80 cows/man.

ii. Individual Stall Parlours: 2 stall/1 unit. The 6 stall/3 unit, or with high yielders the 8 stall/4 unit, tandem parlour is satisfactory for herds of 50–60 cows/man, especially with a dispersed calving policy and wide range of yield. However, it is doubtful if there are many cases when a batch herringbone or chute parlour would not be preferable. Alternatively, the stalls can be arranged as an abreast parlour, and this is popular with many farmers, though the layout should be designed with steps up to the stalls, raising the cow at least $2\frac{1}{4}$ ft above the work position. In some cases, the cow steps up $1\frac{1}{4}$ ft and the cowman down $1\frac{1}{4}$ ft to give a $2\frac{1}{2}$ ft change of level. The main advantage is that the stallwork might be about £100 cheaper and, in some layouts, particularly in a conversion, the building could give a further saving, being a little smaller in floor area than a tandem. In addition, the cowman can see the cow better while milking. However, even a capital saving of £200 might equal only £$\frac{1}{2}$/cow/p.a. in a 60-cow herd, and there are layouts in which a tandem parlour might prove to be cheaper and more convenient.

iii. Batch Stall Parlours: 2 stall/1 unit. The 6 stall/3 unit or 8 stall/4 unit chute parlour is a cheap parlour for batch milking, being suitable particularly for the 50–70 cow/man herd. Alternatively, a 6 stall/6 unit chute should be suitable for a herd of 60–80 high yielders. The

stallwork should be about £20/stall less than in a similar tandem parlour and, in addition, the building should be at least £30/stall cheaper. However, any commercial herd, requiring between an 8 stall/4 unit and a 16 stall/8 unit layout for its parlour, equally could be milked in a batch herringbone parlour and, in the latter,

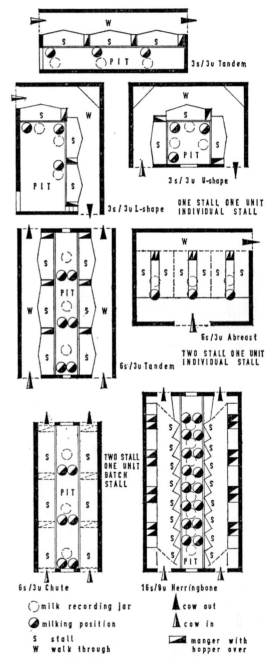

Fig. 55. Basic types of parlour

142

herds of up to 100 cows/man can be milked. The stallwork should cost about £10–£12/stall, plus perhaps £12–£15/stall for a wall-mounted manger, plus £15–£18/stall for remote-controlled feeders, making a total of £37–£45/stall, which is similar to the stallwork for a tandem parlour.

v. Portable Parlours or Bails. Proprietary abreast type and chute parlours are available, some of which include a dairy and food store.

v. Cowshed or Shippon. The traditional housing of cattle with sleeping/feeding/milking stalls, though popular for conservative reasons of stockmanship, can be designed to include modern features which make them reasonably efficient.

e. Collecting Yard

An area of not more than 15 ft²/cow should be allowed, though this could be a dual-purpose area:

i. It may be included as part of the normal exercise area.

ii. It may be divided to form a small concreted apron at the parlour entry plus a larger area normally used for other purposes.

In some cases, 12 ft²/cow may prove suitable, particularly with smaller breeds. The yard, for preference, should be long and narrow, funnelling the cows into the parlour in a straight line (Fig. 56). Cross access should be included for easy cleaning. If essential, due to a difficult site, cows can enter a parlour at right angles to the collecting yard, but the floor areas should be increased. It is possible to suspend a light tubular frame, which can be electrified with a low voltage, from an overhead monorail, the frame or electric dog being pulled along the monorail from the parlour; this can be kept behind the cows in the collecting yard in order to bring them forward to the parlour doors. The entry to the parlour is simple if the parlour floor is only a few inches above that of the collecting yard. This means that the work area or pit has to be below ground level. If this is not possible the work floor may be just above the yard floor, with the standings or stalls raised 2½ ft. Therefore the cows need to have steps up to and out of the parlour, which require considerable space (Fig. 56) and are expensive.

The collecting yard floor should be anti-slip textured and have a fall to a drainage gulley (preferably offset from the tractor scraping routes) of 1 : 40 to 1 : 60. Alternatively, the floor can be slatted, but a concreted area is required near the parlour entry doors which is not slatted to suit the Milk and Dairies Regulations—though this requirement might be amended in the future.

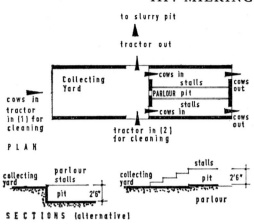

Fig. 56. Collecting yard: pit level and clearing yard

f. Food Storage
Storage requirements are given in IE (p. 72).

g. Milk
One gallon of milk weighs 10 lb.

6. *Equipment*
a. Bulk Tanks (see 3e, above)
A dairy should be planned for the immediate or eventual inclusion of a bulk tank. The size of tank required will be such as to hold the maximum daily yield, but, since the cost per gal is considerably less for a large rather than a small tank and since various tanks are available holding between 80 and 500 gal, a dairy may subsidize the installation of a large tank for a small herd, in order to be able to collect the milk every other day. Tanks have either a stainless steel, plastic or glass-fibre cover to a layer of insulation surrounding a stainless-steel holding tank of double thickness, refrigerated water being circulated within the thickness. Some tanks include an ice-bank and refrigerator at one end, whereas others have them housed separately, and therefore tanks of equal capacity can vary in size according to the manufacturer. Most tanks are rectangular, though a few are in the form of horizontal or vertical cylinders, and overall heights can vary between 2 and 7 ft, though most are about 3½ ft. Thus, one 125-gal tank might be 3 ft × 3 ft on plan, but another 5½ ft × 4 ft. A 500-gal tank might be 12½ ft × 5½ ft. An analysis of tank sizes on the market has been made by the *Dairy Farmer* (9). Space is required around the tank, 2–2½ ft wide, for the cowman to swab the interior, though 1½ ft might be adequate as a poor alternative. In order to calibrate the tank, a floor-to-ceiling height of at least 8 ft, sometimes 9 ft, is required, the tank level being changed by adjustable legs. The legs make it difficult to clean the space below the tank, but make it possible to install the tank on a floor having a fall. Since the tank has to be

swilled out, a free-draining floor profile is essential. A flowmeter, if developed, may make calibration unnecessary. The tanks have an outlet at one end for coupling to the bulk tanker and, since the coupling is flexible, the outlet can be at right angles to the tanker, but the maximum length of coupling is usually 10 ft. Normally there are suction and liquid pipes at the other end of the tank for connection to the condenser in the motor-room, the maximum pipe run being 25 ft placed in a channel in the floor. The milk pipe-line will be taken from the parlour into the dairy, the vacuum being broken through a releasing jar and D-pan, the bottom of which must be above the bulk tank, and therefore an overall height of 9 ft to the pipeline entry to the dairy may be required. The D-pan may drain into the tank through a freely suspended pipe.

There are three main cooling methods used in different types of tank (9):

i. Direct expansion: refrigerant evaporated in tubes against the tank and held by insulation against an outer tank cover. 3-h.p. unit required for 150-gal tank.

ii. Chilled water in an ice-sump below the tank is sprayed between the inner and outer tank cover. $\frac{3}{4}$-h.p. unit for 150-gal tank.

iii. Jacket of chilled water held within the inner and outer tanks. $\frac{3}{4}$-h.p. unit for 150-gal tank.

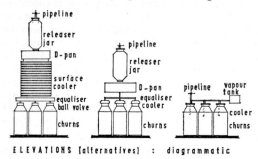

ELEVATIONS [alternatives] : diagrammatic

Fig. 57. Cooling systems with milk stored in churns

b. Cooling with Churns (Fig. 57)

Unless a bulk tank is installed, the milk will have to be stored prior to collection in churns, the common size being for 10 gal, $13\frac{1}{2}$ in. dia × 28 in. high. Milk leaving the cow at blood heat through the pipe-line has to be cooled, and this can be done in two ways:

i. Prior to storage over a surface cooler, the milk being discharged via a releasing jar and D-pan over the cooler and into the churns via an equalizing head or a ball-valve-controlled trough. The releaser and cooler are wall mounted and require at least $7\frac{1}{2}$ ft from the pipe-line to the floor, in some cases 9 ft. If a milk pump is used the height can be reduced

to $6\frac{1}{2}$ ft. To some extent, the height is governed by the size of cooler, which depends on the surface area, the temperature of the water and the quantity of milk to be cooled, a drop of at least 30° C (45° F) being required. The surface area/ft² of cooler varies with different makes, but on average 12 in²/gal cooled/hr is required. Thus, 100 gal/hr cooled would need about 3 ft × 3 ft. The cooler and releaser need about 2 ft of space from the wall. Cooling water at a rate of 2–3 gal/gal of milk cooled will be required, and this water must be drained.

ii. During storage the milk being discharged either via a releasing jar, D-pan and equalizing head into the churns or directly into the churns, which are coupled together with linked lids under vacuum. In the latter case the vacuum should pass through a vapour collecting tank on the wall, normally of about 6 ft³ capacity, before re-entering the pipe-line. In both cases the milk can be cooled with sparge-rings or cooling heads, the former requiring about 6 gal of water/gal of milk, which must be drained. To reduce the water consumption, the churns may be coupled together on a stand, which cools the water by an electric motor and recirculates it. A small stand for 30 gal might measure 4 ft × $2\frac{1}{2}$ ft × 1 ft, and a larger stand for 300 gal 8 ft × 3 ft × $1\frac{1}{2}$ ft.

iii. Typical space requirements for the filled churns, which can be staggered, allowing 2 extra churns for emergency, would be:

Peak yield/ day, gal	Total No. churns	Total a.m.	Total p.m.	Floor area, ft a.m.	Floor area, ft a.m. and p.m.
120	14	8	6	$3\frac{1}{2}$ × $3\frac{1}{4}$	$5\frac{3}{4}$ × $3\frac{1}{4}$
160	18	11	7	$4\frac{1}{2}$ × $3\frac{1}{4}$	$7\frac{1}{2}$ × $3\frac{1}{4}$
200	22	13	9	$5\frac{3}{4}$ × $3\frac{1}{4}$	9 × $3\frac{1}{4}$
240	26	15	11	5 × $4\frac{1}{4}$	$10\frac{1}{4}$ × $3\frac{1}{4}$
300	32	19	13	8 × $3\frac{1}{4}$	$9\frac{3}{4}$ × $4\frac{1}{4}$
360	38	25	15	$5\frac{3}{4}$ × $5\frac{1}{4}$	$11\frac{1}{4}$ × $4\frac{1}{4}$

The cowman has to be able to change lids, check the milk and label the churns. Churns more than 3 deep, i.e. $3\frac{1}{4}$ ft, will need access on both sides. To save labour in handling the churns it is desirable to have a roller conveyor from the releaser to the loading bay.

c. Recirculation Cleaning

The pipe-line has to be coupled to a trough containing water and detergents. Therefore the releaser jar should be near a rubber trough, served with hot and cold water and capable of holding at least 15 gal. A draining board to the trough is desirable, and a combined space of 6 ft × $2\frac{1}{2}$ ft is an average requirement.

45: POTATO CHITTING GLASS HOUSE

Mr. Watson-Jones, Newport, Shropshire

A greenhouse of almost standard construction with glass down to floor level, 90 ft × 24 ft × 7½ ft to the eaves, holding 32 T of seed potatoes in trays 2½ ft long × 1½ ft wide × ½ ft deep. The trays are arranged in 5 double rows, 3 ft wide, with four 2-ft alleys between rows and with ½ ft between external row and glass walling. Within each alley, 5-ft warm white fluorescent tubes are suspended at 7-ft centres from a catenary wire and are connected to an endless rope so that the lights can be moved 1 ft laterally each day, each light being able to be moved 7 ft along the catenary wire. Frost protection is provided by six 3-kW fan heaters controlled by 2-ft rod thermostats discharging through perforated polythene ducting laid along the floor of each alley and capable of raising the temperature to 9° C (48° F). [SEE PAGE 157] Courtesy of Midlands Electricity Board.

46: POTATO CHITTING HOUSE INTERIOR

P. C. Bath Ltd., Nr. Bedford

Existing timber barn converted to form a non-glass, insulated and controlled chitting house. Ceiling and walls are lined with insulation board, and a dry concrete floor is required. Trays of seed are stacked to a height of 8 ft, two abreast with 1½-ft-wide alleys. Warm white fluorescent tubes are suspended from overhead catenary wires at 10-ft centres and can be moved laterally each day. The building can be warmed by means of fan heaters controlled by rod-type thermostats. [SEE PAGE 157] Courtesy of Electrical Development Association.

47: TRACTOR SERVICE SHED

Nackington Farms Ltd.

The tractor is an essential farm tool and its regular maintenance is vital for farm efficiency. Though this photograph was taken in 1951, it demonstrates the need for order in farm machine storage and maintenance. The shed is of simple steel truss construction of 20 ft span. A more modern shed might have a portal frame. Wide entrance doors give access for the tractors and their attachments from a large turning yard with an open-fronted implement shelter on the far side. Four tractors are shown in the tractor service shed, placed ready for inspection. Natural and artificial lighting are limited, but adequate for normal work. A heating stove, essential for successful winter mechanical work, is provided. Other facilities are available for ease of maintenance, and the service area is well organized. [SEE PAGE 161] Courtesy of Farmer and Stockbreeder.

48: POTATO PACKING SHED

East Riding Farm Produce Ltd., Melbourne, York

A steel portal frame of 40 ft span, 120 ft long and 16 ft to the eaves provides a clear work space for a co-operative potato packing station producing 30 T packed potatoes/day for 40 wks. The walls are clad with proprietary galvanized steel panels. Lighting is provided by rooflights, high-level general-purpose industrial tungsten lights and low-level fluorescent strips above the working plane. Sliding doors to eaves ht are provided at each end of the building so that lorries have access into the building. The potatoes are washed prior to grading, the water being collected and filtered in a 50-ft × 8-ft tank outside the building prior to being recirculated. At present buildings of this kind are classed as agricultural buildings, and therefore are exempt from industrial requirements of insulation. Since they are used during the winter months, it is probable that they should be covered by the Industrial Acts. [SEE PAGES 163 & 15] Photo: J. B. W. Courtesy of East Riding Farm Produce Ltd.

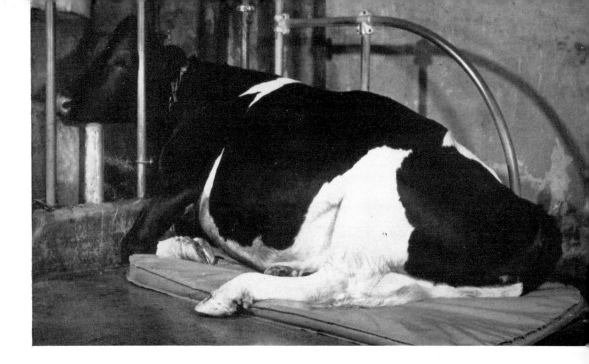

49: COW MATTRESSES

Cows can be comfortable on various types of bedding. Foam rubber mattresses with an impervious cover can be satisfactory. They are comfortable, easy to clean and can have a reasonable life. They can prove economic, especially as an alternative to straw when the latter has to be bought at above average prices. [SEE PAGE 167] Courtesy of The Gourock Ropework Co. Ltd.

50: AUTOMATIC FEEDING WITH DAIRY CATTLE HOUSING

Mr. E. Moffit, Peepy Farm, Northumberland

In 1961 part of the Hunday herd was rehoused so that two 60 cow units could be completely housed, milked, fed and managed by 2 men within a steel portal framed building of 85 ft clear span. The two units are divided by a central auger and manger $4\frac{1}{2}$ ft wide over which is an inspection catwalk. The auger is linked at the near end with two external 300-T haylage silos, the cows being fed automatically three times a day while standing on an 11-ft-wide concrete area at each side of the manger, which is also used as a collecting yard. Just visible is an electric wire which can be lowered to hold the cows on the concrete. At the sides of the building are strawed bedded areas, and at the far end are two parlours, one for each unit. The concrete areas are scraped into a channel which is outside the parlour entrance, the slurry then flowing underground to an external pit. [SEE PAGE 168] Courtesy of the Farmers Weekly

51: CLEANING STRAWED YARDS
Lord Knutsford, Little Munden Farm, Watford, Herts.

A concrete portal frame of 70 ft overall span and 90 ft long with a roof pitch of 18 deg. can provide a clear internal space. The concrete frames are thickened as hauching at the eaves, which are 10 ft high. The portal frame provides an 'umbrella' type of building since the internal layout can be adapted for changes in management policy. Walls are of 6-in. concrete block, except for the frontage which is in brick to improve the appearance. The building provides a strawed yard for up to 80 cows. At the far end is a temporary fencing to form a collecting yard, adjoining a parlour unit over which a bulk feed store is to be built. The floor to the bedded area is of rammed chalk. Clearing the 2–3 ft build-up of dung can be carried out in the spring-to-autumn period to suit the fieldwork with a fore-mounted scoop to a tractor. Work requirements are not excessive for handling dung in this manner. [SEE PAGE 170] Courtesy of Crendon Concrete Co. Ltd.

52: SLATTED FLOORS FOR CATTLE
Royal Show, Cambridge 1960

Slatted floors, both for dairy and for beef cattle, have been proved successful over several years. The slats must be of top-grade quality, being free from cracks, chips, warping or uneven surfaces. The slats should be, for preference, flat on top and normally of 5 in. width. The sides of the slats should taper by $\frac{1}{2}$ in., so that the dung does not stick between the slats. For adult cattle, a gap between the slats of $1\frac{1}{2}$ in. is satisfactory, but $1\frac{3}{4}$ in., or even 2 in., is possible. The gaps should be true throughout the length of the slat, as shown in the photograph. The cattle stand on the slatted floor without discomfort and they should remain reasonably clean, the dirt being pushed into the cellar or pit below the slats by their hooves. Slats can span various distances up to 12 ft, or even 15 ft, without intermediate supports, but should have about 4 in. bearing at both ends. The slats shown include attached spacers to fix the distance between them, but separate wooden spacers, one to each end, can be used. [SEE PAGES 171 & 188] Courtesy of Cement and Concrete Association.

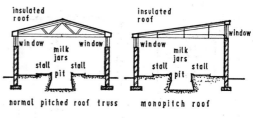

d. Additional Dairy Equipment

i. Clothes cupboard with shelf and hanging space, 4 ft × 2 ft × 6 ft minimum.

ii. Table with drawer and stool.

iii. Blackboard and pinboard.

iv. Hand-basin and towel rail.

v. Bucket tap, and possibly additional wash trough.

vi. Water heater, see below.

In any large unit there should be a small control office leading off the dairy, since careful recording and administration is essential, and some of the equipment and storage could be in the office.

e. Motors

The motors have to be housed in a separate room, which may open to the exterior, but can open off the dairy, but in this case there must be no risk of fumes entering the dairy. Several motors may be required in addition to the main fusebox for the electrical installation.

i. Bulk tank motors, usually $\frac{1}{2}$–3 h.p., require about 3 ft × 2$\frac{1}{2}$ ft × 2 ft, and the condenser will need a cold-air inlet. The heat-extraction rate will range between 4000 and 18,000 B.T.U./hr, and this heat can be used for warming calf pens, etc., if required.

ii. Vacuum motors, perhaps 1–2 h.p., and with an emergency motor, which is a desirable extra, may need 8 ft × 2 ft × 3 ft. It should be possible to couple the motor to a tractor external to the motor-room and, since most tractors require a coupling at not more than 2$\frac{1}{2}$ ft above ground level and the motor connecting may be 1$\frac{1}{2}$ ft off the floor, care must be taken in positioning the motors.

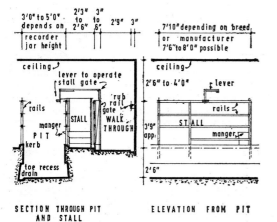

SECTION THROUGH PIT AND STALL   ELEVATION FROM PIT

Fig. 58. Tandem stall: a hopper can be installed above the manger. See Figs. 54 and 61 for herringbone layout

Fig. 59. High level cross ventilation light

f. Stallwork (Fig. 58)

Typical stall dimensions, including feeding arrangements, are shown in Fig. 58.

g. Remote Control Doors

All the cow entry and exit doors to the parlour should be controlled from the pit. The doors should slide, with the gear set at an angled rise of about 4 in., and should have a counterweighted overhead control pulley, with a cable taken to the pit for operation.

7. *Environmental Control*

a. Since the parlour provides an environment for nearly half of the cowman's working life, it should be designed for his comfort. The roof should be insulated and high-level light and cross ventilation under the ceiling are desirable (Fig. 59). An average cow produces 3142 B.t.u./hr (10), which is a little less than the heat from an electric 1-kW fire, and this heat will have a high R.H. Inadequately ventilated parlours will have condensation problems and, if wall openings are impractical, due to adjacent structures, fan ventilation to create a through draught at ceiling level will be essential. The parlour entrance and exit doors can assist the ventilation. However, in order to warm the parlour prior to use, a high-level industrial fan heater above the work area is desirable, perhaps of 1 kW for small parlours. In many cases natural light will be inadequate in the work space and artificial light will be required for at least $\frac{1}{3}$ or even $\frac{1}{2}$ of each year. On this basis it might be argued that no natural light need be provided.

b. Artificial light should be provided on a generous scale both in the parlour and in the dairy. No working plane should have illumination lower than 10 lumens/ft², and 20 lumens/ft² is preferable, particular attention being given so that the cowman does not cast a shadow on to his work and that the udders, the recording jars, the bulk tank or cooler and churns and the wash tub and desk are well lit. Lighting must be uniform, without glare. Two-way control of lighting may be desirable. Since lighting will be required for

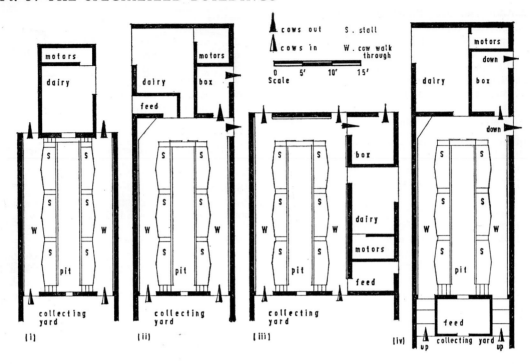

Fig. 60. Dairy units layout with a tandem parlour

prolonged periods, fluorescent strip lighting, with good reflectors, is economic. Consideration should be given to the humidity in protecting the lighting, but, in any case, the light fittings should be cleaned at regular intervals. A bank of tubes either down the centre of the pit or, more expensive, above each kerb to the pit would be satisfactory. Industry has shown that poor lighting is one of the principal causes of fatigue. It is possible to place an angled and diffused tungsten light source under the udder and made watertight, set in the floor of the cow standings, since this will give better illumination at the working plane than overhead lighting.

c. Insect control being essential, the installation of a proprietary electrical insecticide atomizer is desirable, positioned as advised by a manufacturer, but probably on the basis of a minimum of 2 per parlour and 1 each for the dairy and box.

8. *Layout*

a. It is impossible to give a comprehensive description of all the possible layouts for a parlour unit. However, other than the actual choice of parlour and any elaboration of the minimum planning requirements, there are three important variations to consider in relation to tandem, chute and herringbone parlours:

i. To enter a parlour at the side and to leave at one end (or vice versa) will increase the overall length of the parlour by $3\frac{1}{2}$–4 ft.

ii. To enter and leave at the side will increase the length by 7–8 ft.

iii. If the standings are raised $2\frac{1}{2}$ ft above the collecting yard level, rather than having an excavated pit, then four $7\frac{1}{2}$-in.-deep steps will be required, and they will project $6\frac{3}{4}$–$7\frac{1}{2}$ ft from the parlour entrance. Similarly, exit steps may be required. Alternatively, the standings can be partly raised and the pit partly excavated.

b. Fig. 60 shows four possible layouts for a 6 stall/ 3 unit tandem parlour, which could be adapted for a herringbone parlour by having a different width or length or could be increased in length for an 8 stall/3 unit tandem. Chute layouts would be considerably narrower.

i. This layout has a minimum floor area, but it is possible only if the dairy is restricted in width, and one stream of cows has to cross the loading bay, which is undesirable. It is not easy to include a holding box in the layout and the food store has to be in a loft.

ii. The cows leave the parlour at one side. Without feed mechanization, bins have to be stored in the pit or hoppers have to be included with

146

the stallwork, both of which are time consuming to refill.

iii. Provided the roof is designed to give economical wall heights, this layout is economical and easy to work, especially if stall hoppers are filled from the store by conveyor.

iv. The space between the steps up to raised standings can enclose a double feed bin, including space as a walkway for the cowman. Feed could be blown into the bin from the exterior and could be conveyed mechanically from the bin to the hoppers.

In all layouts it is desirable for the cowman to be able to leave the pit, so as to reach behind a cow refusing to enter the parlour. This can be assisted by having steps from the pit into a small area adjacent to the cow entry but railed off from the collecting yard.

c. Fig. 61 shows a herringbone parlour for 16 stalls/8 units, suitable for a large herd managed by the minimum labour.

9. *Siting.* Siting a parlour unit must be in relation to the method of housing (IIIA, 8, p. 176). Bails, being portable, permit the siting to be flexible. Good access on a hard road is essential for milk collection. Not only should the cows be able to enter the collecting yard from the winter housing but the route to and from the fields for summer grazing, if practised, should be considered. At present only a few farmers permanently house their herd. The unit may be sited in relation to calf boxes. A supply of water and electricity are essential. Good drainage must be provided and hosing the unit clean, as well as swilling a bulk tank, will create a considerable amount of effluent, which must drain to a sewer or to a drainage tank (IG, 5f, p. 77).

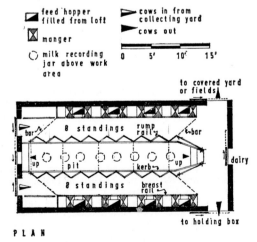

feed hopper filled from loft

manger

milk recording jar above work area

cows in from collecting yard

cows out

0   5'   10'   15'

to covered yard or fields

bar — 8 standings — rump rail — t-bar

up — pit — kerb — up — dairy

8 standings — breast rail

to holding box

PLAN

Fig. 61. Typical herringbone parlour layout

10. *Services*

a. Great attention must be given to floor profiles, since drainage is an essential planning requirement. The minimum fall for the collecting yard, parlour, dairy and box should be 1 : 120. The pit floor as well as the standings should have a fall. In a tandem parlour it is desirable to raise the standings about $\frac{1}{4}$ ft above the walk-through passage. In a herringbone there should be an additional cross-fall from the kerb to the side wall, or from the kerb and wall to the centre of the standings. Where possible, the floors should drain into an external gulley, but an excavated pit should have an internal trapped gulley. The latter, being at least 3 ft below ground level, will mean that the complete run of drainage from the pit must be deeper than normal, and on some sites this may be impossible. It should be possible to rod out all runs of drainage. Equally, good wall and floor finishes are desirable (Vol. 2).

b. The cold supply should be distributed from the stop-tap to the following points:

i. Storage tank (if included in layout).
ii. Parlour pit.
iii. Supply tank to water heater.
iv. Wash tank.
v. Circulation cleaning tank (if separate from wash tank).
vi. Hand basin (if included, as extra to wash tank).
vii. Milk cooler (whether bulk tank, surface cooler or sparge rings).
viii. Bucket tap in dairy.
ix. Pressure taps in parlour, collecting yard, box.
x. Supply tanks for automatic drinking bowls in box.
xi. External trough (near exit to parlour).
xii. Other taps for individual requirements.

c. A hot supply should be taken to:

i. Parlour pit, possibly with mixer for spray udder washing.
ii. Wash tank.
iii. Circulation cleaning tank.
iv. Wash basin.

Hot-water requirements are difficult to assess. Circulation cleaning with most methods will require hot water at about 85° C (185° F) almost immediately after milking has finished and, depending on the layout, this might be based on a minimum of 2 gal/unit plus about 2 gal. Thus, a 6 stall/3 unit tandem might need at least 10 gal and a 16 stall/8 unit herringbone 18 gal. In addition, for washing the cows about 1 gal of water at about 32° C (85° F)/6–8 cows will be required and, for preference, this will be used via a spray nozzle jet provided at every unit, or in a herringbone at every 2 units. Hot water will be required also for general washing. The problem is to decide whether all the water should be heated to 85° C in one tank, some being diluted with cold as required, or whether, after milking, a powerful immersion should boost the water in the tank from 32° to 85° C within 20–30 min. Large herds justify the use of two heated tanks, both of which should be lagged, that for water at the higher temperature being heated in off-peak rate periods (Vol. 2). For the lower temperatures, Calor gas can be used instead of electricity.

d. It is probable that heat pumps will be developed in the near future, and a prototype has heated 130 gal of water to 62° C every day when 170 gal of milk has been cooled with a $\frac{3}{4}$-h.p. motor. Considerable electrical savings are forecast, the unit costing perhaps about £100 (11).

11. Costs

a. Costs for parlour units are impossible to give comprehensively, since there are many variables. Equipment costs vary widely between manufacturers, since different facilities in operation are given by different plant. The cost per standing for the stallwork in different parlours, including mangers, pipe-line milking and recording equipment, and installation (including, in the case of herringbone parlours, automatic feeders and hoppers at about £16/standing) might be given on a comparative basis:

8S/4U herringbone	£85–£100	per stall
16S/8U ,, ,,	£70–£85	,, ,,
6S/3U tandem	£100–£110	,, ,,
6S/3U chute	£80–£90	,, ,,
3S/3U tandem	£140–£150	,, ,,
6S/3U abreast	£80–£90	,, ,,

Direct-to-churn milking and recording:

6S/3U tandem	£85–£95	,, ,,
6S/3U chute	£65–£75	,, ,,

In any parlour additional equipment might add £10–£30/standing for fairly normal extra requirements. Pipe-lines cost about £$\frac{1}{2}$/ft.R. Dairy equipment will be in addition to these figures, and recirculation plant, extra wash-tank, hand basin, drainer, cupboard and two water heaters might cost between £150 and £250. Cooling equipment will vary, but might cost £50–£150, with the alternative of a bulk tank, without any concession, about £8/gal storage space for a small tank, decreasing to £4 for a large tank. The equipment required for a 16 stall/8 unit herringbone parlour and dairy is unlikely to be less than £1500–£1800, excluding a bulk tank, when installed. This represents about £375 p.a. (6–7 yr depreciation) which for 120 cows averaging 1200 gal is less than $\frac{3}{4}$d. per gal, or averaging 900 gal about 1d. per gal.

b. Portable and proprietary bails are relatively cheap. A 6 stall/3 unit abreast unit might cost up to £80–£100/standing, whereas a 4 stall/2 unit two-level chute unit about £200/standing. However, there are many variables possible, including the inclusion of a dairy, a raised food store and the possible need for a concrete standing. Bails can be hired.

c. The building costs are difficult to assess. Many parlours are installed in a converted building, or the structure is an integral part of the housing layout. Not all parlour units include a holding box, few a small anciliary shippon for milking sick cows, etc., nor do many include a food store. The standards of construction, finish and servicing of parlours are probably more varied than any other farm building. The standard required or justified will depend on the efficiency and throughput planned for the enterprise. For example, a 30-cow herd averaging 800 gal could not justify the same investment per cow as a 80-cow herd averaging 1000–1200 gal.

A simple, but well-fitted, 6-stall tandem parlour, with dairy, motor-room, foodstore and box, is unlikely to cost less than £100/standing and could cost £150/standing, if good finishes and mechanical aids are included. A comparative chute parlour might be £10–£20/standing less. A compact herringbone layout, with the same additional accommodation, for 16 standings might cost the same, that is £100–£150/standing. However, a total cost of up to £5000 for the building, including a shippon, race, box, tractor-shed, dairy, office, motor-room and foodstore may be required or, with the equipment, £6500. The latter would represent about £1100 p.a. and, for 180 cows averaging 1000 gal about 1$\frac{1}{2}$d./gal, but, since this might be a 2-man unit to manage, the labour cost would be only about 4d./gal inclusive of relief milking costs. If the housing and food storage and handling unit cost £100/place (IIIA, 11, p. 180) this would represent perhaps £15 per cow p.a. at most, or 3$\frac{1}{2}$d./gal. A total cost of under 9$\frac{1}{2}$d./gal for fixed equipment and labour should give a reasonable profit. However, if the unit was for only 140 cows, that is 70/man, the costs would be increased to about 11d. and 1s./gal respectively, and this might be a reasonable investment in some circumstances.

12. References

(1) ROBERTS, W. P. 'Selecting a Milking Parlour'. *Agricultural Review*, p. 10 (Autumn 1958).

(2) DALTON, H. L., HUFFMANN, C. F. & RALSTON, N. P. 'The effect of feeding concentrates with different degrees of fineness and water content on the eating and milking times'. *J. Dairy Sci.*, Vol. 36 (1953).

(3) Based on information from BELSHAW, D. G. R. & CROFTS, R. B. I.

(4) DODD, F. H. & CLOUGH, P. A. 'Measurement of performance in machine milking'. *NAAS Review*, No. 43, p. 103 (1959).

(5) DODD, F. H. & CLOUGH, P. A. 'Ratio Research'. *Farmers Weekly*, p. 91 (12th April 1957).

(6) Cambridge Report 58. See below, pp. 43–4.

(7) Cambridge Technical Report 1. See below, p. 47.

(8) PHELPS, A. 'Cow comfort counts in a herringbone'. *Dairy Farmer*, pp. 58–63 (October 1963).

(9) HOYLE, J. B. 'Which bulk tank'. *Dairy Farmer*, pp. 37–41 (October, 1963).

(10) STRAHAN, S. L. 'Method of design, insulation and ventilation for animal shelter buildings'. *Agricultural Engineering*, p. 407 (October 1945).

(11) HALL, H. S. & CROMARTY, A. S. 'Combined milk cooling and water heating'. *Farm Mechanization*, p. 299 (August 1962).

SELECTED REFERENCES

a. EASTON, P. H. & HARVEY, C. H. 'The development and performance of the herringbone parlour with special reference to Great Britain'. Agricultural Research Council (1964).

b. NIX, J. S., BELSHAW, D. G. R. & WELLER, J. B. 'The Yard and Parlour: capital costs and work requirements'. Farm Economics Branch School of Agriculture, Cambridge. Report 58. (1962).

c. BELSHAW, D. G. R. & SCOTT, A. H. 'Work routines and work elements for Yard and Parlour and Cowshed systems'. Farm Economics Branch School of Agriculture, Cambridge. Report (Work Study) No. 1 (1962).

d. 'A bibliography of Farm Buildings Research 1945–58 Pt. IV. Buildings for Cattle'. Agricultural Research Council (1960); also 1958–61 (1963).

e. SCOTT, A. H. 'A work study exercise in milking parlour performances'. Farm Economics Branch School of Agriculture, Cambridge. Report (Work Study) No. 3 (1963).

f. CLOUGH, P. A., HALL H. S. & THIEL, C. C., Mechanization of milk production. Farm Mechanization. March, April, May and June 1964.

g. Code of Practice C. P. 11: 1963, Farm Dairy Buildings.

h. 'Building for the dairy cow', National Farm Buildings Conference Report, *Farmers Weekly* (Autumn 1964).

IIG. Dipping and Shearing

1. *Activity*

a. Shearing sheep is a secondary activity within the production of mutton and lamb (IIIG): but the wool crop can be an important by-product to the latter, sometimes accounting for nearly one-third of a sheep farmer's income (1). In fact, wool is the most valuable of all farm products, considered by weight. It would be possible to consider a shearing shed as a production building within Section III. However, wool, like milk, is grown or produced either in the open or within a production building designed specifically for the conversion of coarse foods into more valuable products. After the milk or wool has been produced, in both cases it has to be processed within another building designed for the additional requirement of extracting the product from the animal.

b. A separate activity, but allied to that of shearing, since both involve the handling of sheep through an operation area, is that of dipping sheep. Dipping is compulsory in order to control sheep-scab, though it also kills parasites in the fleece, but the actual requirements vary in different counties. Many flockmasters prefer to spray their sheep rather than to dip them, since:

i. Dipping is a shock treatment which can have adverse effects.

ii. Spraying is cheaper in materials and equipment.

iii. Each sheep is sprayed with clean material, whereas a dip becomes fouled by the animals.

Similarly, foot-baths are desirable in order to keep the hooves healthy. In some cases the holding areas for the flock required prior to dipping and to shearing can be combined, though sometimes these activities are dispersed.

c. There are more than 30 recognized breeds of sheep, divided not only into regional types but also into long- or short-wooled varieties. The fleece of the different breeds is of variable quantity and quality, some breeds having no commercial wool crop and others having wool suitable either for cloth or for coarse fabrics, such as carpets. As discussed in IIIG, 1*b* (p. 235), flocks can be managed both on highland and on lowland; or they may be moved in the winter from highland to lowland pasture; or they can be held on a farm as a temporary, flying flock; or they can be inwintered.

d. Good feeding is essential, for a period of poor nutritional diet can cause weakness within the wool fibre. Therefore outwintering, when fodder is scarce and poor, can be detrimental to the wool growth. In fact, inwintered sheep should have a heavier and better wool yield, which in France has been claimed to be 50 per cent heavier than with outwintered sheep (2). Permanent housing of ewes at the Boots Experimental Farm also has shown that fleece weights are increased (3). It has been claimed that a hill sheep with a 4-lb fleece might produce a 7-lb fleece after one season of good lowland keep (1). Not only is the manner in which the wool is grown important, but the potential income can be reduced by bad shearing, dirty sheep and poor shearing facilities (Ref. *b*).

e. Nevertheless, it is generally accepted that there is a danger in over-capitalizing on sheep. Not only may winter housing be almost non-existent on most farms but the facilities for dipping and shearing may be very simple, in some cases primitive. Since these activities are summer operations, they can be performed in the open, either within an arrangement of holding pounds, walls and hurdles or within a temporary and portable layout formed entirely from hurdles. Therefore many layouts for dipping and shearing can be hardly termed as buildings. A simple sheep yard of hurdles for 300 ewes at the Northumberland Farm Institute, including a race and a footbath, cost only about £⅜/head, and a more elaborate layout for 100 ewes, including yards, treatment pens, race, footbath, weigher, and a spray and a dry race, for the Wiltshire Farm Institute, using farm labour for construction, was under £2/head (4). Similarly, shearing can be in the open, though there is a greater tendency towards permanent shearing sheds than towards permanent dipping yards.

2. *Managerial requirements*

a. Handling sheep quickly and efficiently is a difficult operation and, in order to reduce man-hours and strain, it is important to have a well-planned layout. Good layouts have been studied and developed in Australia and New Zealand. However, in those countries large numbers of sheep are managed by one man and, since specialist shearers may work for 10 months in each year, the cost of expensive buildings can be justified, since the cost per lb of wool may be slight. In the United Kingdom, on many farms dipping and shearing may be confined to about 3–6 days a year, and hand shearing is still practised widely. In fact, machine shearing may not be justified for flocks of fewer than 200 sheep.

b. In shearing, cleanliness and speed are important. These factors can be controlled more easily in specialized buildings rather than in the open. However, well-planned buildings, fully equipped, as opposed to converted buildings providing little else than shelter, may not be justified for flocks of fewer than 1000 sheep. Good shearing is a matter of rhythm, and the shearer should not have any distraction from that operation, all other work being undertaken by assistants.

c. A shearer using hand clippers should have a throughput of 10–16 sheep/hr, but with a machine this can be 40–150/day, though a New Zealand record is 456/day. A team of 10 can shear up to 700 hill ewes/day, with one catching, seven hand clipping, one wrapping and one marking (5). Shearing and dipping are essentially a matter of teamwork. Two men using a simple layout can dip 500 sheep/hr (6). Alternatively in another simple layout one man can dose 400 sheep/hr (7), or on another farm one man can

dose and inoculate 80 sheep/hr (8). Therefore seasonal labour requirements need not be exacting.

3. *Production techniques*

a. There are many different layouts suitable for handling sheep in order to dip them; but, for the most part, layouts include a number of specific areas, though varying in size, in detail and in arrangement. The handling yards may be used not only for the seasonal operations of dipping and shearing but for regular tasks, such as sorting, culling, dosing and the examination of feet. The facilities provided should take into consideration all the aspects of maintaining sheep in health. The basis of all sheep yards is that sheep will follow each other with little hesitation. The main areas required are:

i. Collecting pen: capable of taking the complete flock, both ewes and lambs.

ii. Holding pen: for small units, one holding pen is sufficient, capable of holding a manageable number of sheep taken from the collecting pen; but a large layout will contain several holding pens leading from a main holding pen connecting with the collecting pen.

iii. Shedder pen: it should be possible to extract sheep both from the collecting and from the holding pens into a shedder pen or race for further examination. The race can include a footbath and, if required, can be extended to include a weigher.

iv. Catching pen: the sheep should be able to enter a catching pen from the main holding pen, the former being used to drive the sheep into the dipper. For preference, the sheep should enter the catching pen at right angles to the exit into the dipper, so that the catching pen appears to be a by-pass to the dipper. Many catching pens are circular, containing 2 or 3 gates hinged from a central post, the gates being revolved to lead the sheep into the dipper. In some layouts there may be decoy pens, each holding a sheep, in order to coax the flock forward, and sited so that the other sheep unwittingly are led into the dipper. (These should not be necessary in a good layout.)

v. Dipper: the dipper leading out of the catching pen can include an automatic trap-door in the floor, shedding the sheep direct into the tank.

vi. Draining pen: the dipper should lead into one or more draining pens, each pen holding the same number of sheep as the catching pen, with the floor draining into the dipper.

vii. Drying pens: the drying area for the sheep may be in the form of one or more pens and can include further races and a loading ramp, if required.

b. The collecting pen used for the sheep dipping yards can be also used prior to shearing. However, sheep must be not only clean but dry when sheared, and they must be held under cover the night prior to shearing, close together so that they generate warmth, without being fed. Therefore most shearing sheds include the following basic accommodation:

i. Holding pens: one or more holding pens for overnight housing. (This area could form part of the inwintering house (IIIG), since it should have a slatted floor.)

ii. Catching pens: one catching pen for each shearer.

iii. Shearing area: sufficient space for each operator.

iv. Exit yards: holding areas for shorn sheep if required.

v. Woolroom: for handling and storing wool.

vi. Store: for equipment.

4. *Work routines*

a. Labour requirements for dipping sheep in a good layout are simple, though the flock does have to be driven into the collecting pen, and the dip has to be prepared (see 2, above). Unless there is an automatic trap-door into the dipper, the sheep may have to be manhandled; in any case, the catching pen has to be operated and at least one other man is required for guiding sheep through the yards, except in simple layouts. Obviously, temporary and portable layouts may need many hours for erecting and dismantling hurdles. In a few layouts one man can manage on his own, though this is not desirable except with a skilled shepherd working a simple but efficient layout (7 and 8).

b. Shearing requires specialized labour, with one shearer per operational point, supported by an assistant to catch the sheep, keeping the catching pen full, to remove the wool, to sweep the shearing area, to wrap or pack the wool, to mark the sheep if required and to be in general attendance. In fact, usually two or more assistants are required. The fleece is packed into wool-sacks, and eventually these have to be loaded on to lorries for sale. The space under the slatted floor has to be cleaned. At least one farmer has a mobile trailer for shearing, powered by a diesel engine, and four men can shear from the trailer. With one man to wind the wool, 100 sheep/shearer/day can be managed (9).

5. *Design data*

a. Collecting Pens and Holding Pens
These should be based on 5 ft²/head, though small breeds may require less (IIIG, *a*, p. 235). The collecting pen should have an entrance gate at least 8 ft wide at one corner, so that the flanking walls act as guides for the movement of the flock, with the gate opening outwards. Gates into side holding pens can be smaller. Pen floor surfaces can be of fine aggregate on free-draining rubble.

b. Catching Pen (Dipping)
If circular, this should have a diameter of 12–16 ft, and if it has three revolving gates from a central post it will contain three compartments, with one batch of sheep being forced into the dipper, another held in readiness and the third being open to the holding pens for filling, with the sheep in the second compartment acting as decoys for the third compartment. With a 16-ft-dia pen, each compartment would hold about 10 sheep.

c. Dipper
The tank should hold at least 80 gal or ½ gal/head for larger tanks. Therefore the length of the tank will vary, a short tank being provided for small breeds and a long tank for large breeds, the latter also possibly of a greater depth; a suitable tank in each case for 800 ewes is shown in Fig. 62 (Ref. *a*).

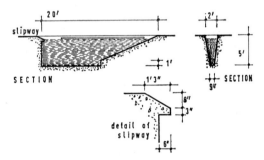

Fig. 62. Dipping tank (large breeds) (Ref. *a*)

The entrance should be vertical, with a sloping lip to the floor from the catching pen, the operator's pit, 3 ft × 2 ft in area, being adjacent to the entry and to the left of it. The exit ramp should not be steeper than 30 degrees, the ramp being slatted for grip. The top of the tank walls should have an anti-splash groove, and there should be 3-ft-high walls guarding the entrance. Many tanks are prefabricated, being sunk into the ground. Usually, tanks are 2 ft wide at the top, with about ¾ ft at the bottom. But if a tipping platform is used, perhaps operated by an overhead counterbalanced arm, this should tip into a pool leading into the tank, the pool being about 6 ft × 3 ft × 4 ft deep. The dipper and pit should be drained through an outlet and valve or outlet pipe.

d. Spray-baths
These can be prefabricated units above ground, approximately 10–20 ft long, 4 ft high, with overhead and side spray pipes along the length, and

with sides sloping from 2 to $\frac{3}{4}$ ft at the bottom. The spray can be operated from a tractor. The effectiveness of the spray is important, dependent to some extent on the length of the spray race; if it should ever supersede dipping, races 40 ft long might be required.

e. Draining pens
Though these should hold the same number of sheep as the catching or collecting pen, their width should be about 6–10 ft. The floor should have diagonal grooves with a cross-fall of 1 in. and a longitudinal fall of $\frac{1}{2}$ ft, draining into a channel and then into a strainer, before the liquid returns into the deep end of the dipper.

f. Footbaths
These should be at least 20 ft long, with longitudinal corrugations to spread the feet open, the bath being 10 in. wide by 4–6 in. deep, with the sides of the bath haunched to give a race width of 2 ft. The bath should have a drain pipe.

g. Race and Pen Walls
Though solid walls $3\frac{1}{2}$ ft high can be used, post-and-rail fences are usual, with 4-in. $\times$ 4-in. posts at 6-ft centres, with four rails $3\frac{1}{2}$ in. $\times$ $1\frac{1}{2}$ in., with the bottom rail $5\frac{1}{2}$ in. above the ground. The rails should be internal to the race or pen.

h. Overnight Holding Pens
Details of slatted floors are given in IIIG, 5a (p. 237).

i. Catching Pen (Shearing)
Usually holding about 12–15 sheep, therefore about 7 ft $\times$ 8 ft or 10 ft $\times$ 7 ft in area. There should be a close-boarded or solid partition between the pen and the shearing area, so that the sheep are not frightened while waiting. The floor should be slatted, with the slats at right angles to the shearing-area gate, possibly with a slight fall towards the gate; the latter, $2\frac{1}{2}$ ft wide, opposite the shearing position, should have a self-closing spring.

j. Shearing Area
The design of the shearing area is important. Machine shearing positions should be not closer than at 5-ft centres, preferably at about 8-ft centres. The work area between the catching pen and the external wall should be about $7\frac{1}{2}$ ft—less prevents access past a man shearing and more increases the distance for fetching the sheep for shearing. The machine should be at least 1 ft from the external wall, with most machines having a gear post about $8\frac{1}{2}$ ft high, plus $1\frac{1}{2}$ ft under the floor with a $\frac{1}{2}$-h.p. motor. The work space itself is about 4 ft square. The floor should be of close-

boarded softwood or of a taut tarpaulin over a firm base. The exit hole should be $1\frac{3}{4}$ ft wide $\times$ $2\frac{1}{2}$ ft high, positioned $\frac{1}{2}$ ft along the wall from the gear post, with a chute for the sheep down into a holding area. Good north light on the shearing area is essential, sunlight and glare being avoided.

k. Woolroom
The woolroom should open off the shearing area and should contain a wool table, 9 ft $\times$ 4 ft $\times$ 3 ft high, with a slatted top and with workspace all round at least $2\frac{1}{2}$ ft wide. The woolroom should include storage space for woolsacks and fleeces, perhaps on the basis of 3 ft²/sheep. The surfaces of the room should be of timber, brick or concrete being too cold and liable to become damp from condensation. Sunlight should be excluded. There should be a loading bay, with doors, to the farm road and away from the sheep.

l. Store
A small lock-up store, perhaps 6 ft $\times$ 4 ft, is desirable either opening off the shearing area or out of the woolroom.

m. Ventilation
Permanent high-level ventilation is desirable to the penning, work area and woolroom, supplemented by controlled cross ventilation for working in warm weather.

n. Lighting
Sheep tend to be drawn towards the light and it is, therefore, desirable for the level of illumination to be increased from the back of the holding pens towards the shearing area. However, they do not like facing direct sunlight, which should be avoided both in the shearing shed and in the handling yards. Similarly, very bright and dark areas should be avoided, and the sheep should not have to move towards a blank wall or odd machinery.

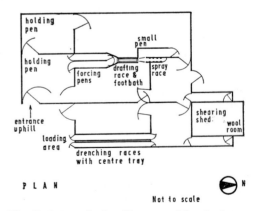

Fig. 63. Layout for handling several hundred ewes (Ref. b)

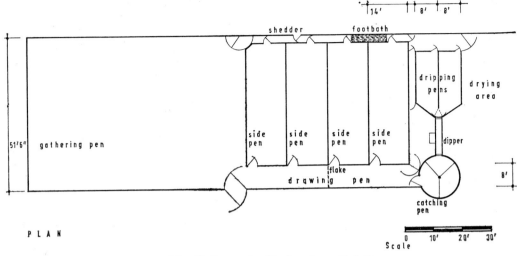

Fig. 64. Layout for dipping sheep (Ref. 2)

o. Levels

Sheep move uphill for preference; therefore the entrance into yards and pens should be uphill.

6. *Equipment.* Generally, equipment is limited, unless all the sheep yards are made from portable hurdles, footbaths, spray races, etc. Reference has been made to the shearing machine, which also includes combs and cutters having to be replaced or resharpened on a revolving disc, driven usually by a 1-h.p. motor, one comb lasting for 80 sheep, and one cutter for 40 sheep. In addition, a hand-towel should be adjacent to the shearing position.

7. *Environmental control.* A shearing shed should have a ventilated ridge and louvred gable ventilation, as well as windows or shutters in the walls. North rooflights on to the working positions are desirable, supplemented by fluorescent lighting. The slatted floors should be in removable panels above a dung cellar $1\frac{1}{2}$ ft deep, sealed against draughts, but with tractor doors for cleaning.

8. *Layout*

a. Moranne has shown one New Zealand layout suitable for several hundred ewes, the pen sizes being adjusted for different flocks, but having several pens which can be used for various purposes, both in conjunction with dipping and with shearing (Ref. *b*), (Fig. 63).

b. The West of Scotland Agricultural College has shown a simple layout suitable for dipping sheep (Ref. *a*), (Fig. 64).

c. Bulmer has shown a simple, conventional layout for dipping sheep (Fig. 65), together with a more advanced layout (Fig. 66, p. 154) (10).

d. Fig. 66 shows a layout suitable for two shearing positions in a shearing shed.

9. *Siting.* The siting of dipping yards and shearing sheds is not easy, since such factors as shelter, transport, sheep access, good drainage and water supply have to be considered, with an electrical supply for machine shearing. In addition, an uphill movement to the dipper and a north light for shearing are desirable. Not only should dipping and

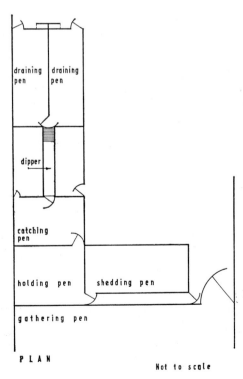

Fig. 65. Conventional layout for dipping sheep (Ref. 10)

153

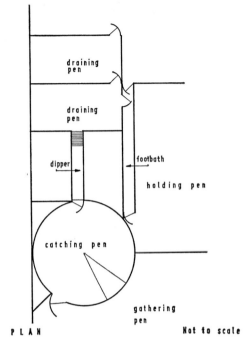

PLAN   **Not to scale**

Fig. 66. Advanced layout for dipping sheep
(Ref. 10)

(5) *Farmers Weekly Supplement*. A Shepherd's Guide',
p. xxiv (10th August 1962).

(6) FLINT, P. 'Dipping the easy way'. *Farmers Weekly*,
p. 101 (21st September 1956).

(7) CHARLTON, R. 'How one man doses 400 sheep an
hour'. *Farmers Weekly*, p. 70 (31st January 1964).

(8) CHARLTON, R. 'Built for speed'. *Farmers Weekly*,
pp. 81–2 (14th June 1963).

(9) 'Farming People: Mr. Ramsden puts shearing on
wheels'. *Farmers Weekly* (14th June 1963).

(10) BULMER, W. J. 'Some sheep handling pens and
dippers'. *Agriculture* (July 1961).

SELECTED REFERENCES

a. FORSYTH, R. J. West of Scotland Agricultural College
Advisory Leaflet 69. 'Sheep-dipping structures'
(1958).

b. MORANNE, N. A. 'Designing your own sheep yard';
'Layout for a shearing shed'; 'Routine for Shearing'.
Farmers Weekly (22nd March 1963; 3rd May 1963;
17th May 1963).

c. CLARKE, H. G. *Commercial Sheep Management*,
Crosby Lockwood, 1963.

shearing operations be together, but they should be
central to the main sheep areas and possibly to
winter housing.

10. *Services.* Though a supply of water and electricity may be required, care in draining sheep dip
is essential, the waste liquid being kept clear of all
water-courses.

11. *Costs.* Costs should be kept to the minimum,
though a well-planned dipping and shearing unit
can cost £10/head for 200 ewes, the cost per head
being less for larger flocks. Simple dipping layouts
should cost not more than £2–£3/head and a
shearing shed £4–£6 for 200–300 ewes. But a cost
of £10/ewe represents only £1½ p.a. Labour costs
are low in a good layout, so the cost of building and
labour per fleece, considering that the fleece should
be of better quality, may not be high.

12. *References*
(1) BRITISH OIL & CAKE MILLS LTD. *Sheep Farmers
Handbook*, pp. 26–7 (1959).
(2) TROW-SMITH, R. 'Sheep, the inside storey'. *Farmer
and Stockbreeder*, pp. 100–1 (14th March 1961).
(3) *Farmers Weekly*. 'When the flock comes in', pp.
99–101 (15th March 1963).
(4) *Farming Express*. 'Simple sheep-yards', pp. 16–17.
(10th May 1962).

IIH. Potato Chitting

1. *Activity.* The annual storage of seed potatoes,
in order to promote preliminary sprout growth
prior to planting, is an essential part of potato production. Some storage is made in sacks, but this is
inefficient, except as a temporary measure; and
other storage is made in clamps in the fields,
though this method has disadvantages similar to
those with ware potatoes (1H). Chitting potatoes is
best within a controlled environment, though this
is not yet common practice. Potato chitting can be
more akin to horticultural practice than other farm
activities, especially since, in some cases, traditional glasshouses are used. However, seed potatoes
are often grown and stored by farmers who do not
handle horticultural produce. For this reason,
potato chitting houses are considered as farm
buildings.

Seed production is principally in areas free from
serious aphid attack, since aphids transmit virus
diseases, which can cause losses in seed potatoes.
Therefore, by tradition, seed is grown mainly in
Scotland and Ireland, and, to a small extent, in
coastal and upland parts of England and Wales.
Thus, not many producers of ware potatoes also
grow their own seed. In fact, nearly 1M tons of
seed potatoes are bought annually for ware production. But not all seed is stored on farms where
it is grown. Chitting houses may be erected either
on the farm growing the seed or on that growing
the ware potato, though they could be at any inter-

mediate point between the two farms, possibly even controlled by a middleman. However, aphids can now be controlled by modern field spraying techniques. Thus, in the future seed and ware production may be combined on many more farms than at present, or seed may be grown on contract for several ware producers within the same district. The quantity of seed potatoes required per acre usually varies between $\frac{1}{2}$ and $1\frac{1}{4}$ T, though $\frac{3}{4}$–1 T might be normal for most planting.

2. *Managerial requirements*

a. All potatoes are dormant for several weeks after lifting and will not sprout unless stored in high temperatures or subjected to certain chemicals. In fact, sprouting can be restricted or prevented at temperatures below 5° C (40° F). The natural period of dormancy differs with variety and locality, sprouting occurring sooner with early varieties and in warmer districts. Growth should be induced in the autumn, when the seed is capable of growing only one or two sprouts, since, if sprouting is delayed, too many stems will be grown, preventing the potato growing to an economical size (1). But this autumn growth will become too long, pale and weak unless controlled.

b. Temperature can control the start and rate of sprouting, and the intensity of light controls the greening and strength of the sprout. The light/temperature relationship is critical, and control is required at all stages during storage. The seed has to be sprouted correctly, ready for the date of planting.

3. *Production techniques*

a. Seed potatoes are handled and stored in buildings within timber trays, which could be designed for movement by fork-lift truck, and the density of the bulk storage depends on each seed being able to obtain sufficient light and air. Seed, being smaller than ware potatoes, packs to a greater density, a factor which tends to raise the temperature among the seed above that normal among ware. However, due to the trays, the total density in the store is considerably lower.

b. Trays can be stored in glasshouses, which, in many parts, should provide sufficient natural heat for autumn sprout growth, but ventilation is essential to restrict excess growth, especially in the spring. However, glasshouses need a high standard of management for success, being susceptible to variations of external temperature, and it is almost impossible to control the light/temperature relationship. During cold weather considerable artificial heat will be required to prevent frost damage. Some recent experiments may show that double glazing, possibly with the use of plastics, considerably reduces or eliminates the need for artificial heat. Even so, the capital cost of a glasshouse, being £20–£30/T, is high, and maintenance can be excessive, unless the best houses are bought, in metal rather than in timber, with well-fitted glass.

c. Alternatively, trays can be stored in insulated barns, without windows and with a completely controlled environment. It has been claimed that this method can increase yields by 25 per cent (2). Almost any building which can be insulated, and in which electricity is available for light and heat, can be converted for potato chitting and used out of season for other purposes. Even if a new building is erected the capital and running costs should be lower than for a glasshouse.

d. As a result of further experiments, some chemical, such as amyl alcohol, may be used in the future to control the sprout growth of seed. At present the yield to be expected from seed treated in this manner has not been established. Application of the chemical would be similar to the method used for fumigation of ware potatoes (1H, 6*f*, p. 83).

4. *Work routines*

a. The principal labour requirements in chitting houses are during loading and unloading, which are seasonal tasks. The former depends both on the method of harvesting and on the place for sorting the seed into trays. It is good practice to load the store early in the autumn, but, provided there is sufficient time for sprouting, loading can be at any time during the winter, though autumn growth may be diminished. Unloading depends on either the date for planting or the date for despatch of the seed for sale. In either case, delay in unloading has to be avoided.

b. Normally, seed trays are stacked and unstacked in the store by hand, which is time-consuming. A fork-lift truck could be used to mechanize the task, but it is unlikely to be economic unless a truck is required for other enterprises. However, to save handling, it is desirable to have transport access doors at both ends of the building.

c. Frequent inspection is essential during storage. The temperature must be regulated, and heaters and ventilators adjusted. However, chitting barns require more labour than glasshouses and demand the same thoroughness in inspection. As soon as sprouting starts, lighting must be switched on for 8–12 hr/day, though this can be controlled by a time-switch, the period being increased until lighting is continuous during maximum growth. Ventilation has to be increased as the temperature rises. During growth the light units are moved daily from one stack of trays to the next.

5. *Design data*
a. Trays

The basis of the store is the seed tray. A standard tray measures $2\frac{1}{2}$ ft $\times$ $1\frac{1}{2}$ ft $\times$ $\frac{1}{2}$ ft, the sides being half open, but other tray sizes are used. A standard tray can hold $\frac{1}{3}$ cwt of seed, but $\frac{1}{4}$ cwt is considered more efficient, even though more space for storage is required.

b. Stacking

Trays are stacked in rows, two deep, except where a row one deep is against a wall, and with alleys between the rows between $1\frac{1}{2}$ and 2 ft wide. Thus, a double row, plus one gangway $1\frac{1}{2}$ ft wide, measures $4\frac{1}{2}$ ft. Stacks are usually 14–20 trays high, i.e. 7–10 ft. Many glasshouses are about 8 ft to the eaves, and light units 10 ft high are economic in barns. In any case, manual stacking above 10 ft is strenuous. A store 20 trays high holds about $\frac{1}{4}$ T/ft.R in double row. Thus, a store 18 ft wide, with 4 gangways, holds about 1 T/ft.R of building. Glasshouses may have no internal gangways, the trays being stacked close together, and with glass walls taken to floor level. Therefore, densities in glasshouses are greater than in barn houses.

c. Temperature

Seed must be protected from frost, and an internal temperature of 5° C (40° F) should be the normal minimum, since this is sufficient to prevent or to check growth. It has been shown that storage at 10° C (50° F) gave higher yields than with storage at other temperatures between 0° and 10° C (3). Some varieties will grow strongly at 6° C (45° F). Temperatures above 10° C are not required, though 20° C (75°–80° F) for a short period might be desirable to stimulate initial growth. Heat may be obtained from the sun, from the potatoes (1H, 5b, p. 82), from the electric lights, if used, or from heaters. Heat from the potatoes and the lights might cause a temperature gradient of 1°–2° C (5° F) from floor to ceiling, affecting the evenness of sprouting.

d. Relative Humidity

A R.H. of 80 per cent has given satisfactory results (4). However, 90 per cent is considered to be optimum, when the temperature is under 5° C (40° F).

e. Illumination

Though natural sunlight gives good illumination, if artificial sources are required, then a warm white light should be provided. Research has shown that sprout growth is inhibited progressively by radiation in the yellow, green, blue, violet, red and infra-red bands (5). Artificial light should have to penetrate for not more than the width of one tray, i.e. $1\frac{1}{2}$ ft, in order to be effective in illuminating stored trays. Glass chitting houses are seldom more than 20 ft wide, in order that illumination may be satisfactory in all parts, though, obviously, the side nearest the sun will grow fastest. Light transmission is assisted if the tray bottoms are white.

f. Ventilation

Fan ventilation is an asset, capable of delivering 40 C.F.M./T stored at 1·5 w.g., if cold air is available for the intake. Perhaps, 15 air changes/hr should be allowed. Thermostats are desirable, one operating at $\frac{1}{2}$° C (31° F), against frost, and the other at the desired maximum temperature. Rod-type thermostats are most suitable. Glasshouses can have natural cross-ventilation coupled to ridge ventilation. Gable ventilators can be used in both types of house. Evaporation losses are less important than with ware potatoes.

g. Access Doors

End access doors for transport should be at least 8 ft wide by 10–15 ft high, depending on the building. However, there ought in addition to be a small pedestrian door.

h. Insulation

Insulation of controlled barn stores should be at least equal to the standards for ware potatoes. In fact, electric fans and heaters in heavily insulated chitting houses may be shown to be economic after further research. Cavity walls, with an internal insulating block or clad skin and an insulated roof with at least 1 in. of glass fibre, are desirable, but floors can be of earth, as long as they are level. Concrete floors are preferable for movement and stacking.

6. *Equipment*
a. Artificial Lighting

Fluorescent units, hung vertically, are the basis of controlled, indoor sprouting. The tubes should be suspended from above the top tray to the floor, being hung on a monorail with a straining wire, so that the unit can be moved. Monorails can be made from curtain track mounted on timber. The tubes should have a choke control. Special units for chitting houses are available, 8 or 10 ft long, including capacitor, choke and starter. The units should be earthed. The tubes should hang central in the passages, since the intensity of light falling on any point varies inversely to the square of the distance between the source of light and that point. Even and uniform lighting is required. For main crops, there should be at least one movable light point per 15 ft.R of passage, preferably one for each 10 ft.R, and, for early varieties, one for every

$7\frac{1}{2}$ ft.R. The units could be coupled to an off-peak lighting rate for much of the season. An 8-ft tube might be of 125 watts to give an average intensity of light suitable for the seed.

b. Heaters

Artificial heat should be required less frequently than fan ventilation and, during some winters in well-insulated glasshouses or barns, perhaps not at all. It is best to install fan heaters, perhaps of 3 or 5 kW, with a high air displacement for a low rise in temperature, either low down in the store or in the roof, with ducting to points near the floor. This helps to give an even distribution of heat. One heater/4 T stored may be necessary to give complete control, though a 3-kW heater per 10 T should be adequate. The fans can be used without the heat banks for ventilation, if they are mounted at high level. Some glasshouses have hot-water heating pipes heated from an external boiler.

c. Ventilators

Fan ventilation is essential, not only to remove excessive heat but more particularly to keep the temperature gradient within the house to the minimum. The fans can be coupled to heater banks. The size of fan depends on the shape of the store, but a very rough guide would be to allow one 9-in.-dia fan per 10–15 T of potatoes. The fans should be mounted at high level on the outside walls, pointing diagonally downwards and slightly inwards, all facing clockwise or anti-clockwise on alternate sides of the store.

7. *Environmental control.* Lighting and ventilation has been discussed above and reference has been made to insulation requirements. However, the degree of environment control which is desirable and economic has not yet been established by research. Though lighting is essential, as discussed, for barns, though not for glasshouses, the heating and ventilation requirements and even much evidence with regard to standards for lighting have not been fully related to subsequent potato yields. However, it seems probable that greater rather than lesser control will be required in the future.

8. *Layout.* Fig. 67 shows a simple layout for a chitting house holding about 80 T of seed. Other layouts are possible, but most would be based on a similar plan.

9. *Siting.* With few exceptions, chitting houses must be near an electrical supply. Good access is

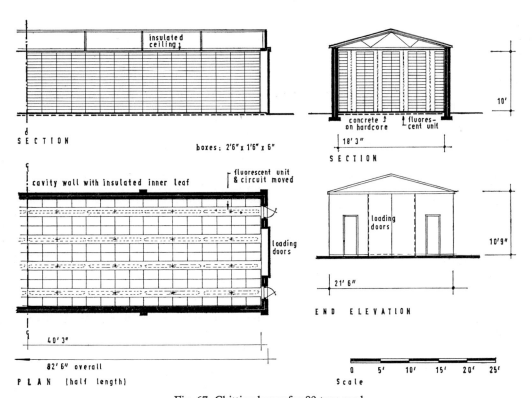

Fig. 67. Chitting house for 80 tons seed

essential, preferably to both ends of the house. The house should be sited close to the store manager's home, since supervision is essential. Reference has been made to whether chitting should be near where ware potatoes are grown. Barn houses may be sited near another enterprise, if they can be used for alternative purposes during the summer. Glasshouses should be away from frost pockets.

10. *Services.* Electrical supply is required for lighting, heating and ventilation in many houses. The supply should be taken internally round the building at high level, protected against humidity. The building must be free from damp, with rainwater taken clear of the footings.

11. *Costs.* As stated previously, a new glasshouse might cost £20–£30/T storage space. A well-fitted glasshouse for 60–100 T is likely to cost in the region of £30/T rather than £20/T. A well-equipped converted barn might cost £10–£15/T storage space. However, provision of lighting and heating is unlikely to cost less than £8/T storage space. A new barn chitting house is unlikely to cost less than £20/T storage space and could be over £25/T. The cost of chitting trays would be additional. A new barn costing £24/T storage space, including £8/T for heating and lighting, might be valued at £4½/T stored. The trays might represent another £3/T, and electrical charges are normally estimated to be £¼/T p.a. Therefore, the total annual cost, excluding labour, might be a little less than £8/T.

12. *References*
(1) TWISS, P. T. G. 'Electricity and Potato Storage'. *Agriculture*, pp. 264–70 (August 1961).
(2) MIDDLETON, O. 'Strip-lights, heat, lift spud yields'. *Farmers Weekly*, p. 61 (2nd February 1962).
(3) MATHUR, P. 'Studies in cold storage of potatoes'. *J. Sci. Industrial Res.*, pp. 224–8 (September 1951).
(4) MONTEAUX, A. 'The use of refrigeration for storing seed potatoes'. *Rev. prat. Froid.*, pp. 29–30 (August 1950).
(5) KRIJTHE, N. 'The effect of light of various wavelengths on sprouting and greening in potatoes'. *Yersl Inst. Landb. Onderz. Wageningen*, pp. 113–17 (1949).

SELECTED REFERENCES
a. TWISS, P. T. G. 'Electricity in Potato Husbandry'. *Electrical Development Association* (1961).
b. 'Potato Chitting Houses'. *Ministry of Agriculture F.E.F. Leaflet No. 48* (1961).
c. A Bibliography of Farm Buildings Research 1945–1958 Pt. II. 'Buildings for Potato Storage'. *Agricultural Research Council* (1960).

IIJ. Workshops

1. *Activity.* The importance of planned machinery maintenance, including its storage, servicing and repair, was discussed in IJ. An efficient farm has efficient machines. But, in order to service and repair machinery, it is essential to have a well-planned and fitted workshop. However, the effectiveness of a workshop depends on the trade skill possessed by the men who work within it. Workshop practice and the detailed fitting of workshops with plant and tools requires a lengthy, specialized study, such as has been given in some standard works (Ref. *a*), and cannot be considered in this section.

Generally, workshops are ill considered on farms. In many cases the workshop is not planned with the same efficiency as may occur in fieldwork or in a livestock enterprise, being under no one's direct charge and no more than a general-purpose collection of tools and spares situated in some building, perhaps no longer required for its original purpose. Sometimes the 'workshop' may be scattered in different buildings, each farm worker having his own private arrangement for repairs. A workshop should be centralized, with one man in charge of the tools and spares, and be planned in relation to the main implement shed, usually in conjunction with the main farm office.

Not every farm requires the same type or size of workshop, even when comparing farms of the same acreage. Obviously, there is a direct relationship between the planning of a workshop and the number and variety of machines on a farm. Occasionally some of the farm work will be under contract to independent contractors, when the latter may be responsible for the maintenance and repair of the machinery. This may be the case, for example, when corn is harvested by a contractor owning a combine. Some specialist machinery may be under guarantee by a manufacturer or machinery agent, whereupon the farmer may not be responsible for it. Similarly, some machinery may be so complex and delicate that only specialists should handle it, as in the case of bulk milk tanks.

The need for a workshop on a farm may be limited by the proximity of a good blacksmith or local workshop. In such cases a farmer may find it cheaper to allow most of his work to be carried out by such independent firms. An engineer or mechanic might be under contract to visit a farm at regular intervals, to service the machinery and to carry out non-urgent repairs. Many factors have to be considered by a farmer before deciding on the type of workshop required. However, one factor must be stressed. Though the servicing of machines can be planned to be undertaken at regular intervals, a machinery breakdown may be of urgent and vital importance, and the time taken to repair the fault may jeopardize a crop, the comfort and health of livestock and, in fact, the annual profit from a farm. A farmer may prefer not to rely on outside help, considering that a workshop and mechanic should be an essential part of the farm.

2. *Managerial requirements*

a. Large farms or estates may maintain an estate labour force as well as its agricultural staff, particularly if timber is grown commercially on the farm. The estate labour force may be no more than handymen, but they may include skilled tradesmen, bricklayers, electricians, joiners and plumbers, as well as handymen. In such cases the workshop for the agricultural machinery may be part of a bigger concern and its siting may be near a sawmill or a builder's yard. A few farmers may include steelwork or other mechanical engineering as one of their enterprises, and at least one farmer manufactures hermetically sealed silo components on his farm and within his general layout of buildings for other enterprises.

b. Basically there are three broad types of workshop which can be classified by the skill of the men using them:

i. A full-time craftsman mechanic would be provided with a well-equipped workshop.

ii. A semi-skilled mechanic, able to carry out normal servicing and minor repairs, might be provided either with a well-equipped workshop or with one restricted to some extent, perhaps having only one form of welding equipment. On many farms there is at least one man with an aptitude for engineering, who would profit by being released for a short period of specialist training. Generally, a part-time mechanic will not be taken from the staff in charge of livestock, but is more likely to be a fieldworker, available for workshop duties, except at peak times for fieldwork.

iii. An unskilled man, capable in servicing and simple maintenance tasks, rather than in repairs or constructional work, would need a small workshop with a few, general-purpose tools.

3. *Production techniques*

a. A well-planned workshop should open into the main implement shed, the latter being used partly as an extension to the workshop and probably containing a service pit to one of the tractor standing positions with a gantry beam over it. However, it is essential to be able to shut and lock the workshop independently of the implement shed.

b. The workshop should include a self-contained store for all spares. The control of spares on a farm, varying in size from a set of tyres to a full range of nuts and bolts, is vital to the efficiency of the workshop. Irrespective of the size and type of workshop, the store should be orderly, with special and named compartments for each spare normally stocked. Frequently storage is confined to a mixture of spares and junk in an odd corner of a workshop, which is inefficient. In a workshop with a full-time mechanic the store may be administered by the mechanic. But if there is no full-time mechanic employed, and sometimes in any case, the store may be under the control of the farm office or of the farmer. Therefore the store and office should be close together.

The arrival of new spares should be invoiced and filed in the office, and their removal from the store should be recorded, together with the date of issue and the name of the person receiving the spare, by the person in charge of the store. Military efficiency is desirable in this matter, though such a system may seem elaborate for a small farm with few machines. Many machines today include some parts which should be replaced after a predetermined period of use, that is, after a fixed number of working hours, irrespective of whether they appear to be worn out or not. Unrecorded use or lack of replacement of spares are bound to lead to waste of time in looking for parts when required.

c. On a well-planned farm all new machines, fittings and spares will be delivered to the workshop, where they can be checked by the mechanic and be adapted, if required, before use.

d. Most large farms will justify having a mobile, breakdown workshop used in conjunction with the permanent workshop. A truck, fully equipped with tools for normal repairs, should be available for instant use, even though this may mean doubling up some of the tools required on the farm. Sometimes it is more convenient to take the workshop to a machine which has broken down in the fields, than it is to take the damaged parts back to the workshop. In many cases speed in repair is vital, and the mechanic should not have to spend time collecting tools from his workshop.

e. All workshops will require workbenches, to a greater or lesser extent, but not all will include facilities for welding, even though little repair or structural work can be carried out without welding operations. There are three methods of welding, each of which requires equipment varying from about £10 to £100 in cost. There are few workshops which should not have one of the methods available and, since the methods complement rather than repeat each other in usefulness, any large workshop will include all three facilities.

i. Coke forge: the traditional method of heating metals for blacksmith work is desirable. Though a large forge and chimney may be expensive to construct, small portable forges, including a metal hood, are available, costing £10–£20, and these might have a metal exhaust flue available for a fixed position when used internally. They can have either manually or electrically powered fans.

ii. Oxy-acetylene welder: with its fittings, such as nozzles and goggles, might cost £30–£40, plus a small annual rental for the gas cylinders. It is the basis of most modern welding. However, if there is an arc-welder also available the oxy-acetylene might be set up almost permanently for cutting metal.

iii. Electric arc-welder: this, costing £80–£100, may not be considered essential, particularly if a forge and oxy-acetylene equipment are available, but in some cases it may prove safer and cheaper in use.

4. *Work routines.* Most workshop routines are based on trade skills and cannot be discussed in this section. However, work is of three main types, including servicing, repairs and constructional work. Servicing machinery, particularly tractors, should be based either on a strict time-table or on the number of operational hours. A chart in the workshop should record each machine, the hours used, the servicing dates and any minor faults not requiring immediate attention, and the mechanic should be able to plan his work from this chart, allowing for interruptions for emergency repairs. Obviously, the more workspace and benches available, the easier it is to have several jobs in the process of completion, thus allowing for some flexibility in the work. Though a workshop with a bench and a work passage about 6 ft wide could be adequate, it is desirable, for anything other than small jobs, to have a large room with benches and fittings spaced around a wide circulation area, which can be filled with temporary equipment for specific jobs. In fact, equipment for specific tasks may be grouped together. For example, tyre replacement and repair can be a frequent task when there are many wheeled machines on a farm, and a vulcanizer and other tools required for the job, placed together on one trolley, is an asset, since it can be taken easily to any position (1).

5. *Design data*
a. Workpit
This can be sited in or near the workshop, but, if a tractor shed adjoins the workshop, it is likely to be most convenient in the shed (Fig. 30, IJ, p. 89). A convenient size for most pits is 7 ft × 3½ ft × 4½ ft deep. There should be a rebate between the pit wall and shed floor to take 1½-in. board cover strips. The pit should be drained, which may be difficult on some sites. The wall of the pit may include a recessed shelf, to take small tools, and there may be a light and power plug, though it is usual for these to be provided on a lead from an electric point away from the pit, where they are not so liable to damage.

b. Gantry beam
A gantry beam, capable of carrying at least ¾ T, for use in lifting engines with a hoist on to tractors, should be suspended from the roof or carried on cross-walls, giving a clearance of about 12 ft. This might be positioned over the workpit. Alternatively, the beam could be supported on a wheeled trestle, so that it could straddle any tractor, and it might be designed to lift as much as 2 T (1). Otherwise, a work height of 8–10 ft should be adequate in the workshop.

c. Workbenches
There is no ideal type of workbench, though stability is an essential requirement. They are positioned, usually, against the workshop walls, though a large central worktable, with working positions on all sides, could be an asset, and a mobile worktable might be of use as well as a trolley. Work heights of 2½ or 3 ft are usual, though, in a large workshop, it would be desirable to have benches with different heights between 2 and 4 ft. Similarly, though a bench may be only 1½ ft wide, others up to 3 ft in width can be useful. On the benches, vices and other equipment will be mounted, and there may be shelves under and above some of the benches. Generally, most free wall space can be used for racks or shelves. A drawing board and bench is desirable.

d. Forges
A large blacksmith-type forge might be 8 ft × 8 ft × 2½ ft high, with brick surrounds, coke riddle, and hood and chimney, but a small portable forge might be under 2 ft in diameter. A chimney will be required.

e. Temperature
Most workshops are too cold for winter work, and it is desirable to keep normal working temperatures throughout the year, comparable with the best industrial standards, especially if the workshop is in frequent use. Storage should be cool and dark, especially for tyres.

53: CATTLE YARDS (FEED AREA)

Lord Forbes, Harthill Farm, Aberdeenshire

A light steel frame with triangular trusses to a central span supporting, without purlins, a roof of corrugated aluminium sheets. The roof has ventilation underdrawn from the eaves to a continuous ridge ventilation strip. The central span covers the feed area, including a tractor passage for discharging food from a self-unloading trailer into a continuous manger with yokes on either side of the passage. The cattle feed from a slatted standing area 10 ft wide with concrete slabs over a dung channel which can be emptied for organic irrigation from a sluice gate. The feed area can be entered from the cattle yards, adjacent under lean-tos, but can also be used as a collecting area to the parlour seen at the end of the building. [SEE PAGES 176 & 75] Courtesy of the British Aluminium Co. Ltd.

54: CATTLE YARDS (BEDDED STRAW)

Lord Forbes, Harthill Farm, Aberdeenshire

The lean-to on each side of the central span is formed with 2-ft-deep lattice girders, which give clear headroom, supporting, without purlins, a roof of corrugated aluminium sheets. Dwarf side walls have timber boarded panels above them to the eaves and include ventilation flaps. The dwarf walls hold the strawed bedding to a depth of 3–4 ft and the cattle on the bedding. The remains of a straw stack used for the bedding is shown. Small holding pens or crushes can be formed against the external walls. [SEE PAGE 176] Courtesy of the British Aluminium Co. Ltd.

55: HEATED DRINKING TROUGH
Mr. J. S. Latham, Averham Flash, Newark-on-Trent

An open exercise yard, adjoining a self-feed silage and covered-yard unit, is flanked by a range of loose-boxes and calf-boxes, divided from them by a race leading to a service pen and the bull box. Drinking troughs placed in open yards should be protected from frost. They can be mounted within an insulated raised brick enclosure having a thermostatically controlled element under the trough to keep the water at about 15° C (60° F). The access panel to the element is at the far end of the brickwork. The open yard, which can be cleaned from end to end into a slurry pit, has a fall of 1: 30 to aid drainage. The surface of the concrete is roughened to prevent the cows slipping. [SEE PAGE 174] Photograph J. B. W.

56: CATTLE YARDS
Mr. Maitland Mackie, Westertown, Aberdeen

An existing building, with conventional steel frame and truss roof 120 ft long × 50 ft wide, was converted to house 150 cows in 1960. A central raised feed passage, with troughs and yokes on each side, is flanked by 8-ft-wide slatted feed areas. The slabs are 6 in. wide 'T' sections of prestressed r.c. above a 2-ft-deep channel falling 10 in. in 120 ft to a sluice gate of steel sheet on rubber mountings. Water to a depth of 6 in. at the shallow end lies permanently in the channel. The sluice gates are raised once in 3 wks during the winter, the diluted slurry being discharged through a 12-in. glazed pipe to the slurry tank. At the side of the slatted areas are strawed yards. Chopped straw is blown through an overhead pipe with several outlet points: the yards being littered while the cattle are milked. Naturally, the system causes dust, which can be seen on the trusses. At the far end is a self-feed silage clamp and, at the near end, the parlour unit. [SEE PAGES 176 & 75] Courtesy of Farm Intelligence Ltd.

57: CUBICLES AND SLATS
Westmorland

Cows sleeping in cubicles can keep clean on sawdust. Various tubular divisions can be used; shown here is a simple 3-bar design. The dimensions for the cubicles depend on the breed of cow. The position and profile of the kerb at the edge of the cubicles is important. The exercise area between the rows of cubicles can be concreted, but this will require cleaning daily. Alternatively, as shown, it can be slatted with concrete slats or with welded mesh. The slurry tank beneath the slats, depending on size, will need infrequent emptying, and labour requirements in housing cows in a cubicle and slat layout are therefore simple. [SEE PAGE 176] Courtesy of the Farmers Weekly.

58: CUBICLES AND CONCRETED EXERCISE PASSAGE

There are many variations practised in the layout of cubicle housing for dairy cows. Cubicles are normally 6¾–7 ft long, depending on breed, by 3¾ ft wide. Divisions between cubicles may be of timber or, as shown here, of galvanized tubular steel. Differences of opinion exist concerning the design of the tubular divisions. The kerb should be high, as shown, so that when the central exercise passage is cleaned with a scraper slurry does not press over the kerb. The top of the kerb should be carefully profiled. Bedding, normally, is of sawdust, though the base may be of crushed, fine chalk or of concrete. [SEE PAGE 171] Courtesy of Dairy Farmer.

PLATES 59 (ABOVE) AND 60: (BELOW). HAY RACK AND MANGER, FROM CATTLE YARD AND FROM EXTERIOR

Two views of an adjustable hay rack and manger which are slung between the steel uprights of a covered yard barn for cattle and which are of simple timber construction. As the depth of the bedding in the yard increases during the winter, additional baulks of timber can be placed between the uprights to form a retaining wall. The height of the rack and manger can be adjusted so that they are at a comfortable level for feeding. They can also be placed at different levels to suit the fall of ground and they can be filled from a tractor-and-trailer along the external road. [SEE PAGES 173 & 188] Courtesy of Messrs Done, Hunter & Co.

f. Lighting

Natural and artificial lighting, to a minimum standard of 15 lumens/ft² on all working planes, should be allowed, and a general diffused light should be supplemented by point lights.

g. Power

An electric arc-welder requires a 30-amp. socket, and there should be five or more 13-amp. outlets for drills, a grinder, a lathe, a compressor and a distilled-water jar. All power plugs should be usable at any point and should be fused accordingly.

h. Storage

Storage should be of two types. Certain equipment, such as tyres, may be stored on the floor, space being provided. Most other equipment and spares should be stored in industrial-type storage racking, with each item in a separate area, even allowing for each size of nail, screw and bolt. Proprietary storage units are available, but simple racks can be made from slotted angle frames, mesh and hardboard. Even a small farm should have a store of 100 ft², and a large farm might need 300 ft².

6. *Equipment*. A brief summary of normal equipment used in reasonably fitted workshops can be given, though each farm will have different requirements (Ref. *a*):

    i. Drills: heavy duty, $\frac{1}{2}$–1 in. dia, fixed to mounting block, with drill as portable extension, and a small electric drill as an extra fitting.

    ii. Vices: heavy duty, fixed to mounting block, and bench vices as extra fitting.

    iii. Grinder: heavy duty, powered bench model.

    iv. Greaser: high-pressure model, 2-man unit preferable to 1-man unit.

    v. Spray gun: for external use.

    vi. Bar-cutter: various types.

    vii. Jacks: heavy duty for tractors, single or double hydraulic.

    viii. Engine stand.

    ix. Distilled-water jar for batteries.

    x. Power lathe.

    xi. Vulcanizer.

    xii. Steam jenny.

    xiii. Compressor.

    xiv. Anvil.

    xv. Fire extinguisher.

    xvi. Full range of hand tools.

    xvii. Pinboard and blackboard.

    xviii. Wash trough or basin.

7. *Environmental control*. An insulated roof is desirable, especially since the extra cost for this, in a workshop of 200 ft², may be only about £15. If a coke forge is included a fan ventilator will be desirable, otherwise cross-ventilation should be provided with doors and windows. At least one wall will probably be fitted with a workbench, with a window for the full length. Rooflights can be an asset, though, unless of double skin, they will break the insulation. Background artificial light should be provided from fluorescent strips, but these should be supplemented by anglepoise lights on the workbench and by a tungsten light to the welding area.

8. *Layout*. A small workshop might be 10 ft × 12 ft, plus a store 5 ft × 10 ft, though a more general size might be about 12 ft × 20 ft, plus a store 10 ft × 12 ft, as shown in Fig. 30, IJ, p. 89, provided the workshop opens into the implement shed. A large workshop might be about 30 ft × 20 ft, plus storage. It is preferable to be generous in providing space, especially since providing areas in excess of 200 ft² might cost only £$\frac{3}{4}$/ft², or, if the workshop is a lean-to adjoining the implement shed, under £$\frac{1}{2}$/ft². It is desirable to have at least 10 ft width as a door opening into the workshop. The actual layout within the workshop will depend on its relationship to the other buildings, and, in any case, this should be planned in conjunction with the mechanic who will use it.

9. *Siting*. The siting of the workshop has been discussed above; it should be adjoining the implement shed and, possibly, near the farm office. Some large estates, having several combines and other big equipment as well as tractors, may have a workshop adjoining the combine shed, since the harvesters have to be serviced during the winter months.

10. *Services*. Electricity and water are essential services, and the former may require a considerable power loading. As stated above, a 30-amp. socket is required for electric arc-welders, and at least five 13-amp. sockets for other normal equipment, though eight sockets may be more satisfactory, placed at strategic positions for flexibility in using tools. There should be a ceiling-light socket for about each 100 ft² floor area, with a wall socket for each 15 ft. R. of workbench and at each major tool position. Lighting should be generous.

11. *Costs*. Obviously, expenditure on workshops, can vary between wide limits. Simple, covered floor space, without fittings and as a lean-to structure, might cost in the region of £$\frac{3}{4}$/ft² for up to 300 ft². However, a workshop and store of 300–400 ft², as in Fig. 30. IJ, including racks and benches, mounting blocks and services, but excluding all tools, is unlikely to cost less than £2/ft²,

M

with $\pounds\frac{1}{2}/ft^2$ for extra space up to about 600 ft². The cost of providing minimum equipment for a workshop has been given as about £40 and, for a larger farm with powered tools, about £100 (2). Specialist equipment, such as for welding, would be an additional cost. A well-built workshop should be depreciated over 20 years, as should be the implement shed (IJ, 11, p. 89), and therefore a structural cost (excluding tools) of £800 represents an annual charge of about £69, which, plus the depreciation on the tools and the power charges, might equal about £100 p.a. This is only a small addition to the mechanic's wages, in order to provide him with reasonable facilities, and it can be recovered, on most farms, by lower charges for maintenance and fewer delays for repairs than would be charged by a local workshop.

12. *References*

(1) PARIS, A. 'He makes sure the wheels keep turning'. *Practical Power Farming*, pp. 32–3 (September 1962).
(2) MOORE, H. I. *The Agricultural Notebook. Farmer and Stockbreeder*, pp. 570–1. (1962).

SELECTED REFERENCE
a. HINE, H. J. *The Farm Workshop*. Crosby Lockwood.

IIK. Packing

1. *Activities*

a. The detailed design for packhouses requires a study separate from that for modern agricultural buildings. Packaging is a complex industry with its own specialized requirements, equipment and work methods, an industry, in any case, more akin to horticulture than to agriculture. However, no study of the function and design of modern farm buildings can be complete without some reference to prepacking, not only because some producers either prepack on their farm or have joined a co-operative packing enterprise but because prepacking influences the type of produce required.

b. The rapid growth in the prepacked food trade has been associated with the development of supermarkets and other self-service stores within the last few years. During 1962 more than 500M prepacks were marketed within the United Kingdom by farmers, farm co-operatives and wholesalers through 10,000 self-service stores, whereas, 8 years earlier, produce prepacking was almost unknown, even though there were about 2500 such stores.

c. Many types of produce may be prepacked. In the poultry enterprises both eggs and broilers are in considerable demand as prepacked commodities. Over one third of the eggs and four fifths of the chickens produced are prepacked. The success of the broiler trade has encouraged the packaging of other joints, such as pork, veal and beef. Such packaging, which involves slaughtering, cannot be carried out on the farm. However, horticultural produce and, to some extent, farm vegetables can be prepacked either on the farm or elsewhere at packing stations. Over half the strawberries and raspberries sold in the shops are prepacked and perhaps one-third of the other soft fruits. But, with the exception of potatoes, only a few of the vegetables sold at present are prepacked, as has been shown by a survey of home-grown vegetables in 1960–61 (1):

Vegetable	Output, tons	Shop sales, tons	Estimate prepacked shop sale, per cent
Beetroot	101,400	52,800	2·5
Carrots	383,500	145,700	5·0
Parsnips	44,100	18,400	1·0
Turnips/swedes	97,800	45,400	1·0
Potatoes	4,500,000	180,000	25·0
Onions (dry)	25,000	17,500	3·0
Leeks	19,700	10,900	2·0
Sprouts	163,200	75,600	6·0

d. The trend for prepacked goods will continue. In order to suit the supermarket meat trade with its prepacked joints, there will be two important factors which will influence, and perhaps eventually control, meat production on the farm. In the first place the demand at present is for lean meat, with little or no fat, uniform and tender, produced regularly throughout the year. In order to produce a uniform grade of meat, control over the diet of the animal is essential. Sudden or frequent changes in diet, environment or movement can be detrimental to the grading of the carcass. Secondly, meat will have to be produced on contract in fixed quantities, types and intervals.

e. In the future there will be more vegetables prepacked, even though this may not be as economic for some roots and green vegetables as for potatoes. However, many markets and shops will not be able to handle loose vegetables and therefore, from necessity, vegetables will be prepacked if they are to be sold within the self-service stores. High-class produce is required for packaging. This has led to the problem that there are considerable quantities of lower-grade vegetables, difficult to market, much of which was previously sold mixed with the top-grade vegetables. The wastage from the prepack line may be edible, though difficult to sell, or inedible, having to be treated as refuse.

2. Managerial requirements

a. If a farmer wishes his produce to be sold as a prepacked commodity he will have to negotiate his market through a packhouse operator. As discussed within the sections on production buildings (Section III), the size of unit and the type of building may be governed by the supermarket trade. A few potato packing units have been installed on farms, usually serving more than one grower. In a few cases they have been installed within a disused barn. However, it is unlikely that many more units will be developed essentially as a farm enterprise. Though farm co-operatives may erect packing stations, usually sited to suit labour and distribution rather than any particular grower (though the station should be suitable for all the members of the co-operative), it is probable that most stations of the future will be owned either by a marketing board or by an independent company or by a supermarket group.

b. The best location for a packhouse has not been resolved, even in the U.S.A., where many stations were erected by the chains of supermarkets, since both the growers and the wholesalers were indifferent to public demand (2). In many cases packing stations have a limited season for any one produce, and seasonal labour may be difficult to obtain in many areas, especially towns. Similarly, the disposal of waste can be an expensive operation in some localities. Handling of the produce cheaply, efficiently and safely must usually be based on expensive machinery. A small- to medium-sized packhouse may cost more than £20,000. Generally, these problems of labour, services, distribution and finance make packaging a job more for a market town rather than for a farm.

3. Production techniques

a. Even if packhouses are not considered as farm buildings, being sited away from agricultural land, the exact division between production techniques required on the farm and those in a packhouse are difficult to determine. It is true that livestock leave the farm ready for slaughter. However, vegetables, especially if stored like potatoes, may receive some preliminary grading and cleaning on the farm, but such grading has been criticized severely as being inefficient and ineffective (2). Since most packers assess the grade of an incoming bulk load of produce when delivered at the packhouse, perhaps even washing the potatoes on arrival, grading should possibly not be carried out on the farm. It is possible, especially with pallet harvesting, that no storage should be situated on the farm. It might be more efficient to have the point of storage combined with the packhouse. Such a

system would incur some increase in transport costs, due to the removal of soil and rubbish from the farm. However, it is generally conceded that it is better to centralize cleaning and grading into one efficient system, using the best equipment and labour.

b. The main distinction in the preparation of potatoes for packing is between machines which dry brush and those which wash the crop.

i. A dry brush machine may have a feed hopper and an elevator, a brushing unit and a roller grading table, requiring perhaps 30 ft × 5 ft plus space for the operators. Dust extraction may be required and a heater can warm the rollers to prevent the potatoes sweating. Dry brushing helps to keep the humidity in the plastic pack at a lower level than with washing.

ii. Wet potatoes, or very dirty crops, should be washed and a small washer, perhaps 8 ft × 4 ft, can be used, fresh water being used for a final rinse, though some potatoes may have to soak for up to $\frac{1}{2}$ hr. A fitter can remove large particles, but small-sized dirt has to settle for removal. Large-scale washers are available.

iii. Drying potatoes after washing is essential, but overdrying has to be avoided. Warm air driers, perhaps 8 ft × 4 ft, can be used, or alternatively, a foam roller drier which will be longer.

iv. Grading, sizing and packing require some 40 ft × 8 ft for each flow line.

4–11. It is not intended to give details of packhouse design. However, one recent potato prepack syndicate in East Yorkshire has erected a building 40 ft × 120 ft × 16 ft to the eaves as a prepack unit producing 30 T/day over a 40-wk season, with a team of 10 women and 5 men on a 12-hr shift. There is storage space for one month's supply of potatoes. A water tank, 50 ft × 8 ft external to the building, is used to collect the sediment, so that the water can be recirculated. The plant for a throughput at this level might cost £4000 and the building perhaps about £10,000 including services. However, a packhouse of this kind, which is larger and more efficient than for any one farm, should be classed as an industrial building, with insulation, heating and worker's facilities being provided.

12. References

(1) 'The potential for prepackaging of fresh fruit and vegetables: based on home grown 1960–1961'. The Produce Packaging Development Ass. Ltd. (1962).
(2) STANSFIELD, G. H. 'An Examination of the problems of the produce prepacker'. *Produce Packaging*, pp. 18–23 (January 1963).

examined, and the relationship between the production units and those for storage and processing must be considered as an essential part of the production of meat and dairy produce.

SECTION III

PRODUCTION BUILDINGS

Introduction

The design of production buildings for livestock is of prime importance in the production of food, and therefore in the national economy. It is true that not all farmers keep livestock; true, also, that produce, such as most vegetables, require no buildings other than for implements, while other produce, such as grain or potatoes, may need several buildings for storage and processing, without involving any of the specialist production buildings within this section. Nevertheless, most investment in farm buildings is for livestock production units, designed for the specific purpose of converting coarse foods into those for human consumption.

Of the eight specialist buildings included, half are for cattle, two for pigs and one each for sheep and for poultry. The latter has been kept to a brief outline, since, though housing for poultry and for eggs has become so specialized that it needs a book to itself, the research into the design of poultry housing has had a profound effect on all livestock buildings. Two of the eight buildings are specifically for young stock.

All the livestock buildings have three important requirements. They must be designed to give low food conversion ratios, minimum demands on labour and hygienic conditions for the stock. These basic requirements seem obvious. However, few livestock units being erected today are so designed that these requirements are taken to their logical conclusion, in spite of the national investment in new buildings through the Farm Improvement Scheme. It is probable that in future greater emphasis will be laid on more efficient buildings. This will have two effects: there will be a greater capital investment per head of stock and larger production units, with a greater throughput per man. The design of livestock units being in process of rapid transition, there is at present little knowledge by which the efficiency of different designs can be related to specific management policies. The basic principles must be constantly re-

IIIA. Milk

1. *Activity*

a. The value of dairy cattle buildings is an enigma in the production of milk. Their basic function is to assist the conversion of bulk foods into milk. Therefore, they are a production building. The other production buildings discussed within Pt. III are used to obtain a product which is ready for sale; but milk, after production, has to be processed (extracted, cooled and stored) on the farm. Hence the need for milking buildings (IIF). In a few instances both the production and the processing of milk occur within the same building. This arrangement is discussed in this section, rather than in IIF.

Milk production may have a subsidiary activity requiring buildings, in that simple shelter for the cows may be provided. Though shelter affects the food conversion ratio, in designing cattle buildings there is a tendency for the true importance of these functions to be reversed, with a good environment for food conversion considered as subsidiary to providing simple shelter from the elements. However, as in the production of meat, food conversion is of vital importance, since food may represent nearly two-thirds of the total cost of milk production.

b. In some regions, as in parts of Hampshire and Wiltshire, the climate and soil make it possible for cattle to be outwintered. The cows may be fed from silage conserved in open pits, possibly with other bulk foods, and milking may be done in a bail. In this system of milk production little capital is required for permanent buildings. But if labour and food costs are increased by more than 6*d.*, possibly even by 4*d.*, per gallon, the system is unlikely to be economic when compared with winter housing. However, in some cases labour costs may be reduced, since there are no bedding requirements, and it may be difficult to fix true comparative feed costs.

In contrast, in many parts of the country not only would the cows lose condition if kept in the fields during the winter but the grass would be damaged by poaching, and therefore milk yields and land productivity might be depressed. In such conditions winter housing is essential, varying normally from 3 to 6 months, being on average from mid-November to early April, though in some parts cattle may be housed only at night until late November. However, it can be argued that grassland is reduced in value, perhaps by 10–20 per cent, if the cows are allowed to graze in the fields, since:

i. there are variations in grazing habits between cows;

ii. the grass is poached, particularly at the entrance to fields;

iii. part of the grass is hidden by dung deposits; as much as 15 per cent has been claimed;

iv. if the cows have a long walk to and from their grazing in order to be milked, food is consumed to provide the additional energy which could have been used to produce milk.

For these reasons, on a few farms, the cows are permanently housed; and if housing is anyway provided for use during several months in the year it can act in many cases as permanent housing without extra capital being required.

c. Housing can help to increase the stocking density on a farm by giving greater control over the rationing of fodder, especially during the winter. Traditional densities may be based on 2 acres/cow, which, if combined with a concentrate ration of $\frac{1}{2}$ T/cow, may produce 850 gal/cow. However, with good grassland, particularly if combined with irrigation, the same performance may be achieved at a density of $1\frac{1}{2}$ acres/cow; and there are farmers obtaining more than 850 gal/cow, allowing 1 acre/cow, with $\frac{3}{4}$–1 T of supplementary concentrates (1). Conversely, if 1–$1\frac{1}{4}$ T of concentrates are fed, 1000 gal/cow may be averaged per acre, though this is unlikely to occur except with exceptionally good and uniform grass. A few small farms stock at $\frac{3}{4}$ acre/cow, buying hay as well as concentrates. In fact, it is possible that milk could be produced with the cows kept on concrete with all their food being bought, but this policy has not, at present, been undertaken in this country. High stocking rates depend on a liberal fertilizer policy, good grassland management, little poaching and well-conserved grass for the winter. Buildings can assist the last two aims and can make winter feeding more effective. National yields and herd sizes have been given (IIF, 1a, p. 134).

d. Grass can be grazed or cut and fed direct to the cows in summer. Alternatively, it can be conserved as hay, silage or haylage. In Devon, for example, in one survey between 35 and 70 per cent (average 54 per cent) of the food required came from grass or its conservation (2). Other forms of silage can be made and fed, notably arable, maize or pea-haulm silage (IIC, 1, p. 105). Other bulk foods can be grazed, such as kale, or can be either cut or lifted and fed in buildings, such as kale, roots or beet-tops. These bulk foods are normally used between the end of the autumn grass and the start of the silage or other conserved grass, perhaps at the New Year. Sudden changes in diet can depress the yield and reduce its quality, as can fodders poor in protein and starch. As discussed in IIF, 2b, (p. 135), bulk foods should not only maintain the cow in health but also produce at least 1, and preferably 2, gal of milk/day, the remainder of the yield being obtained from concentrates. In the early summer up to 5 gal/day may be obtained from good grass without concentrates. Each extra gallon obtained from bulk foods in winter may save about £6 in concentrates over $4\frac{1}{2}$ months or, if the winter period extends to 6 months about £8. Thus, if it could be shown that the method of conserving and feeding the winter bulk foods, perhaps by having haylage rather than silage, could produce an extra gal/cow without concentrates, then, for an 80-cow herd, this could justify a capital investment of over £3000, or £40/cow, before it would be cheaper to waste food by less efficient methods. Unfortunately, such assessments are not easy to make.

e. Milking tends to limit the herd size/man, and therefore possibly the herd size for any farm, though the acreage and quality of food which can be grown more often limits the herd size. Work planning should be based on an 8-hr day, though in practice many milkmen work longer than this averaged over the year, and milking should be limited to under 4 hr/day (IIF), in two sessions. Thus, if the maximum milking rate is 30 cows/hr/man, then the herd size will be limited to 50–60 cows/man or, since usually some cows in the herd are dry, 60–70 cows/man. However, if the milking rate can be increased to 45 cows the herd size might be 80–100 cows. In either case an additional $1\frac{1}{2}$ hr should be allowed for work in the dairy, with at least $\frac{1}{2}$ hr for rest periods. Therefore, possibly not more than 2 hr/day should be allowed for milk production in addition to processing (milking and cooling), that is, either about 2 min/cow or $1\frac{1}{4}$ min/cow in the two examples for such matters as feeding, littering and cleaning. The cowman could divide each milking into two sessions of about $1\frac{1}{4}$ hr, with an interval of $\frac{1}{4}$ hr and, on this basis, at least 100 cows/man could be managed, provided that all work external to the parlour and dairy could be completed within $\frac{1}{2}$ hr. As with other enterprises, the unit for the future must be based on a 5-day wk for the cowman, with relief help. For maximum efficiency, units of 180–200 cows, managed by two men with a third man as relief, should be considered. However, this normally would only be possible with dairy farms of at least 250 acres. If production costs are to be kept low units of 60–70 cows on 100 acres with one cowman, plus relief, should be an alternative. But these sizes of unit may be too large if the cowman has to manage the calves and followers.

f. Replacements for the herd can be reared either as part of the milk enterprise, thus forming a self-contained herd, or may be purchased in the case of a 'flying herd'. Replacements are required for old, diseased, injured or low-yielding cows, which should be culled as well as for deaths in the herd. The method of replacement will affect the herd size/man. Though cows do not normally attain their peak yield until their sixth lactation, the average life within a herd is about 5 lactations (3). With an average calving age of 33 months, though many may calve at under 27 months, the number of followers should equal 55 per cent of the milking herd size, plus an additional 25 per cent to allow for deaths and culling. Therefore the followers should number about three-quarters of the milking herd, though often they are of equal number. The unwanted calves will have to be fattened or sold. The time required to look after 42 calves has been given as $\frac{3}{4}$ hr/day (4). In this case a milking herd might have to be limited to 60 cows/man. Generally, it is cheaper to rear the heifers, when the land is available, rather than to buy them, but another 25 acres may be required for the one-man unit. It may be, however, more economic to increase the number of cows, when this can be done without requiring more men, or the acreage of cash crops, when these are also included in the farm system, rather than to rear the heifers.

g. An investigation of 500 producers in 1962 showed that 57 per cent produced milk for less than 2s. 4d./gal, compared with only 36 per cent in 1958 (5). In a large, well-planned unit a building and labour cost of 6d.–10d./gal may be required (IIF, 11c, p. 148), but even so it should be possible to produce at less than 2s. 3d./gal.

2. *Managerial requirements*

a. Feeding Techniques

As previously stated, the system of feeding and food conversion are important. A long-term research programme is being carried out at the University of Durham to compare high-quality silage and hay with bulk silage and hay as winter fodder. Bulk foods can be fed in a number of ways, and this is discussed in greater detail in 4 below:

i. *Tower Silos*. Within the last year or two, several dairy layouts have been erected, including mechanical feeding of haylage from tower silos. Though this system reduces wastage and can make it possible to increase the stocking density, the main advantage can be that the labour required for the feeding of bulk rations is negligible, and therefore more time can be given to milking and stockmanship. With large herd sizes/man, especially over 80 cows/man, this can be important. The main disadvantage is that feeding alternative bulk foods, such as cut kale, may be restricted. This can be overcome by using a side-unloading trailer in conjunction with the tower, which can also be used for other chopped foods, but, of course, this might take $\frac{1}{3}-\frac{1}{2}$ hr/day of the cowman's time, thus reducing the herd size possible.

ii. *Rationed Silage*. Silage can be cut and carted from a clamp and delivered into a manger or feeding area, using a side-unloading trailer. Though this is satisfactory with beef cattle, it is likely to be too time-consuming for a milk enterprise, unless carried out by someone other than the cowman, since up to $1\frac{1}{2}$ hr/day for 60 cows could be required for this task (6). However, more efficient systems with better mechanization for cutting, lifting and carting might reduce this to under $\frac{3}{4}$ hr/day. Alternatively, silage can be cut and dropped direct into adjacent mangers for easy-feeding, and this considerably reduces the labour required.

iii. *Self-feed Silage*. Allowing the cows to have *ad-lib.* access for self-feeding at a silobarn has been a popular method for reducing labour within the last 6–8 yrs. The system has much to commend it, except that it may prove wasteful of fodder compared with rationed methods. However, cleaning and managing the silage face does require some labour, perhaps $\frac{1}{3}$ hr/day for 60 cows (7). If herds of 80–100 cows/man are desired, then self-feeding may take too much time within the work programme in order to keep the silage face clean.

iv. *Hay*. Hay can be a principal part of the winter ration, or may be used to supplement a mainly silage ration. In the latter case a little hay may be placed in a hay rack, perhaps allowing 5 lb/cow/day and, in a well-planned unit, taking only about 5 min/60 cows/day (6); whereas bulk hay feeding, perhaps 20 lb/cow/day, if carted by trailer and fed to a fence or manger, might take 30 min/60 cows/day (IIIB, 3a, p. 186). Mechanized hay feeding, using a bale separator and conveyor along a trough, might require only 10 min/40 cows/feed for a capital cost of £15/cow (7), though simple conveyors might cost under £5/cow.

v. *Roots, Kale, etc.* In the autumn the cows may graze or eat roots, kale, tops, etc., in the fields, returning to their housing at night. In many cases these foods will be carted and fed at mangers, and many layouts, even when self-feeding is practised, have to include manger space or a forage fence which can be filled from a trailer. Since providing eating space for this requirement can make a layout less compact than with self-feeding, and generally more expensive, it is worth considering whether all the fodder should be fed this way, including silage, using a self-unloading trailer wherever possible.

vi. *Zero-grazing.* Reference has been made to housing cattle permanently, which normally is termed zero-grazing, whereby grass is cut once or twice a day and is delivered at a forage fence by side-unloading trailers, the same fence being used for other fodder during the winter. This system received considerable attention a few years ago, but depends on good grassland management with fields near the housing. Herds of 140 cows have been fed this way (9). Extra labour and machinery costs are incurred, but the grass can be more productive. Extra bedding is required for strawed yards, but a cubicle and slat layout, if coupled to organic irrigation, could be satisfactory. Comparative details are not available. An alternative system of zero-grazing may be based on holding the cows in a small paddock near their parlour, provided the ground is free-draining, the grass being eaten direct from the trailer (10), 1 hr/day being required for cutting and carting for 35 cows. However, if tower silos are included in the layout these might be used and filled at the same time, so that grass cutting, as with beef-fattening, could be concentrated into short periods every few weeks, rather than being done every day.

b. Rations

The daily requirement (depending on starch and protein equivalents) for dairy cattle has been given (11):

Jersey 23 lb d.m. or 115 lb fresh grass
Ayrshire 30 lb d.m. ,, 150 lb ,, ,,
Friesian 34 lb d.m. ,, 170 lb ,, ,,

With self-fed silage, 10 lb/1 cwt livewt/day, or about 1 cwt/11 cwt cow, may be consumed (12); though, in many cases, especially with well-wilted silage, consumption may be little more than ¾ cwt/day (30 lb d.m.). Hay will probably be limited to under 20 lb/cow/day, some additional fodder being provided. Grass, if it is good, may provide for maintenance plus 5 gal from 150 lb/day in May and June; but, even so, there are few farmers not feeding some concentrates in the parlour even with good summer grazing. Silage will seldom give more than maintenance plus 2 gal, and frequently only 1 gal (IIF, 2b, p. 135).

c. Bedding

Bedding techniques for dairy cows have received considerable attention in recent years:

i. Straw is the traditional form of bedding, but is an expensive material to handle, even in grain growing areas (IIIB, 2b, p. 184).

ii. Slats for beef cattle are satisfactory, but have been criticized for dairy cows due to damage to their teats and feet, though this may be no worse than in a shippon, and in some cases no damage may occur (13).

iii. Rubber flooring has been tried on several farms with success. Non-slip rubber blocks are best, but, unless second-hand, are expensive. Sheet rubber will require sawdust over it, but should last at least 5 years in a stall or cubicle, costing no more than about £1½/cow p.a.

iv. Removable plastic-covered rubber mattresses, costing £12–£14 each, can be used in stalls, perhaps assessed at £3/cow p.a.

v. Various forms of deep litter, straw, shavings, fibre, peat, etc., can be used and, in some parts of the country, are much cheaper than straw (IIIB, 2b, p. 184) (14).

vi. Concreted cubicles, covered with a layer of sawdust, which can be used as a sleeping area can be combined with an exercise area, the latter being either concreted or slatted.

vii. There have been experiments using under-floor heating instead of straw, the cables being laid in an insulated concrete floor, consuming off-peak electricity. In one case, during the cold winter of 1962–63, yard temperatures were heated to 40° C (55° F) and with heating for 134 days over the winter costs were 5½d./cow/day or £3½/cow/winter, proving cheaper than straw and requiring less labour (26).

d. Fast and Slow Milkers (see IIF, 2c, p. 135)

In a large yarded herd there is some advantage in dividing the herd into two, so that the fast and slow milkers can be separated, especially if calving is not concentrated into a short period and if batch milking is practised (IIF, 2a, p. 135, and 3c, p. 138).

3. Production techniques

a. Basic Types of Housing

Until about a decade ago, dairy cattle were housed in cowsheds or shippons (the term varies in different parts of the country), which sometimes included a feed passage behind the mangers, if space was available, but otherwise were almost standard in basic design, though not in detail. Machine milking eventually led to the parlour, thus divorcing the function of milking from that of housing cattle, though much machine milking is still carried out within shippons. With the introduction of loose housing in conjunction with a parlour, the function of feeding, as well as that of milking, came to be divorced from the bedded area. Many permutations of layout were possible, which included separated areas for feeding, sleeping and milking, though most were based on self-fed or easy-fed silage plus some rationed foods, strawed bedding and simple abreast or tandem parlours.

However, today the choice of housing system is complex. Not only are there many types of parlour available, but the sleeping area may be in several forms, including bedded yards, slatted yards and cubicle layouts, with concreted or slatted exercise areas combined with the various systems of feeding listed above, and the areas for these basic functions may not be clearly defined. In particular, cubicles have received considerable attention within the last two years, and cubicle housing with slatted exercise areas appears to have many advantages for low running costs. In spite of these changes, many farmers prefer a shippon, and if this is well planned it may be suitable for all except the largest throughput/man (15).

b. Breed of Herd

Milk production in relation to breed of herd has always been a subject for argument; with the introduction of payment according to milk quality, this has become more critical. Quantity without quality will be less economic in the future. With regard to planning a layout, a more important distinction is that between the commercial and the pedigree producer. This is probably more relevant with dairy cows than with other animals; there is, perhaps, a greater element of sentiment between a farmer and his pedigree herd than in other production units. Some practices, suitable for commercial production, would not be tolerated for a pedigree herd, the latter commanding more individual attention for each cow, and a shippon, rather than loose housing, may be preferable or, if milking in a parlour is accepted, a tandem rather than a batch parlour may be required. In particular, Channel Island herds are more delicate than either the Ayrshires or the quantity milk producers, the Friesians.

c. Followers

The need for followers has been discussed above and, normally, these are housed in a yard separate from the milking herd. The introduction of a heifer into a herd can be critical, especially for milking, and work routines have to be planned accordingly.

d. The Bull

A.I. has removed the necessity for having a bull. However, pedigree and some medium and large herds usually include one or more bulls in the herd and the bull-pen is sited in close and visible relationship with the yarding (IIIC).

e. Dry Cows

A cow is dry for about one-sixth of each year. In a small herd the dry cows may be run with the milkers, passing through the parlour with the others, though this is not desirable with a batch parlour. Alternatively, the dry cows may be housed separately in a small yard or pen, but this may add to the work routines if food has to be handled specially for them. In a large herd the dry cows should be yarded together, the layout being similar to that for the milkers, with the same feeding arrangements, but without requiring access to the parlour.

4. *Work routines*
a. Generally

More attention has been given to the work requirements in milking and housing dairy cows than for those in many farm enterprises. As discussed above, milking, together with its allied work in the dairy, takes the major part of the cowman's working day, unless the latter includes substantial amount of overtime. Stockmanship in milk production, as within fattening and rearing units, must be skilled. Therefore the three major chores in housing the cows, feeding, bedding and cleaning, must be kept to the minimum in order to attain the maximum throughput/man combined with skilled stockmanship. Estimates were made some year's ago for work requirements in winter milk production (16):

Man minutes per cow per week

System	Cowshed		Yard and parlour		Yard and cowshed		Outwintered and parlour	
	Av.	Good	Av.	Good	Av.	Good	Av.	Good
Milking	59	42	51	32	67	45	51	32
Dairy work	27	18	23	12	26	16	23	12
Cleaning	37	26	24	12	24	12	12	7
Feeding	34	16	35	11	35	11	22	6
Other work	20	20	10	10	10	10	15	15
	177	122	143	77	162	94	123	72

Thus, with the exception of the special case of out-wintering, the yard and parlour requires the least work, needing $\frac{3}{4}$ hr/cow/wk less than a cowshed—though the cowsheds examined were based on milking to churns rather than on pipe-line milking, the latter becoming successful only recently for long lengths of pipe, and the parlours considered were stall rather than batch parlours. However, it is worth noting that, on a working-day allowance of $7\frac{1}{2}$ hr, based on these requirements, a cowman could manage a herd of only 41 cows, with a good yard-and-parlour layout; and, excluding the milking and dairying, nearly 5 min/cow/day would be required for other work. On the basis, as previously suggested, of not more than 2 hr/day being available for this other work, then, with a large herd and a batch parlour, only about 25 cows/man could be managed in the yards. Thus, again on these estimates, a 75-cow herd might need three men to feed, bed, clean, etc. the cows, even though one man might do the milking. This is an important distinction in planning for high through-put/man, but it must be appreciated that more modern work methods have made it possible for one man to look after 60–80 cows in a yard as well as milking them. However, the relationship between the work in the parlour and all other work for the herd is very important.

b. Feeding

Traditionally, hand feeding of hay into mangers in a shippon absorbed a great deal of labour. Feeding hay to yarded cattle has been examined (IIIB, 3*a*, p. 186). Self-feeding silage has proved an important method for saving labour; but, though the silobarn should be designed with floor profiles to assist drainage, keeping the silage face clean and moving the silage barrier may require 18 min/day/60 cows (7). However, the main difficulty is to coordinate the work so as to maintain the silage face, which is done usually while the cows are being milked so that another man is required in addition to the milker. If the cowman has to do the work himself he has to shut the cows away from the silage. In addition, time could easily be wasted in this task due to unforseen factors, such as the variations in the quality of silage and the extent to which the wastage could be cleaned away at the same time as the exercise yards were scraped by tractor. However, a decision to forgo the advantage of low labour requirements in self-feeding methods must be based on several considerations:

i. With herds of 80–100 cows/man, automatic feeding may prove to be desirable, since rather more than $\frac{1}{2}$ hr/day required for cleaning the silage face could be a disadvantage.
ii. Unrationed feeding may be considered wasteful.

iii. Insufficient silage might be available to self-feed for long periods.

For intensive milk production labour required for feeding could be eliminated by the use of a tower and auger, as in beef production. However, where such fodder as beet tops is to be fed, a slatted trough conveyor may be preferable to an auger, capable of removing waste fodder at the end of its run. (With beet tops, waste may be equal to 15–25 per cent.) Though this method requires some labour in filling a hopper to feed the conveyor, it should prove to be less than that required for self-feeding silage and maintaining the silage face. However, a self-unloading trailer filled from a tower silo, which could also be loaded from a hopper with chopped roots and possibly kale, should be able to place the fodder for 100 cows at a manger within the same time, i.e. perhaps under the $\frac{1}{2}$ hr, and probably 180–200 cows in little over the $\frac{1}{2}$ hr. Cutting silage from a clamp and distributing it with a self-unloading trailer while possible with beef cattle, unless the stockman has tasks other than managing the beef enterprise, might prove too time-consuming with an intensive milk unit if carried out by the cowman. However, for example, if the cows were housed in a cubicle and slat layout, then it might be feasible to feed in this manner and still leave 6 hr/day for milking and dairying.

The times required for the more traditional feeding methods have been examined fully by Belshaw and Scott (Ref. *b*), covering various methods of rationing silage into mangers (and cowsheds) with either a trailer or fore-end loader, feeding hay, and either forage harvesting kale or cutting it by hand and carting by trailer. These may be summarized:

i. Easy-feeding silage, cutting clamp with knife and forking into mangers about 4 ft away from clamp:
60 cows at $\frac{3}{4}$ cwt/cow, medium-density silage 45·8 min
60 cows at $\frac{3}{4}$ cwt/cow, high-density silage 73·7 min
60 cows at $\frac{3}{4}$ cwt/cow, 10–14 ft from manger 85·4 min
ii. Cutting clamp with knife, forking into trailer and placing from trailer into manger 50 yd from clamp, moving trailer every 16 ft along manger.
60 cows at 84 lb/cow, medium-density silage 99·86 min
iii. Cutting clamp with knife, removing 4 cwt with foreloader and placing in heaps at manger 50 yd from clamp, then forking heaps into even rations.
60 cows at $\frac{3}{4}$ cwt/cow (12 loads) 80·81 min
iv. Kale forage-harvested in field (yield 20 T/acre, cut at 2 m.p.h.), taken to mangers 500 yd distant

and shovelled from the trailer, moving trailer every 16 ft along manger.

60 cows at $\frac{1}{2}$ cwt/cow 61·86 min

v. As *iv*, but self-unloading trailer 35·96 min.

It is obvious that the time required for handling bulk foods to the cows is critical to the overall productivity of the cowman. The alternative is for grass, kale, roots, etc., to be cut and carted by the fieldworker rather than by the cowman, and on most farms this division of labour will be essential.

c. Bedding

Strawing a bedded yard should take 25–35 min/60 cows/day. (IIIB, 4c, p. 187.) This can, of course, take longer if the work methods are unplanned; but, in any case, littering is a chore which restricts productivity, though it does mean that the cowman will be working among the herd for a short time each day and this may be considered an advantage. Moreover, many farmers like their cows to sleep on straw. The straw store should be adjacent to the yarding, possibly on top of a silage clamp. Chopped straw may be blown into the yards while the cows are being milked, but this does create dust. Alternatively, with cubicle or slatted housing, a sprinkling of sawdust may take only a few minutes each day, and the $\frac{1}{2}$ min/cow saved may be critical with large herds.

d. Cleaning

Cleaning is a daily and seasonal chore, the requirements varying on each farm. Concreted areas should be cleaned every day, using a tractor and scraper, and quick methods depend on well-placed gates, long straight runs the width of the scraper and a well-sited slurry pit. Moreover, cleaning is easiest when the cows are being milked, which suggests that it should not be the responsibility of the cowman. In some cases a farmer may clean the yard only two or three times a week. A time of $\frac{1}{4}$ hr/50 cows twice a week, plus about 6 min/day for cleaning a run of mangers, has been suggested as adequate for well-designed layouts (17). Cleaning a self-feed silage face will increase this time. However, intensive housing can be based on a bedded or cubicle yard plus a slatted exercise strip, 10 ft wide in front of the manger, whereby cleaning requirements are reduced.

Cleaning out a strawed yard during the spring or summer might take 35 hr for 40 cows housed for 5 months, allowing 10 lb straw/day/cow, if cleaning is by foreloader and a manure spreader (17). Alternatively, with a slatted layout the slurry can be piped and spread with irrigation equipment automatically or can be removed and spread by tanker (IG, 4, p. 77).

e. Fetching Cows when Grazing

When grazing in summer, the cows should be fetched from and returned to the fields twice a day for milking, within about the same time as is required for feeding, littering and cleaning in winter, in order to keep the routine balanced. If the cows are $\frac{1}{2}$ mile from the parlour, $1\frac{1}{2}$–2 hr/day will be required, unless the cows can return to the fields by themselves after milking (17).

f. Inspection

The cows should be inspected in the parlour. However, more detailed examination should take place through a crush, which should be sited perhaps in conjunction with the collecting yard, so that the herd can be held in the latter, pass through the crush and return to their yarding.

5. Design data

a. Strawed Yards

The requirements and main variations for strawed yards have been examined fully (Ref. *a* and *f*). Partly covered yards should be based on the following (Fig. 68):

i. Bedded Area: 40 ft²/cow normal (36–45 ft²/cow possible range), preferably with a clear height of not less than 10 ft (preferably 12 ft), with structural walls 8 ft high on three sides probably taken to eaves, unless overall height greater than 12 ft), with a bonded floor, normally level but with a slight fall towards the opening for a concreted edge about 8 ft deep into bedded yard.

ii. Open Concreted Area: 20 ft²/cow (15–30 ft²/cow possible range) to S.E.–S.W. of bedded area, with longitudinal fall of 1 : 40 towards slurry pit, and with gates opening full width of yard at each end, with a slip gap for easy access.

iii. Forage Fence or Manger: 2 ft.R/cow, 5 ft high, $2\frac{1}{2}$ ft wide, against a farm road.

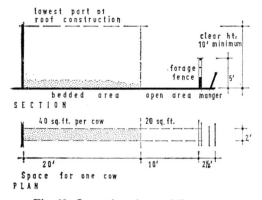

Fig. 68. Strawed yards: partially covered

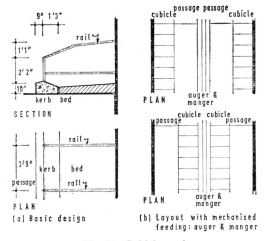

Fig. 69. Cubicle yards

(a) Basic design

(b) Layout with mechanised feeding: auger & manger

iv. Straw Storage: say 10 lb/cow/day for 5 months, allow 200 ft³/cow (IA, 5, p. 55).

v. Fully Covered Yard: 70 ft²/cow, of which at least 40 ft² is strawed, plus straw storage, generally similar to partly covered yard, except that it is difficult to include for a forage manger, which is filled by self-unloading trailer, unless there is a central feed passage (IIIB, 8a, p. 193).

vi. Bed-and-Breakfast Yard: part of the bedding can be on top of a clamp silo, provided there is a 30-degree access ramp for the cows, but this will not save space if straw has to be stored on the ground instead of on the silage. Layouts of this kind may be particularly suitable in a conversion.

b. Slatted Yards (Ref. *n*)

About 30–35 ft²/cow should be allowed, the yard being combined with one side as a forage fence, manger or opening into a silobarn. The clear height should not be less than 10 ft. Slats should be 5 in. wide on top, tapered to 4 in. and spaced 1½ in. apart (IIIB, 5i, p. 190). Alternatively, proprietary metal grids may be used.

c. Cubicle Yards (Ref. *k* and 25)

The design of the cubicles needs careful detailing if the cows are to lie clean, an area 6 ft 10 in. long × 3 ft 7 in. wide being required, or possibly 7 ft × 3 ft 9 in. for large breeds such as Friesians (Fig. 69a). Bedding the cubicle should be based on sawdust, 8–10 lb/cow/wk, though shavings or chopped straw may be used. Divisions between cubicles may be solid or tubular, the division and floor profile being detailed correctly. Some farmers, to allow for freedom in choice of lying positions, prefer one or two additional cubicles more than the herd number; others, having a slatted exercise

area, allow for more cows than cubicles, perhaps half as many again. The passage between two rows of cubicles, which is used for exercise and access, should be 8 ft wide, though 10 ft may be preferable, and may be concreted or slatted. Therefore, the total stocking density will vary between 40 and 45 ft²/cow.

Though a few farmers feed a little hay in their cubicle layouts and some layouts are combined with self-feed silobarns, feeding by auger within a cubicle house has not been attempted. It might prove unsatisfactory to combine an auger and manger with the cubicle (Fig. 69b), but mechanized feeding could be planned down the centre of the house, if the latter was 35 ft wide and the density decreased to about 68 ft²/cow. However, feeding, littering and cleaning for 100 cows could be managed by one man within ½ hr/day, thereby making a 100 cow/one-man layout possible; though summer grazing, which can cause the cowman to need longer than this for moving the cows, would be unsatisfactory. Alternatively, the cows could be permanently housed, possibly having access into a sheltered open yard for exercise during the summer.

d. Cowsheds

Cowsheds (or shippons) have received considerable attention in the past; their design is detailed in the Ministry of Agriculture's Leaflet F.E.F. No. 1 and examined in practice by Ingersent and Manning, together with early yard-and-parlour layouts (Ref. *g*). With a feed passage, the density may be about 55–60 ft²/cow, which is comparable with that for semi-strawed yards (Fig. 70a). With pipe-line] milking it is unlikely that the milking routine need take longer than batch milking in a herringbone parlour, though adequate time studies are not available for each method using the best equipment. Work routine times for a cowshed and 2 stall/1 unit tandem parlour have been given as about 1½ min/cow in each case (18). But, with a shippon, the cows do not have to be taken to and from a collecting yard, as is required with a parlour, though it must be appreciated that milking is not as easy in a shippon as in a two-level parlour which has all the equipment to hand.

The main disadvantage of a cowshed can be in the time required for littering, cleaning and feeding, rather than in milking. Littering straw at 7 lb/cow can take nearly ½ hr/60 cows, when using a tractor and trailer with straw stored 50 yds away from the shippon (Ref. *b*). But other forms of bedding can be used, which take less time. Though cleaning out can be done with a tractor and scraper, a mechanical scraper in the dung channel can reduce the work required considerably. Therefore it may be mainly the feeding of bulk and concentrate foods which cause difficulty, and few attempts

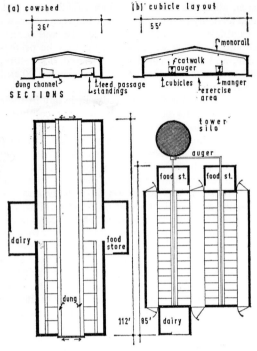

Fig. 70. Cowsheds for 60 cows

would need a floor area of 30 ft × 60 ft for 360 T. Alternatively, 100 cows being fed 25 lb d.m. haylage/cow/day for 5 months would need 25,000 ft³ of storage, which could be held by one 25-ft-dia silo 50 ft high. Rationing with either of these methods requires a forage fence or manger, based on 2 ft.R/cow (IIIB, 5d, p. 188). Feed passages should be 7–10 ft wide (IIIB, 5g, p. 189).

g. Water Requirements

Water is provided *ad lib.* and consumption will vary with temperature, feeding and breed, but may be as little as 5 gal/cow/day, increasing to 14 gal on hot days, though consumption for cows-in-milk has been given as 8 gal + 2 gal for each gal milk yield (20).

h. Heat and Moisture Produced

Few milk production buildings are designed to have a controlled environment, though the need to prevent condensation from the roof by under-drawing ventilation is well recognized. Heat produced has been given per 1000-lb Friesian cow as 2000–3200 B.t.u./hr, per 750-lb Jersey as 1800–2400 B.t.u./hr, and moisture produced per 1000-lb cow as 9·7 oz/hr at a temperature of 10° C (50° F) (21). (See also IIIB, 5j, p. 191.)

have been made to mechanize this work. However, at least one recent cowshed has used an auger for haylage from a tower, though in this case the cows are milked in a parlour (19). In such layouts the stalls should be on either side of the auger and concentrates could be fed from a raised feed walk, using a hopper running on a monorail (Fig. 70b). A layout of this kind might prove efficient, but it would be difficult to assess whether it has any advantage over a mechanized cubicle-and-slat layout.

e. Self-fed Silage

Normal depth of settled silage should be 6 ft for self-feeding, which means that a silobarn should have 14–16 ft of unobstructed headroom for filling the clamp. The width of the clamp should be based on ½ ft/cow, allowing ¾ ft/cow as a maximum, with 24 hr access. Restricted feeding will require up to 2 ft/cow at the silage face. Requirements are given in detail in IIC, 5, p. 107. However, Fig. 71 shows a silobarn suitable for 60 cows with self-feeding for 4½ months; assuming 100 lb/cow/day is consumed, about 360 T would be required, which, with lacerated grass, could be stored in a barn of 30 ft span × 90 ft length, allowing for wastage.

f. Rationed Silage or Haylage

Silage for cutting and carting could be stored in a clamp 9 ft deep, which means that a barn 20 ft high

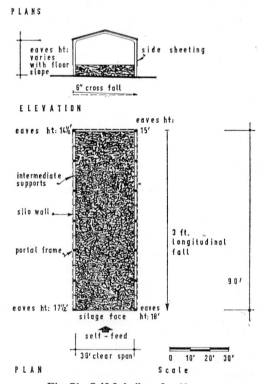

Fig. 71. Self-fed silage for 60 cows

i. Temperature Requirements

Findlay has shown that the following effects occur with Jersey cows when the temperature exceeds 10° C (50° F), following experiments at the Hannah Research Institute (22):

10°–12° C   Desirable temperature
(50°–54° F)
15° C (60° F)   Breathing rate increases
24° C (75° F)   Food consumption decreases, body temperature rises
30° C (85° F)   Body weight and milk production declines
37° C (100° F)   Pulse rate increases

Yield also will decline below 4° C (40° F), particularly with Jersey cows, and food consumption will increase. Sharp changes of temperature should be avoided.

j. Ventilation Requirements

The volume of fresh air required in order to remove the moisture released by a cow when housed at 10° C (50° F) has been given (21):

External Conditions		Air change/
Temp., °C	R.H., per cent	cow/min, ft³
−7 (20° F)	75	34
5 (40° F)	75	75
5 (40° F)	80	88
8 (46° F)	75	140

k. Cattle per Yard

Square yards holding 60–100 cows can be satisfactory, care being taken that 'boss' cows cannot block openings to a self-feed silo, etc.

l. Races, Crush and Footbath

There should be a cattle race and crush, about 2½–3 ft wide, with railings 5 ft high, allowing inspection from both sides within every dairy layout. The crush should be under cover, with good artificial light. This could be sited in conjunction with the calf housing and bull pens; the cows could be deflected from the parlour through the crush, which means that the parlour would be fouled during inspections, or, alternatively, the cows might be held in the collecting yard to the parlour, being able to return to their housing via the crush. The crush should have a yoke form of gate for the cow's head. At the rear of the crush the cow should be held by a fall gate to restrict entry by a second cow. The internal width of the crush should be restricted to 2¼ or 2 ft for small breeds and the length with a yoke gate should be 6 ft, the crush walls being between 3½ and 6 ft in height, provided that access for inspection to each side is available. The crush can be formed in

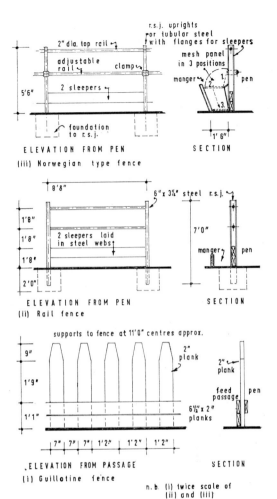

Fig. 72. Forage fences

tubular steelwork with corner posts buried in a concrete floor, costing about £60, or it can be portable, or constructed fairly cheaply in timber, being perhaps under £30 for a simple crush (23).

m. Forage Fences (Fig. 72)

Various fences are satisfactory, three of which are shown in the diagram:

i. Guillotine fence: suitable for adult stock, reduces wastage.

ii. Rail fence: can be constructed in various simple ways.

iii. Norwegian fence: used with a manger to reduce waste.

In addition, yoke fences can be used with a long ratchet arm, so that cattle can be held at the manger, but these are more expensive.

6. *Equipment*

a. The Tractor

The tractor can be an essential tool in the daily management of a dairy herd. It may be used with a scraper blade for cleaning concreted exercise areas, whether covered or uncovered, the slurry being pushed into a pit. It may be used with a self-unloading trailer for handling bulk foods to a forage fence. Moreover, it can have seasonal uses for cleaning yards and slurry pits, or for making silage, as well as occasional use for acting as an emergency power unit in milking. The main problem is to decide whether the tractor should be housed with the herd, either in conjunction with the yarding or the parlour unit, or with the main implement storage. If the cowman uses the tractor, it should probably be housed within the dairy layout, but if it is used by another man, then it should be kept within the central tractor shed.

b. Self-feed Silage Barriers (see Fig. 39)

Various types of barrier are available. Silage should be self-fed through a barrier to save waste, so that any silage dropped from the face will not be trampled under foot. There are three basic types:

  i. Tubular barrier fences, with lateral braces, free-standing on the floor, costing up to £2¼/ft.R.
  ii. Tubular bar, with spikes for fixing into silage face, so that the bar remains clear by 1–2 ft, costing up to £1/ft.R.
  iii. Suspended electric cable, possibly the cheapest and easiest to handle, but the electric charge may discourage the cows from eating.

c. Slats (see IIIB, 6*v*, p. 192)

d. Water Troughs

Water should be provided in troughs with raised automatic filling valves, possibly on the basis of one trough per 20–30 cows. One trough should be near the parlour exit. Troughs should not obstruct the daily cleaning of concrete yards, nor should they be over a bedded area, nor in corners where a boss cow can restrict access. They are best recessed into a wall adjoining a concreted exercise area and they should be mounted about 1½ ft above the floor level, insulated round the exposed sides and preferably with a thermostatically controlled heating element under them.

e. Yard Gates

For preference yard gates should be of a heavy stockyard pattern and should open for the full width of a concreted area to allow for easy cleaning by tractor.

f. Slip Gaps

Gaps, 11–13 in. wide, should be provided for pedestrian access adjoining gateways or through fences, in order to save yard gates being opened.

g. Augers

As in other layouts with augers, the latter should be positioned above a trough 5 ft wide, allowing access for eating to both sides at 1 cow/ft.R, with a cattle standing area on each side of the trough 8 or 12 ft wide, the former if access is unrestricted, the latter if access to the feeding strip is only from the ends.

7. *Environmental control*

a. Since it is well known that a controlled environment is desirable for poultry and pigs and that one for beef cattle is being acknowledged as beneficial in the reduction of food consumption, it is probable that in the future a controlled environment for dairy cattle will be examined. A constant temperature, without the sudden fluctuations usual in present-day housing, might increase the food conversion efficiency of dairy cattle. As stated previously (1*d*, above), each extra gal/cow obtained from bulk foods, by saving the concentrates required, may be worth while, provided that the capital expenditure does not exceed about £40/cow. Provision of a low-pitched portal frame, with an insulated roof, and an environment controlled by electric fans, could be obtained for under £10/cow extra, possibly for under £5/cow. However no evidence exists to show how much food could be saved by this method, but it appears that a controlled environment might be desirable, even if an additional pint could be obtained from bulk foods. American research has shown that yield and quality of milk was not materially affected by temperatures between about 0° and 25° C (32° and 80° F), but substantial changes occurred outside this range. However, this has not been related to food consumption (24).

b. At present most cows are housed in uncontrolled environments. Warmth is obtained from a build up of temperature in straw bedding or from the dung pit under a slatted floor, temperatures of up to 20° C (75°–80° F) being obtained. However, this benefit is not obtained from sawdusted cubicles. Additional warmth is generated by the animals, but this has to be obtained from food consumed, and an uninsulated building will dissipate this warmth. Not only are buildings for dairy cows uninsulated but many are open on at least one side and most have an air-flow under the roof cover from eaves to ridge to prevent condensation. A few shippons and yards, if fully enclosed, are fitted with electric fans, but generally this is considered an unnecessary refinement. Generally, ventilation inlets are baffled above the cows' heads with a ridge extract system.

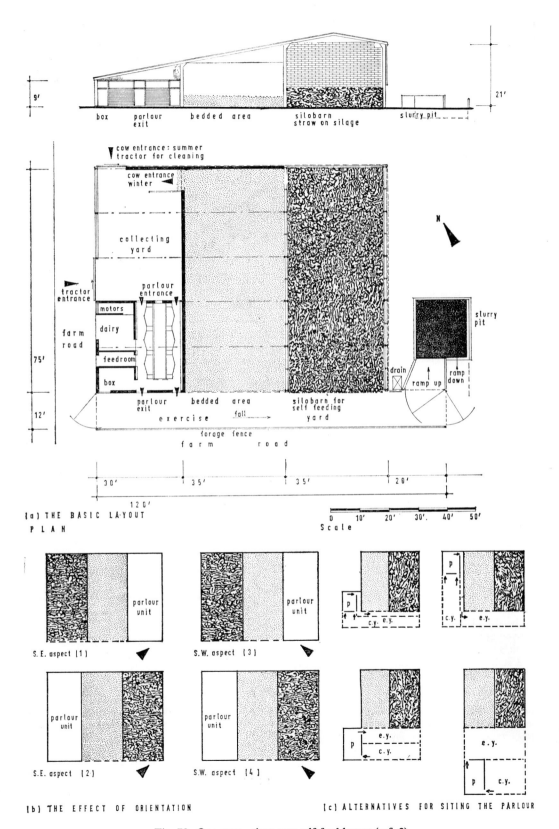

box | **parlour exit** | **bedded area** | **silobarn straw on silage** | **slurry pit**

9′   21′

▼ cow entrance: summer
    tractor for cleaning

cow entrance
winter

N

collecting
yard

tractor
entrance ▶

parlour
entrance

slurry
pit

motors

dairy

farm
road

75′

feedroom

drain   ramp up   ramp down

box

parlour
exit

exercise   fall ⟶

silobarn for
self feeding
yard

12′

forage fence
farm   road

30′   35′   35′   20′

120′

**(a) THE BASIC LAYOUT
PLAN**

Scale   0   10′   20′   30′   40′   50′

parlour
unit

parlour
unit

p   c.y.   e.y.

p   c.y.   e.y.

S.E. aspect [1] ▶   S.W. aspect [3] ▶

parlour
unit

parlour
unit

e.y.
p   c.y.

e.y.

p   c.y.

S.E. aspect [2] ▶   S.W. aspect [4] ▶

(b) THE EFFECT OF ORIENTATION   **(c) ALTERNATIVES FOR SITING THE PARLOUR**

Fig. 73. One man—sixty-cow self-feed layout (ref. 2)

c. Artificial lighting is not essential in simple yards, but generally it is an asset for stock inspection, especially during calving, etc. Therefore, it is desirable to include for one socket, perhaps for each 300–400 ft² of floor area. In some cases a low intensity of illumination is provided permanently, so that the cattle are not disturbed by the light being switched on, and this is valuable in any case with self-feed silage layouts, when some cows may eat during the night. A high-level yard light with wide-angle reflector is desirable when the layout includes an open exercise yard.

d. Insect control within the housing areas is desirable and atomizer insecticides should be installed, positioned as advised by a manufacturer.

8. *Layout.* There are so many layouts possible for dairy herds that it is difficult to indicate all the variations which can be satisfactory within certain managerial policies. The many variations, which may be suitable in some conditions, for strawed yards combined with a parlour have been discussed fully in Report No. 58 (Ref. *a*). Some of the layouts discussed here are based on that report and on articles by the author (Ref. *e* and *f*). Unless otherwise stated, the diagrams are based on layouts suitable for 60 cows.

a. Fig. 73 shows various basic layouts suitable for a partly covered strawed yard, including a parlour unit and a silobarn holding sufficient silage, with straw on top of the silage, for about 4 months winter housing. It is an economy to use the bedded area as a lean-to adjoining the silobarn and to continue the lean-to over the parlour unit. Obviously, if required, the plan can be reversed. The open yard, which includes a forage fence at one side, can be cleaned from end to end into a slurry pit. The total floor area is in the region of about 130 ft²/cow, excluding roads. The latter are essential to the success of the scheme. One man should be able to manage the herd and have time to look after followers and young stock in a separate building. Either a 6 stall/3 unit tandem, a 6 stall/6 unit tandem or an 8 stall/4 unit herringbone parlour could be included in the layout (a chute parlour would be less wide).

i. Fig. 73*a*: The basic layout, showing the grouping of the specialized buildings (Ref. *e*).

ii. Fig. 73*b*: Showing the effect of orientation (Ref. *e*):

> *S.E. aspect (1):* Dairy faces N.E., bedded area sheltered from N. and N.E. winds and receiving early morning sun, but straw needs protection from S.W. rain.

> *S.E. aspect (2):* Dairy faces evening sun, but bedded area is protected from S.W. rain, though, as straw is used, N.E. winds blow into building, unless side is clad.

> *S.W. aspect (3):* Dairy faces S.E., bedded area protected from N. and E. and receiving late morning sun, but straw needs cover from S.W. rain.

> *S.W. aspect (4):* Dairy faces N.W., bedded area well protected if clad to E.

iii. Fig. 73*c*: Showing alternative positions suitable for the parlour unit, though if separated from main building some economy in design is lost, and it may not be economic to cover the collecting yard (Ref. *a*).

b. If silage is not self-fed, then the straw should be stored adjacent to the bedded area, which will be more expensive, but the open yard can include a forage fence. The latter is suitable for rationed bulk foods and can be coupled with a tower silo. But the feeding of all bulk foods in the open may not be desirable (Fig. 74), (Ref. *f*).

c. The complete yard and silobarn can be covered. This is essential on exposed sites and in the north of the country and may not be much more expensive than partly covered yards. The main difficulty is that bringing in rationed fodders by trailer can be time consuming unless the cows can be segregated from the tractor passage. Bed-and-breakfast layouts can be suitable within a fully covered yard. Care has to be taken to provide adequate high-level ventilation (Ref. *f*).

i. Fig. 75*a*: A simple layout, relying on self-fed silage plus a little hay, which can be kept on top of the silage with the straw, as the feeding policy, and with an internal concreted area, used both for exercise and as a collecting yard, as well as for access to the silage from the

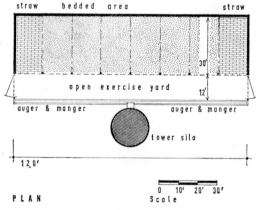

Fig. 74. Sixty-cow strawed yard and mechanized feeding

61: INTENSIVE BEEF UNIT (EXTERIOR)

J. Sainsbury Ltd., Inverquhomery, Longside, Aberdeenshire

A unit for 400 beef erected in 1962 divided into four sections, each for fattening 100 head on a slatted floor over a dung cellar, which partly uses a natural fall and is partly excavated to give tractor access to each cellar from one end. The liquid is drained off to allow the dung to be handled by tractor and foreloader. Adjustable wall louvre panels and a continuous ventilated ridge are used for ventilation. A ramp provides access for cattle into the building. At the far end of the building is a double-bay silage clamp 90 ft long with access for loading at the sides and end. Walls are of rendered blockwork. [SEE PAGE 193] Courtesy of North of Scotland Agricultural College.

62: INTENSIVE BEEF UNIT (INTERIOR)

J. Sainsbury Ltd., Inverquhomery, Longside, Aberdeenshire

A 4-ft-wide passage-cum-trough separates 12-ft-wide slatted yards, which, at 2 ft run/head, allow 24 sq. ft/head. Feeding is carried out by an electric powered trolley which is filled from the silo and travels along the passage, emptying into the trough. The 9-in. block walls with piers are 8 ft high, over 18-in. walls 9 ft to the dung cellar, and support timber trusses of 28 ft 9 in. span at 12-ft centres. The louvre wall ventilators are visible. The roof is of asbestos insulated sandwich construction. Slats are 5 in. wide with $1\frac{1}{2}$-in. gaps between them. The overall dimension of the 8 runs of yards, subdivided to hold 10 head, plus four feed passages is 120 ft × 115 ft 9 in. [SEE PAGE 193] Courtesy of North of Scotland Agricultural College.

63: BEEF YARDS
Mr. E. Arnold, Ulting Hall Estate, Essex

Six strawed yards on each side of a central auger and manger have chalk floors and a 10-ft-wide concrete feed area adjacent to the manger. The yards are 21 ft 8 in. wide, with those on one side being 24 ft deep and those on the other 20 ft deep, holding 14–25 head depending on the size of animal. The feed area division gates fold back to hold the animals in the strawed yards when the concrete is cleaned out by tractor. [SEE PAGE 193] Courtesy of Dairy Farmer.

64: MECHANIZED BEEF FEEDING
Mr. E. Arnold, Ulting Hall Estate, Essex

A central manger between two runs of beef yards is filled from an auger with rolled barley and concentrates from an external moist grain silo. The frame of the building is in two spans forming a rigid timber frame of composite members bolted together. The gables are formed from 'hit-and-miss' ventilation boards. Galvanized catching posts in the feed area receive division gates between yards. [SEE PAGE 193] Courtesy of Dairy Farmer.

65: CONTROLLED ENVIRONMENT BEEF UNIT

Vitamins Ltd., Henhaw Farm, Surrey

This building, 120 ft × 38 ft, with a central tractor passage having mangers on each side of it to slatted floor pens, holds 120 head. Ridge air-inlet shafts are not visible. At each side of the building are fan extractors placed a little above slat level. Half the fans are thermostatically controlled. The underside of the roof slopes is smooth, the insulation being finished with a vinyl-faced fibreboard. The steel portal frame does not project into the interior. The plastic-sheeted gable strip windows can be opened, if required, as can the gable louvre panels. Below slat level are the pressure inlet and sunction outlet pipes for cleaning the dung cellars, 4½ ft deep, below the slatted floors. [SEE PAGE 193] Photo: J. B. W.

66: CATTLE FEEDING FENCE

An old barn converted for intensive beef production has a simple timber slatted floor over a dung cellar and has a feed-passage-cum-manger beyond a feeding fence. The latter is based on a Norwegian design which has been pioneered in this country by the West of Scotland Agricultural College. The uprights are at about 1⅛ ft centres and can be up to 4 ft 2 in. high, depending on the age and breed of stock. They can be used for dairy cows. The cattle feed through alternative gaps, which are 8½ in. wide. With their heads between the uprights, cattle cannot flick their fodder out of the manger. [SEE PAGE 188] Photograph J. B. W.

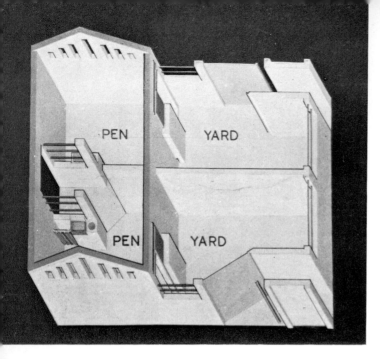

67: BULL BOX

The model shows a double bull box, each unit including a pen and an open yard. The pens have a central feed and control area, with a door to each pen and railings above the trough and bowl. High-level ventilation is provided by vents in the gables. Access from pen to yard is through a sliding door which can be controlled from the exterior. The yard leads into a service pen through a gate which can swing into two positions. The yards, as shown, exclude safety gaps. [SEE PAGE 199] Diagrammatic Model: Courtesy of West of Scotland Agricultural College.

68: CALF HOUSE

Mr. J. Ross Anderson, Boquhan Estates, Kippen, Stirlingshire

The calves are housed in individual pens until about a month old, when they can be put together into larger pens. The calf house is a converted building. A suspended and insulated ceiling has been added, in which are extract grilles for ventilation. Cross-ventilation and light are provided by hopper windows in the side walls. There are 11 single pens and 5 pens taking two or more calves. The pens are divided by rendered dwarf walls and have a yoke-type gate at the front. The floors of the pens are of timber slats a few inches above the concrete floor, which slopes into a dung channel along the front of the pens. The calves have straw on the slats for bedding. White plastic buckets, which can be kept clean, are used for feeding. In addition, for the older calves, there are small hay racks. An infra-red heating bulb is suspended from the ceiling above each pen. The bulb can be raised or lowered by means of a counter and weight. The central passage leads to a feed room. [SEE PAGE 200] Courtesy of Mr. J. Ross Anderson.

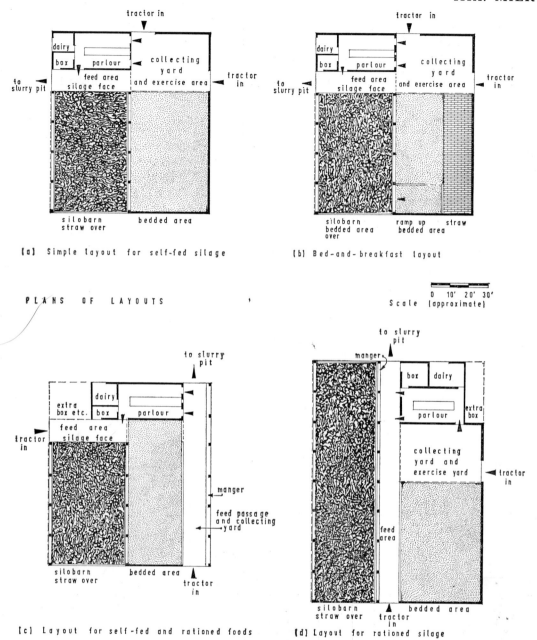

PLANS OF LAYOUTS

Scale (approximate) 0 10' 20' 30'

(a) Simple layout for self-fed silage

(b) Bed-and-breakfast layout

(c) Layout for self-fed and rationed foods

(d) Layout for rationed silage

Fig. 75. Totally enclosed strawed yards

strawed bedding. The total area is about the same as Fig. 73a.

ii. Fig. 75b: The advantage of a bed-and-breakfast layout is lost in a new building if straw storage has to be provided (this is true equally in a partly covered layout). However, if saw-dust and shavings are used as bedding, instead of straw, then there is an advantage in that about 20 ft²/cow of covered space may be saved.

iii. Fig. 75c: If rationed foods are fed at a manger, then it is possible to have an access road through the building, which can be used for a tractor and self-unloading trailer, the road being used also as a collecting yard to the parlour.

iv. Fig. 75*d*: It is possible to cut the silage and place it in a manger, the complete unit being under cover, and with a strawed yard, 10-ft-wide feed area and silobarn all under one roof, with parlour attached. The mangers are moved into the silobarn as the latter is emptied, providing more exercise space for the cows. The total area may be similar to Fig. 73*a*. The feed area can be slatted.

d. Slatted yards can be used instead of bedded yards and, since only 35 ft²/cow may be allowed instead of about 40 ft² for bedded and 20 ft² for concreted exercise areas, the total area per cow may be reduced by 25 ft², a reduction which can pay for the slats and slurry pit in some cases (Ref. *f*).

i. Fig. 76*a*: Slatted yard with self-fed silage and hay.

ii. Fig. 76*b*: Slatted yard with silage hand cut into troughs.

iii. Fig. 76*c*: Slatted yard with fodder delivered by side-unloading trailers into troughs.

e. Fig. 77 shows two cubicle layouts combined with self-fed silage and an alternative layout having an auger and trough coupled to a tower silo. There are many advantages in the layout shown in Fig. 77*c*, since labour requirements are considerably reduced over most other layouts. The exercise area between the cubicle rows can be slatted, which saves the need for cleaning out the concrete every day, and should not add more than £15/cow to the cost (Ref. *f*).

f. Fig. 78 shows a cubicle-cum-slat layout, with tower and auger feeding of haylage and a parlour unit for 100 cows, which might be managed by one man plus relief help. The total floor area should be less than 75 ft²/cow, and all feeding, cleaning and milking is highly mechanized, so both the building and running cost may be low, which can justify the mechanical equipment (Ref. *f*).

9. *Siting.* Siting a diary unit correctly is one of the most important planning problems on a farm and it is not easy to assess away from a particular site and layout.

a. Access

There must be good access both to the highway and to the fields, the latter being especially important if the cows have to return from a milking parlour to the fields for grazing. The unit may have to be planned in relation to summer grazing. Access may be required both for milk and grain tankers, though the dairy unit may have to be sited in relation to a farm mill-and-mix plant. If

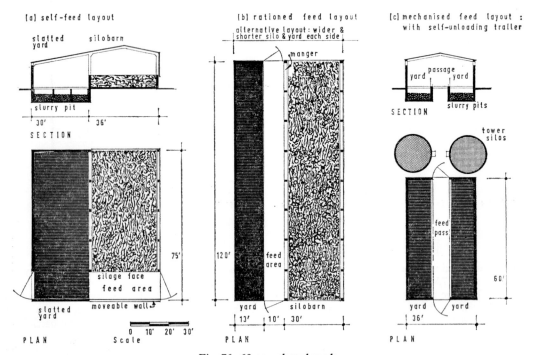

Fig. 76. 60-cow slatted yards

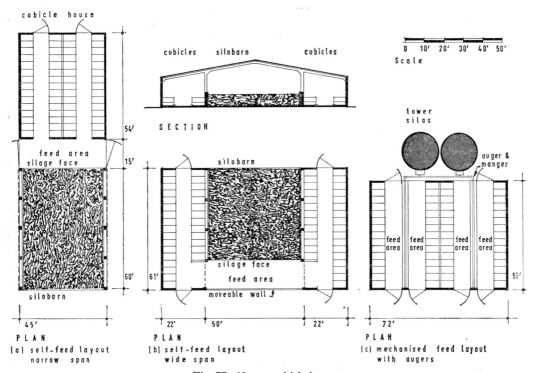

Fig. 77. 60-cow cubicle layouts

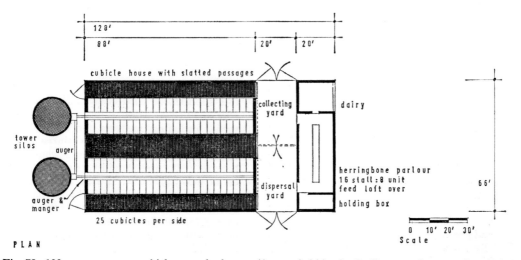

Fig. 78. 100-cow—one man cubicle-cum-slat layout. (An untried idea for feeding cows by auger in cubicles)

silage or haylage is made the route for bringing the grass from the fields is important. Similarly, hay and straw may have to be handled to the unit. Kale, roots or tops may be lifted from the fields every day in the autumn to be fed to the cows. Slurry or manure may be piped or carted by spreader from the buildings to the fields. It is obvious that the dairy unit can have an important bearing on the economics of the fieldwork.

b. Services
Roads, drainage, electricity and water are of vital importance to the success of the layout, which should be planned to reduce the cost of providing these services.

c. Aspect
Layouts which are partly open should face S.E. to S.W. and should be planned to take into account prevailing or local winds; wind-tunnel effects should be avoided. Shelter is important.

d. Ground Slopes
Silobarns and open yards have detailed requirements for floor profiles. Falls of 1 : 30 are expensive to construct on flat sites. Considerable economy can be obtained by making use of existing ground falls, though these may contradict the principles of orientation.

10. Services
a. Electricity
As previously stated, not all layouts have electric lighting to the yards, but it will be a disadvantage if none is provided, and self-feed silobarns, open yards and parlours should include good lighting, as should totally enclosed yards. However, little work should be carried out in the yards after dark, therefore, since most of the light is required for the convenience of the cows and for casual inspection, the installation of light sockets is mainly common sense. However, it is useful to have one high-level, wide-reflector yard light commanding any open yards, forage fences, etc. Fully insulated and enclosed yards in the future may require fan ventilation. There should be a thermostatically controlled low-intensity heating element under each water trough, the latter being insulated and encased to prevent the water dropping below 15° C (60° F) in winter. Electric supply cables should be at least 15 ft, and preferably 20 ft, above roads and yards, especially when silage trailers are used, or they should be taken underground.

b. Water Troughs
As previously stated, troughs should be insulated and heated, be away from bedding and tractor runs, and should preferably be near the parlour exit. Great care should be taken at the planning stage to site the troughs correctly.

c. Floor Profiles
Reference has been made to the care required in draining concrete floors and the need to take advantage of ground slopes. These falls can be difficult to relate to a site and to the required heights in the building, and care should be taken to examine the levels at the design stage.

d. Roof Drainage
Since large roof areas of 100–150 ft²/cow may be required, considerable drainage from the roof will occur. Rainwater can be stored for use or should be taken clear of the building, roads, gateways, etc. However, rainwater can be drained to a ditch.

e. Foul Drainage
All drainage from the floors must be treated as a trade effluent and should therefore be taken into a slurry pit, for return to the land. Obviously, the siting of the slurry pit needs considerable attention, since it usually has to be at the lowest point of the yard levels. The disposal of effluent may possibly govern the design of a layout and even the basis of the management of the herd.

11. Costs
a. Overall costs for dairy layouts, including milking equipment and food storage, may vary from under £30/cow in a conversion to over £200/cow in a new, well-equipped layout. A new lean-to yard and open exercise yard, excluding a slurry pit, but including a forage fence, should cost probably less than £30/cow; whereas, if the yard is a self-contained barn, including straw storage, the cost might be £40/cow. A fully enclosed, lean-to barn, connected to a silobarn for self-feeding, might be a little over £40/cow. Most fully covered strawed yards, including mangers for rationed feed, slatted yards with 4-ft-deep slurry pits or cubicle yards, if constructed as a lean-to, perhaps to a silobarn, should cost about £45/cow or, at most, £50/cow. If slats are added to a cubicle layout the cost might be £60/cow and, if the layout includes an auger and trough, perhaps £75/cow. In contrast, a traditional cowhouse with feed passages is unlikely to cost less than £70/cow.

b. A capital cost of £40/cow for a normal type of strawed yard (and several types of yard are possible) represents £6/cow p.a. or, for a 1000-gal cow, a little over 1½d./gal. However, the cost of bedding and the labour costs in handling straw and cleaning yards can be very high, to which might have to be added wastage due to high food conversion ratios, if such were known. Bedding costs may represent at least another $1\frac{1}{2}d$./gal (IIIB, 2b, p. 184) and, at a general labour requirement of $\frac{1}{2}$ hr/day for cleaning, etc., during the winter, and for fetching cows to be milked in the summer, labour costs might be assessed as at least at $\frac{1}{2}d$./gal. However, labour costs are directly related to milking costs. Thus the total cost of housing, including labour required, might be $3\frac{1}{2}d$./gal, though this could be easily increased due to many other factors.

c. A mechanized layout, with cubicles, slatted exercise areas, and auger and trough, costing £75/cow, represents about $2\frac{3}{4}d$./gal. However, there are no bedding costs (the slurry also will be more valuable as a fertilizer than the manure, which has greater organic losses) and labour costs may be negligible. It might be argued that the mechanized layout would prove cheaper than the strawed-yard layout, but the effect of the cubicle-and-slat layout should be also to increase the throughput/man. Since the cost of housing should be considered in relation to all the other factors, such as food conversion, food conservation, milking, etc., it is impossible to assess a standard cost for housing suitable for all managerial policies. However, the cheapest housing may not produce the cheapest milk.

12. References

(1) ATTLEE, P. 'Milk begins with grass'. *Farmers Weekly*, p. 75 (18th January 1963).
(2) BEYNON, V. H. 'Cashing in on grass'. *Dairy Farmer Supplement*, pp. 43–5 (February 1963).
(3) WITHERS, F. W. 'Surveys of disease in dairy cattle in G.B. 1950–54'. *Outlook on Agriculture*, Vol. 1 (1956).
(4) Ref. *a*, p. 55.
(5) *Dairy Farmer*, p. 19 (April 1963).
(6) Ref. *b*, p. 20.
(7) Ref. *a*, p. 50.
(8) *Dairy Farmer*, p. 22 (January 1963).
(9) WELLESLEY, R. 'Zero grazing experiment in Berkshire'. *Times Agricultural Supplement*, p. viii (July 1958).
(10) PHELPS, A. 'Grazing a la carte'. *Dairy Farmer*, pp. 55–7 (November 1962).
(11) *Farmers Weekly Supplement*. 'Off the Grass', p. xxi (14th September 1962).
(12) *Farmer and Stockbreeder*. 'Grassland Handbook', p. 225 (1957).
(13) LONG, D. 'New ideas in bedding'. *Farmers Weekly*, pp. 92–5 (24th March 1961).
(14) Ref. *h*.
(15) Ref. *f*.
(16) Ref. *d*, p. 32.
(17) Ref. *a*, p. 47.
(18) Ref. *b*, pp. 47, 49.
(19) MILLAR, G. C. 'A farm factory on a concrete raft'. *Scottish Farmer*, pp. 24–6 (16th June 1962).
(20) MOORE, I. *Agricultural Notebook*. Farmer & Stockbreeder, p. 660.
(21) Ministry of Agriculture Fixed Equipment on the Farm Leaflet No. 35. 'Ventilation & Insulation' (1958).
(22) FINDLAY, J. D. *Agricultural Review* (Dec. 1955).
(23) Ministry of Agriculture Fixed Equipment on the Farm Leaflet No. 13. 'The Cattle Crush' (1958).
(24) Ref. *i*, No. 32.
(25) LONG, D. 'Cubicles—770 cows give their verdict'. *Farmers Weekly*, pp. 86–9 (26th April 1963). 'Cows like Cubicles. *Dairy Farmer*, pp. 26–7 (March 1963) and pp. 91–3 (April 1963).
(26) 'Under-floor heat cuts bedding bill'. *Farmers Weekly*, p. 59 (22nd November 1963).

SELECTED REFERENCES

a. NIX, J. S., BELSHAW, D. G. R. & WELLER, J. B. 'The Yard and Parlour', University of Cambridge School of Agriculture Farm Economics Branch Report No. 58 (July 1962).
b. BELSHAW, D. G. R. & SCOTT, A. H. 'Work routines and work elements for Yard and Parlour and Cowshed Systems'. University of Cambridge, School of Agriculture Farm Economics Branch Technical Report (Work Study) No. 1 (1962).
c. STURROCK, F. G. & BRAYSHAW, G. H. 'Planning the Farm to Save Labour'. University of Cambridge School of Agriculture Farm Economics Branch Report No. 47 (1958).
d. STURROCK, F. G. Ministry of Agriculture Bulletin No. 172. 'Planning Farm Work' (1960).
e. WELLER, J. B. 'Planning the one-man yard-and-parlour layout'. *British Farmer*, pp. 27–45 (4th August 1962).
f. WELLER, J. B. 'Which housing system'. *Dairy Farmer* (November 1962–April 1963).
g. INGERSENT, K. A. & MANNING, P. 'New housing for dairy cows in the East Midlands'. University of Nottingham Dept. Agricultural Economics (1960).
h. PRICE, W. T. 'U.K. development of Farm Buildings with appendices on methods of flooring and bedding for livestock'. Harper Adams Agricultural College Technical Bulletin No. 9 (1962).
i. 'A Bibliography of Farm Buildings Research 1945–1958'. Pt. IV. Buildings for Cattle. Agricultural Research Council (1960); also 1958–1961 (1963).
k. LIVINGSTONE, H. R. Cow cubicles. Experimental Farm Buildings Rep. No. 1. Agricultural Research Council.
l. Dairy Cow Feeding. *Farmers Weekly Supplement*. (11th Sept. 1964).
m. Code of Practice C.P. 11: 1965 Farm Dairy Buildings.
n. LIVINGSTONE, H. R. 'Slatted Floors'. Experimental Farm Buildings Report No. 3 (1965).
o. 'Building for the dairy cow', National Farm Buildings Conference Report, *Farmers Weekly* (Autumn 1964).

IIIB. Beef

1. *Activity*

a. Annual consumption of beef in the United Kingdom is a little under ½ cwt/head, of which approximately two-thirds, representing over ¾M tons, is fattened within the home industry, with over one-fifth being imported from the Argentine and the remainder from such countries as New Zealand and Yugoslavia. In contrast, consumption per head in the U.S.A. is about ⅞ cwt, in New Zealand 1 cwt and in the Argentine nearly 2 cwt (1). In recent years the United Kingdom beef industry has been stimulated by Government subsidies, which in 1961–62 amounted to £52M. Methods of beef production are extremely varied. Not only are many breeds of cattle used for fattening and numerous different management and rationing systems adopted, but the cattle may be slaughtered at any age up to 3 years and at any weight up to 13 cwt. At present about half of the cattle are fattened in yards and about half in the fields (Ref. *a*). Many grades of carcass are marketed. Economic beef production has been retarded by farmers keeping cattle for the value of the manure produced, rather than for a realistic profit from the enterprise, and by a lack of scientific knowledge concerning breed, food and liveweight gain. Moreover, cheap imported meat has discouraged farmers, except in the production of prime beef, and has led to difficulties, such as in the spring of 1963, when deficiency payments rose to about £1½M per week and to over £30/beast.

b. Today beef production is in a period of rapid transition and it is probable that within a few years only three main types of meat will be marketed, though there may be some variation in quality and grade within each type. Meat will be graded from carcasses produced under contract to a specified weight and age from cattle fed intensively with standard and uniform rations. One grade will be veal, fed on milk or milk substitutes and marketed at 250–400 lb liveweight at 10–14 weeks (IIID). The most important grade will be beef, frequently prepacked, reaching 7–9 cwt in 10–18 months, obtained partly from intensive and partly from semi-intensive feeding and housing. In addition, there will be a limited production of luxury meat obtained from non-intensive methods over 2–3 years. The main stimulus for these marketing changes will be from the needs of the supermarkets, and it will possibly be

intensified if a Meat Marketing Board is developed. Moreover, there will be some vertical integration within the industry whereby certain groups will own or control not only the breeding, fattening, slaughtering and marketing of beef but also the production of the raw materials required for fattening (2). In fact, as stated in a leading article by the *Farmers Weekly* (Ref. *a*):

'Beef production is on the threshold of development patterns reminiscent of the broiler industry. Large scale operators whose methods will affect the future of thousands of farmers raising cattle on traditional lines are being attracted to the barley beef system.'

Though there are several traditional breeds used for beef production, such as Shorthorns, Aberdeen Angus and Herefords, one-fifth of the beef slaughtered in recent years has probably been culls from dairy herds, with as much as two-thirds originating from dual-purpose cattle (3). A recent estimate gives sources of beef from animals slaughtered in Britain as (Ref. *a*):

	Percentage of total
Irish store cattle	18
Home-breed beef stores	21
Fat cows, etc.	25
Stores bred in dairy herds	36

Therefore, there are five main sources for beef fattening:

i. Steers or bullocks (castrated) and heifers from beef cattle.

ii. Steers or bullocks (castrated) from dairy herds.

iii. Culled cows or heifers from dairy herds.

iv. Bulls (limited number used for beef) (1).

v. Calves from dairy herds used for veal.

Fraser has shown that meat to suit modern requirements, which must have little or no fat, can be best obtained from late-maturing animals killed at an early age, since their fat develops only when fully grown, that is perhaps after 18–21 months, and they have a rapid liveweight gain in the early stages (4). The value of beef production from dual-purpose cattle was shown:

	Av. for breeds up to 15 months	Daily livewt. gain, lb, 15–21 months
Beef steers	2·34	1·97
Dual-purpose steers	2·49	2·18

The traditional fattening process can be summarized by a quotation from the Ministry's publication on Beef Production published as recently as 1959 (5):

'If fed generously they can be brought to slaughter weight at 10 cwt. or thereabouts at under two years of age. Many cattle, however, are three years old before they are fit for slaughter, by which time they may be expected to weigh 11–12 cwt, or even more.'

On this basis production included a rearing-calf period of 6–8 months, followed by a store period of 15–24 months and, finally, fattening within a period of 3–4 months, the animals usually having several owners before slaughter. This extensive method of production is the antithesis of the recent trend for intensively produced beef animals within 12–21 months of age. Lamming has shown that fattening 2-year-old Friesian bullocks off grass is considerably less efficient than yearlings, since for every lb liveweight gain twice the value of the extra weight could be consumed in food than if fed intensively to attain the same weight at an earlier age (6). Therefore the emphasis for the future must be on a quicker throughput for the producer, which has important implications for the economics of housing and equipment. Moreover, the traditional store period for cattle prior to the final fattening process no longer has the same emphasis. In fact, the movement of cattle on long journeys and through markets, with the inevitable changes in environment and diet, can cause growth setbacks, reflected in their carcasses, and therefore uneven grading.

c. Beef production, as in pig fattening (IIIE), requires a supply of two basic raw materials. In the first place there must be a source for obtaining the young stock. Calf rearing is described in IIIC, but it is important to appreciate that there is no fixed age when a calf becomes a fattening animal. In fact, the fattening process might be considered to start immediately after weaning, which traditionally is at 10–14 wks, but, with early weaning, may be at 3–5 wks. However, with traditional fattening over 2–3 years the calf period was normally taken to be until an age of 6–8 months, but, with modern intensive fattening, may be considered as 3–4 months. The calves may be reared on the farm, but they should be considered as an enterprise, with its own costings, separate from that of the fattening enterprise. Alternatively, they may be bought in the market or, as is the trend for the future, on contract or from 'calf banks', the latter being a group of registered calf producers acting through an agent, such as the N.F.U. or an auctioneer.

Secondly, there must be a supply of sufficient fodder both for maintenance and for fattening. In sheltered districts beef cattle can graze all the year round, being outwintered and given,

possibly, some additional hay in the fields. Obviously the need for buildings is limited to field equipment sheds, unless there are cattle shelters in the fields. In many similar extensive fattening enterprises the cattle are brought into open, partly covered or fully covered yards during the winter, and are fed on roots, silage or hay. In some cases the enterprise is planned to suit the existing yards and buildings, rather than the amount of fodder which could be grown on the farm. Many farmers buy a few store or fattening beasts as a sideline, perhaps using a building which, for example, is used for storing potatoes for part of the year. Intensive beef enterprises should be planned to use the bulk foods available to their best advantage, perhaps with tower silos for haylage. Alternatively, stimulated by research at the Rowett Institute, beef fattened entirely from barley plus supplements has proved an economic method of production and has led to a new form of intensive housing which can be divorced from normal arable farms since bulk foods are not required. Intensive systems can be on such a scale as to be called a 'feedlot', which is a term describing the U.S. beef units holding between 1000 and 10,000 head at a time. In the United Kingdom most large units hold at present no more than between 400 and 700 head, but a few units of more than 1000 are coming into operation, with units of up to 10,000 being pioneered by at least one company. Feeding policy determines the layout required.

2. *Managerial requirements.* Reference has been made to the effect basic management decisions can have on the building needs of a beef enterprise. Other management factors have to be considered.

a. Spring or Autumn Calving
The cost of winter housing is critical to the success of beef production. Whenever it is considered undesirable to rear the calves externally autumn calving may be preferable:

i. Spring calving, using a calf house or yards, has to be followed by a winter housing period, one summer for grazing and a second winter indoors, to obtain a 2-year-old beast.

ii. An autumn calf spends its first winter indoors and has two summer grazing periods to only one winter fattening period to reach the same age.

Thus, winter calving may increase the throughput in the buildings, which reduces the capital cost/ beast. Suckling in yards is discussed in IIIC. In contrast, intensive production may require a constant source of calves, perhaps on a monthly basis, to maintain a regular contract throughput instead of one annual sale.

b. Bedding

Straw is the traditional material for bedding yards, considerable quantities, perhaps more than 20 lb/beast/day within the grain districts, being used either in open or in partly covered yards in order to make manure. However, the straw allowance, when straw is in short supply, may be restricted, perhaps, to under 7 lb/beast/day. The national average used for dairy cows is 11 lb, with 9 lb for semi-covered yards and 17 lb for fully bedded and covered yards (7). If, for example, the allowance is 12 lb/beast/day, about 10, 13, 16 and 19 cwt/beast p.a. would be required for winter housing periods of 3, 4, 5 and 6 months respectively. An allowance of $\frac{3}{4}$ T p.a. might be a reasonable average for about 5 months housed, though many farmers would consider 1 T to be the minimum for cleanliness in the cattle.

i. Unfortunately, inadequate costings are available for modern methods of baling, harvesting and handling straw. This matter requires research. However, it can hardly be less than £5/T and might be more than £10/T, if the cost of storage and of lifting the manure by foreloader from the yards and of spreading in the fields is added to give a total cost. In the Eastern Counties the average cost of straw collection in 1956 was given as £2/acre (8), which, at $1\frac{1}{2}$ T/acre, might equal a cost of about £1$\frac{1}{3}$/T. Another recent estimate has been made (24):

'Surveys show that the time taken to ted, bale and stack a straw crop of a ton per acre is on average four manhours and two tractor and machine hours. The former will cost £1–£1$\frac{1}{4}$ (depending on how much is overtime). The latter could well cost £1 also. By the time that the cost of twine is thrown in and allowance is made for bad weather, the straw may easily have cost between £3 and £4 per ton to gather.'

Recently, it has been reported that baling costs £3/T and carting and stacking another £2/T. Storage can cost another £1/T and a merchant may charge £2–£3/T to handle it, making a purchase price of up to £9/T (24).

In any enterprise in which straw has to be bought, particularly in the north and west, an average cost of £5–£7/T should be allowed, though in 1960–61 the price reached £14T. A new straw barn might cost £1$\frac{1}{2}$–£2/T stored (IA, 11, p. 56), though in many cases an existing storage building may be considered to have negligible cost. Handling into and out of storage, allowing 60 bales/T at 2$\frac{1}{2}$ min/bale might cost £1–£2/T, cleaning out another £2–£4/T, on the basis of labour costs given (Pt. 1,

Ch. 1). However, yards can be emptied at a rate of $\frac{1}{3}$ hr/T, including spreading on nearby fields, with modern methods and a cost of £1–£2/T might be reasonable. Thus, handling into and out of storage could cost about £2/T from the barn to spreading the manure, but £2–£5/T might be considered in difficult conditions as more probable.

ii. Therefore it might be reasonable to assess the cost of bedding, including manure handling, as £4–£8/T, when the straw is harvested on the farm, and £8–£12/T, when the straw is bought. In many cases these costs might be exceeded.

Therefore, at $\frac{3}{4}$ T/beast, annual bedding costs might be £3–£6 and £6–£9 respectively, which, on the basis of the higher figures and if considered as an annual building cost, would equal a capital investment of either £40 or £60 depreciated over 10 years. The latter could be used to provide a slatted layout with mechanical disposal of slurry, thereby eliminating the need for straw (see below). Bedding costs for stock housed for two winters could become an exceptionally important percentage of total production costs. The average cost during 1961–62 for fattening in Yorkshire, excluding the cost of the store or calf, has been given (9):

Winter fattened 144 days and sold at 9·5 cwt aged over 2 years £28 10s. 8d.

Winter fattened 174 days and sold at 9·1 cwt aged 1$\frac{1}{2}$–2 years £31 5s. 11d.

Intensive fattened 1 year and sold at 8 cwt £56 5s. 4d.

Though these costs do not include the total cost for handling straw, as discussed above, and have low building and equipment costs of between 3s. and 7s. 10d./beast, they indicate the important part straw handling, if fully costed, would have within production costs. The value of the dung as a liquid rather than as a manure has been discussed (IA, 1a, p. 54, and IG, 1b, p. 76).

Straw is not the only material used for bedding cattle. One beeflot for 400 head is housed on 1 ft of wood shavings. In some yards sawdust is used. Costs for shavings and sawdust usually vary from £0 to £6, plus handling costs, and therefore the overall bedding cost may be less than when straw is used. Experiments at Harper Adams Experimental College included the use of a mixture of shavings, peat moss and chopped straw, costing £2$\frac{1}{4}$/beast for the materials using 1 T/beast over 148 days (10).

Since no straw is used, slatted floors for beef cattle have the advantage of reduced running costs. It is normal to use a sprinkling of sawdust on the slats, perhaps amounting to $\frac{1}{4}$ T/beast for 4–5 months and costing less than £$\frac{1}{2}$. Higher stocking densities in the slatted buildings (5, below) help to make the building cost equal to that for normal yards. Moreover, the slurry can be handled as a free-flowing solid or as a liquid when returned to the land from under the slats.

c. Weighing

In the past few beef cattle were weighed on the farm, except sometimes prior to sale, and stockmanship is still frequently a matter of visual appraisal. However, modern grading, intensive fattening and the economic use of expensive fodders justify more frequent weighing, perhaps fortnightly, and at least once a month. Not only is it important to know the weight of incoming and outgoing cattle, to give the overall liveweight gain in relation to food consumed, but frequent recording makes it possible to control the rationing policy in relation to weekly, or even daily, gain, and this is important, particularly with grain-fed beef. Therefore the layout must include weighing facilities.

d. Liveweight Gain

Under traditional management a calf was expected to require 12 lb d.m./day at 8 months, perhaps increasing to 25–30 lb before slaughter at 12–13 cwt, with an average liveweight gain of 1, $1\frac{1}{2}$ and 2 lb at 7, 8 and 11 cwt liveweight respectively (11). Under modern forage feeding the daily d.m. requirements have been given as $14\frac{1}{2}$, 19 and $23\frac{1}{2}$ lb for stock weighing 5, 7 and 10 cwt respectively (12). However, d.m. has to be related to the Starch and Protein Equivalents, plus their digestibility, required for maintenance and fattening. A semi-intensive system, particularly for autumn calves having one summer at grass, can prove economic with a winter diet of hay and concentrates, fattening to 16–20 months. With intensive fattening the aim may be to fatten to 8 cwt within 12 months of age. If a calf weighs 200 lb at 3 months a liveweight gain of at least $2\frac{1}{2}$ lb/day is required with a conversion ratio, if fed 28 cwt of rolled barley and concentrates, of under 4·5. This can be obtained, and gains of $3\frac{1}{2}$ lb/day from $10\frac{1}{2}$ lb concentrates have been recorded (13). Average gains and ratios in an experiment at the Rowett Institute for barley-fed Friesian steers have been given as (14):

Age, wk	Livewt, lb	Daily gain lb	Conversion ratio
16–20	229–280	1·91	3·46
24	332	1·85	4·34
28	387	1·97	4·42
32	466	2·86	4·04
36	563	3·46	4·56
40	669	3·86	4·38
52	891	3·15	5·79

If bulk foods are fed, in order to obtain a liveweight gain of at least 2 lb/day, which is required for beef to reach about 8 cwt at 15 months, it is essential to have very good silage and hay (12). Though gains with silage of $2\frac{1}{2}$–3 lb/day, or occasionally more, have been recorded, gains of under $1\frac{1}{2}$ lb/day are frequently experienced, even when 2–4 lb/day of supplementary concentrates are fed (15). Such differences in liveweight gain affect the throughput and can make a fundamental difference to the economics of housing. The building should be costed in terms of the annual cost per cwt liveweight gain.

e. Feeding Policies

Reference has been made to feeding policies based on summer grazing, followed by winter rations of roots, haylage, silage, hay or concentrates. The rations may be mixed and the fodder may be varied with the season. However, even grading depends on uniform and consistent rations, since changes in the diet can be reflected in the carcass quality. This could lead eventually to a widespread departure from summer grazing/winter housing policies to the permanent housing of beef cattle, whether with tower haylage or self-feeder concentrates, as practised by a few specialist beef farmers. A *Farmers Weekly Supplement* discusses modern feeding methods (Ref. *a*).

The average haylage ration over 12 months might be 40 lb/day (20 lb d.m.) plus 2–5 lb of concentrates. Rolled barley should have a m.c. of at least 17 per cent and, if barley is stored below this m.c., water must be added. Alternatively, storage can be wet within hermetically sealed silos. Usually the barley ration includes about 15 per cent of concentrates. At present many beef units are self-fed silage, which saves the capital cost of mechanized feeding, but the method is unsatisfactory for large, intensive units due to wastage in the silage (IC, 1*b*, p. 58), lack of control over rationing and labour requirements in cleaning the silage face. The layout must suit the feeding policy, though some layouts can be adapted or used for more than one fodder. Alternatively, chopped straw, sometimes with a liquid feed supplement, may be fed with barley.

f. Mixed Units

A few intensive fattening enterprises house pigs among the cattle, in one case having a pig/2–3 cattle without extra space, with the pigs sleeping between the cattle's legs or beneath a manger (16). This system would be unsatisfactory for a slatted layout. Many units, strawed or slatted, are used for pigs or poultry for part of the year, especially if the cattle are fattened within 9 months.

g. Size of Production Unit

One man can manage 500 cattle in a feedlot, including feeding, weighing, littering if required and cleaning, plus all external office work. With automation, a 5-day week is possible. However, average annual labour requirements for beef cattle have been given as $4\frac{1}{2}$ days/head (17), which would limit the unit size to 80 per man. Many units have a lower stocking/man rate. But even without complete mechanization it is doubtful whether units holding less than 400–600 justify the employment of a full-time, skilled stockman costing perhaps £4–£5/beast p.a. on the basis of labour costs given (Pt. 1, Ch. 4, p. 11). In the Yorkshire costings for intensive production (9) the manual labour/beast was rated at £3½, plus overheads at a little over £5, part of which would be labour overheads, perhaps giving a total labour cost of about £6/beast. In contrast, yarding $1\frac{1}{2}$–2 year olds costs only about £4¼/beast for labour and labour overheads. One man should be able to manage 300–400 head, including the mechanical cutting of silage from a bunker and its distribution with a self-unloading forage trailer. With a tower and auger, feeding becomes a push-button operation. If the stockman has to manage a rearing unit in addition to a fattening unit the latter might have to be limited to 150–200 head. Not only must there be relief help, but additional labour would be required for fieldwork in conserving fodder, unless the latter is bought.

3. *Production techniques*

a. Feeding Techniques

Traditional feeding arrangements, still followed by many farmers, are based on manhandling hay bales either direct from a haystore or via a tractor and trailer. Obviously these methods can be time consuming. Studies for dairy cattle have shown the following times required for feeding hay (18):

i. Hay stored in 35-lb bales in nearby barn alongside yard, and put into mangers or against feeding fence a few yards from stack:
   60 cows at 20 lb/cow/day, 34 bales, 12·57 min (if manger covered by a wire mesh, 15·97 min).

ii. Hay stored in 35-lb bales in barn 50 yds from yard, and tractor and trailer used, being moved forward every 36 ft at manger:
   60 cows at 20 lb/cow/day, 34 bales, 30·12 min (0·73 min saved if tractor and trailer are ready hitched, and 0·95 min if they are not put away after use).

Thus, feeding hay by trailer once a day to 200–300 head of cattle with 120–180 bales might take $1\frac{1}{2}$–$2\frac{1}{4}$ hr. At 2 hr/day, 300 hr p.a. are required for feeding, if the stock are housed for 5 months. This might be costed as £250–£300 (Pt. 1, Ch. 4, p. 11); but mechanized feeding equipment, if installed at a capital cost of about £1000–£1500, that is, about £5 per place, and depreciated over 6–7 years, would

cost about the same. But the skilled stockman could manage more stock with the time saved, thereby increasing throughput. A few farmers have adapted chain and flight conveyors to handle bales from a store on to a run of mangers, costing less than £5 per place. But in some cases hayracks are positioned within yards and the stockman has to handle the bales from a road or passage into the yards. Such systems are non-intensive.

Self-feeding silage is described in IIIA, but reference has been made to the improved use of fodder by rationing silage at a manger or fence. Though cutting and loading silage on to a trailer has not been fully mechanized, it should be possible for one man to cut, load and distribute enough feed for up to 400 head and still have time for stockmanship and recording. In such systems a tractor and foreloader with an easy-hitch, self-unloading trailer may be used. Alternatively, the trailer can be loaded directly from a tower silo, unless an auger is used with the tower. Mechanization decreases the drudgery and can increase the time available for stockmanship, making it possible to increase throughput, which helps to offset the additional capital cost.

b. Barley Beef

The cost of calves and the price of barley largely govern the profits possible from fattening beef with a barley concentrate. In some circumstances it can prove cheaper to sell the barley than to convert it into meat. Otherwise barley beef units would probably be concentrated around the barley-growing districts, as skim-fed pigs are around the main creameries. So far, this is not the case. Barley is fed *ad lib.* from self-feeders, the production methods being similar to concentrate-fed pigs. An average margin of more than £30/beast, including the calf subsidy, above the feed and calf costs has been claimed (19). (With barley at £18½/T, margin £35; at £28/T, margin £24.) On this basis capital building costs of £60–£80/place might be justified, representing perhaps £1–£1¾/cwt liveweight gain, depending whether 800 or 1000 lb gain/place p.a. is obtained. Alternatively, a capital cost of £80–£100/place with a slatted layout, so that there are no straw costs, can prove economic. It is unwise to switch animals rapidly from a bulk to a concentrate ration and, therefore, most barley beef is planned as a self-contained enterprise without grazing or grass products.

c. Feedlots

As with concentrate fattening, mechanized haylage systems can be similar to industry in their production techniques. A slatted unit with mechanized feeding from tower silos can require a high capital outlay, perhaps of £100–£150/place. At £120, allowing £80 for the slatted building and

£40 for haylage equipment, this might represent as much as £2½/cwt liveweight gain, if the building and equipment is depreciated over 10 and 6 years respectively. If the margin/beast over food and the calf is only £24 and the capital depreciation represents £15 and labour £4 on a 500 beef-lot, then the margin for other factors and for profit would be £5/beast. However, some industrialists would depreciate a specialist unit of this kind over as much as 15 years for the building and silo and over 8 years for the machinery, reducing the cost to under £2/cwt liveweight gain. With investment at this level, good haylage with high throughput and low running costs are essential, and it is desirable for the unit to be in operation continuously, with only occasional breaks as a rest period against disease. However, if the cattle are fattened to slaughter weight within nine months, then a hog-fattening enterprise during the remainder of the year will improve the return on the investment.

d. Small Units

Since small units as a side-line enterprise are usually housed in existing buildings, perhaps with minor conversions, there are few design considerations other than shelter and the provision of as simple work routines as possible.

4. *Work routines*
a. Feeding

Feeding forms a major part of the work requirements and, as discussed above, can be based on manual labour, on automation or on self-feeding principles. Rationed feeding may be made once, sometimes twice, a day. Feeding from an auger should be planned so that the auger is centrally above a manger, wide enough for feeding from both sides. Obviously, long, straight runs of manger are desirable. Similarly, filling mangers with a self-unloading trailer or manually from a trailer depends for economy of movement on straight access roads or passages. Dimensions are given below. Feeding should be under cover and, in order to give a controlled environment, it is necessary sometimes to cover the work route. As with pig production, central feed routes with pens on either side are the basis of most designs.

b. Weighing

Some layouts are planned with an external race around the building, having access into each yard and connecting with a crush and weighbridge, which makes fortnightly or weekly weighing an easy task, the cattle being able to circulate back to their yard around the perimeter of the building. If the cattle are fed from an auger down the centre of the building, then a perimeter race may be essential and, to maintain warmth, this should be enclosed within the building. Alternatively, with a slatted layout, the mangers can be designed to give access on to the central passage from the yards, making it possible to use a portable weigher within the passage. This is not easy to arrange with strawed yards, due to the build up of manure.

c. Littering

Strawed yards, or those with other forms of bedding, have to be littered, usually every day, but in some cases about 3 times/week. The bale strings have to be cut. Sometimes the straw is spread by fork, but with intensive housing this can be left to the cattle. However, handling straw for large numbers is a lengthy job. One unit holding 600 head, given 240–320 bales/day, takes 2 men half a day to distribute the bales (16). If the cattle are housed only during the winter labour may be available on an arable farm for strawing the yards. The work can be mechanized by handling the bales by conveyor to the yards rather than by trailer. However, time studies for littering partly covered dairy yards have been given (20):

i. Straw stored in 35-lb bales in nearby barn alongside yard, spread by fork—
60 cows at 10 lb/cow/day, 17 bales, 24·68 min
ii. Straw stored in 45-lb bales as above—
60 cows at 10 lb/cow/day, 13 bales, 22·27 min
iii. Straw stored in 60-lb round bales as above—
60 cows at 10 lb/cow/day, 10 bales, 24·43 min
iv. As above, but straw stored 50 yds from yard—
35-lb bales, 33·33 min
60-lb round bales, 31·76 min

and, on this basis, littering 600 head from a barn away from the yards could take about 5 man hr.

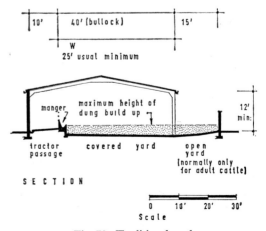

Fig. 79. Traditional yard

	Age of animal			Type of animal	
				Bullock	Horned bullock
	½ year	1 year	2 year	Bullock	bullock
Area/head, including manger, ft²	40	60	80	100	130
Manger/head, ft.R	2	2¼	2¼	2½	2¾
Width, including manger, W ft	20	27	35	40	47

d. Cleaning Out

The yards should be cleaned out once a year, which, with 4–5 months housed, could mean that there would be 3½–4½ ft depth of manure at the end of the season to handle. Similarly, with slatted layouts, the slurry should be removed once a year by tanker or, with intensive housing 2–3 times, or, if organic irrigation is used, as frequently as desired to suit the fields. The frequency of removal will govern the depth of the manure pit under the slats which is required. Generally, removal should be the job of the fieldworker rather than stockman.

5. *Design data*

a. Traditional Yards (Fig. 79)

Space allowances for beef cattle in strawed yards and with a manger have been given, see above table (21).

In the cases of the larger yards of over 70 ft²/head, part of the yard may be uncovered, but the covered width should seldom be less than 25 ft.

b. Modern Strawed Yards (Fig. 80)

Bedded areas of 35–40 ft²/head are adequate for modern fattening (16), though other layouts are based on a bedded area of about 30 ft²/head plus an exercise area of 20–30 ft²/head (10). The former

requires plenty of straw, since the cattle eat and sleep in the same area, whereas the latter can have the concreted exercise area behind the manger, which saves straw, though this area has to be kept clean. Some intensive houses are based on under 30 ft²/head for cattle fattened to 12 months of age.

c. Slatted Yards

Floor area and slat sizes have been given (22):

	Ft²	Slat top	Slat bottom	Gap between slats
Yearlings	15–20	4 in.	3 in.	1½ in.
Over 10 cwt	20–25	5 in.	4 in.	1½ in.

These dense stocking rates reduce the size of building required compared with strawed yards. A width of pen of 11 ft is recommended, which, combined with the space requirements for the manger, gives a building flexible for most stock. Recently, a form of cubicle for beef animals has been tried, 7 ft long and with divisions which can be moved from 1¾ ft spacing at 3 months, to 2 ft at 6 months, to 3 ft at 9 months (26).

d. Mangers and Troughs (Fig. 81)

The dimension of the building is governed by the length of trough/head required. With slatted lay-

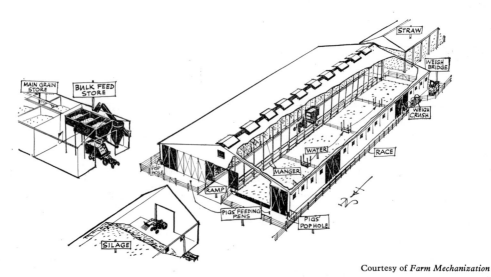

Courtesy of *Farm Mechanization*

Fig. 80. Modern intensive strawed yards. Court Lodge Farm, Harrietsham, Kent. See also Fig. 81, below.

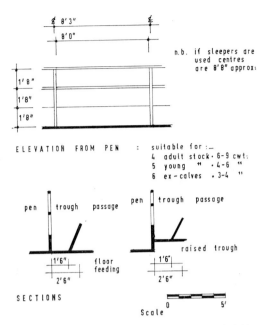

ELEVATION FROM PEN : suitable for :—
4 adult stock • 6-9 cwt:
5 young " • 4-6 "
6 ex-calves • 3-4 "

Fig. 81. Mangers—see also Figs. 72, 80 and 83

outs, yearlings require 15–20 in. each and 10-cwt cattle 24 in. Similar dimensions are adequate for strawed layouts, though some farmers use $2-2\frac{1}{2}$ ft/head. However, $9\frac{1}{2}$ in./head has been used in intensive strawed housing, on the basis that the cattle take it in turns to eat and that the fodder is delivered several times a day (16). Self-feeders should be based on 3 ft.R/12 head. The width of the trough should seldom be less than $2\frac{1}{2}$ ft at the top, though this may taper at the bottom to $1\frac{1}{2}$ ft, the height of the bottom board to the cow being 16 in., with rails above the board to hold the cattle. (See diag.) The bottom of the trough can be on the floor, which is cheap, but for preference is $\frac{1}{2}-\frac{3}{4}$ ft above floor level. If the manger is adjacent to the strawed bedding the build up of straw can be a problem, and, either the manger has to be raised, being slung by chains from posts, or the floor of the yard has to be about 3 ft below the bottom of the trough. As an alternative system, with floor feeding, there can be a forage fence between the yard and feed passage, but the cattle should not be able to push their fodder out of reach, which is a maximum distance of about $2\frac{1}{2}$–3 ft.

e. Self-feeding

As with dairy cows, self-fed silage should be based on $\frac{1}{3}-\frac{1}{2}$ ft.R/head for youngstock and $\frac{1}{2}-\frac{3}{4}$ ft.R/head for adult cattle with 24 hr access. Restricted access to under 8 hr/day should be based on $1\frac{1}{2}$–2 ft.R/head.

f. Height of Yards

Strawed yards should allow for a build-up of dung to 4 ft in 4–5 months plus the cattle on top, the latter requiring a height of not less than 7 ft. Slatted yards should have not less than 7 ft above the slats. However, an asbestos roof at these levels can be fractured by a bulling animal, and an additional 2 ft is desirable. Cleaning out strawed yards is easiest when the overall height is at least 12 ft. Excessive height is undesirable, since the conservation of warmth is essential, and therefore for preference roof pitches of 4–15 degrees are required.

g. Feed Passages

Hand feeding from barrows is undesirable. Haylage can be fed by auger. Alternatively, haylage or silage can be fed from a trailer self-unloading into the manger. In some cases a feedway 7 ft wide is adequate, but some large unloaders require over 8 ft, and a width of 9–10 ft may be desirable.

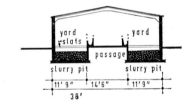

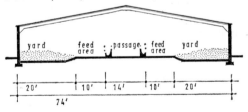

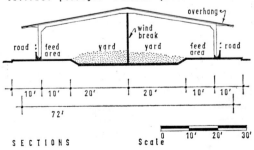

Fig. 82. Feed passage for tractor-and-trailer with different types of yard

189

No food should be exposed to the rain and should therefore be under cover to prevent wastage. The roof should project several feet beyond the manger, if feeding is along the external wall of the yard, but since, in most cases, a central feed passage is desirable, this passage should be covered (Fig. 82). This has the following advantages:

i. Good food conversion depends on a controlled or semi-controlled environment.
ii. If part of the manger can be removed the central passage can be used for weighing.
iii. The passage can be used for filling both manger runs, thereby halving the length of roadway required.

A covered central feed passage may appear to be expensive. Fig. 82 shows sections for three types of yard based on 2 ft.R of manger/head, where one yard has an external passage at the side and two have a central passage, in one case for a strawed and in the other for a slatted yard. A central passage should not be uncovered, since this will create a draught-tunnel effect. With a 10-ft-wide passage the extra insulated roof represents 10 ft²/head, which, plus a proportional increase in the cost of the yards, due to a more expensive frame being required for the wider span, might add £4–£5/head on the capital cost. In contrast, the overhang for an external passage, plus the extra road required if there is an external passage to both sides of the building, might cost about the same. In any case, the difference in the cost p.a. will be small.

h. Auger and Manger

Augers can be used to distribute haylage and concentrates and, if placed above a combined run of mangers (Fig. 83), can be used to feed yards on either side of the auger, thereby feeding one head/ft.R. The cost of the auger might be £5/head. However, 10 ft²/head less covered space may be required compared with a layout having a central tractor passage and, if the roadway was of 6 in. r.c., at least £5/head on the cost of the building should be saved and no self-unloading trailer is required. Thus, the reduced size of building required should make it as economic to include auger feeding. The

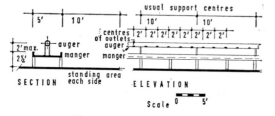

Fig. 83. Auger and manger

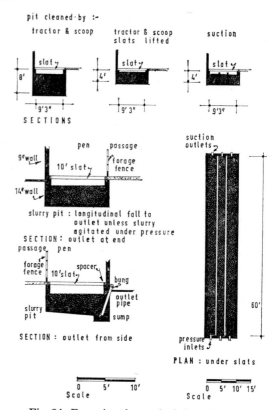

Fig. 84. Emptying slurry pits below slats

disadvantage may be that there has to be a less flexible rationing policy, since kale and roots may not be handled efficiently by many augers, though some augers will handle chopped kale or roots. Self-feeders can be filled from an overhead auger.

i. Slats and Slurry Pits

The depth of the slurry pit below the slats is normally 4 ft, unless emptying every few weeks with a vacuum tanker is intended, when only 2 ft may be required (IG). In a few cases a dung cellar which can be cleaned with a tractor and scoop may be desired, especially on sloping sites, and this will need a cellar 8 ft high. The pit design should be detailed in relation to the method of disposal. Generally, there is no limit to the size of the pit compartment. But if the dung is to be agitated by water added under pressure by a tanker, then the size should be related to that of the tanker and the width of the pit might have to be formed in compartments 3–4½ ft wide. Each compartment would need a pressure inlet and a suction outlet at alternate ends (Fig. 84). If cleaning is by suction under pressure the pit floor may be level to save cost. Alternatively, if no agitation is intended, the pit floor may slope to the external walls, draining into a sump with draw-off points at about 15-ft centres, with falls of 1 : 80 to 1 : 120 being allowed. Otherwise, the slats can be removed and a tractor-and-scoop used to clean the pit, no floor profile being required. Since the slurry exerts a lateral pressure on to the pit walls, an excavated pit is desirable. In any case, a 14-in. wall should be used to give 4–5 in. bearing for the slats, with a 9-in. wall above. The slurry should have no smell, but should give off sufficient heat to help keep the cattle warm. The pit walls should be rendered.

j. Heat and Humidity

Since intensive beef housing in this country is of recent development, neither the heat nor moisture generated by different classes of stock being fed with different rations, nor the temperature and humidity at which the different stock and ration combinations give the best conversion ratios, are known. This is a matter for urgent research. It might be assumed that evidence from dairy cattle (IIIA, 5) is relevant. Sudden fluctuations in temperature and draughts must be avoided.

A leading manufacturer, who has studied environmental problems and requirements relating to beef cattle, has assessed from observation and tentative recordings the heat and moisture which may be given off under normal conditions of feeding and housing (25):

i. Heat losses

Cattle livewt, lb	Heat loss, B.t.u./hr
150	845
250	1190
500	1890
750	2475
1000	3000
1250	3480

ii. Total evaporation loss

°F	°C	lb/hr/1000 lb livewt
20	− 7	0·6
30	− 1	0·8
40	$4\frac{1}{2}$	1·0
50	10	1·1
60	$15\frac{1}{2}$	1·2
70	21	1·4
80	$26\frac{1}{2}$	2·0

iii. Percentage latent heat

Environmental temperature		Percentage
°F	°C	
69	$20\frac{1}{2}$	40
58	$14\frac{1}{2}$	23
52	11	20
43	6	18

N.B. Total heat (sensible heat + latent heat) decreases at approx. 16 B.t.u./hr/1000 lb livewt for each ° F rise in temperature. Heat output generally quoted at 60° F ($15\frac{1}{2}$° C), when, for normal purposes, 25 per cent of the total heat is latent heat.

k. Water Requirements

Water requirements in relation to class of stock, feeding and temperature are unknown, but water is usually provided ad lib. (perhaps 6–8 gal/head/day being required) either by tongue-operated bowls or by troughs (IIIA, 5, p. 172, dairy cattle requirements). However, the number, size and position of water points is difficult to assess. In semi-intensive housing one 6-ft trough or three bowls per 20–30 head may be adequate, usually positioned in the open away from the sleeping area. In intensive housing, particularly with slats, no distinction is made between the areas for sleeping, exercise and eating, and the water point usually projects into the general area, perhaps being a water bowl attached to a division between the pens on the basis of one bowl per 10–15 head. It may be preferable to recess the bowl or a 4-ft trough into a wall, since it will be subject to knocks, though it can be protected by a metal hoop.

l. Cattle per Yard

Traditionally, about 15–25 head/yard was considered adequate, but yards holding 60–100 head are accepted today, especially if nearly square in shape.

m. Food Storage

The size of food storage allowed will depend on the feeding policy, but, with an average of 20 lb d.m./head/day, each animal will require about 40 ft³ of storage space per month for good haylage or silage, or about 14 ft³ for rolled barley (though the latter should be mixed at weekly intervals).

6. *Equipment.* Beef housing has little in the way of standardized, specialist equipment, other than tower silos, augers, self-unloading trailers, slats, gates, mangers, troughs and bowls, and weighers. Partially prefabricated intensive cattle buildings are becoming available as the investment in this kind of housing continues to be increased. For the most part, these items are discussed elsewhere. However, a few points should be considered:

 i. With auger feeding from a tower it should be possible to add concentrates to the haylage at the base of the silo.
 ii. Not all unloading trailers require the same dimension for manoeuvrability and unloading, but a turning circle of at least 45 ft may be required outside the building (Fig. 85).

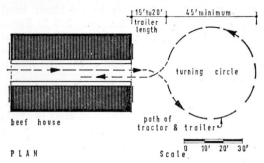

Fig. 85. Turning circle for self-unloading trailers

iii. Self-feeding of silage, with barriers, is discussed in IIIA.

iv. Proprietary troughs, mangers and feeding fences are available, but may not suit all schemes.

v. Slats should be movable, but should not move under the weight of the cattle, and adjustable spacers between the slats are an advantage for flexibility. (Heavy hogs may be housed in the unit.) Slats should have at least 4 in. bearing at each end, and normally, at present, proprietary r.c. slats are not longer than 10 ft. Slats should not be cracked, chipped or warped, and should be uniform throughout their length.

vi. Heavy stockyard gates or barriers should be used and, in intensive housing, it is desirable for all the pen divisions to be flexible, perhaps positioned at every 6-ft centre to give a choice of pen size in 6-ft multiples (i.e. 3 head at 2 ft.R of manger/head).

vii. The entrance and exit doors to the central feed passage should be draught-proof, preferably insulated, and easy to handle, the latter possibly by remote control so that the tractor-driver does not have to dismount to operate them. Such doors, perhaps 10 ft wide by 12 ft high, do not exist as an economic unit for farm buildings, but could be developed.

viii. Water points should be clear of positions where they can be fouled, and, if used over strawed bedding, will have to be lifted as the bedding level is raised. The water supply, if exposed, may be damaged by cattle.

ix. Proprietary air inlets for extraction boxes and thermostats are available, but their applications to a layout requires the advice of individual manufacturers.

7. *Environmental control*

a. Due to the factors given in 5*j* above, it is not possible to give details of adequate methods for the control of the ventilation in intensive hous-ing. In semi-intensive housing it is normal to allow an air flow under an asbestos-cement or aluminium roof by having a gap above the cattle a few inches deep at the eaves and a ventilated ridge capping. Alternatively, Yorkshire board-ing, slotted asbestos-cement or aluminium sheets can be used. These methods, in the right conditions, should give reasonable ventilation and prevent condensation. However, intensive housing should include an insulated roof, with controlled or semi-controlled means of ventila-tion. The underside of the roof slope should be smooth, without projections, to give no obstruc-tion to an air flow from a continuous eaves gap of about 6–8 in. deep leading to a roof ventila-tion shaft and fan, equidistant from the corners of the house. To reduce the internal volume, the roof pitch should be kept low (Fig. 86). The principle is not quite the same as in some pig fattening houses, since in the latter the air flow is forced towards floor level by the division of the dung passage from the main part of the house, thus ensuring proper ventilation. In the direct eaves to ridge shaft ventilation there is a danger that in some circumstances the air flow will be direct and will not remove the hot, humid air from the house, which will be trapped below the air flow. In a slatted layout one method is to have controlled ridge air inlets and an extract fan mounted in the external walls about 6–9 in. above slat level. For satisfactory removal of moisture, an extraction rate of 240 c.f.m./9 cwt livewt may be required. An 18-in. fan at 1400 r.p.m. may extract 3400 c.f.m., being adequate for 15 cattle at 9 cwt. An air inlet, designed to prevent down-draught, of 24–30 in²/place may be required and the position of

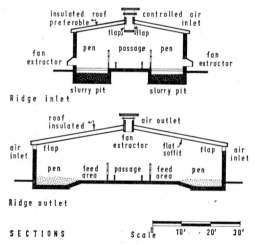

Fig. 86. Ventilation of intensive houses

69: CALF HOUSING

Calves, other than for veal, benefit from light and air. The high-level windows on both sides of the house above the pens include hopper ventilation panels with side cheeks to prevent down draughts, but give cross ventilation to a ridge extraction panel. The ceiling is insulated. Fluorescent strip lighting is included. Pens, on either side of a central work passage, hold 3–5 calves each and have a simple galvanized panel front and gate. Division walls are rendered and solid, with rounded edges, $4\frac{1}{2}$ ft high, to prevent cross-infection and draughts and to allow for easy sterilization after use. Pen floors are strawed over a concrete base, draining into a longitudinal gulley in the passage. Cleaning out is a manual task with fork and barrow, there being an access door at the far end. Access to a feed room is at the near end. [SEE PAGE 200] Courtesy of the Farmers Weekly.

70: VEAL HOUSING

Not all veal is produced in intensive crates which restrict the animal's movement. Some allow 4 or 5 veal calves to each pen, though all natural light is excluded as in the more intensive housing. Timber slatted floors and pen fronts will become worn after a time. The stakes to the front are placed so that every second or third gap can act as a feeding place, bucket holders being attached to the front within the central passage area. Pen division walls are rendered. [SEE PAGE 204] Courtesy of British Farmer.

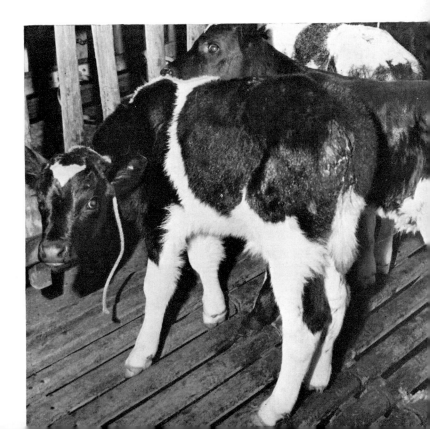

71: BACON FATTENING PEN

Mr. G. T. G. Shepherd, Pitmillan, Newburgh, Aberdeenshire

The pens are designed to hold 40 baconers with space for 20 to feed at each side from controlled feeders. The feeders and the end-gate partition in the foreground, which open into a central passage, are demountable so that the building of 50 ft clear span could be used for other purposes with little alteration. There are narrow transverse passages for the pigman between the rows of feeders. Rations can be released into the troughs by pressing the levers. The pigs have shavings on the concrete floor for bedding and a pop-hole at the far end of the pen into a dung passage. The volume of the building is not restricted in order to maintain maximum temperatures, and the large number of pigs per pen is unusual but successful. [SEE PAGE 208] Courtesy of North of Scotland Agricultural College.

72: PIGS ON A MESH FLOOR

Pigs can sleep on concrete, slats or mesh. Mesh floors can prove satisfactory, the pigs keeping clean. For stability, 5 gauge mesh should be used with supports at about $1\frac{1}{2}$-ft $\times$ 1-ft centres. [SEE PAGE 214] Courtesy of Mr. D. S. Soutar.

73: MECHANICALLY CLEANED DUNG PASSAGE

The dung passages of fattening houses can be scraped clean automatically with a scraper blade conveyed along an endless chain. At the end of the passage the blade passes up a ramp and deposits the dung into a manure spreader below the ramp. The passage can have a slatted floor above the blade so that the pigs do not have to be disturbed while being cleaned. The dung passage is uninsulated with timber framed and boarded walls and an asbestos-cement roof. A dado is formed with external-grade plywood above a concrete plinth. Doors cover the pop-hole access into the pens, and when the doors are open the passage is turned into dung compartments, one to each pen. The passage is lit with clerestory windows above the pens, some of which are seen on the left. The roof of the pens drains into a gutter below the windows. [SEE PAGES 213 & 45] Courtesy of McMaster & Co. Ltd.

74: ADJUSTABLE PEN FRONTS

One proprietary pig-fattening house includes a trough unit complete with a swing-panel front. The panel can be closed, as in the foreground, so that the feed can be placed in the trough or open, as shown beyond, for access during feeding time. Thus, rations can be placed at any time prior to feeding, the front being opened quickly by the turn of a ratchet. [SEE PAGE 212] Courtesy of Pig Farming.

75 : INTENSIVE FATTENING LAYOUT
Haywold Farm, Southburn Estates, E. Yorks

Three bacon fattening houses, the nearest of which holds 396 pigs and the other two 198 each, are grouped near a provender mill. Each house includes a raised food store at the near end, coupled to two automatic, travelling hoppers which distribute the feed into the troughs on each side of a central walkway down the length of the house. The amount of feed delivered to each pen is controlled by the number of steel pegs placed in the pen to trip release the feed from the hopper, pulled by a chain at predetermined times. At the same time water is released into the troughs. The feed is conveyed from the mill to each food store by an overhead chain-and-flight conveyor mounted on a gantry. The mill, which produces 2000 T of feed p.a., is sited off-left in the photograph and over 14 T per wk is conveyed to the three fattening houses. The dung passages at the

side of the houses are cleaned automatically with a chain-and-scraper, the muck being deposited into a culvert outside the near end of the houses. Another scraper in the culvert conveys the dung to a below-ground pit, with a ramp access road between brick retaining walls visible in the right foreground. The scraper deposits the dung into a trailer, prior to being towed and distributed on the land. The houses are connected to a series of external pig races, with walls of horizontal galvanized sheeting, and which lead to a ramp, seen in the centre foreground, for loading the pigs on to a lorry. [SEE PAGES 218, 45, 72 & 77] Courtesy of Southburn Estates.

76 : CENTRAL DUNG PASSAGE

With a slatted dung passage, as shown, it can be particularly economic to have the passage central between the pens rather than to have a central feed passage and the dung areas at the edge of the building. The top of the slats are a few inches below the pen floor level and there is a sloping skirting from the slats against the walls. The passage is 4 ft wide. The length of each dung compartment can be half the length of each pen, so that the compartments can alternate with a pen on each side of the passage. Vertical sliding galvanized panels can be used as divisions between the dung compartments on which can be mounted the drinking bowls, coupled to a flexible rubber connection above pig level when the panel is lowered. It is possible for the central passage to be divided from the pens by walls taken to the ceiling with pop-hole access into the dung area, rather than to have dwarf walls. With a separate dung area, it is possible to have roof lights over the dung passage and to have an insulated roof over the pens. [SEE PAGE 218] Courtesy of West of Scotland Agricultural College.

inlet to fan is important (Ref. *a*, p. xxxii). Thermostats may be required (see 10, below). Further research is required. Walls should be of 9 in. hollow block, rendered externally, for insulation.

b. Maintaining an even temperature range of 15°– 20° C (60°–70° F) should be possible from the warmth of the cattle themselves, even during the winter in uninsulated but draught-free buildings on straw bedding at straw level. This has not been proved yet in practice. In the Harper Adams College experiments (10) the temperature of the litter in semi-enclosed yarding did not drop below 18° C (64·4° F) during the winter of 1961–62. In insulated buildings, with controlled ventilation, low internal volume and slatted yards, it should be possible to maintain temperatures of over 15° C, even in cold weather. High temperatures can hold more moisture than low ones, without condensation, and thus with fans more moisture is removed from the building for the same air flow.

c. As in pig fattening, natural light is probably not required, though many farmers will prefer to have it. It is possible that the eaves ventilation strip can be used to admit light by being combined with translucent sheeting. To break the roof insulation with roof lights is undesirable. In fully covered strawed, but uninsulated, yarding a rooflight/floor area ratio of 1 : 20 has been recommended (23).

d. Adequate artificial lighting is essential over the feed passage, perhaps on the basis of one socket/ 30 ft.R. It may be desirable to vary the lighting from low-intensity illumination as permanent lighting to a normal minimum intensity of 5 lumens/ft² along the mangers during feeding and weighing.

8. *Layout*

a. Fig. 80 shows a typical semi-intensive, uninsulated strawed layout with a central feed passage used for feeding a variety of bulk and concentrated foods. The building, 240 ft × 120 ft (a converted hangar) plus an external race around the perimeter, can hold either 680 (2–4 cwt) or 520 (6–8 cwt) cattle, plus 200 fattening pigs. This represents a density of 55 ft²/adult animal, or about 4¼ adult stock/ft.R of building. The wide span and restricted manger space helps to keep the layout near to a square on plan, thus reducing capital costs.

b. In contrast, Fig. 82 also shows a layout with a central feed passage but based on 1 animal/ft.R of building. The example shows a strawed and a slatted yard having densities of 55 ft²/head and 37 ft²/head respectively. These layouts, in order to house 520 stock, would have to be 520 ft long. This would give an extra perimeter of

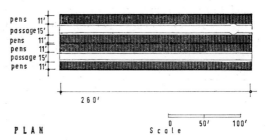

PLAN

Fig. 87. Double-banked yards for 520 head of cattle

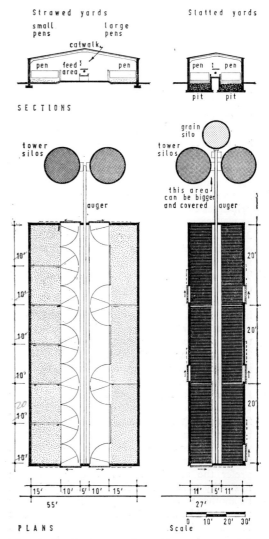

Fig. 88. Mechanized feeding with strawed or slatted yards

walling, compared with Fig. 80, of over 140 yd.R and 130 yd.R respectively. In the case of the strawed yard, this might represent an additional cost of £450–£500, and for the slatted yard of £800–£900, since walling forms a major part of the total cost of a building after the roof and floor costs have been considered. In addition there would be increased costs for the passage and mangers, perhaps totalling another £1500–£2000. Therefore unrestricted manger access might be expected to add another £4–£6/place, but, of course, this might amount to at most 12s.–18s./head produced. Alternatively, the units could be half the length, being double-banked, as shown in Fig. 87. In this case the external walling is less than in Fig. 80.

c. Fig. 88 shows two layouts based on auger feeding from tower silos. Fig. 88a allows 30 ft²/head of strawed yard plus 20 ft²/head of concreted exercise and feeding space adjacent to the manger. The total density is 55 ft²/head. The main problem lies in keeping the concrete clean and, in a long building, in dividing the layout into smaller yards, at the same time being able to handle the stock. It should be possible to pen the cattle in the strawed area. This is easy to do if the yards are small, holding 10 head each, and if the gates are doubled, as shown. Alternatively, larger yards can be formed by accepting some restriction. (See diagram right side.) To save having to clean the concrete by tractor and scraper, the feeding space can be slatted. These principles can be used with feed-passage layouts as well as with auger feeding. Fig. 88b allows 22 ft²/head of slatted space, giving a total density of 27 ft²/head. Access has to be from the perimeter walls.

d. The number and size of tower silos required depends not only on the number of cattle, their ration and period housed but also on the harvesting policy. In some cases one large tower may be adequate. For example, a 30-ft-dia × 60-ft-high tower, with central unloading core, might hold 240 T d.m. and, if this had to last 9 months, it would allow ⅞ T/day, which at 20 lb d.m./head/day would provide food for 100 cattle. However, loading the tower would probably take place over a period of 6–8 months, perhaps finishing with a maize silage crop, and either a bottom-unloading tower or two smaller towers would be required. Even though two towers increase the capital cost, many producers would prefer the additional harvesting and feeding flexibility obtained. In some cases there might be another tower to store wet grain. Though the towers will be external to the main building, the food should be augered under cover as soon as possible, perhaps receiving additional concentrates from a hopper placed above the auger.

9. *Siting*. Siting a unit will depend on its size, feeding policy and method of housing. Semi-covered yards should be open to the S.E. to S.W., and shelter should be provided from prevailing winds. Self-feeding of silage and concreted yards require floor profiles which may be assisted by natural ground slopes (IIIA). Supervision will be required, but slurry tanks when agitated may cause an offensive smell. Good access is essential. The unit might be sited in relation to silage or haylage harvesting requirements, to a grain store and mill/mix unit or to the method for returning the slurry to the land, especially with organic irrigation.

10. *Services*. Both electricity and water will be required, though in some layouts the unit might be managed without lighting. Except in intensive housing, natural ventilation will be required. Roof ventilators, drawing air from shielded perimeter inlets and fitted with fans, should be designed as in pig housing, but with the extraction rate suited for the larger stock. Alternatively, extract fans may be in the perimeter walls (see 7a, above). Intensive layouts, with controlled temperature and humidity, will require thermostats. Siting the latter to be effective may be difficult and will depend on individual layouts. All concreted yards, as in IIIA, should drain into a slurry pit, unless the Local Council permits drainage into a sewer. Roof water may drain into the same pit, if it is large enough, otherwise it should be drained clear of the building.

11. *Costs*

a. Costs of housing will vary between wide extremes. Simply converted existing yards may cost only £5–£10/place. New units will have costs similar to those for dairy cattle without a parlour (IIIA, 11). Partly covered yards might cost about £30/place, that is £4½/head p.a., if combined with a self-feed silo, the latter costing about £28/T d.m. storage space (IIC, 11, p. 112). Thus, if the cattle ate 25 lb d.m./day for 6 months during winter housing the silobarn holding 2 T/head would cost about £9/head p.a., plus the labour cost for making the silage. A slurry pit would be required, and the total building cost for the yarding, silobarn and pit might be over £14/head p.a., which, if only 3½ cwt livewt. gain is obtained over 6 months, represents £4/cwt livewt. gain or a little under 9d./lb livewt. gain. In addition, there are the costs of straw, silage, labour and general overheads to consider.

b. In contrast, a strawed yard as shown in Fig. 88a, with a central feed passage, but uninsulated and cheaply constructed, might cost about £60—£65/place, plus the storage of fodder. If the feed strip area was slatted an additional £15/place might be required. If a total housing cost of £80/place is allowed, this might equal £12/head p.a.; with a silobarn for a year's supply, a total of about £26/head p.a. Therefore for a gain in wt. over 12 months of 6½ cwt, the cost is £4/cwt livewt. gain or a little under 9*d*./lb livewt. gain. There would be additional costs in making extra silage and in cutting and carting the silage, using a self-unloading trailer as well as for the straw required for bedding. But, controlled feeding could be an advantage. Obviously, if the building was only used for half of each year the cost/lb livewt. gain might prove uneconomic. Proprietary strawed yards, central supports, an 8-ft passageway, insulation and fan control, can cost under £40/place in some circumstances.

c. A slatted yard as shown in Fig. 88*b*, including the manger and auger, being smaller in area than Fig. 88*a*, should also be erected for about £80/place. But in this case there would be no straw costs, which for permanent housing might be costed as much as £12/head (see 2*b*, above), reducing the comparative cost of the building apparently to no charge. Moreover, if straw was produced on the farm, and could be sold, this might be an additional asset, rather than in using it for the beef fattening enterprise. Of course, some expense is incurred in the handling equipment for the slurry. Labour costs per head can be very low. Proprietary slatted yards with a 2-ft-deep dung cellar, narrow feed passage, but with insulation and fan control, can cost under £60/place in some circumstances.

d. The tower silos might cost £40–£80/place. For example, two towers plus blowers and unloaders, and a wet grain store plus a mill/mix unit and hopper might be erected, costing £12,000 for 200 places, that is £60/place. The towers and equipment, if depreciated over 10 years, would cost about £9/head p.a. This would be a cost equal to that of a cheap silobarn and cheaper than one holding a year's supply of fodder and would have the advantage of the grain storage, perhaps proving considerably cheaper if the cost of cutting and carting the silage was considered as part of the true comparative cost when considering a silobarn.

12. References

(1) FRASER, A. *Beef Cattle Husbandry*, p. 26, Crosby Lockwood (1959).

(2) Personal communication from Harvestore Owners Association.

(3) RAMSAY, A. 'Dairy production in Britain'. p. ii *The Times Supplement* (3rd April 1963).

(4) FRASER, A. *Breeder & Boffin*. Crosby Lockwood (1962).

(5) *Beef Production*. Ministry of Agriculture Bulletin 178, p. 23 (1959). Revised 1965.

(6) LAMMING, E. Report of Experiments at Nottingham University (1962).

(7) HARVEY, N 'Straw—how little do you need?' *Farmer & Stockbreeder*, p. 103 (16th Oct. 1962).

(8) NIX, J. S. 'Wheat and Barley: cost and returns 1956'. Farm Economics Branch, Cambridge (1957).

(9) 'Costs of Producing Fat and Store Cattle in Yorkshire'. Economics Section, Department of Agriculture, Leeds, Report 157, pp. 7–8 (1963).

(10) PRICE, W. T. 'U.K. Development of Farm Buildings with appendices on methods of flooring and bedding for livestock'. Harper Adams Agricultural College. Technical Bulletin 9, p. 12 (1962).

(11) *Beef Production*. Ibid., p. 19.

(12) *Farmers Weekly Supplement*. 'Off the Grass', pp. xxi and xxv (14th September 1962).

(13) *Farmers Weekly*, p. 53 (15th June 1962).

(14) PRESTON, T. R. *Farmers Weekly*. 'Barley into Beef', pp. 100–1 (1st December 1961).
See also—RILEY, K. P. & HURST, D. 'The Rowett system in practice', *Farmers Weekly*, pp. 92–3 (13th September 1963).

(15) BARBER, D. & YOUNG, W. 'Does grass silage work for young beef stores?' *Farmers Weekly*, p. 105 (13th April 1962).
BALL, C. 'Appetite begins with quality'. *Farmers Weekly*, p. 89 (11th May 1962).

(16) CLIFTON, D. 'Beef at a profit', *Farm Mechanization*. Report Oxford Farming Conference, pp. 52–3 (February 1963).

(17) STURROCK, F. G. 'Planning Farm Work'. Bulletin No. 172. Ministry of Agriculture, p. 6 (1960).

(18) BELSHAW, D. G. R. & SCOTT, A. H. 'Work routines and work elements for yard and parlour and cowshed systems'. Farm Economics Branch, School of Agriculture, Cambridge, Technical Report (Work Study), No. 1, pp. 30–2 (1962).

(19) HURST, D. 'Barley into Beef'. *Farmers Weekly*, p. 83 (8th December 1961).

(20) BELSHAW, D. G. R. & SCOTT, A. H. Ibid., pp. 6–12.

(21) *Beef Production*. Ibid., p. 59.

(22) SOUTAR, D. 'Design for beef'. *Farmers Weekly*, pp. 100–1 (30th November 1962).

(23) *Beef Production*. Ibid., p. 65.

(24) HOPE, H. 'Bale or burn?' *Farmers Weekly*, p. 75 (22nd November 1963). 'Disposal of surplus straw sets problems'. *The Times* (Sept. 31st 1964).

(25) Personal communication from FFISKE, G. of Stockbuildings Ltd.

(26) 'Beef cubicles to grow with the calves'. *Farmers Weekly*, p. 80 (10th July 1964).

SELECTED REFERENCE

a. 'Profit from Beef'. *Farmers Weekly Supplement* (4th October 1963).

b. See Ref. *i.* IIIA.: Ref. *n.* IIIA.

IIIC. Calves

1. *Activity*

a. The calf crop is essential for the production of milk (IIIA), of beef (IIIB) and of veal (IIID). More than 4M calves are born annually. Calf production, in the past, has tended to be casual with regard to health, nutrition and housing. This situation has been stressed in the foreword to a *Farmers Weekly Supplement* on calf rearing (1):

> 'An appalling number of calves die within a few weeks of birth, and many more that survive are marred for life. A survey gave losses of 6 per cent of home-bred calves in England and Wales and 11 per cent in Scotland. Losses of bought in calves are much heavier. This wastage, particularly for the beef man, may make all the difference between profit and loss. But such losses can be substantially reduced if the calves' nutritional and housing requirements are met and precautions taken against bringing in and spreading disease.'

In fact, a mortality of 15 per cent is not uncommon, and estimates have been made that 20 per cent of calves die within their first three months (2). Even in veal production, where standards are higher than with normal rearing, mortality and wastage represent a loss of 10 per cent in production (Pt. 3, IIID, 1*b*, p. 202). It is probable that the annual mortality within the calf crop is between $\frac{1}{2}$M and $\frac{3}{4}$M calves. This wastage may represent a national loss of some £10–£15M, to which has to be added the loss of the potential value of meat in the slaughtering of bobby calves for veal (Pt. 3, IIID, 1*a*, p. 202), such calves from dairy herds mainly being sold for under £3/head within a few days of birth.

b. Bull housing is an ancillary requirement in the production of calves except in the cases where A.I. is used. In 1962 the M.M.B. had nearly 1000 bulls at 23 centres for their A.I. scheme, and almost $1\frac{3}{4}$M cows, that is about two-thirds of the national dairy herds, were treated in this manner. Such specialized centres are not considered in this study. However, there are sufficient bulls still kept on farms, both for milk and for beef production, to warrant a description of bull housing. Bulls are essential on a farm with a pedigree herd used for breeding.

c. Good calf housing, when required, can be akin to veal housing (IIID) having many requirements in common and being similar in design.

d. Calves may be born, weaned and reared on a farm where they are required to supplement a dairy or beef enterprise. Alternatively, they may be sold after birth, though seldom before they are at least a week of age unless for slaughter, or after weaning or at any stage during the rearing process, though usually in the latter case this will be when they are about 3–4 months old. Calves, whether bought or home-reared, are required as replacements within a dairy herd (Pt. 3, IIIA, 1*f*, p. 166) or for fattening (Pt. 3, IIIB, 1*c*, p. 183), though some will be required for future breeding, both for dairy and for beef herds. Breeding stock may be pure or cross bred in each case, though dual-purpose cattle suitable either for milk or for fattening can have economic advantages. Good genetic recording is essential in calf production.

e. As has been stated, calf production has been, and still tends to be, casual, with a high disease incidence, whether the calves are marketed or required on the farm. Few specialized calf houses have been built, many farmers relying either on cheap conversions to existing buildings or on raising their calves in the fields. However, during recent years there has been a rapid growth of calf banks and even of contract rearing of calves. A calf bank is operated through an agent who registers calf producers in the district and is able to keep the movement of calves from breeders and rearers to fatteners without their passing through a market where they are liable to a growth setback and to disease. It is probable that these new methods of marketing, since only good calves will be wanted, will increase the importance of good housing, and this, in turn, will help to reduce the mortality rate.

2. *Managerial requirements*

a. Spring or autumn calving

Calving can be planned to occur at any time so that the calf crop from a herd may be spread more or less evenly over the year. However, it is usual for calving to be concentrated either in the spring or in the autumn period both in the case of milk production (Pt. 3, IIIA, 2*a*, p. 166) or of beef fattening (Pt. 3, IIIB, 2*a*, p. 184). Spring calving in milder districts may have the advantage that it can be carried out in the fields without specialized housing. Autumn calving, in contrast, except in exceptionally mild districts, can rarely be completed without winter housing for the young stock.

b. Hygiene

The *Farmers Weekly* has stated (3):

> 'Disease in a calf indicates a failure in animal management, or a lapse in the hygiene which calf rearing demands. Disease prevention requires positive thought, intelligent planning and the careful and persistent application of those prin-

ciples which are recognised as consistent with good animal husbandry.'

A common source of disease is in the excreta and saliva from one animal when contacted by another, especially when young. Similarly, a diseased calf can spread air-borne infection quickly to others. Therefore, housing should be cleaned and disinfected prior to the arrival of new calves and bought calves should be isolated for a period before entering a calf house. A calf unit must contain a number of isolation pens. Calves are particularly susceptible to pneumonia viruses and bacteria and warmth and ventilation are essential to reduce this risk. Sunshine is beneficial, ultra-violet light killing many of the air-borne bacteria. All surfaces should be smooth for ease in cleaning and so that bacteria cannot be held in the fabric of the building, and lead paints should be avoided. Failure to provide proper calf-housing and poor discipline in hygiene contribute to the high rate of mortality. Expenditure on good housing may be recovered quickly if fewer calves die.

For example, a cheap calf house with 20 places used three times p.a. and costing £20/place represents a building cost of £60 p.a. or £1/calf. If a 15 per cent mortality occurs there is an annual loss of 9 calves, valued perhaps on average at £20/head, so that the annual loss represents £180. However, if the capital expenditure is doubled to £40/place, that is £120 p.a. or £2/calf, and mortality is reduced to 10 per cent the annual calf loss equals £120. Thus, the increase in capital expenditure of £60 p.a. is recovered by a reduction in mortality of 3 calves a year.

c. Size of unit

A few producers rear as many as 1000–1500 calves a year, though most, perhaps, rear less than 100 and many less than 50. Therefore there are few specialist calf producers, which partly accounts for the general lack of good housing. If calving is concentrated into a 1–3-month period each year it is difficult to justify an expensive calf house perhaps used for less than half each year. Though some types of calf house might be suitable for pig production during the remainder of the year, this policy might complicate the farm management. However, if calving is split into both spring and autumn periods, then the calf house might be in use for more than three-quarters of each year. Specialist calf producers, who will become more common especially for beef fattening, can plan their calf unit to be full almost all the time.

Calf units should be planned on the basis of one calf per cow each year, though twin calves, or even triplets, are not unknown, and twinning is encouraged in some beef experiments to increase production. The period during which a calf is treated as young stock varies, but normally in modern practice represents the first 3–4 months of the animal's life. In a well-planned layout this period will be divided into two, with a nursing house for up to 7–8 wk of age and a rearing house up to 15–16 wk. The number of calf places required will depend on the size of the breeding herd, the calving dates and whether any of the calves are to be reared in the fields. When breeding replacements for a dairy herd approximately one individual and one group pen are required for every 12 cows when calving is not concentrated into one period.

d. Type of housing

The type of housing required depends partly on the method of rearing, which is discussed below, on the emphasis placed on reducing disease and mortality and on whether the plane of nutrition is to be restricted. As with other stock, warmth and comfort can reduce the amount of food consumed, that is the food conversion ratio. Generally, pail-fed calves need a more controlled environment than suckled calves, especially when fed synthetic diets.

3. Production techniques

a. Weaning

A calf from a dairy cow is normally removed from its mother very soon after birth. However, in beef production suckling may be continued for 10–14 wk, though in recent years artificial rearing or early weaning have become common practice. Normally, weaning from whole or synthetic milks takes place at about 8–12 wk of age, though with early weaning this may be at 3–5 wk followed by a diet of dry concentrated foods, hay and water. Early weaning reduces labour requirements, making it possible to house the calves in groups at an earlier age.

b. Suckling beef calves

Several systems may be adopted when beef calves are suckled. Single suckling is the basis of traditional practice, and has been described by a Ministry publication as (4):

> 'Suckling is the traditional method for rearing pedigree beef cattle; it is the only practicable method of rearing commercial cattle on hill or marginal land. Mortality amongst beef calves suckled by their dams is low.'

Generally, single suckling depends on cheap land, low labour costs and good management, but autumn-born calves if winter housed with generous feeding, including self-fed silage for cow and calf, may gain good prices when one year old. Occasionally, double suckling is practised, whereby a bought calf is suckled alongside the natural calf. However, multiple suckling is practised more widely, in some cases the cow keeps the same calves for a full lactation and in others calves are suckled in batches, the time for each batch depending on management policy. Though much suckling of calves is practised in the fields, autumn-born calves usually entail winter housing.

c. Artificial rearing

Artificial rearing is essential for dairy calves and is often considered economic for beef cattle, usually being based on a ration of either fresh skim milk or whey or reconstituted milk replacements plus supplementary vitamins until after weaning. The amount fed depends on the system of rearing, but is in the region of 6 pints/day or $1\frac{1}{4}$ per cent in powder of the birth wt fed thrice a day for the first week and twice a day thereafter at a temperature of 38° C (100° F) in individual buckets. The powder has to be added to the warm water prior to whisking. Obviously, labour requirements are high, but can be reduced by early weaning. Calves can go out to grass or into specialist fattening houses when about 3 months old.

d. Liveweight gain

A livewt gain on a moderate plane of nutrition has been given as 1·0 lb/day for Friesians, 0·9 lb/day for Ayrshires and up to 1·5 lb/day for beef calves during the first three months, though 1·75 lb/day can be obtained with single suckling (5). Heifers should continue at the same rate of growth for another 9 months, but beef cattle with a high plane of nutrition should grow at about 2·5 lb/day (Pt. 3, IIIB, 2d, p. 185), though less than 1·5 lb/day may be experienced with poor grazing.

e. Veterinary attention

Dehorning should take place before the calves are 3 wk old and castration of bull calves for beef production before they are 9 months old. Various injections may be administered. Frequent attention and vigilance are required to detect the disorders to which calves are prone. Isolation pens are essential to prevent the spread of disease. Pens should be cleaned and disinfected immediately calves are taken from them and should be, for preference, left empty for 3–4 wk before the next batch of calves are housed in them. Thus, if calves are kept in a nursing house for 8 wk and then in a rearing house for a further 8 wk, each house should be planned on an occupancy and sterilization period of 11–12 wk. Intake into the houses might be planned on a 3-monthly basis, though intake frequently is at random intervals.

f. Housing systems

Various types of housing have to be considered. Suckled calves may be yarded with their mothers, though usually this is only for autumn-born calves when winter housed. The yards should be provided with a creep area for the calves where they can be fed with their own rations, preferably enclosed and insulated for greater warmth. The yards may be basically similar to those for older cattle, though they may be restricted so that each cow and her calves, in multiple suckling, have their own yard and creep. Weaned calves may be housed together in their own yards. Bucket-fed calves may be penned individually or in groups of 3–5 as in veal production (Pt. 3, IIID, 3c, p. 203). Alternatively, calves may be yarded together with the bucket-feeding area separate, either in the form of an enclosure with adaptable and individual feeding units grouped around a central work space or even as a herringbone layout. Whether suckled or artificially reared, isolation pens, bull boxes and service pens are required in addition. Calving boxes also may be required.

4. *Work routines*

a. Work routines with artificial rearing are similar to those in veal production (Pt. 3, IIID, 4, p. 203). The distribution of a large number of plastic buckets containing the liquid feed, mixed in the feed room, can be time consuming, though the buckets can be conveyed on a hand trolley along a central work space. Alternatively, if only one ration is being used it is possible to have a milk container with a tap suspended from a monorail passing above the bucket positions. However, it is essential that the milk does not cool below 38° C (100° F) and that the buckets are cleaned after use. Suckled calves and their mothers can be fed in a variety of ways. Though after weaning self-fed silage might be practised, the mothers require a high plane of nutrition for suckling, possibly with a hay and concentrate diet fed by a self-unloading trailer at a manger. Within the creep area the calves may be fed concentrates *ad lib.* from a self-feeder plus a little hay in racks. Supplying feed to the creep areas mechanically is unlikely to be economic. A passage for a feed-barrow is sufficient. Though cows may calve in the fields or in yards, they may be put into special calving boxes a few days prior to calving.

b. Techniques for dehorning, castration and sterilization of pens have been given in detail in the Ministry publication (Ref. *a*). The work required in maintaining and feeding a bull has to be based on safety rather than on speed. A side-unloading trailer can be used for delivering food into a manger, which is sensible if this technique is used for the herd. Generally, feeding is manual with the aid of a fork, the fodder being placed through a controlled opening into a manger within the bull house. It is desirable that the bull can be contained either in its yard or in its house, so that each can be cleaned in turn, that easy escape for the herdsman is provided from the yard, and that the yard leads into the service pen with a simple gate arrangement.

5. *Design data*

a. Artificial rearing pens

Generally, the data given for veal calves (Pt. 3, IIID, 5, p. 203) can be taken for normal calf housing, though if calf housing is divided into a nurse and rearing house the latter will need less insulation but more ventilation. The main difference between calf and veal housing is that in the former direct sunlight is a desirable feature. The temperature in the rearing house can be about 15° C (60° F), whereas that during the first few weeks of the calf's life should be nearer to 20° C (70° F). Artificial ventilation is desirable for nurse houses, but is not essential for the older calves unless they are to be fattened intensively. Ventilation should be based on 10 c.f.m./100 lb livewt of calf.

Some general data for heat and moisture given off by beef animals are given in the section on beef production (Pt. 3, IIIB, 5*j*, p. 191). Natural ventilation, which might be included in addition to and as an alternative to artificial ventilation, might be based on hopper windows on both sides of the calf house about 2 ft deep under the eaves plus ridge extract ventilators. Total inlet and outlet areas each should be based on a minimum of 6 in²/100 lb livewt, double glazing being used for insulation. R.H. may be about 80 per cent. Size of pens may be less restricted than in veal production, being perhaps as much as 15–20 ft²/calf in the nurse house and 25–30 ft²/calf in the rearing house. For older calves walls should be 4½ ft high. Usually, not more than 3 or 4 calves are grouped together in a pen until 8 wk of age, thereafter about 8 calves being penned together. Most farmers will provide some straw over the slats, some ½–1 ft in depth at the end of the 8-wk period when the pen is disinfected.

b. Suckling yards

Yards for cows plus their calves should be restricted in size to hold at most 25 mothers, allowing some 70–80 ft² for each cow plus calf, with an additional creep area of about 10–15 ft²/calf. Provided *ad lib.* straw is available, perhaps on the basis of 20 lb/cow/day, then the complete area of yard and creep should be strawed. If straw has to be restricted the area behind the manger may be concreted or even slatted. Each cow should have 2 ft.R of manger, though if calving takes place in the yards this might be 2½ ft.R. Access from the yard to the creep should be 1½ ft wide. The creep should be away from the manger area, completely enclosed, with an insulated ceiling 8 ft from the floor, and with hopper windows for ventilation. Multiple suckling should be based on a pen and creep area either for each cow plus calves or for 2 cows plus 8 calves held together. Suckling yards should be completely covered, though in mild districts partly covered yards might be suitable provided the creep areas were sheltered.

c. Individual pens

Loose boxes or pens for calving or for isolation should be about 10 ft × 12 ft in area, preferably with a stable door facing south, with hopper windows and an insulated ceiling.

d. Bull boxes and service pens

Bull pens can be enclosed within a larger building, or they may be separate with their own pen and yard. Bull pens should be about 180–200 ft² in area with a raised bedded floor free from draughts and with a standing area away from the bedding complete with trough, water bowl and hay rack. The trough should be 2 ft × 1½ ft × ¾ ft deep and the bowl an automatic pressure type, both being set in a concrete surround 2½ ft from the floor, with an adjoining area 2½ ft × 1½ ft for hay, all of which should be operated and cleaned by the herdsman from outside the pen through stout railing.

A door should open out of the pen to the outside adjacent to the feed area, there being tying rails available. High-level ventilation should be provided, though light should be restricted. The pen should open into the yard through a sliding door controlled from the exterior. Both doors should be clad with metal sheets. The yard should be about 300 ft² inclusive of service pen, perhaps 20 ft long × 15 ft wide, with either tubular fencing or 9-in. walling surround 6 ft high. There should be escape gaps in the surround 13 in. wide, and if tubular work is used this can be set 12 in. above the floor so that a man can roll under the fence. If walling is used this should be only 4½ ft high in places with one rail above. It is desirable that the bull should be able to see out of the yard, preferably in sight of the cows. The service pen should be 3½ ft wide internally, 7 ft long and 6 ft high, with a control gate for admitting a cow while the bull is in the yard which can be swung to a second position to admit the bull. The cow should be tied to a ring. Some pens include footrests or a small sand-pit. All walls should be of 9-in. solid construction, with piers if excessive in length. The roof can be uninsulated. Good electric lighting should be provided to the feed area, and possibly above the bedded area. Comprehensive details of modern bull housing have been given by the West of Scotland Agricultural College (Ref. *d*). Bull housing is frequently paired, there being no objection to bulls being in adjoining yards.

e. Storage

The feed store should act as a draught lobby to the nurse house, being equipped for artificial rearing as for veal housing. When straw is used, perhaps at an allowance of ½ bale/calf/wk, this should be adjacent to the housing, though with yarded animals the straw may be delivered via a tractor and trailer every day.

f. Water

Generally, after weaning, water is provided *ad lib*. Individual or group pens and creeps should be fitted with automatic pressure bowls.

6. *Equipment.* Little specialist equipment is normally required except as for veal housing (Pt. 3, IIID, 6). Proprietary service crates, whether portable or fixed, are available. Similarly, individual and adaptable calf pens with metal sides, a rear chain and a tubular front with bucket holders can be bought or made easily, such pens being flexible, since they can be erected for temporary use. Alternatively, portable timber stalls can be made cheaply and can be used until calves are weaned at 5 wk. They are similar to veal stalls.

7. *Environmental control*

a. Nurse houses should have background electrical heat, or preferably, for localized warmth, infra-red pendant heaters which can be raised and lowered above each pen.

b. Ventilation is similar in principle to that for intensive beef houses. The internal volume of the calf house should be restricted, the ceiling being low, including a flat soffit, vapour seal and insulation. Controlled air inlets at the ridge with extractor fans in the walls or natural eaves inlets with ridge extractors can be used. The internal temperature should be thermostatically controlled. Walls should be of insulated block.

c. Though timber slats are used for most calf pens, recent developments have included buffed expanded metal, the sub-floor draining to an effluent tank as in other stock housing.

d. Lighting should be similar to that for veal housing. (Pt. 3, IIID, 7*d*, p. 204.)

8. *Layouts*

a. Layouts for bucket rearing are similar in principle to veal housing (Pt. 3, IIID, 8, p. 204). A large layout with a nurse and a rearing house is shown in Fig. 89 the overall number of pens being designed to suit a 3-monthly throughput.

b. Fig. 90 shows a simple layout for a multiple suckling unit.

c. Fig. 91 shows a large layout for suckling yards with creeps. Such a layout can be suitable when an existing farm yard with a range of buildings around three sides can be converted, the yard

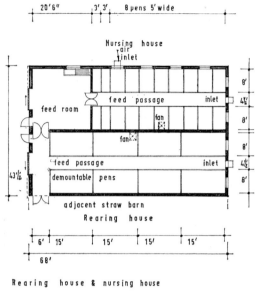

Fig. 89. Layout for bucket rearing (Ref. *a*)

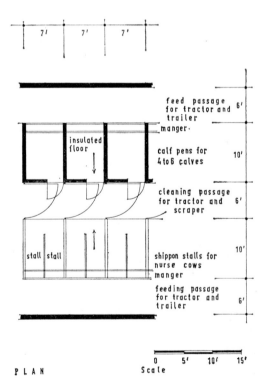

Fig. 90. Layout for a multiple suckling unit

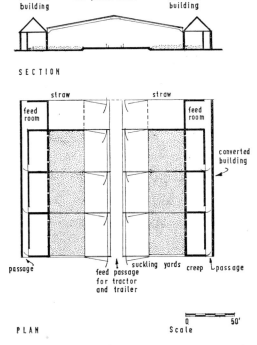

SECTION

PLAN   Scale

Fig. 91. Layout for suckling yards and creeps

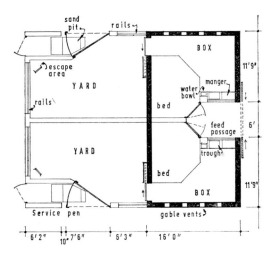

Layout for two bulls
on an island site

PLAN

Scale

Fig. 92. Bull pens (Ref. d)

being covered, including a central tractor passage, and the existing buildings being converted into creep areas and looseboxes.

d. Fig. 92 shows a double bull box, yard and service pen layout on an open site, perhaps adjacent to loose housing yards for the herd (Ref. d).

9. *Siting.* The siting of calf and bull units is not simple, since much depends on the farm layout and the relation of the calf housing to other enterprises, especially milk or beef production. In a few cases the calf housing may be enclosed within one building including a dairy herd layout or even beef yarding. Sometimes calf housing is separate from but adjacent to the adult yarding, especially when, as often is the case, calf housing is within converted buildings. Usually, the herdsman in charge of the adult stock also manages the calves. If there is separate management for the calves the calf housing can be sited away from the adult stock. In either case good management is essential, especially when calving takes place. Therefore, many calf units should be sited close to the farmhouse. Bull yards, which should be sunny and sheltered, should be adjacent to the housing of the herd, even if this means it is sited away from the calf housing.

10. *Services.* An electrical and water supply is essential. Rainwater must be taken clear of the site, dry conditions being essential. Foul drainage must be treated as a farm effluent. A high-pressure hose for cleaning the bull yard is desirable.

11. *Costs.* There are wide variations of cost which may be incurred in calf housing due to different standards. Generally, costs for new units need not be greater than for veal housing, i.e. £25–£30/place; since space is usually less restricted costs of up to £40 may be reasonable.

Conversions should cost less. Good bull housing, including house, yard and service pen, may cost £500–£750/bull. A simple timber calf stall might cost £5–£10 each. The provision of artificial ventilation should not be more than £1/place. Special pen fronts including yoke and bucket holders might cost about £5/calf.

The importance of good housing has been stressed, and a reduction in the mortality rate may easily justify an addition of £20/place, see 2b above. The cost per calf is more important than the cost per place, and this depends on the number of calves reared within each place p.a.

Staggered calving dates, especially in beef production, may mean that the house is kept full throughout the year except for the sterilization periods. Though a nurse and rearing period each of 8 wk plus 3 wk sterilization has been suggested, it may be more profitable to restrict the calf period to 3 months, which, plus the rest period, means that 3 lots of calves can be reared per place p.a. Thus, a capital expenditure of £40/place would represent £2/calf. Alternatively, if the nurse and rearing houses are filled and emptied every 3 months, then 4 calves/place can be housed each year, but if the combined cost of a nurse and a rearing place was £60 representing £2¼/calf.

12. *References*

(1) Selected Ref. *a*, p. ix.
(2) Calf rearing—a B.O.C.M. Survey, p. 1 (1962).
(3) Selected Reference *a*, p. x.
(4) Selected Reference *c*, p. 15.
(5) Selected Reference *c*, p. 8.

SELECTED REFERENCES

a. 'Calf rearing'. *Farmers Weekly Supplement* (20th April 1962).
b. 'Calf rearing'. *Farmers Weekly Supplement* (2nd October 1959).
c. PRESTON, T. R. 'Calf rearing'. Ministry of Agriculture Bulletin No. 10 (1960).
d. FORSYTH, R. J. 'Safer buildings for bulls'. West of Scotland Agricultural College Bulletin No. 148 (1958).
e. SMITH, A. K. 'The healthy calf'. *Farmers Weekly* (2nd October 1964).

IIID. Veal

1. *Activity*

a. Veal has been a popular Continental meat for many years, specially produced to give a white tender carcass at between 250 lb and 400 lb livewt. In contrast, veal in the U.K., for the most part, has been a by-product of the milk industry, coming from unwanted dairy calves, termed bobby calves, and killed at about 80 lb livewt, when four days old. However, within the last few years commercial veal markets for imported and home-reared meat have expanded and veal production is promoted now by the Quality Veal Producers' Association. Unlike Continental production, the U.K. market is based mainly on veal calves, reared from dairy breeds, such as the Ayrshire and Channel Island, though many producers use Friesian calves, slaughtered at 200–240 lb livewt, at about three months old. Calves from beef crosses tend to be too expensive.

b. Successful, commercial veal production depends on the raw material, management and environment in order to obtain the lowest, quickest and most economic food conversion ratio:

i. There are two raw materials. Strong, vigorous calves should be used, and culling is essential, particularly after about 4 wk. A mortality of about 4 per cent, and a wastage of up to 6 per cent, can be expected. Good-quality skim milk or milk substitutes should be correctly rationed.

ii. The production of white veal meat has similarities to that for broiler chickens, except for one major difference. Mass-production methods are undesirable. In order to obtain maximum livewt gains, individual attention and feeding are vital. Good stockmanship and management are essential, since the margins for error are small. The largest veal farm in Europe has a throughput of 1500 calves p.a., operated by 2 women (1).

iii. Veal production depends on the calves having restricted movement, the minimum of disturbance, the correct diet and a controlled environment. Veal calf houses are specialized buildings, which can be obtained as proprietary prefabricated units, or may be constructed on the farm, in many cases as a conversion of existing buildings, perhaps from an abandoned broiler enterprise. Some veal is produced from small, sideline enterprises conducted in cheaply converted buildings for the minimum of capital outlay.

c. Conversion rates of under 1·4 : 1 should be obtained, with 1·25 : 1 as the average, representing an intake of about 1¾ cwt of liquid food for a livewt gain of 150 lb. The rate can be as low as 1·15 : 1.

2. *Managerial requirements*

a. Most producers market the calves in batches at about 3-monthly intervals, being able to clean and sterilize the building between batches. At least one producer markets every week (1). In this case four compartments holding 96 calves each are filled in rotation at 3-wk intervals and each compartment is marketed in batches at the end of the tenth, eleventh and twelfth week, depending on size. Veal production should be by contract.

b. Most calf pens are made of timber, since if the calves lick metal their carcass may be tainted. Deliberately produced anaemia, coupled to exceptionally restricted quarters, has led to a charge of cruelty for veal production (2).

c. The pens may be planned to have a short life. In this case they should be designed as removable crates. One producer uses a crate holding 5 calves, costing £7½, which is destroyed after being used ten times, giving a cost of 3*s.*/calf (3).

3. *Production techniques*

a. Some calves remain in the same pen or crate from weaning or purchase at 4–6 days old to slaughter at 3 months. However, as a precaution against disease, it is worth keeping the young calves on straw in isolation pens for the first 7–14 days. Sometimes the younger stock lie on straw on top of the slats for the first few weeks within the main calf house.

b. No visitors to the calf house should be allowed, the only disturbance being the visit of the stockman at feeding times. Continual unrest can adversely affect food conversion by as much as 0·5, perhaps representing £5 in food costs (4). In addition, the carcass can become discoloured.

c. In some cases one calf/one pen is the rule, and, in the Netherlands, the crate may be designed almost to prevent the calves lying down, this restriction being claimed essential for economic production (2). However, many producers are convinced that 4 or 5 in a pen, with room to lie down, is satisfactory. Production becomes similar to a small-scale slatted beef unit (IIIB), except that all calves must be fed individually from plastic buckets instead of from a communal manger.

4. Work routines

a. The main work requirement, other than veterinary attention, is feeding, which may be at 12-hourly or at 8-hourly intervals. Feeding, and mixing, the rations must be carried out with care. Techniques vary, but in some cases the milk powder may be mixed with water at 75° C (165° F), then diluted with cold water to give a feeding temperature of about 40° C (105° F). The food is prepared and rationed in a feed room, which leads directly into the calf house, the plastic buckets being carried and placed into holders for each calf. Mixing can be by machine, either in an adapted washing machine or in a stainless-steel mixer emulsifier. In a large unit the food can be pumped through a pipe, the buckets being filled in situ with a trigger-operated nozzle (1). Equipment should be sterilized in the feed room.

b. The calves are not weighed, since disturbance would taint their meat, but progress can be checked with a tape measure, visual appraisal being the normal method.

c. The floor and dung channels can be hosed down, but the additional moisture may lead to excessive humidity. The house must be cleaned thoroughly after a batch has left.

5. Design data

a. The pen or crate (individual)
Restricted individual crates may be 51 in. × 23 in. wide, i.e. just over 8 ft²/calf, plus the bucket-holder projection, giving an overall length of about 5 ft. The height of the timber crate from the top rail at the front and sides can be 37½ in. to the slatted floor, the latter being about 4 in. above a sloping floor to the house. The back rail may be about 4 ft above the slatted floor. Less restricted pens allow nearly 12 ft²/calf, perhaps being 4½ ft × 2½ ft wide.

Individual pens should have access at the back for veterinary inspection, i.e. a passage at least 3 ft wide.

b. The pen (group)
A group pen might be 5 ft × 4 ft wide for 3 calves, allowing only 6⅔ ft²/calf (1). Alternatively, a pen 6½ ft × 9 ft wide would house 5 calves at a little under 12 ft²/calf.

c. Slatted floor
All calf-pen floors should be slatted, usually of beech, elm or imported hardwood, with slats parallel to the front and feed buckets, 1½ in. × 1 in. deep, with 1¼-in. gaps, supported on battens, about 3 in. deep, preferably in a removable panel to facilitate cleaning. The sides of the slats should be tapered and the battens should be cut to suit the floor profile, giving a level slatted floor.

d. Pen fronts
Various types of timber pen fronts are used, about 3–3¼ ft high, usually in a yoke design with vertical and adjustable slanted members, preferably removable, and including bucket holders.

e. Division walls
Individual pens usually have timber division rails. Group pens may have plywood panels on hardwood framing or may be in 3-in. concrete block, preferably rendered. Walls may be 4–4½ ft off the concrete floor.

f. Feed passage and floor drainage
A passage between two pen rows is required for feeding, cleaning and access, and this, for convenience, should not be less than 3 ft (sometimes 4½ ft) wide between bucket holders. The floor should include channels at the sides having a fall of at least 1 : 30, draining to a draught-free external trapped gulley and picking up drainage from a floor profile of 1 : 30 under the slatted pens (Fig. 93). Individual pens drain into a channel along the rear access passage.

g. Temperature and R.H.
A constant internal temperature of 20° C (70° F) is required, though some producers may prefer 22–23° C (75° F) (5). For heat produced by calves, see IIIC, 5, p. 199. The R.H. should be about 70 per cent. The internal volume should be restricted, perhaps to an overall height of 7 ft.

h. Light
Some producers exclude all natural light, whereas others believe that bright illumination, excluding direct sunlight, will not cause carcass discoloration (1). However, a new layout should exclude windows, which otherwise should be double glazed,

therefore adding to the cost. Permanent low-intensity artificial illumination may be desirable, perhaps tinted.

i. Food store

Since there should be no direct access from the exterior into the calf house, the food store is normally used as a draught lobby leading into the feeding passage. The store may be small, perhaps 50 ft²/50 calves. However, it should contain:

i. Storage space for interlocking buckets, perhaps 3 ft².

ii. Wash tub, perhaps $2\frac{1}{2}$ ft $\times$ $1\frac{1}{2}$ ft, plus drainer.

iii. Water heater, insulated, perhaps wall mounted, approximately $1\frac{1}{2}$ ft dia, say 20 gal/100 calves.

iv. Store cupboard, perhaps 4 ft².

v. Table or writing top, with pinboard on wall, perhaps 4 ft² and 10 ft² respectively per 50 calves.

vi. Mixer, or mixing tub, approximately 4 ft². Large unit, 100 gal.

vii. Food: at least 1 week's supply, i.e. approximately 16 lb/calf, or say 10 ft³/50 calves, though with milk powder (well contained) a month's supply may be allowed, or even more in some cases.

6. *Equipment.* Equipment is limited mainly to removable crates, if used, or removable pen fronts and floors, bucket holders, buckets and food-storage fittings, described above. In addition, there should be thermometers, etc., for measuring internal temperature and R.H.

7. *Environmental control*

a. Artificial heating may be required during the winter months, which may be based on under-floor, off-peak electrical heating, oil-fired central heating or infra-red pendant heaters for localized warmth.

b. Artificial ventilation is essential and follows the form of most intensive calf-housing (IIIC, 7, p. 200). Ventilation may be provided by manually controlled ridge inlets, excluding external moisture, with thermostatically controlled, fan-operated outlet ducts, running internally along the eaves with perforation slots into the duct.

c. The roof should have good insulation similar to pit-fattening houses, with 2 in. glassfibre or similar insulation and a vapour seal between a top and bottom sheet (IIIE, 7c, p. 200). The roof should have a sealed and smooth internal surface. Walls should have similar construction or may be of rendered hollow concrete block.

d. One light socket central above the feed passage per 9–10 ft.R should be adequate, controlled from the store, possibly with 1 extra socket/25 ft.R for a 25-W tinted bulb. The food store

should have good natural and artificial illumination to the table, mixer and wash tank.

8. *Layouts.* Layouts are normally based on a central feed passage with pens on either side. Therefore, an internal span of 19 ft may be required for individual crates, or 15–20 ft for a pen layout (Fig. 93). Individual crates might have 1 calf/ft.R of

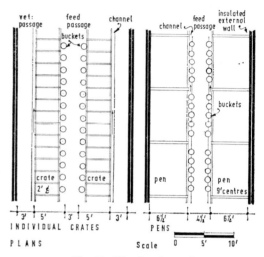

Fig. 93. Housing for veal

building at a minimum stocking density of 19 ft²/calf or 130 ft³/calf, and a pen layout 1 calf/$\frac{7}{8}$ ft.R at a density of about 14 ft²/calf or 96 ft³/calf. A large unit should be double banked to reduce walling and capital cost, as well as to help conserve warmth. However, the layout should be divided into compartments to suit the marketing and cleaning requirements.

9. *Siting.* Siting should allow for good management supervision, exclusion of noise, no contamination from other stock, the ease of handling calves off and on to trucks or lorries, disposal of urine and reasonable shelter without air restriction to the fan ventilation.

10. *Services.* An electrical supply is essential, probably including power for heating the building and water, as well as mixing the food. A supply of pure water is essential. Rainwater must be taken clear of the building. Foul drainage must be treated as a farm effluent.

11. *Costs.* Costs for converted veal houses may be as low as £1/calf place, but most cheap conversions will cost £5–£10/calf place. Special crates may cost £1$\frac{1}{2}$–£3 each. Prefabricated units might cost

£22–£26/place, and well-fitted, load-bearing new units perhaps £24–£30/place, including food storage and services. A capital cost £24/place represents a cost of 18s./calf.

Food at £6¼/cwt might represent about £11½/calf. Labour is unlikely to be full-time, since large veal units are uncommon, but an allowance of 1½ hr/calf (i.e. approximately 1 min/calf/day) might be a reasonable assessment. Therefore labour might be valued at about £1/calf, and production costs, without general overheads, would represent nearly £13½/calf. Allowing an average wastage value of about 8 per cent, the production cost is nearly £14½, say, £15 overall. The investment should allow a good profit over the calf and production costs on this basis.

12. References

(1) PHELPS, A. 'Europe's largest veal farm'. *Dairy Farmer*, pp. 22–4 (September 1962).
(2) TROW-SMITH, R. 'I would not keep a calf this way'. *Farmer and Stockbreeder*, pp. 92–7 (13th September 1960).
(3) 'Calf rearing'. *Farmers Weekly Supplement*, p. xlvi (20th April 1962).
(4) 'Calf rearing'. A B.O.C.M. Survey, p. 10 (1962).
(5) 'Blueprint for British broiler veal'. *Farmer and Stockbreeder*, pp. 99–101 (13th September 1960).

IIIE. Pork and Bacon Production

1. *Activity*

a. The conversion of coarse foods into pigmeat is a technical problem. About 9M pigs are slaughtered annually in Great Britain. The method of obtaining the basic raw material (weaners) for fattening is discussed in IIIF, and the supply and storage of the subsidiary raw material (coarse foods) is described in IE. The fattening of weaners for pigmeat can be within adverse conditions and many farmers are convinced they obtain satisfactory results with inexpensive methods and equipment. But the industrial production of pigmeat requires accurate control over the genetics, production methods, feeding and environment of the pig.

Weaners are fattened until they obtain one of several accepted weights (90–300 lb being the limits, though 120–260 lb is the more normal commercial range of weights) suitable for different marketing requirements, their rations being planned accordingly for that purpose. The time taken to reach the prescribed weight and the food consumed affect the economics of housing the fatteners, though the farmer is concerned also by the quality and grade of pigmeat obtained, since these will determine his payment. The chart which follows summarizes the normal types, weights and age of pig at slaughter:

Type of product	Wt in lb	Age in days (approx.)
Early weaners *	14 approx.	18–24
Weaners *	45 approx.	50–56
Porkers 1	120	130
Porkers 2	140	147
Porkers 3	160	165
Cutters	180	175
Baconers (restricted feed)	200–220	186
Baconers (*ad lib.* feed)	200–220	170
Heavy hog	260	210

* Early weaners and weaners—see IIIE. It is claimed that early weaners should reach finishing weights 7–10 days earlier than as given. There can be a variation of 20 lb (i.e. 35–55 lb) between the largest and smallest weaner in one litter at 8 wk, and this may become 50 lb, equal to 5 wk growth, at slaughter.

A farmer may fatten for one or several of the finishing weights or he may wish to vary his product to suit the market. Linear programming can be used to indicate the product which will yield the highest profit in relation to the pigs, labour and building available, but depending on an estimate of the pigs' potential performance and an appraisal of future market prices (1).

b. There are three basic management decisions to be made before designing a layout:

i. Whether to fatten intensively or extensively. This section will consider intensive systems in which the pigs are kept indoors until slaughter. In extensive systems the fatteners are kept out of doors either until about 12 wk old or until slaughter. Obviously, extensive systems do not require buildings, except for food storage, though portable arks or huts are normally placed in the fields as shelter for the pigs.

ii. Whether to rear or to buy the weaners for fattening. In the former case one skilled pigman should manage about 80 sows plus progeny until bacon weight (i.e. about 1600 fatteners p.a.). In the latter case the weaners should be bought on contract, and one man could fatten from 2000 to 4000 p.a., depending on the layout. Relief labour must be available, and in either case a two-man unit is desirable (see 2a, below).

iii. Whether to grow or to buy grain for feed. In either case a mill/mix unit will be justified in an industrial production unit. If only home-grown grain is available the unit must be limited to the grain yield p.a.—though this is seldom a reasonable policy, since probably it will be more economic to supplement the harvest with bought-in foods.

2. *Managerial requirements.* Successful fattening depends on the economical conversion of coarse foods into flesh. The pig industry requires some 4M tons of feed every year. Coarse foods can consist of either various meals with barley as a base, fed either dry or wet, in the form of pellets or cubes or skim milk or whey. The food may be rationed, being fed once to four times a day, or may be fed *ad lib*. It is acknowledged that within efficient systems, where the food conversion ratio is low and the throughput/man is high, the cost of coarse foods (at market prices) can account for 80–90 per cent of the total cost of production. Even with an average conversion ratio, it can account for 70 per cent of the cost if labour is assisted by little mechanization and the throughput/man is not high. In addition to the feeding techniques, the management must determine the level of hygiene desired, the method of dung disposal, whether the pigs will be weighed during fattening and the size of the production unit.

a. Food conversion

The conversion rate depends on several factors:

 i. Genetics: the sex, age and weight of pig at weaning, together with the natural characteristics of the breed of pig in being able to convert coarse foods efficiently.

 ii. Feeding: the type of coarse food used and the method of feeding (as above).

 iii. Environment: the design of the house to give recognized optimum conditions; but there has been little research to relate environment to genetics and feeding policy—especially on comparative methods.

The optimum conversion rate, obtained with some breeds and under some managerial systems, is less than 3·0, but rates greater than 5·0 are known, especially during winter months in poor housing conditions. It would appear that the national average conversion rate is rather more than 4·5. The conversion rate can be affected considerably by the temperature in the pig house as well as by the comfort and hygiene for the pigs. However, the conversion rate must be related to the liveweight of the pig, since an average conversion of 3·0 may be obtained for a pig converting at weaning at 2·0, at 100 lb liveweight at 3·0, and at bacon weight at 4·0. This is a normal sequence, since a larger pig needs more food for maintenance. Heavy hogs with a high lean content, quick growth and a low weaner cost have been shown to have economical conversion averaging 3·7 lb of feed to 1 lb of food and reaching 260 lb in wt. A difference of 0·1 in the conversion rate, with food costing £30/T, will be equal to 4·2s. in the production cost of a baconer, which is about one-tenth of the average profit. However, the conversion rate

has also to be related to the nutrient value of the food, since food costing £25/T and converting at 4·0 will be as economic as one costing £30/T and converting at 3·2, provided that the time taken is the same and that there is no difference in the grade of pig or in the environment of the house. The food cost per lb. livewt gain can be given for different conversion rates and costs of food (Ref. *i*):

Con-version rate	Price of food per ton				
	£24	£26	£28	£30	£32
	d.	*d.*	*d.*	*d.*	*d.*
3·0	7·7	8·3	9·0	9·7	10·3
3·2	8·2	8·9	9·6	10·3	11·0
3·4	8·7	9·5	10·2	10·9	11·7
3·6	9·3	10·0	10·8	11·6	12·3
3·8	9·8	10·6	11·4	12·2	13·0
4·0	10·3	11·1	12·0	12·9	13·7
4·2	10·8	11·7	12·6	13·5	14·4
4·4	11·3	12·3	13·2	14·1	15·1

Common practice is to feed *ad lib.* for pork, up to 120 lb livewt for baconers and up to 140 lb livewt for heavy hogs, but to ration the feed thereafter, though a few farmers gradually increase the ration from weaning to finishing weight. However, completely *ad lib.* feeding for heavy hogs, and even for baconers, is practised, and can make considerable savings in capital building costs. With *ad lib.* feeding the daily liveweight gain may average about 1¾ lb. Water may be provided *ad lib.*, or it may be rationed, usually being given in fixed quantities in the meal at feeding time.

b. Standards of hygiene

Intensive production needs high standards of hygiene, though different farmers have varying interpretations of the standards required to make buildings hygienic. At a minimum standard, all surfaces at pig level should be impervious and smooth, though many farmers will use unrendered brick or timber for walls without apparent harm from disease. However, there is a good case for all the internal surfaces being impervious and smooth. Since the internal surfaces of walls and ceilings should amount to not more than 5 yd²/place, a moderate surface could be provided at £1½/place, and a good surface at £3/place. The latter should represent a building cost of about 4s./baconer, without grant.

Most pig houses have a common dung passage, through which all drainage must pass. This can be a disease risk and a slatted dunging area may prove to be more hygienic. Similarly, most houses are designed to have one air space for 100–300 pigs, but it is better to restrict the volume into smaller compartments, each for about 50 pigs or equal to each intake batch into the house. The design should encourage dunging to occur within the dunging area, and the trough and water bowl must be designed to prevent soiling. To prevent the build up of bacteria in the fabric, the house should be cleaned after use, preferably with a disinfectant, possibly by steam, and should be rested for 3 wk. Systems for disinfection are described in standard works on pig husbandry (viz. Ref. *f* and Ref. *j*). This is another reason why compartments equal to each intake batch are desirable. The rest period represents a loss of potential throughput and many farmers will risk omitting it between some, if not all, batches of pigs. For baconers the rest period means that one-seventh, or possibly one-sixth, additional pig places are required. Therefore, a house for 200 baconers would need about 230 pig places, which, at £15 per pig place, represents an additional capital cost of £2¼ on each of the 200 pig places always in use, i.e. about 3s. per baconer. To be really effective, the complete house should be clear of pigs during the rest period.

c. Methods of dung disposal

Dung can be valuable as a fertilizer (IG, 1, p. 76). A slatted dunging area may reduce the risk of cross-infection inherent with a dunging passage and will be suitable both for organic irrigation and for vacuum tanker methods of returning the dung to the land. It will also help to reduce labour requirements in cleaning the house. It is the simplest and, probably, the most hygienic method of dung disposal. Alternatively, if the dung passages are cleaned daily into an external dung pit the latter can be emptied either by organic irrigation methods or by vacuum tanker, or they may be scraped directly into a manure spreader. A few farmers advocate open dunging yards used in conjunction with a deep layer of straw. This will dictate the design of the layout, and not only can it be an expensive method of making manure, but probably the food conversion rates will be less efficient in winter than in completely enclosed houses. Dung-disposal methods are considered in more detail below.

d. Weighing

There are two opposed ideas concerning the recording of pig weights during fattening. A farmer may not weigh the pigs, except perhaps in the last fortnight of growth, due to the labour required for weighing and to the disturbance to the pigs which might cause a small check in growth. This attitude in particular may be combined with *ad lib.* feeding techniques. Conversely, some farmers believe that full recording, i.e. weighing at least at fortnightly intervals, is essential. Since weighing normally takes place in a portable crate placed within the dunging passage, the design of the building should

not be affected. However, *ad lib.* feeding would make it possible to have a permanent weighing point at one end of a central inspection passage, provided there was a screen between pen and passage so that pigs not being weighed were undisturbed. This arrangement would reduce labour requirements during weighing. Alternatively, a weighing room can be sited at one end of the building, but if access is not possible into the central inspection/feed passage this means the pigs have to move along the dung passage, which can lead to cross-infection. However, a permanent weighing position is more accurate than using portable scales.

e. Size of production unit

The economic size of fattening unit is in a period of transition. There is no standard size of unit, since farmers may fatten any number between a few dozen and a few thousand pigs each year. However, pig production will inevitably come under contract to established markets, farmers fattening a contract number of pigs available at specified times, weights and grading. This will be successful only if the pigman is a skilled herdsman, able to devote all his time to pig production. With automation, there is almost no limit to the size of unit possible and manageable by one man, provided that there is no restriction to the supply of weaners and food, and that he is not responsible for rearing the weaners in addition to fattening them. A mechanized, but not automated, unit might be designed in which one man could manage 1000 pigs at one time, but there is no evidence from available research to indicate either the optimum or the maximum size of unit. The unit should be designed to have a constant cycle of pig production, with weaners bought or reared and fatteners sold at the same regular intervals.

A reasonable and efficient unit might be based on 700–800 pigs controlled by one man, which, on the basis of a 40-hr week, would allow a maximum of 2 min/pig/wk within the houses and 1½ min/pig/wk outside the houses for milling/mixing, distributing feed to the houses, marketing and general administration. This is examined in (4) below, but it assumes that the dung would be taken to the fields or drainage system without the pigman's assistance. An additional man would be required for veterinary work, weighing and relief. Therefore a two-man unit is more satisfactory, perhaps able to manage 1500–2000 pigs, and in which the men work together for 3 days/wk and on their own for 2 days. Few units have a throughput per man at these levels, since in most cases the layouts are either inefficient and inadequately mechanized or the pigman has duties other than pig keeping.

If x weaners are bought in weekly batches when

8 weeks old, and the house is rested 3 weeks between batches, then:

	Pork	Bacon	Hog
No. of weeks in house	13	18	22
No. of pig places required	16x	21x	25x

Since some fatteners will not reach the required weight within the specified time, a number of shedding pens are desirable, but fatteners from different pens in the house should not be put together at this stage, since they would fight. An allowance of $\frac{x}{10}$ shedding pens might be made, each capable of taking 3 or 4 fatteners. If 720 pigs are managed at any one time, then:

	Pork	Bacon	Hog
Weaner intake per week	56	40	34
Total fattened per annum	2912	2080	1768

However, the weekly intake numbers would be governed to some extent by the optimum pen sizes, see (8) below. Many smaller units can prove economic, for example, if a small pig unit is run as a subsidiary enterprise, perhaps, to a beef unit—the stockman being responsible for both.

3. *Production techniques.* Some of the techniques for production have been discussed above, but, in addition, production is governed by the work routines, level of mechanization and environment. However, the feeding policy should be the basis of any design, coupled to the optimum number of pigs per pen.

a. Skim milk and whey

It has been claimed that 12s. on pork pigs and £1 on baconers can be saved by using skim (3), and it would be natural to find skim and whey fed pig production units centred around the main butter and cheese manufacturers. Since the feed is liquid, it can be piped from a storage tank direct to the troughs. Therefore pig feeding is economical in labour requirements compared with meal rations, it being possible to feed 50–100 pigs/min without installing equipment as expensive as that required if meal is handled mechanically. Humidity within the house will be increased, since more dung will be produced.

b. Rationed meal

Meal can be placed manually in the troughs by a measured scoop from a barrow or it can be conveyed mechanically direct from a store. Meal, which is normally a mixture of barley and additives, is the normal pig food, and rationed feed at some stage of the pig's life is practised by most farmers (see above) fattening pigs, though *ad lib.* feeding can prove economic.

c. Ad lib. meal

Self-feeding hoppers each holding about a week's supply of food can be placed in the pens, and since troughs are not required, with space for all the pigs to feed at one time, the building can be cheaper than when rationed feeding is required.

d. Floor-feeding

Floor feeding with meal, or preferably with cubes, is practised, especially for heavy hogs, and has the following advantages over trough feeding:

i. Saves the space and cost of troughs.
ii. The shape of pen is more flexible (see below).
iii. More pigs may be kept in each pen (see below).
iv. Increased density of pigs per ft³ helps to raise the temperature in the house.
v. Pigs are reputed to keep cleaner and quieter.

e. Pig-to-pen ratio

Traditionally, one pen is designated to each litter from a sow, and therefore pens are normally designed to hold ten fatteners. However, it is better to grade the pigs into groups of similar weight at weaning and the mixed litters may be grouped into pens holding from 10 to 35 fatteners. At least one farmer keeps 45 pigs to a pen, with a slatted dung area, and the pigs both keep clean and have a low conversion ratio of 3·1 (12). Larger pen sizes may reduce capital costs, especially with floor feeding, since a shorter and wider building is possible than when troughs are required. The density of the pigs in each pen is important, both in relation to keeping the house warm and to reducing the capital cost. If the weaners are graded and placed, say, 12 to a pen, and left until they are ready for slaughter the house will not have the maximum density except during the last few weeks. This can be overcome in three ways:

i. The pen can be restricted in area by a partition, which can be moved as the pigs grow, but this will not reduce the capital cost, though the pigs may keep cleaner with restricted space while young.
ii. The pigs can be moved from a small pen to a larger pen during the fattening period, but some farmers prefer not to move their pigs nor to have two sizes of pen. It may be difficult to improve the density per cubic foot, unless there are two houses, one for grower weights and one for finishing weights. This system has other advantages, see (7) below.
iii. All the pens can be the same size, half the fatteners being removed at mid-growth and placed in another pen, which gives a second chance for grading the pigs. The main disadvantages of dividing the pigs during their growth are cross-infection and the difficulty for adequately resting the pens between batches.

77: LAYOUT OF FATTENING PENS

The two basic layouts for fattening houses are shown by the models. The side dung passages are the normal form of layout, since they have two advantages. With manual placing of rations in the troughs, the central feed passage is easier to manage and the pigman can inspect all the pigs more quickly from the central passage. Secondly, it is best to have warm, insulated pens and a colder dung passage, the former being without windows and the latter having some natural light. If the wall between the dung passage and pen is taken to the roof, the roof having a lower pitch, and access between the two being limited to pop-holes, this is easy to arrange. However, the central dung passage can have advantages, particularly if feed is conveyed to the troughs automatically. If the dung passages are cleaned out by tractor, a central dung area is quicker and easier to clean. Moreover, if the dung passage has a slatted floor over a channel this will be cheaper to construct as one central unit. [SEE PAGE 215] Diagrammatic Model: Courtesy of West of Scotland Agricultural College.

78: PIG FATTENING UNIT
Mr. A. Duff, Southwaite Farms, Carlisle

The external view of the intensive fattening unit shows eight adjustable, baffled outlets along the side

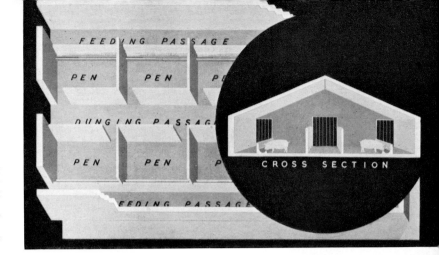

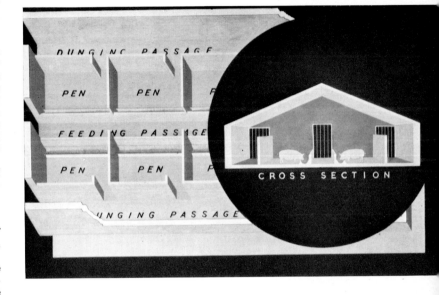

of the house, which has a central passage with eight self-contained rooms on each side of it. Two ridge air inlets and a gable louvre panel supply air to a duct above the central passage, which, in turn, ventilates each room through a thermostatically controlled fan. Thus, each room is a separate air compartment, reducing the risk of cross-infection, and is divided into two pens by a raised catwalk. Each pen will hold 30 pork or 20 bacon pigs. An intake of 60 weaners is allowed to each room, from which at a later stage 20 are removed as porkers and the remainder are fattened to bacon weight. The rooms are completely insulated and include slatted dunging areas over a slurry channel which empties into a 28,000-gal tank. Feeding is either on the floor or from self-feeders, which can be automated. The feed store has a raised roof at the end of the production building and a second production unit is to be built on the other side of the store. [SEE PAGE 215] Courtesy of Farmer and Stockbreeder.

79: FATTENING HOUSE WITH MECHANIZED FEEDING
Messrs. R. Howie & Sons, Ayr

The fattening house has a slatted central dung passage and has work passages along the external walls. The sliding door opens into a work and feed room at one end, above which is a raised feed storage bin. The latter is filled from a trailer, the feed being blown through the external supply pipe. Feeding is semi-mechanized. The bin discharges into a chain-and-flight conveyor which circulates above the pens and fills a hopper suspended over each pen floor, holding a ration for each pen, the quantity being controlled by a sliding ratchet bar set by the pigman. At feeding time the pigman walks along each side passage, inspects each pen and pulls a cord releasing the ration on to the pen floor. [SEE PAGE 209] Photograph: J. B. W.

80: SLURRY TANK: FATTENING ENTERPRISE
Messrs. R. Howie & Sons, Ayr

A series of fattening houses with slatted dung passages discharge their slurry into a common tank, shown under construction. The tank is 6–7 ft deep with rendered walls. Sleepers are used to cover the tank, being supported by the side walls and a central reinforced concrete beam and brick piers. In the foreground is the inspection chamber collecting the slurry from the dung channels before discharging it into the tank. [SEE PAGE 209] Photograph: J. B. W.

81 & 82: FARROWING PEN: SOLARI-TYPE

Harper Adams Agricultural College

   The Solari farrowing kennel, named after Mr. Solari of Shropshire, is a simple brick compartment, 5 ft wide, and partly open to the south if required. The insulated ceiling slopes to an internal ht of 3 ft at the back. The kennel is in two parts. The rear portion has a raised, insulated floor as the farrowing and sleeping area. Farrowing rails and a creep area, which are available as a unit construction, can be removed after weaning so that the kennel can be used for the growers. The length of the farrowing area is about $8\frac{1}{2}$ ft. In the background is a dunging area which includes an automatic water bowl, a feed bin and a trough. The floor drains to an external gulley. The kennel has to be cleaned out through a door at the south side. The overall length is $16\frac{1}{2}$ ft. [SEE PAGE 230] Courtesy of Pig Farming.

83: FARROWING CRATES

Mr. G. T. G. Shepherd, Pitmillan, Newburgh, Aberdeenshire

The design of the farrowing crate is important to obtain low piglet mortality. The sow is held in the tubular crate throughout farrowing and the 6-wk rearing period. Crate and pen are strawed and drain into a gulley in the work passage, and the length can be adjusted by the rear guard into three positions depending on sow size. The piglets have a generous-sized pen, including water bowl and adjustable infra-red heater. The sow has a manger bowl, and the pigman has to enter the pen. The rear wall is rendered and the other partitions are low timber barriers. The crate and barriers are easily removable when the house is cleaned. [SEE PAGE 230] Courtesy of the North of Scotland Agricultural College.

84: DRY SOW HOUSE

Messrs. R. Lawson & Son, Parkhill Stock Farms, Dyce, Aberdeenshire

Dry sows can be housed in groups or in individual stalls, though the latter has not been tried over a long period, so veterinary experience is limited. The house holds 200 sows. Feed passages are next to external walls, mangers being filled from hoppers above them, which are not visible. The hoppers, in turn, are filled by a horizontal chain-and-flight conveyor from the feed room. The operator is turning a ratchet in the hopper to feed a sow. The sows have straw for bedding : their insulated floors fall to a central passage including a mechanical scraper in a channel. Normally, the latter has a grille over it. The stalls are 2 ft wide, with reinforced concrete divisions and top rails to prevent the sows climbing. Tubular rear gates lift out. Baffled air inlets are at the side of the building, and the insulated ceiling includes air extract chimneys. Good artificial lighting is essential. [SEE PAGES 46 & 227] Courtesy of North of Scotland Agricultural College.

4. *Work routines.* The work involved in fattening pigs is of two kinds, one external to the house and the other within the house.

a. External work

Pig production requires efficient methods of keeping records, and an office is essential (IK). Feed has to be distributed to the houses, each house for preference having its own store capable of holding at least 7–10 days supply of rations, whether meal or liquid. Distribution should be mechanized, with the meal handled in bulk, since, except in small units, sack handling is to be avoided. Meal can be conveyed mechanically from a central mill/mix unit to each house. The most efficient method may prove to be chain-and-flight conveyors in an overhead trough (Pt. 2, IVC, *b*, ii, p. 45). This may cost about £4–£6 per ft.R. Blowing meal might cause a displacement in the mix. However, the labour saved may not justify the cost unless the overhead run is short. More normal methods of distribution will be by a tanker, from which the meal may be blown into an overhead bin or loft to each house. Cubes might have to be handled by an auger, rather than by blowing. Liquids will be pumped into an overhead tank.

Dung should be removed from the houses into a storage tank, unless it is held under a slatted floor. Alternatively, it can be cleaned directly from the dung area into a manure spreader or it can be emptied into a lagoon, where the solids can be decomposed by bacteria and the liquids evaporated. Removal or disposal of the dung to the fields should not for preference be the pigman's duty, especially in a unit of any size. Methods of handling dung are discussed in Pt. 2 and in IG.

The pigs, when ready for sale, have to be taken from the houses to load them on to a lorry. Normally, the pigs leave the houses via the dung passage. They should be able to enter a race leading directly to the lorry position and, in any large scheme, the race may include a ramp up to the lorry height (see 8 below).

b. Internal work

The methods for distributing the feed to the pigs within the house is of major importance. It is essential for the pigman to see all the pigs at least once a day and it is claimed that this is assured only if the pigman personally places the food in the troughs. On this basis, it is claimed that the only satisfactory method is for the pigman to fill a wheeled trolley from the overhead store, push it down the house and, with a graded scoop, place the food in the troughs. Alternatively, instead of the trolley, a hopper may be mounted on a monorail. Liquid foods will be piped above the troughs and the pigman will turn on a tap to supply each pen. These requirements usually prescribe a house designed with a central feed passage flanked by a trough to pens on each side, unless a central slatted dung area is required when feed passages may be down each side of the building.

In addition, it is claimed that the cost of mechanized feeding methods cannot be recovered by the labour saved, since one man may only take 8 min to feed 300 pigs with a well-designed trolley, scoop and manger (4). For a baconer, feed twice a day, this is equal to about 6 min from weaning to sale, perhaps costing 2*s.*, including all labour overheads. In contrast, fully mechanized feeding with automatically travelling hoppers may cost about £5 per pig place, which may represent about 8*s.*/baconer. Machinery, based on equipment developed originally for poultry housing and using a chain-and-flight within a tube, can convey meal for several hundred feet and may be cheaper to install than a hopper on a monorail. The cost may be less than 6*s.*/baconer. Semi-mechanical feeding can convey the meal in this manner either to self-feeders or into holding boxes. The pigman, in the latter case, will release a catch on the box, to tip the meal into a trough or on to the floor. It is possible that costs may be reduced to under 5*s.*/baconer with this method. However, mechanized feeding, by automatic travelling hoppers or by chain-and-flight conveyors, is accepted within many large production units. Mechanized feeding makes it possible to feed a small ration four times a day. This is claimed to give quicker and cheaper food conversion, especially if the pigs are kept in darkness, with an automatic light switching on a few minutes before feeding, than feeding twice a day. The pigman is free to visit the house at any feeding period and, moreover, can devote all his time to an observation of the herd. A feeding rate of 8 min/300 pigs with a barrow and scoop leaves little time for good stockmanship.

Dunging passages should be cleaned out daily, unless a slatted layout is used which eliminates the necessity for cleaning. With one exception in layout design, the pigs have to be shut in their sleeping areas before cleaning, which means that all the dung-passage doors have to be shut and then opened after cleaning has been completed. This disturbs the pigs, and may take at least 1 min/50 pigs (5). With fully automatic cleaning, the pigs need not be disturbed, if their dung passage has a slatted floor and a powered scraper blade operates under it. Otherwise cleaning is simplest with a small 'horticultural type' tractor, fitted with a fore-mounted scraper, which may or may not include a seat for the operator. Manual cleaning with a squeegee may take as little as $2\frac{1}{2}$ min/50 pigs (5), but manual muck-shifting is to be discouraged and simple powered cleaners cost less than £100.

Automated cleaning might cost £$1\frac{1}{2}$ to £2 per

pig place, which perhaps equals 5s./baconer, whereas a tractor and scraper in a large unit might cost 6d. to 1s. plus about 1s. 6d. for labour. Manual cleaning, if efficient, taking not more than 10 min/baconer will be cheapest, but may frequently take 20 min, thereby being the most expensive if labour and overheads are considered.

Moving and weighing pigs, and veterinary work, normally takes place within the dung passages, unless there is a special weighroom at the end of the building. If open dung yards are included these should be strawed, the straw being delivered by tractor and trailer or stored on top of the pens. Straw allowances may equal 1 bale/10 pigs every other day.

5. *Design data*
a. Space requirements
Floor areas required can be summarized in ft²/pig place:

	Growers 120 lb	Finishers Bacon	Heavy hog
Sleeping and feeding	$3\frac{1}{2}$	5	$5\frac{1}{2}$
Dunging—slatted floor ★	1	$1\frac{1}{2}$	2
Dunging—concrete passage (if required)	$2\frac{1}{2}$	3	$3\frac{1}{2}$
Trough	$\frac{3}{4}$	1	$1\frac{1}{4}$

★ Sizes of slatted areas are still under review for optimum requirements.

A solid-floored dung passage should be about $\frac{1}{4}$ ft lower than the sleeping area.

Self-feeding hoppers need only about $\frac{1}{2}$ ft²/pig, being about 4 ft × $1\frac{1}{4}$ ft for 10 pigs, and can be placed anywhere along the perimeter of the pens. Circular self-feeders, if filled automatically from an overhead conveyor, can be placed in the centre of the pens. With floor feeding, hoppers can be suspended above the pens. Self- and floor-feeding techniques do not control the pen shape, whereas

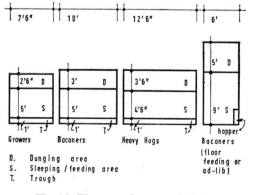

D. Dunging area
S. Sleeping / feeding area
T. Trough

Fig. 94. Floor area for pens of 10 pigs

a trough filled from a feeding passage will create a long narrow house (Fig. 94).

Feeding passages, to take a barrow, should be $3\frac{1}{2}$ ft wide, but this can be reduced to a walkway 18 in. wide, if a hopper is suspended from a monorail or if the feed is mechanically conveyed. The walkway can be above the troughs, which saves floor space and is desirable, provided the internal volume of the house is not substantially increased (Fig. 95). Well-designed houses for baconers can restrict the volume to 20 ft³ for the dunging passage and 40 ft³ for the house, though some may give a combined volume of over 80 ft³/baconer. Equally important to the volume is the surface area per pig. Fig. 95a represents nearly 20 ft²/baconer (excluding the dunging passage) for a house holding 300 pigs, whereas Fig. 95b, nearly 18 ft²/baconer and Fig. 95c, nearly 24 ft²/baconer.

Food-storage requirements, though depending on conversion rates, may be based on total rations (IE, 5c, p. 72):

Pork	at $3\frac{1}{2}$–$4\frac{1}{2}$ cwt
Bacon	at 5–$5\frac{1}{2}$ cwt
Heavy hogs	at $6\frac{1}{2}$–7 cwt

Therefore a week's storage space for $\frac{1}{8}$ cwt food/pig should prove sufficient. Skim-milk feeding will require storage for about 6–7 gal/wk, and whey about 10–11 gal/wk, though in addition some meal may be fed. Water requirements vary with temperature, age and type of food, but with meal will increase from $\frac{3}{4}$ to 2 gal/day, and with liquids will be about $\frac{1}{2}$ gal/day. Milk and whey should be delivered every week, but meal may be less frequent.

b. Temperature generated and required
Heat generated by the pigs should be used to warm the house. Moreover, the body temperature of a pig is extremely important related to the efficiency of its growth, including its livewt/gain per day, the food conversion ratio and its carcass quality. Though temperature is important for the health and performance of the pig during fattening, this must be related to humidity, air velocity and radiation from the surfaces of the building.

Until recently, the most comprehensive research on temperature and environment has been from experiments in America, which have established some criteria. Research in California has shown that the optimum temperature to give the best food conversion is 24° C (75° F) for pigs from 70 to 160 lb livewt, but this may be reduced to 18° C (65° F) at bacon wt and to 15° C (60° F) by the time hog wt is obtained (6). In the tests the air velocity was 25–25 C.F.M. with a R.H. of 50 per cent. The tests showed that a 100-lb pig converted at 2·5 at 24° C, but at a little over 3·0 at 15° C (Fig. 96). These figures have been insufficiently tested

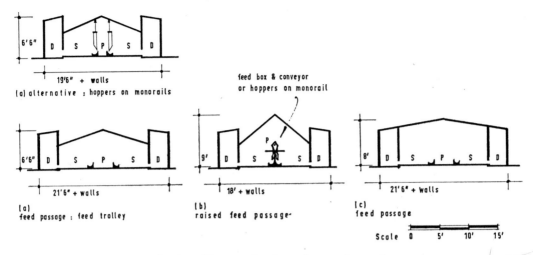

Fig. 95. Section of houses related to volume and to surface areas

to be reliable for U.K. conditions, breeds and feeding policies. However, the same research showed that each pig produced heat in B.t.u./hr:

	100-lb pig at 24° C (75° F)	300-lb pig at 15° C (60° F)
Latent heat	129	110
Sensible heat	301	750
Sensible heat used to evaporate water from pig	158	230

Therefore, a 100-lb pig will produce 143 B.t.u./hr of sensible heat, which may be used to cover heat losses from the structure of the pig house, and a 300-lb pig 520 B.t.u./hr. But it was also shown that the heat-loss rates changed continually throughout the day, possibly reaching a peak in relation to food digestion, with low rates occurring during the night. The body heat available to warm the structure, when the external temperatures are at the lowest, will be less than indicated by these figures. However, it might be taken, pending further research, that the average heat generated by 10 growers and which warms the house is equal to not much more than $\frac{1}{3}$ kWhr, and by 10 finishers perhaps $1\frac{1}{4}$ kWhr, these figures being reduced by at least one-third at night when the building heat losses may be at their maximum. In summer, when external temperatures exceed 24° C (75° F), the building will gain heat in excess of that generated by the pigs, and excess heat above the optimum temperature in relation to livewt will have to be removed from the house.

Recently, in the U.K. at Cambridge, the Pig Industry Development Authority has begun to investigate temperature requirements by experiments within a controlled-climate pig house. The correct temperature is important for efficient fattening, since body composition will deteriorate with temperatures higher or lower than the optimum which will give the best carcass. Moreover, as the air temperature falls, the heat loss from the pig will eventually exceed the heat produced to maintain body temperature, and food will have to be consumed which could have been used for productive purposes. Similarly, as the air temperature rises, eventually the body temperature will rise and, as the pig has few sweat glands, excess heat will be fatal, but loss of appetite and, therefore, of growth, will occur at an earlier stage.

With adult pigs, 30° C (85° F) may be excessive for efficient fattening. However, it is not easy to establish the limits of the range of optimum temperatures, since age, diet, acclimatization and the microclimate at the pig's skin rather than the

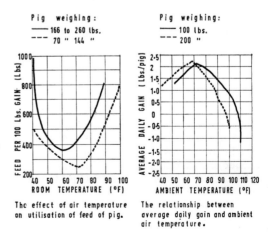

The effect of air temperature on utilisation of feed of pig.

The relationship between average daily gain and ambient air temperature.

Fig. 96. Optimum temperatures (Ref. e).

general climate in the house can affect the optimum range (14). It has been established that for each 1° C (1·8° F) fall below the air temperature at which body temperature is maintained an extra 1·4 oz of food/day/fattener will be required, that is, 120 lb/wk for 200 pigs, and the conversion ratio will be increased. The highest wt gain for pigs, with a conversion as low as 1·57, can be obtained at a temperature of 26° C (80° F), though the optimum temperature drops as the pigs get older (13). The Californian experiment showed that pigs of over 150 lb lost wt when the temperature rose above 38° C (100° F).

To maintain the internal air temperature to the range required the density of the pigs in the house, as well as its insulation, is important. This is a reason why growers should be separated from the finishers, being given less floor area, and possibly being housed within a better-insulated structure.

c. Humidity

Humidity will occur from moisture vaporized from the pigs, from their water and to some extent from the dung passage. U.S. research (6) indicated that the total might be:

100 lb pig at 24° C (75° F) $\frac{1}{8}$ lb/hr approx.
300 lb „ at 15° C (60° F) $\frac{1}{4}$ „ „

increasing in relation to water consumption to temperature ratio. This would be equal to $\frac{3}{4}$–1 gal/day. The level of relative humidity is contested, but 80 per cent can be taken as normal, with some experimental work indicating that more than 90 per cent is an advantage for conversion rates, and up to 98 per cent in 'sweat-box' conditions, especially when temperatures are above 25° C (78° F). A R.H. of 45 per cent has been shown to be harmless.

d. Ventilation and light

Natural ventilation can be successful, but with an average stocking density of 25 ft³/100 lb livewt, the possibility of excessive temperatures and foul air can be avoided only by artificial ventilation. It is more important to avoid sudden changes of internal temperature than to design a house for a permanent temperature of 24° C (75° F). Ventilation should be designed at a maximum rate of 40 C.F.M. per fattener, that is about 20–25 C.F.M./100 lb livewt for normal sites, and of under 30 C.F.M. per fattener for exposed sites and the north of the British Isles (7). The maximum rate is equal to about one air change/hr, but other authorities would suggest a lower rate of 15 C.F.M./100 lb livewt as being adequate and equal to about one air change/1½ hr (8). However, pigs over 200 lb in wt might need as much as 50 C.F.M. in hot weather. The intake should be capable of reduction to 3 C.F.M. for winter use and the fans should be

reversible, fitted with thermostats and automatic time controls, as well as with five variable intake speeds. It is desirable that the entrance to the house should be through a draught lobby or food store. Natural light should be excluded, except in a dunging passage, where it will encourage the pigs to dung, since windows will increase the heat loss from the house dim artificial light rather than natural light may be better for keeping the pigs quiet.

6. *Equipment.* Reference has been made already to equipment for feeding, cleaning and weighing. In addition, temperature and R.H. thermometers should hang freely at pig level, but out of their reach. Since pigs have a considerable capacity for gnawing and pushing any projection from the structure of the building, equipment needs careful detailing, and timber at pig level should be avoided. In particular, such details as gate catches and water-bowl connections need consideration.

a. Feeding equipment

The design of a typical trough and pen front to a feed passage is shown in Fig. 97, based on a 12-in. half-round glazed trough and tubular front rails. The latter can be designed to include a sliding panel, perhaps by having a section of the railing telescopic, so that the pigs can enter the central passage for weighing (if this is required). Alternatively, the front of the pen above the trough can be in the form of a galvanized sheeted and swinging panel which may be held in two positions. This makes it possible for the feed to be placed in the trough prior to feeding, the front being swung to the second position when required to give the pigs access to the trough. Feeding can be mechanized by having a meal box above the trough which can be filled by an endless conveyor, usually in the form of a chain-and-flight, the pigman having to pull a graded lever to let the meal fall into the trough. Many producers prefer to board the opening from the roof to the trough, so that the pigs can remain undisturbed in the dark when the pigman moves about in the feed passage, but allowing a shutter in the boarding to act as a viewing hatch into the pens.

Various techniques have been devised, both proprietary and home-made, to distribute a rationed quantity of meal into the troughs from a travelling overhead hopper carried on a monorail. The monorail may be moved either automatically or manually. The feed release normally works on a ratchet-to-peg connection, the pegs being placed above the trough, and graded in numbers to control the meal released by the ratchet. For example, a 4-cwt hopper which might be used for feeding 5 lb of meal each to 150 pigs into a trough allowing 1 ft.R/pig might take 3 min for the operation.

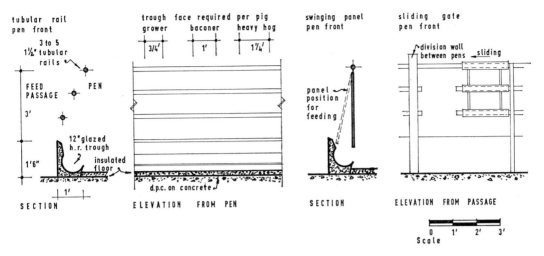

Fig. 97. Trough and pen front design

The lowest rail to the trough front can be used to distribute water, if rationed, or even liquid foods into the trough on the basis of a sprinkler action and a control tap. Some farmers consider that the meal mixed with water is more digestible than dry meal. With piped liquid feeds, mixing, pumping and distribution are equally important operations. Storage of the skim milk or whey is discussed in IE, 5 (p. 72). Mobile mix/pump units operated from a tractor can be used, holding perhaps 250 gal and complete with flexible piping for distribution to the troughs. A unit of this kind might cost around £400 and could be quickly filled from overhead storage hoppers. Alternatively, the mixer can be in a large vat or tank capable of mixing 750 gal of liquid with a 3-h.p. electric motor, being filled from overhead storage hoppers. A centrifugal action created by an impeller blade within a cylindrical tank can be effective for mixing skim milk and meal. A pump similar to those used for handling sludge can drive the liquid through the supply pipes, with an impeller action and a 5-h.p. motor for several hundred yards, preferably on a circular layout so that the feed can be returned to the mixer through a 2-in.-dia main supply. The circuit can be drained easily and the flow reversed to remove a blockage. Secondary circuits, with their own control valves, or lateral pipes in $1\frac{1}{2}$-in.-dia piping can be used to supply the troughs, being controlled by releaser valves or cocks. Sharp bends of under $\frac{1}{2}$ ft dia in the supply should be avoided (17).

b. Drinking equipment

If the water supply is not combined with the trough, water bowls are normally provided, and these should be sited with care, for preference within the dunging area rather than the sleeping area. However, they should be positioned to avoid being fouled and, except in slatted layouts, to avoid being damaged while the dung passage is cleaned. They should also be sited well away from the access from the dung passage into the bedded area. They can be fixed on the passage doors between dung compartments with a flexible connection above pig height to the water supply. When the passage is cleaned the bowl can be positioned on the door so that it will be within the sleeping area at the pop-hole. Alternatively, the bowl can be on a plinth $\frac{1}{2}$ ft high and recessed into the dung passage/sleeping area wall with access from the former. The lip of the bowl should be $\frac{1}{2}$ ft above floor or step level. At least one bowl per 10–12 pigs is desirable. Proprietary drinkers are of several types, being reviewed in *Pig Farming* (15), and having bowls with different forms of water supply (16):

i. Snout-operated flaps, particularly suitable for finishers.

ii. Float-and-valve chambers at the back of the bowl.

iii. Non-return valves, supplied from an independent cistern with ball-valve control from the supply and placed at the same level as a series of bowls.

iv. Plunger in pipe-outlet, without a bowl, and operated by sucking.

c. Cleaning equipment

Fixed automatic cleaning by a scraper blade, drawn the length of the passage by means of an endless circulating chain and under a slatted floor set $\frac{2}{3}$ ft above a sub-floor, is a proprietary mechanism. The slats help to keep the pigs clean, since the dung is pressed between them. The scraper will deposit the dung into a pit at the end of the house or up an artificial ramp into a dung trailer. The ramp should rise 1 : 4 or 1 : 5, at the foot of which a grating should drain the urine. This system can be adapted, for example, by having scraper bars on two endless chains set about 4 ft apart, that is nearly the width of the dung passage, with the bars at 1-ft intervals on the chains. The bars push the dung into prepared gaps in the floor, dropping into a sloping channel under the floor, the gaps being under the dung passage doors. A $\frac{1}{2}$-h.p. motor with reduction gear will clean a 70-ft-long passage and, since the bars move slowly, the pigs need not be harmed (18).

d. Slats

Slatted floors can be formed in several materials, welded wire mesh probably being the cheapest. The mesh should be 3 in. $\times$ $\frac{1}{2}$ in., with 10-gauge wires supported at 1-ft centres, though finishers after reaching 150 lb livewt can be comfortable on 6 in. $\times$ $\frac{3}{4}$ in. with 5 gauge wires supported at $1\frac{1}{2}$-ft centres transversely. Proprietary metal T-bars are available with 1-in. $\times$ 1-in. $\times$ $\frac{3}{16}$-in. sections, $\frac{3}{4}$-in. gaps and supported on cross-members or, alternatively, U-bars in 16-gauge high-tensile non-corrosive steel which slot into dovetailed metal spacers with $\frac{3}{4}$-in. gaps have been developed economically in the U.S. Reinforced-concrete slats can be used with a width of 2–3 in. tapering $\frac{1}{2}$ in. on each side to the bottom, spanning $3\frac{1}{2}$–$4\frac{1}{2}$ ft with a depth of $2\frac{1}{2}$–3 in. Gaps can be formed with hardwood spacers giving openings of $\frac{3}{4}$ or $\frac{7}{8}$ in. for older pigs, but the hardwood spacers must be out of reach of the pigs, though it is better for the slats to be formed into panels with concrete ends.

e. Weighers

Fig. 98 shows how a fixed weigher could be positioned in a central walk-through inspection passage 2 ft wide, when self-feeding or floor feeding is practised. Alternatively, a semicircular weighing room with a rotating swing gate to drive the pigs into a fixed weigher, similar in principle to shearing pen control for sheep, can be used. In an intensive layout, with a high throughput per man, the cost of a weigher would be justified.

7. Environmental control

a. It should be unnecessary to include artificial heat in addition to the natural animal warmth. A U.S. experiment with fatteners on electrically warmed floors in a Danish type piggery, with inputs varying from $5\frac{1}{2}$ to $11\frac{1}{2}$ W/ft^2 of floor area, showed that there were no benefits to be gained (9).

b. Artificial ventilation is essential for an intensive fattening house. The fans should be designed on the basis of the data given in *5d* above, with baffled air inlets to suit the size of fan, as instructed by the manufacturer of the fan chosen. Approximately, the size of inlet might be 6–10 in^2/fattener or a maximum of 4 ft^2/1000 C.F.M., but the shape of the house has some effect on the air flow. It is preferable for the inlets to be equidistant from the fan, and a long narrow house should have several smaller fans rather than one large one (Fig. 99a), even though this will be more expensive. In any case, fans should not be more than 50 ft apart. One fan per 50–60 pigs is usual, positioned in the ridge of the house with the inlets at the sides (Fig. 99b), but sometimes the reverse is practised (Fig. 99c). A general guide for fan sizes for fattening houses can be given (Ref. *j*), though each house should be considered on its own design:

Fan, in.	R.p.m.	Max. C.F.M.	Number of pigs Baconers	Porkers
12	1400	1000	20	25
15	1400	2500	50	60
18	900	2500	50	60
18	1400	3600	72	90
24	700	4500	90	110
24	900	6000	120	150

c. Insulation for the floor of the sleeping area, the walls and the ceiling is essential. Fig. 100 indicates some of the normal methods of insulating these areas.

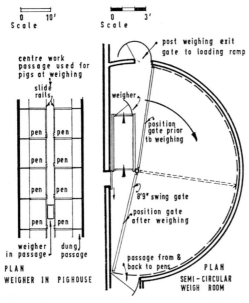

Fig. 98. Weigher position

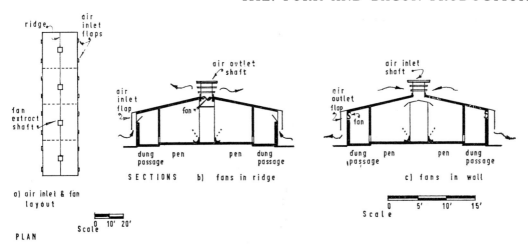

Fig. 99. Artificial ventilation

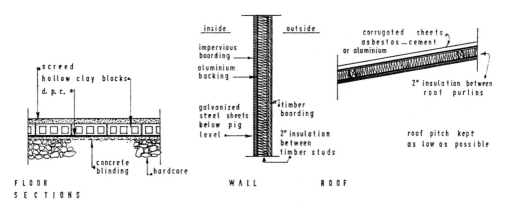

Fig. 100. Some normal methods for insulation

d. Rooflights are not desirable in an insulated roof, though they can be included in an uninsulated roof to a dung passage which is separated from the sleeping area. Otherwise, and in layouts which include the sleeping and dunging areas within one volume, small double-glazed windows to give light to the dunging area are desirable, in order to encourage cleanliness. Electric light, giving permanent low-intensity illumination, which can be increased in intensity at feeding times and for inspection, is desirable, perhaps amounting to one socket per 30–40 pigs. There should be a master control switch in the adjacent food store or draught lobby.

8. *Layout*

a. Though a few circular piggeries exist abroad (10), which can be economical to construct, most fattening houses are multiples of a basic unit forming a long rectangle. The unit usually has a central access and feed passage with a pen on either side, with a dunging passage against the external walls. A few layouts have a central dunging area, with access passages against the external walls. However, so many variations are possible within these two basic layouts that complete classification of all the layouts in common use is impossible. Some of the layouts which are possible are shown in the diagrams:

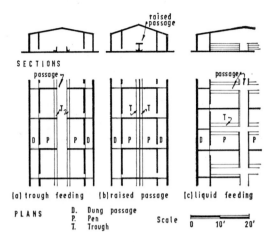

Fig. 101. Pen layout in relation to feeding method

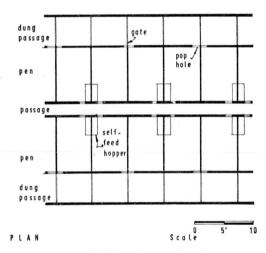

Fig. 102. *Ad lib.* or floor feeding layout

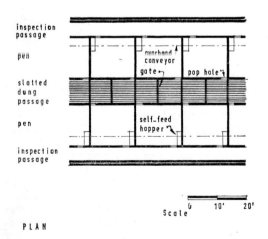

Fig. 103. Central dung passage: *ad lib.* feeding

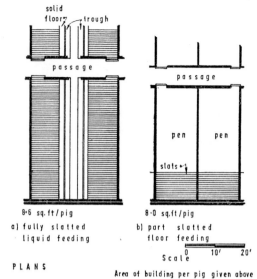

Fig. 104. Slatted pens: 20 pigs/pen

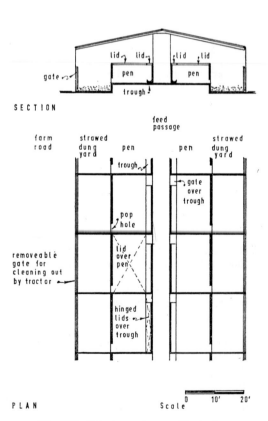

Fig. 105. Solari-type house: 10 pigs/pen

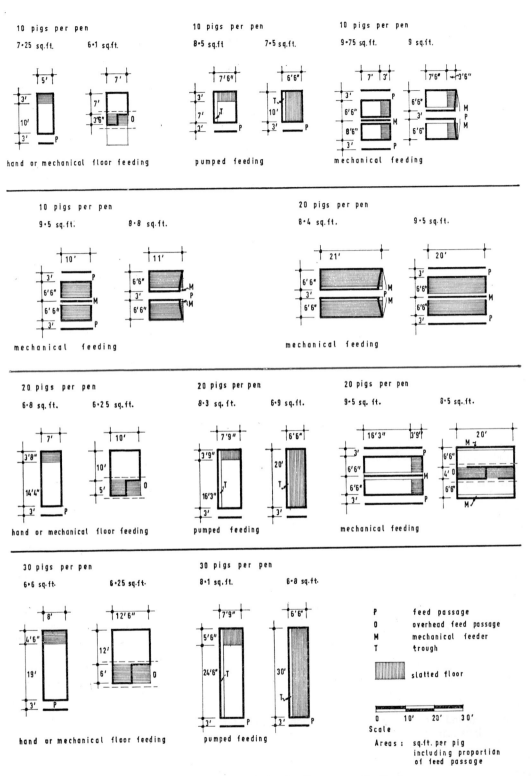

D. Dunging area   S. Sleeping feeding area   P. Feed passage

Fig. 106. Basic plans for pen layouts: based on analysis by D. S. Soutar ARIBA in *Farmbuildings*, Winter 1963/64

i. Fig. 101. With rationed feeding, the shape of the house is governed by the length of trough required. Fig. 101a shows the normal layout, with a central feed passage having troughs parallel to the passage. The passage can be raised above the troughs to reduce the floor area, Fig. 101b. With mechanical feeding the passage can become a walkway 2 ft wide. However, the length of the house can be reduced, which is more economical, by having the mangers at right angles, Fig. 101c, but this is suitable only with liquid feeding, since considerable effort would be required for distributing meal into the troughs.

ii. Fig. 102. *Ad lib.* or floor feeding makes it possible to reduce the width of the central passage to a walkway and to have the pens with their short sides to the walkway. Since no trough space is required, the floor area/pig is reduced, and the squarer plan shape is an additional economy. It is possible that such layouts might be at least 25 per cent cheaper than Fig. 101a.

iii. Fig. 103. The dunging passages can be slatted, which reduces the floor area required. A central dung passage should prove more economical than two dung passages and, with mechanical feeding aids or *ad lib.* feeding, the work routines should not be increased. The slurry pit should be about 3–4 ft deep.

iv. Fig. 104. The slatted dunging passage can be omitted, a slatted area being included within the pen. Alternatively, the complete pen can be slatted, which, coupled to *ad lib.* feeding, can reduce the floor area required to 6–8 ft²/place. This arrangement is suitable particularly for heavy hogs.

v. Fig. 105. Semi-intensive layouts, in which the environment is not fully controlled, can reduce capital costs. The Solari type house is economical and popular in sheltered districts.

vi. Fig. 106. Soutar has shown the complexity of designing standard layouts due to the many types of pen suitable for different management policies common in the North of Scotland, considering pens designed to hold 10, 20 or 30 pigs, with part or completely slatted floors and with different forms of feeding. Pen sizes can vary from about 6 to 9½ ft²/pig.

b. Many proprietary prefabricated timber fattening houses are available, some of which include special features within their design, but the specification and the standard of construction can have important variations. Generally, they should prove to be cheaper to construct than a house built without prefabrication, unless the latter is either a conversion or is built with farm labour. A few two-storey houses exist and they can prove economical, when there is a natural

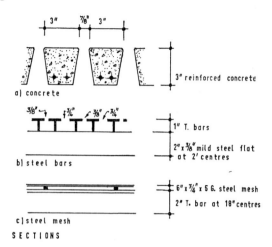

Fig. 107. Slatted floors

access to both floors due to a ground slope along the length of the building. Slats may be either concrete or a steel mesh (Fig. 107) (11).

c. As previously discussed, though pens holding 10 pigs are traditional, larger pens holding up to 35 pigs or more are possible, and larger pens should prove cheaper to erect. It is desirable that the pen size should be related to the size of the intake batch, and the latter should be based on a regular contract. A unit for 800 baconers, which might be managed by one man with part-time help, could have a weekly intake of 50 weaners divided into two pens holding 25 each. This could form a self-contained compartment within the house. The house could be divided to form a growing unit holding the pigs, for 8 wk (i.e. 400 pigs in 8 compartments, plus 3 compartments to act as a rest period, giving a total of 550 pig places), and a finishing unit of 8 compartments plus 4 small pens for any pig not reaching the prescribed weight in 16 wk (i.e. 420 pig places). A central mill/mix unit could supply the feed to a local store to each unit. A total of 970 pig places could have a throughput of 2600 baconers p.a., representing 2·4 baconers/place p.a. (Fig. 108).

9. *Siting*

a. Siting the unit will depend on several factors:

i. Management supervision: an office near the unit is desirable, and the office may be part of the farm, but many units are sited away from permanent supervision.

ii. Mill–mix unit: unless the feed is conveyed automatically to the houses, taking the feed by tractor will not limit the distance of the houses from the mixer.

iii. Dung disposal: unless the dung is drained into

a sewer or a lagoon, it must be returned to the land by spreader, tanker or pipeline, and this may determine the siting.

iv. Access: good roads are required for supplying the unit. If there are several houses there can be an external pig race, 2½ ft wide, linking the houses to a central ramp for despatch on to the lorries.

b. Siting the buildings should allow unrestricted air flow for ventilation and, therefore, the houses should not be in the vicinity of trees and other buildings, but at the same time the site should not be in an exposed situation. It is best for the long axis of the houses to lie N. to S. so that the sun will reach both sides.

c. A dung pit should have a longitudinal fall of 1 : 160 and a dung passage one of 1 : 60. In the latter case the fall may be related to a natural ground slope for economy. A free-draining soil is desirable.

10. *Services.* An electrical supply for lighting and ventilation is essential in all except the most simple layouts. Similarly, pure water is required and, since the drinking bowls cannot be taken off the mains, a header tank is necessary. However, the low building height normal for most piggeries is insufficient for a header tank, which must therefore be placed on external framing, with the resulting problem of insulation against frost, or be sited within a nearby tall building. In some cases the tank can be included within a raised feed store. Rainwater must be taken clear of the building.

11. *Costs.* Costs of proprietary or customer-designed fattening houses normally vary between £8 and £25 per pig place. Simply constructed 'Solari' type houses may cost as little as £8–£10 per place for a unit of 200–300 places. The cheaper 'package-deal' houses with conventional dung passages are often quoted at £10–£13, but normally £14–£16 should be allowed to include for a food store, services and a few extras; allowing up to £18, should the site need more than minimum attention. Units of 800–1000 places should save more than £1 per place, if erected at one time. Non-prefabricated houses, if erected by contract, seldom cost less than £2–£4 per place more than a package-deal house of similar design. These costs do not allow for the rest pens and, therefore, the cost per pig place in use at any one time will be considerably greater. A unit to hold 800 pigs, costing £15 per pig place and having 170 additional places, would cost nearly £18 per operational place. As stated previously, automatic dung-passage cleaning might cost £2 per place, automatic feeding £5 per place, with semi-automatic or mechanical aids for feeding £2–£3 per place. Slatted floors might cost about £⅓/ft² for welded wire mesh to £½/ft² for T-bars or £⅓/ft² for concrete, plus the cost of the dung channel. A unit

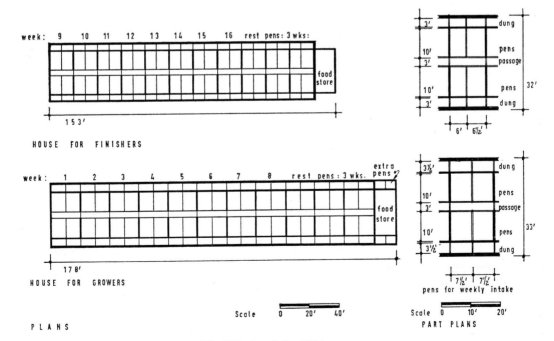

Fig. 108. A unit for 800 baconers

planned with a partly slatted floor, semi-mechanized feeding, labour-saving devices, facilities for weighing, good finishes, access with pig runs and ramp for a lorry may cost £20–£25 per place. However, the cost per pig fattened or per lb livewt gain is more important than the capital cost. The 800-pig unit costing £20 per place would cost £19,400, which, without grant, would equal £2910 p.a., representing on a throughput of 2600 pigs p.a. about 22s. 4d. per baconer. But if the weaners took 18 wk to reach bacon weight, which is not uncommon, the throughput would drop to 2288 pigs p.a., since the weekly intake would be 44 weaners to give a total complement of about 800. Alternatively, a total of 952 places would be required, which, at £20 per place, would cost nearly 25s. per baconer. Therefore capital cost must be related to the throughput, and provision of the best environment to give the maximum throughput is important, in order to use the skill of the pigman to advantage.

12. *References*

(1) THORNTON, D. S. & STEWART, J. D. 'Making the best use of capital resources'. *Pig Farming*, p. 60 (May 1961).
(2) LODGE, G. A. 'Expecting too much from your baconers?' *Pig Farming*, p. 44 (September 1962).
(3) HAYNES, C. 'Bring the pigs to the skim'. *Pig Farming*, p. 32 (December 1962).
(4) *Manual* (see below), p. 19.
(5) Ibid., p. 27.
(6) KELLY, C. F. & BOND, T. E. 'Heat and moisture loss from swine, based on *Jnr. Animal Sc.*, Vol. 8, May 1949, Heitman & Hughes'. *Ag. Eng.* (March 1952).
(7) 'Housing fattening pigs'. *Farmers Weekly Bulletin*, p. xi (18th August 1961).
(8) SOUTAR, D. S. 'Pig housing'. *Scottish Ag.* (Spring 1962).
(9) BARBER, R., BRAUDE, R. & MITCHELL, K. 'The value of electrically warmed floors for fattening pigs'. *J. Agric. Sci.*, pp. 31–6 (June 1955).
(10) *Manual* (see below), p. 35.
(11) SOUTAR, D. S. 'Plan for a piggery'. *Farmers Weekly*, pp. 86–7 (7th February 1962).
(12) SOUTAR, D. S. *Farmbuildings*, p. 23 (Winter 1963/64).
(13) HOPE, H. 'P.I.D.A. primes the research pump'. *Farmers Weekly*, p. v (14th February 1964).
(14) FULLER, M. F. Ref. *i*, p. xvi.
(15) 'Guide to drinkers'. *Pig Farming*, pp. 48–9 (March 1964).
(16) SAINSBURY, D. W. B. 'Site with care'. *Pig Farming*, p. 47 (March 1964).
(17) PHELPS, A. 'Pipeline feeding'. *Pig Farming* (March–April–May 1964).
(18) CHARLTON, R. 'Slats: do pigs like them?' *Farmers Weekly*, p. 79 (13th December 1963).

SELECTED REFERENCES
a. Part of this section is based on articles by the author in *Pig Farming*, April, May and June 1963.
b. AGRICULTURAL RESEARCH COUNCIL. *Bibliography of Farm Building Research*. Part 1. Buildings for Pigs (1945–58) and Supplement (1958–62).
c. *Manual of Modern Pig Housing*. Vitamealo Advisory Service (1962).
d. FISHWICK, V. C., revised HICKS, N. *Pigs: Their Breeding and Management* (1961).
e. 'Housing fattening pigs'. *Farmers Weekly Bulletin* (18th August 1961).
f. MINISTRY OF AGRICULTURE. *Housing of Pigs*. Revised edition (1962).
g. KRAGGERUD, H. *Hus for Gris* (1960).
h. TUITE, P. J. *Specialised Pig Housing*. Dublin Agricultural Institute (1963).
i. 'Pig feeding'. *Farmers Weekly Supplement* (7th February 1964).
j. SAINSBURY, D. W. B. *Pig Housing*. Farming Press (1963).
k. 'Pig Housing and Disease'. *Farmers Weekly* (24th December 1964).

IIIF. Weaners

1. *Activity*

a. There are nearly $\frac{3}{4}$ M sows and gilts in England and Wales used for breeding. The rearing of weaners is essential for pork and bacon production (IIIE) and either may be organized as part of a fattening enterprise, the weaners being reared and fattened on one farm, or after weaning the piglets may be sold for others to fatten. In the latter case it used to be general practice for the piglets to be sold in the market. In recent years, however, there has been a growing practice for piglets to be reared by producers under contract to supply a fixed number of weaners at standard times and of standard breed and quality to trade buyers or to specialized fattening units.

In the past there has been a tendency for pig production to be haphazard, litters being born at random times for an unplanned market. It is probable that within a few years pig production will be as planned and as intensive as poultry and that most weaners will be reared under contract by specialist producers to a prescribed specification. Therefore, in planning a weaner enterprise, it is essential that litters are produced to a schedule suiting a fattening unit, either on the same or on another farm. This is discussed below. The economics of intensive pig production are such that fattening houses must be kept full all the year round except for the rest pens (IIIE 2a, p. 206). This factor is important in the design of a weaner house. Some of the weaners will not be fattened, being required as boars or gilts to form replacements for the breeding herds.

b. Though there are several main breeds of pig, such as Large Whites and Landrace, each with particular attributes for fattening to different weights and carcass quality, genetic selection is an essential part of pig production. In large pig breeding herds the organization of breeding records and litter statistics is one of the most critical tasks, the records office requiring modern equipment for this purpose. There are great variations both in breeding performance and in managerial ability. Future genetic selection may be aided by the use of computers (1).

c. A design for a breeding unit must include for a number of different functions, the most important including:

i. Farrowing—the mother usually coming into her quarters a few days before farrowing.

ii. Weaning—the mother and her litter are kept together until after weaning, possibly within the same area as farrowing.

iii. Dry sows—these must be quartered and usually require individual feeding, particularly during the time before farrowing. Individual attention for the dry sow is now generally recognized as being of great importance.

iv. Boars—housing with a service pen is essential for a breeding herd except in the few cases (36,500) where A.I. is accepted (2).

v. Food storage and mixing.

d. Mortality is one of the most serious aspects of poor management, $2\frac{1}{2}$ M piglets dying each year. Most losses occur during the 48 hours after farrowing, but a total of at least 20 per cent of piglets die before fattening begins. A dead weaner represents a loss of about £6. Therefore, the national loss due to infant mortality represents about £15 M, though losses have been put as high as 26 per cent before 8 wks of age, 16 per cent being within the first wk (3). Losses usually are due to three factors:

i. Many litters include a runt or weakling which, with large litters, may be unavoidable.

ii. After birth many piglets are crushed by the sow. This can be avoided in most cases by a good farrowing crate and correct management.

iii. Disease, due to poor housing, malnutrition or bad management should not occur, but frequently does.

Mortality losses should not exceed 10 per cent, and with some good producers is considerably less. Certain producers rear minimal disease pigs, in which the litter is removed from the sow two days before she is due to give birth. The sow is used for meat. The operation is expensive, the piglets have to be reared artificially and skilled labour is required, but the pigs may reach bacon weight within 150 days and with 15 per cent less food being required compared with natural birth and weaning (4). These litters

should be free from virus pneumonia, but even so, mortality may be 12–14 per cent.

2. *Managerial requirements*

a. Number and Size of Litters

The economics of a breeding herd will depend both on the number and the size of the litters produced by each sow in the year. The average number of litters per sow is $1\frac{3}{4}$ p.a., some 10 per cent of herds failing to have more than 3 litters in 2 years ($1\frac{1}{2}$ litters p.a.), though 25 per cent have nearly 2 litters p.a. (5). The aim should be to have at least 2 litters/sow p.a.—with advanced breeders, having good housing and practising early weaning, even obtaining $2\frac{1}{2}$ litters. Obviously, if sows farrow every 160 rather than every 210 days the number of litters a year will affect the layout of a breeding unit as well as decrease the unit cost of rearing.

The size of a litter is equally important, and this can be expressed both as the number of piglets and as the livewt per litter. The average number of live piglets is less than 10/litter, with less than $\frac{1}{3}$ of the herds having more than 11, but the aim should be to have at least 12/litter. A few sows have had litters with about 2 dozen piglets. Nationally, only about 17 weaners/sow p.a. are born, whereas a good producer will aim for about 25, an increase of nearly 50 per cent above the average. In the latter case rearing houses could cost considerably more than those for the average producer yet give a greater profit. This is discussed below.

The livewt/litter, coupled with the rate of growth after birth, is a better economic valuation than litter numbers. Livewt varies partly with the number born per litter, taking into account that a large litter may have smaller piglets than those within a small litter, but particularly due to sows' breeding ability and to the care and feeding policy during gestation. Good feeding in a comfortable environment may increase the weight of the piglet at birth from $3\frac{1}{2}$ to 5 lb. This difference can become 20 lb at 8 wks (IIIE 1*a*, p. 205).

Thus, the total livewt at birth of piglets/sow p.a. can have wide variations, perhaps from an average of 60 lb to a desirable minimum of 100 lb.

b. Weaning

With natural weaning, the piglets should reach about 45 lb within 7–8 wks, though if born lighter than 3 lb and with a low plane of nutrition may weigh less than 35 lb. With early weaning, usually at about 3 wks of age (18–24 days), the sow is removed and the piglets remain in their quarters, being about 12–15 lb in wt. Early weaned piglets may enter the fattening units at 6 rather than at 8 wks and they may reach bacon wt 3 wks sooner. Thus early weaning may give an increased throughput in the rearing and fattening units, but hygiene is more critical.

c. Size of Farrowing Unit

Obviously, the number of farrowing places will depend on the number of sows in the herd. However, since good farrowing accommodation may cost £120–£220/place, it is important to use each place as much as possible. The sow should have up to a wk in the house before farrowing: weaning takes 8 wks and the pen should be rested for sterilization for 3 wks. Thus, throughput should be planned so that each pen is used 4 times a year. On this basis a pen costing £120/place or £220/place would represent £4½/litter or £8¼/litter respectively, perhaps, with good litters, the latter being equal to a max of £⅗/piglet or 3s./lb livewt at birth. Planning on a 3-month schedule can have exceptions:

i. Semi-intensive rearing (see below)—the pens may be used only for 4 wks at a time, thus they could be re-used 7–8 times p.a.

ii. Early weaning—the pens can be re-used every 7–8 wks.

iii. Pre-farrowing—a few producers house their sows in their farrowing pens, where they can be fed individually, for all or nearly all of the gestation period of 16 wks. The advantages can be a reduction in the food required by the sow, easier farrowing and an increase in the livewt of the piglets at birth. On this basis the throughput would be reduced to about 2–2½ litters/place p.a., though no separate pre-farrowing individual-feeders are required.

It is not always possible to plan farrowing with the precision indicated above. There are natural causes which can upset the planned routine. At least 10 per cent, or even 20 per cent, extra farrowing places should be provided above the theoretical minimum. In any case, the farrowing programme must be planned to suit the fattening house for which the weaners are intended. The latter may be planned to take a batch of weaners every wk, 3 wks or 18 wks, for example (IIIE 2e, p. 207). On many farms farrowing pens may be used only once, or at most twice, a year. In the latter case the capital expenditure could be only £60/litter or £110/litter to give costs/litter equal to the example discussed above. An expenditure of £60/place could not give a suitable standard of insulation, fittings and finishes, and the food-conversion ratio and livewt/litter would be less efficient. In fact, it might prove to be undesirable accommodation. Thus, it is important for farrowing dates to be planned to keep the farrowing house almost full all the time, except for sterilization periods, rather than for farrowing to be concentrated into short periods once or twice a year.

d. Birth Weights and Liveweight Gain

Reference has been made above to the importance in the piglets having a good wt at birth. Many piglets weigh less than the desired minimum of 3½ lb (on average about 2½ lb), and their chance of survival is reduced and the time taken to reach bacon wt. is increased the lighter they are born (6). Normal livewt increase should be about ½ lb/day until weaning (*see* table at foot of page.)

e. Feeding Policies

Feeding is a complex subject, and the three stages can be only briefly discussed:

i. Maiden gilts: mated at about 8 months when weighing 250–280 lb, with 6 lb feed/day when 200 lb in wt to 7 lb/day at service—approximately 6 cwt over nearly 4 months. However, many gilts are grazed with little if any supplementary feed.

ii. Gestation period: about 5 lb/day for 3 months (gilts—6 lb/day), increased to 7 lb/day during last month—approximately 5½ cwt. Though individual feeding has proved desirable, in many cases in-pig sows are grazed during the first months.

iii. Suckling: about 5 lb/day plus ¾ lb/piglet suckled—approximately up to 7 cwt. Piglets should start creep feeding at 10–14 days.

f. Hygiene

As previously mentioned, a high standard of hygiene is essential if the litter is to thrive. Though good management is the basis of hygiene, much depends on the design of the building. The provision of smooth internal surfaces, which can be sterilized easily, is an obvious advantage. However, many buildings are designed where the internal walls are not rendered. This is an economy. It is impossible to prove the degree of disease risk incurred. In some cases a compromise is made in that a render dado to about 3–4 ft from the floor is allowed. Not only is it important to stress that, though cheap construction may not cause disease, economy may be regretted, but also that all should be done to assist the pigman in the supervision of farming and in keeping the building clean.

Birth wt, lb	1–1½	1½–2	2–2½	2½–3	3–3½	3½–4	4
Alive at 8 wks, %	35	42	62	85	90	90	95
Av. wt at 8 wks, lb	28	31	36	38	40	43	48
Av. age at 200 lb, wks	34	32	30	28	26	23	21

3. *Production techniques*

The type of accommodation, the feeding and management policy before, during, and after farrowing, and the degree of supervision—in fact, the technique of producing weaners—are not only complex but are also confused by conflicting opinions. The correct management of farrowing sows is, to some extent, a personal problem, and certainly depends on the skill of the pigman. It is, perhaps, less easy than in any other enterprise to define the different techniques practised.

a. Indoor or outdoor farrowing

Outdoor farrowing can prove successful, particularly in the milder parts of the country. It is probably the cheapest method of housing, using simple portable timber arks, and, therefore, is favoured by some producers when the climate is mild. It is suitable principally for the smaller producer. A well-insulated ark can provide satisfactory accommodation which can easily be coupled to fold runs in a field. In severe weather the arks may be placed on concrete, sheltered by the farmstead or by trees, or they may even be placed inside a barn. Supplementary heat can be provided if an electrical supply is available. The advantage of outdoor farrowing is that it simulates natural conditions, the piglets being able to take advantage of sunlight and of trace elements in the ground.

In some ark systems the piglets only have contact with ground uncontaminated by the sow. It is claimed that the piglets prove hardier than those reared indoors. Moreover, the system is flexible to suit changes in the herd numbers or in farrowing dates. The main disadvantages, other than the climate, are that each farrowing requires clean ground, thus ark and fold must be moved, and that the labour required can prove excessive, especially if the herd is large with frequent farrowings. Not only does food and water have to be provided, though the latter can be piped, each day, and usually at least twice a day, but the inspection of the sow and, eventually, of the litter is made more troublesome and the possibility of emergency assistance at the right moment more remote. Expert management in bad weather is less easy than with indoor farrowing, and the pigman should keep the sow under frequent supervision during the farrowing period. Nevertheless, in general, chronic or fatal illness is more common with indoor than with outdoor farrowing. But this is a reflection more on the quality of most indoor accommodation and management than on the merits of the different systems. In fact, indoor farrowing is becoming accepted as the better system, since it reduces the work requirement and permits greater control.

b. Dry Sows

The sow is a valuable animal whether she is farrowing and nursing a litter or whether she is pregnant. Since the sow should be served within a week of weaning and has a gestation period of about 115 days, varying with breed, but does not enter her farrowing quarters normally until a few days before giving birth, she has a long period when alternative accommodation has to be provided. In fact, the annual cycle can be based on at least two litters a year:

Nursing period to weaning:	8 wks
Between weaning and stocking:	1 wk
Gestation period:	16–17 wks
	————
	25–26 wks

Thus, sows may have some 36 wks p.a. dry or in-pig when they can be kept successfully out of doors in a field or fold, though they should be kept in small batches of not more than about 10 or 12. Moreover, it is preferable that each batch should contain sows at the same stage of gestation. Keeping in-pig sows out of doors, naturally, depends on the climate. As observed above, some in-pig sows farrow in the same pen used for gestation. In mild districts the sows may be kept in the folds at any time of year, except when farrowing, perhaps with some form of rough shelter. But out-wintering or even external folding at any time of the year has disadvantages, and the value of individual attention for sows at all times is beginning to be widely recognized, though not by all farmers (7). There are several advantages:

i. Accurate feeding of the sow is essential for healthy and regular litters since, though the rations are relatively small, a balanced diet is vital with feeding twice a day. Therefore, individual feeding stalls are desirable. Communal feeding leads to unbalanced rations for each sow. The pigman should observe the sows feeding, since lack of appetite is an indication of ill-health, and individual feeders makes observation easier.

ii. Warmth and comfort are important factors for the health of the in-pig sow. Though completely enclosed housing is not essential, decent shelters and yards are desirable.

iii. Except in dry conditions, folded sows can lead to poaching of the fields, which is both bad for the pasture and for the sow. Cleanliness is desirable for healthy stock. Thus, concreted yards with straw may be preferable, especially if an adjoining paddock can be made available when the weather is fine.

iv. Individual attention is easier in proper yards near the farmstead than in outlying fields, and the economy in labour and feed can prove to be valuable.

v. After serving and prior to farrowing, rations for the sow may be increased and, again, individual feeders with the sows grouped into small batches makes this easy.

The advantage of outdoor folds in mild weather and on well-drained pasture is that the sows eat less meal, grazing may suit a ley pasture in an arable rotation on a farm and accommodation is cheap. However, the disadvantages may well outweigh the advantages in most management systems. In contrast, at least one producer has experimented with sows housed individually in small pens, each with a semi-automatic feeder (8). In this case, since acreage was limited, restricted housing was valuable, but though the long-term effect has not been established, it appears that individual attention, accurate feeding, higher fecundity index, stronger piglets and easier management are better or more easily obtained. This is a reversal of normal management, where intensive systems are not considered necessary or desirable for in-pig sows. Most producers consider exercise vital during this period. More research is required concerning the best management system and type of building for the period of gestation.

c. The Boar

As stated above, 1*b*, iv, most breeding herds require accommodation for a boar. The health and genetic pattern of the boar is important for the success of the breeding policy, though feeding and housing requirements can be simple. A mixture of green food and of in-sow rations and exercise are the normal basic needs. A paddock with a hut and run is adequate, but normally a pen and yard near the sow accommodation is easier for management, with provisions made for the boar to see out. There should be ease of access to the boar from the dry-sow pens. Generally herds of more than 30 sows will need 2 boars. The boar, like the sow, should be recorded for performance, and his health will depend on hygienic surroundings as well as on rations (9).

d. Farrowing: Pen or Crate

The difference of policy between outdoor and indoor farrowing is discussed above, 3*a*. However, even with indoor farrowing there are important differences in practice. It is not desirable to move a sow just before farrowing, and she should be in her farrowing area several days earlier, perhaps as much as 1 wk. Not all producers agree that the pigman should be present during farrowing, unless difficulties are expected, since the sow can be made restive. Certainly no one except an expert pigman should be present (10). Close-circuit television may be the best system, especially for night farrowing. The main difference in farrowing layouts indoors is between a farrowing pen or crate or

crate pen. In some cases producers allow the sow to farrow in a pen with no more than creep rails so that the piglets can move into a safe area after birth. The crushing of piglets by their sows is a common cause of mortality during the period after birth. Some of the rails may be removed so that the sow and litter can remain for the full period of weaning in the same pen. A safer system is to include a crate, as well as the creep rails, which can be used for farrowing and removed after a few days. Weaning can be within the pen with the crate removed. However, alternatively, special farrowing crates can be designed in which the sow and litter remain for only 3–10 days and are then moved into a special weaning pen or sometimes into external huts with runs. External weaning in mild areas may be favoured even on large, intensive farms (11). Generally, moving sows and litter into special weaning quarters is preferred for the large, specialized producer and removing the crate for the smaller unit.

Another difference in management is that some farmers allow the sow to move in and out of the crate at will, while others keep her movement restricted or even restrict movement completely for about 3 wks. The latter method requires expert management to detect any loss of health in the sow, otherwise the choice is mainly one of personal preference (12). More important is the need to keep the construction of the farrowing quarters simple, since complexity may make the sow restive (12). Any form of communal dunging area should be avoided, and hygiene is essential. After farrowing or weaning the quarters should be sterilized before being re-used.

e. Gilts

Some of the litters will be kept as herd replacements, either as gilts or as future boars. The selection of breeding stock is a skilled job, and depends on accurate records being kept. Some producers may buy their replacements, others raise their own or raise extra breeding stock for sale. Gilts may be served at 8 months of age, though some may be as much as a year old. Some producers allow the boar to be in the gilt pen. Since the gilt should not become fat, care is required in feeding, particularly the older she becomes, and her growth rate should be rapid but steady. Rationing of feed should take place at about 100 lb livewt. Thus, gilts may have to be housed for 6 or more months after weaning. They should be penned separately from the sows. However, their accommodation requirements are similar; either external, partly covered or internal housing being practical, though there may be less emphasis on individual feeding, except, perhaps, during the last weeks before being served.

f. Pedigree Herds

As with all livestock breeding enterprises, some

85: GILT HOUSE AND YARD
T. Wall & Son Ltd., Experimental Farm, Tring, Herts.

Four houses and yards each hold 50 pigs. The houses are coupled as two pairs, each pair having access to a feed area including 25 individual feeders so that feeding is in two batches. Gilts in the first two yards have access to pasture, one group being for gilts after service to 5 days before farrowing and the other for those having left the fattening house by a fortnight to reaching 200 lb weight. The third yard holds a group of gilts during the first fortnight after leaving the fattening house and the fourth yard gilts from 200 lb onwards. The latter have access to pasture near the boar pens to aid detection for their service date. Dividing the gilts into groups prevents fighting, and feeding is simple, each group having one type of ration. The houses are of open-fronted monopitch construction and the yards can be cleaned by tractor. [SEE PAGE 226] Courtesy of Pig Farming.

86: SOW YARDS
Mr. S. Chapman, Blois Hall Farm, Ripon, Yorks.

After being served, sows are housed in groups of six. Indoor farrowing pens on the left are combined with external, strawed dunging yards. At the right the yards are coupled to individual feeding crates. The tubular gates to the yards can be removed and the straw and dung cleaned out by tractor. [SEE PAGE 226] Courtesy of Pig Farming.

87: SHEEP SHED

The Farmers Weekly, Cowbyers, Northumberland

A lean-to timber-framed sheep shed for 150 ewe hoggs was erected in 1962 with concrete block walls to 3 ft above floor level and with timber ventilation slats above. The floor is of 2-in. tapered timber slats, with $\frac{5}{8}$-in. spaces, laid parallel to the entrance doors and formed in panels on bearers. The panels are supported by 8-in. × 4-in. timber beams at about 4-ft centres, resting on concrete block piers in a dung pit about 3 ft deep. The panels, beams and piers can be removed for cleaning when the doors at the far end are opened. Due to a site fall, the sheep can enter the house at ground level at the near end. [SEE PAGE 237] Courtesy of the Farmers Weekly.

88: SHEEP SHED

Invercauld Estate, Braemar, Aberdeenshire

The timber-framed and clad building, made from estate timber, is 120 ft long × 20 ft span, with a food store 30 ft long at one end, and is used to winter house 200–220 hoggs in four pens. The pens are 7 ft wide on either side of a central feed passage-cum-manger $2\frac{3}{4}$ ft wide. Timber slats, $2\frac{1}{2}$ in. wide × $1\frac{1}{4}$ in. deep with $\frac{5}{8}$-in. gaps, are made in 6-ft × 7-ft panels which can be raised for cleaning out by tractor through doors at the end of the building. Water troughs are between the pens. The house is ventilated with baffled wall air inlets and ridge ventilators. [SEE PAGE 237] Courtesy of the Farmers Weekly.

89: SHEEP YARD

Mr. C. G. Hitchcock, Ringshall, Nr. Stowmarket, Suffolk

A slatted sheep yard, 187 ft × 32 ft, holds 400 ewes from the autumn until lambing begins in spring. The slatted floor is formed in 8-ft squares, with 3-in. × 1-in.-deep slats and with ¾-in. gaps, 2½ ft above ground level. The slat sections can be removed for cleaning out by foreloader in the spring. Along the four sides to the yard there is a ¾-ft-deep × 1-ft-wide feeding trough, fitted with a chain conveyor, similar to a cowshed dung-scraper. The conveyor feeds the sheep automatically with haylage from tower silos, also used for a dairy unit. Wind breaks are formed by the side of an existing building and by low walls of straw bales. [SEE PAGES 238 & 239] Courtesy of Pauls Foods Ltd.

90: TRADITIONAL WINTER SHEEPYARD

Though sheep may be outwintered, in some parts they may be housed during the winter in unspecialized courts or yards with various types of partially enclosed shelters around them. Traditional buildings and farm yards can be easily converted for this purpose. Straw for bedding may be required in considerable quantities, and it may be difficult to mechanize the feeding arrangements. The more enclosed buildings may be difficult to ventilate. [SEE PAGE 235] Courtesy of Farmer and Stockbreeder.

91: INTENSIVE BREEDING HOUSE FRAME

School of Veterinary Medicine, Cambridge

A timber frame with 4-in. × 2-in. studs and cill plate mounted on a dwarf concrete wall and with 6-in. × 2-in. rafters is lined externally for the walls and roof with plywood. The panels are lined with building paper as a damp-proof membrane. On the left are flaps under the eaves to form air-inlet panels. Between the studs insulation is formed with mineral-wool quilts wrapped in polythene, which acts as a vapour seal. Internal surfaces are then lined. [SEE PAGE 242] Courtesy of Dr. Sainsbury.

92: INTENSIVE BREEDING HOUSE: INTERIOR

School of Veterinary Medicine, Cambridge

Plywood sheets with cover strips line the internal wall and ceiling surfaces of the timber-framed house. Smooth internal surfaces are essential for good hygiene and good ventilation. The double doors are insulated. The air-inlet flaps at the eaves are shown on the right. The floor includes a damp-proof membrane and insulation. [SEE PAGE 242] Courtesy of Dr. Sainsbury.

herds may be pedigree and some commercial. There will be differences in approach to housing requirements for the herd between the farmers concerned. Owners of pedigree herds are likely to be exceptionally particular, though in fact all successful production depends on expert management and attention to hygiene. Moreover, even a commercial breeder should record the genetic differences and growth rates as much as for a pedigree herd.

4. Work routines

The work required in producing weaners cannot be skimped, nor can it be completely mechanized. Attention to detail is essential, as has been stressed in the discussion of management and production above. It is difficult to summarize the work pattern: much depends on management policy and housing layout, and the attention which should be given to a farrowing sow and to a litter prior to weaning is technical. However, certain principles or detail can be given which affect or control design.

a. Feeding

Rations vary at the different stages of a sow's cycle as a gilt, during gestation and farrowing, while nursing the litter and after weaning. Moreover, rations may vary within each stage. Though the sows in a herd may be planned to farrow more or less at the same time, especially with outdoor-management policies, so that their rations may be uniform at any particular time, this is unlikely to occur in practice. Moreover, in order both to use the farrowing accommodation to the maximum advantage and to keep a steady throughput in the fattening unit, farrowing should be planned to occur, with a large herd, at regular intervals throughout the year. Thus, many different types of ration will have to be prepared each day. The feed room is an essential part of a layout, and the preparation of rations and the sterilization of feeding or mixing equipment an essential part of a pigman's day. The work in feeding a sow can take up to 5 min/sow/day, especially with feeding twice a day. In practice, some sows may take longer to feed, especially if they are out of phase with the others in their requirements. Rations may have to be handled in individual buckets which can be tipped into the mangers. However, since usually sows' requirements will be in groups, some standardization and bulk handling may be possible, though the rations should be weighed before being placed in the mangers. In fact, it is possible to convey feed mechanically in a dry sow house, provided different weights of ration can be fed to each sow. Of course, if individual feeders are not used, then such care will not be necessary. The weaners will be fed a special ration, given to them in the creep area, and the amount given depends on their age.

b. Cleaning

Yarded sows may be housed on straw and have strawed or concreted exercise yards. Yards should be planned so that, with gate control, the sows can be penned in their shelters while the yards are cleaned out at intervals by tractor and scraper. Likewise, empty shelters, after a batch have been moved, should be cleaned. In most layouts this will be probably by fork into the yarded section where mechanical cleaning is possible. Between batches, shelters, yards and feeders should be sterilized. Folded sows should be accommodated on sterile ground, old ground not being re-used, preferably for several seasons or at least for one year. Particular care must be taken to sterilize farrowing and weaning accommodation after use. Short straw may be used for bedding both for the sow and for the weaners, but an insulated floor may be both sufficient for the former and more hygienic, especially if movement is restricted in a crate. Not much cleaning is practical during farrowing and weaning, though individual attention will be required to clear any particular mess and to keep passages clean. The risk of cross-infection should be avoided. Much cleaning and sterilization will be manual, methods being similar to those for fattening houses (IIIE 2b, p. 206).

c. Recording

Full records must be kept in a central office, and record cards should be placed near each sow and litter. Recording must not be skimped, and adequate time must be allowed for it, perhaps with a herd of 30–50 sows as much as 1 hr/day. With a large herd of several hundred sows the manager's job may be largely one of recording, and he will require clerical help. Records must be kept of each sow and her dates of service, farrowing and weaning, as well as of her litters and of her rations. In addition, the weight of the litter at birth and at weaning is required. In fact, it may be preferable to wean by weight and not by age, for example when the litter has reached an average wt of 30 lb and each piglet is eating a minimum of 1 lb/day of the creep food (12). Thus, the weight of the litter is an important part of the records. Marketing weaners may take considerable time, but this can be reduced by contract sales.

d. Veterinary Attention

The sow needs constant observation before, during and after farrowing, and may need veterinary attention. The piglets will have to be injected, castrated and looked after with care. Sows need attention so that they are served at the right time. The design of accommodation must allow for ease

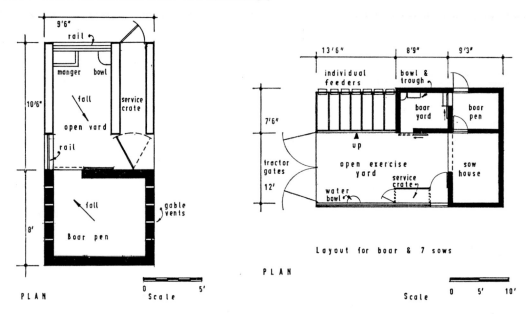

Fig. 109. Boar housing

of veterinary work and of attention. Close-circuit television is a useful aid to management, particularly during farrowing. The creep should be planned for ease of access, though some layouts place the creep away from the pigman's passage so that he has to go into the pen for his inspection.

e. Crates and Arks

Crates, when used for farrowing, have to be placed before the sow comes to the house, and normally have to be removed a few days after the litter is born. With a layout using arks, moving the folds and arks can be a lengthy job if the fields are not satisfactory in their arrangement.

f. Moving Pigs

In a weaner enterprise handling is an important part of the work routine. Naturally, great care is required, especially in moving pregnant sows and young weaners. The main times for care are when moving a sow into her farrowing quarter, moving sow and litter from a farrowing pen into a weaning pen, unless a movable crate is used, and moving the weaned pigs into a grower house. Movement can be made safer and easier with care in detailing both the buildings and the circulation routes between building.

5. Design data

Since much of the design data in this section depends on particular management policies and building layouts, some detail normally given in sub-section 8 will be given here.

a. The Boar (Fig. 109)

Accommodation for the boar should be generous rather than restricted in area, with at least 40 ft² of covered housing and 80 ft² of concreted exercise yard, though any grass fold provided should be in addition to these areas. An internal dimension of 8 ft × 6 ft for the house is satisfactory, with a yard of 8 ft × 12 ft including a built-in service crate and trough, though both the latter and the water bowl are better within the house away from the bed. The house should be about 5½–6 ft high, and yard walling should be 4½ ft high, though part of the walling should be reduced to 3¼ ft with rails over, so that the boar can see into the sow yard. Alternatively, the boar yard can open into a small yard for 5–10 sows. A sow yard to hold 5 sows should have a house of 50–60 ft² and an exercise yard of about 200 ft², including a service crate plus space for individual feeders of 75 ft².

b. Dry Sows and Gilts (Fig. 110)

Each sow or gilt should have 40–50 ft² of concreted exercise area or, if they are folded on grass, perhaps 150–300 ft², depending on the state of the pasture, the soil and the frequency with which the fold is moved. Seldom should more than 10–12 sows or gilts be yarded or folded together. Walls between yards should be 4½ ft high and electric fences for folds 10–19 in. high. In addition to the yard, it is preferable for the sows or gilts to have a house allowing 8–10 ft² each. The floor, walls and roof of the house should be insulated, though usually some daylight is included. Access into the

226

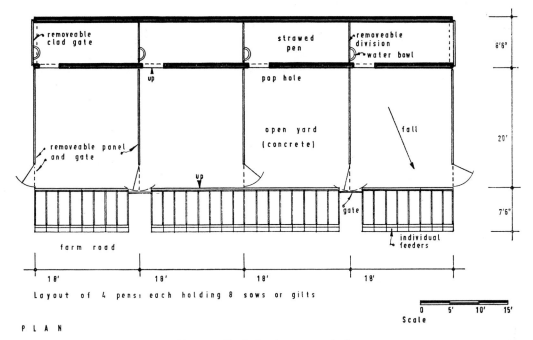

Fig. 110. Yards for dry sows and gilts

house for the pigs should be restricted to an opening of about $3\frac{1}{2}$ ft $\times$ $4\frac{1}{2}$ ft high. Some bedded areas are open fronted into the yard, forming a shelter instead of a house. In such cases, for preference, the roof should have a big overhang. The yards should be divided by gates $4\frac{1}{2}$ ft high and usually sheeted to prevent contact between yards. Similarly, it is best for there to be sheeted gates between each house so that it is possible to clean out mechanically. Straw may be used for bedding, even in addition to an insulated floor.

Each sow, or gilt, should have an individual feeder, with access from the yard requiring about $7\frac{1}{2}$ ft $\times$ 2 ft, see 6, below. The yard floor should drain into a channel, also collecting drainage from the floor of the feeders, and connecting to a foul-drain gulley positioned external to the layout. If the open yards are strawed the feeders should be raised on a concrete step about $\frac{1}{2}$ ft above the yard level. Water bowls should be placed for warmth within the house. Access will be required around at least 3 sides of the layout.

c. Straw Storage
Dry sows, gilts and boars, and usually weaners, require straw for bedding. Straw requirements are not standard, the allowance being dictated partly by the amount available and partly by comfort and cleanliness. An allowance of $\frac{1}{4}$–1 bale per sow or gilt or sow and litter each week might be given. The straw store should be near the layouts requiring bedding, but, unless it is adjacent, the bales

should be conveyed by tractor. However, manual spreading of the bedding will be essential.

d. Sow Stalls (Fig. 111)
Instead of communal yards and houses, in-pig sows may be kept in individual stalls within an insulated house. Each stall, water bowl and manger requires 8 ft $\times$ $2\frac{1}{2}$ ft with division walls 2 in. thick and $3\frac{3}{4}$ ft high of reinforced concrete, otherwise rendered 4-in. block walls are required. To prevent the sow climbing above the wall, rails are required across the top of it to form a cage. The front of the stall includes water bowl, manger and hopper, and the rear has a vertically sliding gate control. The floor of the stall should be insulated and should have a fall of 4 in. to drain into a channel beyond the rear gate. Alternatively, the rear third of the stall can be slatted above a slurry channel.

The house should have a central feed passage with the mangers and stalls on each side of it and an access passage $3\frac{1}{2}$ ft wide at the sides of the building providing access for the sows to reach their stalls. It is possible to reverse the layout and to have a central dung passage, which can have a mechanical scraper, and side feed passages. However, generally, it is considered best for the rows of pigs to face inwards. The feed passage should be $3\frac{1}{2}$ ft wide if the pigman has to use a feed trolley. But feeding can be partly mechanized, since the type of feed, if not the quantity to each sow, can be standardized. A chain-and-flight conveyor from

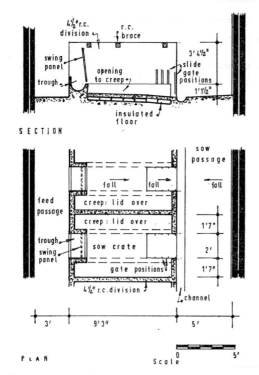

Fig. 111. Sow stalls: based on work by the North of Scotland College of Agriculture

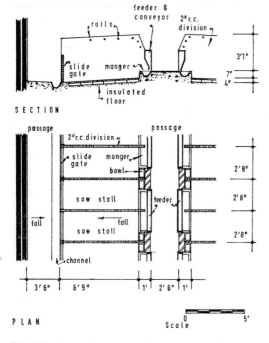

Fig. 112. Farrowing crate: based on work by the North of Scotland College of Agriculture

the food mix room can connect to a hopper above each manger, fitted with a ratchet release and operated from the centre passage, which in this case, need be only 2½ ft wide (8). Thus, each sow needs a total of about 34 ft² of space in the house.

e. Farrowing (Fig. 112)

A sow only needs about 7 ft × 2 ft in which to farrow, provided there is additional space for the weaners after birth. In fact, it is better that space for the sow should be restricted so that she cannot turn or move to crush her litter. Thus, an open pen for the sow in which she is not restricted, though cheaper, can lead to increased mortality. Portable farrowing crates are available, see 6*b*, below. However, a permanent sow crate with adjoining creep areas is desirable and justified for a large herd with staggered farrowing dates. The crate is not unlike that for in-pig sows, but has an overall dimension of 9¼ ft × 2 ft with a trough and water bowl in front and vertical gate control at the rear. It should be possible to place the latter in three or four positions, depending on the length of the sow, so that it is from 6¼ to 7 ft from the manger. There should be an additional ¾ ft, giving a max overall length of 7¾ from the manger, so that piglets can move behind the sow, to the back position of the crate. The insulated floor of the manger should have a profile, falling 1½ in./6 ft from the manger, then 3 in. into a channel beyond the line of the crate. The side walls should be open for 10 in. from the floor, to give access for the piglets into the creep areas, and have an overall ht of about 4¼ ft.

f. The Creep (Fig. 112)

The piglets should have a safe area to lie on each side of the sow, known as the creep and where they cannot be crushed by the sow, and a safe area to move from one creep to the other behind the sow. The creep should be designed as a nest about 1¼ ft wide and for the full length of the farrowing position. The floor should be insulated and be bedded with straw, and the creep should be heated with an infra-red lamp. The creep should be about 3–3½ ft high and have a hinged lid to give ease of access for inspection. Alternatively, an unheated creep can be only 1¼ ft high, but this is not as satisfactory as one with artificial heat. Access to the sow should be restricted in ht to 10 in. Creep walks are included in some farrowing pens with a rail set 10 in. above the floor and 10 in. out from the walls. Some layouts have creeps in different forms, such as the circular creep in the Ruakura farrowing ring, see 6*b*, below.

g. Weaning Pens (Fig. 113)

If the sow and litter are moved from a permanent farrowing crate to a weaning pen the latter should

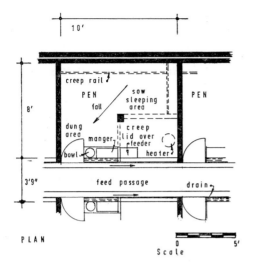

Fig. 113. Weaning pens

measure 10 ft × 8 ft with a creep area 5 ft × 3 ft, a trough and bowl for the sow, and with the main floor area for the sow divided into a bedded and a dunging area. The creep should include a lamp and a self-feed hopper.

h. Work Passages

Most layouts for intensive farrowing or in-pig sow quarters will include pens on crates on either side of a central work passage. The latter may be 2½ ft wide in some cases, but more normally will be 3½ ft. Passages for handling sows into crates or pens should be 3½ ft wide.

i. Food Storage

Food processing and storage may be combined with that for other enterprises, especially for a pig-fattening unit. The amount of storage required is not easy to establish. An in-pig, sow on grass, may need only about 2–4 lb/day of meal, but one kept indoors may need 4–8 lb/day of meal plus 4–6 lb/day of green food. Thus, storage for meal would amount to, perhaps, 6–8 cwt per period of gestation, but it is more probable that the meal would be mixed or bought at more frequent intervals. The sow, after farrowing and being fed a little green food, may be fed about 8 lb of meal/day plus ½ lb for each piglet nursed. Thus, if she has 10–12 piglets her ration might be 13 lb/day or about 6 cwt during the weaning period. In addition, the piglets will be fed in the creep as soon as they can take solid food, and this may amount, by gradual increases, to a total of 20–25 lb by the time they are weaned, or, perhaps, 2 cwt for a litter of 10 piglets. Gilts may be fed about 6 lb/day of meal, plus green foods, or at least ½ T before service. Total consumption for a sow may normally

be about 1¼ T p.a. or rather more than 1½ T for a sow farrowing a large litter twice a year.

j. Water Requirements

Water should be provided *ad lib.* for in-pig sows and for nursing sows.

k. Temperature Generated and Required

Generally, the sow will give off body warmth per 100 lb live wt in the same ratio as other pigs (IIIE 5*b*, p. 210). Since the density of stocking in the house is lower than in fattening houses, the natural warmth of the animals has to be supplemented, especially in the case of the piglets. It has been established that piglet mortality is greater in badly insulated houses than in good modern buildings and that the loss can increase from an average of about 20 per cent in the summer months to over 35 per cent during the winter. The piglet is susceptible to cold, especially in the hours after birth (13). During the first 2–3 days the creep should be kept at about 26–32° C (80–90° F). This temperature can be reduced by degrees to 20–26° C (70–80° F). In addition, the background temperature in the farrowing house should be about 15–20° C (60–70° F). The maintenance of the temperature within the stated range, without sudden fluctuations, is essential to the success of the enterprise. In-pig sows should also, for preference, be housed at 15–20° C.

l. Humidity

The humidity for farrowing houses has not been established in relation to the specific needs of sow and litter. It is probable that the humidity for adult pigs, that is about 80 per cent, is satisfactory, but a wider range, though not harmful for older pigs, should be avoided for a farrowing house.

m. Ventilation and Light

Ventilation for farrowing houses has been given as satisfactory at a max for sow and litter of 350 CFM or 20 air changes of the volume of the house, whichever is the least. This rate can be reduced to 25 CFM in the winter (14). Natural lighting is not essential. Artificial lighting has to be provided. In a farrowing house it is best that this should not be of high intensity for normal use, since this would disturb the sows. It is best to have a general low plane of illumination for general observation. This should be supplemented by a bright light for working, ideally as an independently switched socket to each farrowing pen or crate. Alternatively, a lead light and stand is suitable with outlets placed at suitable points. Most dry sow houses have a greater density of livewt/cubic capacity. Therefore ventilation rates should be greater, and fluorescent lighting to give a moderate plane of intensity is satisfactory.

6. *Equipment*

a. Outdoor Farrowing Huts, or Arks (15)

Portable shelters for gilts, dry sows, in-pig sows and for farrowing are normally used with outdoor folds in the fields under extensive or semi-intensive forms of pig rearing. The shelters can be elementary, being no more than bales, planks or canvas. Prefabricated and proprietary huts or arks in various forms are available. Some are very simple, being corrugated, galvanized sheets over a light steel frame, and cost as little as about $£\frac{1}{4}$ ft² but are not suitable for farrowing. Others are of timber or a mixture of timber and galvanized sheeting, those which are easily portable are built on timber skids and can be moved with a tractor. Some are in the form of huts, and others include a hut and a run. Most of the huts provide about 50–70 ft², costing $£\frac{1}{2}$–$£\frac{3}{4}$ ft². Farrowing huts include a creep area, with rails, which may be in the hut or as a projection from the hut. The better farrowing huts include insulation in a double-skin construction. Some may be of plywood and others are A-framed. At least one proprietary make is circular and includes a Ruakura-type creep ring. Some huts have a farrowing crate. Entrances should be baffled, floors draught-proof and there should be no projections which can be gnawed. There should be an inspection door to make observation both of the sow and of the litter easy. Prices vary normally between $£\frac{1}{2}$ and $£1$/ft². Huts and arks are sometimes mounted on a concrete yard, especially during winter months, and may even form permanent housing, but usually they are used as mobile equipment.

b. Farrowing Crates (16)

Some crates are fixtures, *3d*, above. Many forms of proprietary portable crates are available, though some are farm constructed, being mainly of galvanized tubular rails. Simple, tubular crates are 2 ft 10 in. high with 3 rails, the bottom rail normally being $2\frac{1}{2}$ ft apart and 10 in. from the floor with the middle and top rail being $1\frac{3}{4}$ ft apart at 1 ft height intervals. The crate may be placed between walls with a gate at one end, or it may be self-contained with its own gate and end. For preference, the rear gate should be able to be placed in 3 or 4 positions to vary the length from $6\frac{1}{4}$ to 7 ft. The piglets should be able to move under the bottom rail into a creep area on each side of the crate. A few proprietary crates include the creeps, but, normally, the crate is placed centrally in a pen $5\frac{1}{4}$–$5\frac{1}{2}$ ft wide forming creeps about 1 ft 8 in. wide. There are several variations to the normal type of crate, described above, which is made of 1-in. rails. The Ruakura crate is circular with a metal frame and galvanized sheeted side wall 4 ft high. It includes an off-centre inner ring 3 ft in dia and 3 ft high set 8 in. from the centre

of the external ring, which is 7 ft 8 in. in dia., towards an opening in the external wall. The inner ring forms a creep and is fitted with creep rails and lamp. In addition, there is another circular creep rail set 10 in. within the outer wall. Because of the curved pen wall, the sow has to lie with her back against the outer creep and her teats towards the inner creep. Though intended for external use in New Zealand, it can be used indoors and various adapted designs have been made using permanent block walling. The disadvantage is that if used for the full period of weaning an exercise area for the sow is required, in addition to the ring, of about 50–60 ft² (17).

c. Farrowing Rails

The Solari-type farrowing pen includes the traditional perimeter creep rail, 10 in. off the floor and 10 in. from the side walls, with a rail at one end and a tubular-framed gate to the creep area at the other end. The rails have a telescopic action and can be removed, while the gate folds back against the end wall. Though this is based on traditional, simple and cheap farrowing pen design, allowing the sow free movement, since it is removable equipment it facilitates cleaning and the pen can be used both for weaning and for the growers.

d. Individual Feeders (18)

Individual feeding pens or crates form an important part of the layout for gilt, dry sow or in-pig sow yards, *5b* above, if an attempt is to be made to ration each sow accurately. Though it is possible to some extent to achieve individual feeding with a normal-type trough, with divisions at 20-in. centres and 2 ft deep, it is better to form individual feeding crates. These may be of timber or metal, and many proprietary units are available. Though the feeders are usually placed in permanent positions with access from a sow yard, they are essentially portable equipment, and some are mounted on skids for ease of movement by tractor. Dimensions vary a little between units, but they are about $7\frac{3}{4}$–8 ft overall in length, including the manger, with the stall about 7 ft long and about 1 ft 11 in. wide. A few types have detachable troughs, others pivot and some are fixed. The latter are not easy to clean. Some feeders have tubular-rail sides, others sheet metal. For the most part, the rear sow-entry gates can be operated by remote control from the front either upwards or outwards, the former being suitable particularly in strawed yards. Some feeders have gates which are opened in groups, others open individually, which allows greater flexibility.

e. Creep Heaters (19)

Infra-red heat is the most satisfactory in the creep area, providing warmth which also attracts the piglets away from the sow where they may be crushed. Several proprietary electrical heaters are available, though others can be powered either by gas or paraffin. Two 250-watt lamps are required, though in a well-insulated building, which has an overall temperature of not less than 30–32° C (86–90° F), one lamp per creep may be satisfactory. The temperature under the lamp should be checked. The lamp should be securely fixed at least 2½ ft above the creep floor, and the ht should be increased as the piglets grow. Heaters should include a good reflector and, for preference, a guard, though most do not.

f. Feeders

The sow may be given a fixed trough in her pen. This is usually a 12-in. half-round glazed pipe 1½–2 ft long. However, rather than have the pig-man take rations twice a day, a hopper can be fitted above the trough with a ratchet that, when turned, lets a fixed amount of feed go into the trough. The hopper may hold about 3 days supply. The hoppers can be connected to a chain-and-flight conveyor, especially in dry-sow housing, which eliminates all carrying of feed. A portable self-feeder for the creep will be required, several small feeders for this purpose being available.

g. Water bowls

These can be similar to those for fattening pigs (IIIE 6b, p. 213).

7. Environmental control

Many traditional farrowing houses and sow yards do not include artificial ventilation or heat, depending on windows or permanent openings, though most include some insulation, especially round the creep area. Modern intensive accommodation should include artificial ventilation, generally on the lines of that for fattening houses, though the air flow required is proportionately less. Insulation should be generous, especially in the farrowing quarters. One modern timber-framed and clad house, on an exposed site, includes 3 in. of glass fibre in the roof and 2 in. in the walls (20). This is not too much insulation. All floors under crates, creeps or other lying areas should be insulated. Brick or block walls should include a cavity. On this basis, the heat generated by the sows will be largely contained in the house, but, even so, it is unlikely that the house will attain the background heat required (5k above) without artificial aid. Several farrowing houses include either floor heating or strip wall heaters to boost the temperature during the winter or if the house is not full (8). Natural ventilation will be inadequate for a well-insulated house. Ventilation, generally, will be similar in technique to that for fattening houses, the air inlet and fan size being selected to suit the building. It is desirable, particularly in farrowing houses, to divide the accommodation into groups of 4–8 sows, preferably with each group having its own air volume and control. The creep area should have its own heater (6e above).

8. Layout

Some details of layouts have been given in 5 above, including several basic diagrams. However, there are numerous layouts which can be suitable both for dry sows and for farrowing. Much depends on individual preference. This is so, particularly in a weaner enterprise, since mechanization is less satisfactory than in other enterprises. There are many specialized pieces of equipment available,

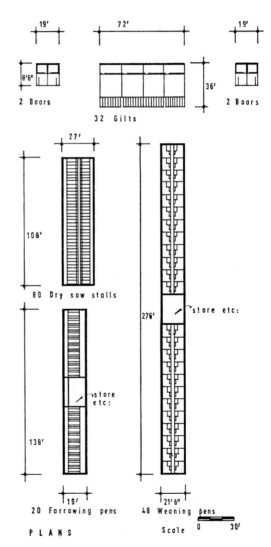

Fig. 114. Rearing layout for 120 sows/2 man unit: siting of buildings as required in relation to farm

principally to assist individual feeding and farrowing, but, perhaps, rather fewer prefabricated layouts, complete with all necessary equipment, than for other enterprises.

a. Complete Rearing Layout (Fig. 114)
A rearing unit, as discussed in 2 and 3 above, is difficult to plan. The pigman, free of all other duties than the rearing unit, must be the basis of the plan, and he will need both assistance and relief. Thus, a two-man unit might be required. Though no real yardstick is possible to estimate the number of sows which can be managed by each man, a unit of 120 sows with 4 boars and some 20–30 gilts at any one time might be a suitable enterprise for two men to manage. There are claims of one man being able to manage some 70 sows and progeny, including fattening, with only occasional assistance. However, it is desirable to keep the work content of the enterprise within a reasonable industrial standard, and some producers would consider 60 sows, even without fattening, difficult for one man to manage.

It would be desirable to plan farrowing to occur at regular times throughout the year, and, with an average of 2 farrowings/sow p.a., there would be about 20 farrowings each month. It is possible that there would be a specialized farrowing house and a special weaning house for a unit of this size. The sow would come into the farrowing house some days before farrowing, so that her total time in the house might be about $2\frac{1}{2}$ wks. Allowing for some overlapping of farrowing dates, at least 16 farrowing crates would be provided and some producers would prefer the extra cost and greater flexibility in having 20 places. In addition, there would be about 40 weaning pens in an adjoining house. On the basis of normal weaning at 8 wks, each litter would be in the weaning house for about 7 wks. Thus, allowing for a rest period after each litter and some overlapping of farrowing dates, a total of 48 weaning pens would provide adequate flexibility. It is probable that the farrowing and weaning houses would be each divided into two buildings around a centralized storage area for food, utility work, straw storage if required, and a couple of isolation pens. Since the sows need additional housing for the remainder of the year, other than when farrowing and weaning, yarding will be required for at least 80 sows, and some 30 gilts, plus the 4 boars. Alternatively, the dry sows might be housed in a specialized house with individual crates.

b. Combined Farrowing and Weaning Pen Layouts (Fig. 115)
The basis for a simple pen which can include removable farrowing rails for a time, then can be used by the sow and her litter until weaning and, if required, can also be used for fattening has been developed by Solari into a design generally named after him. A row of these pens, in mild districts, can be open to the south on to a sheltered work yard. In more exposed areas a similar type of pen has been developed within a totally enclosed building. There are various different adaptions of the same principles, depending on the degree of air isolation between pens which is required (8). The cheapest form includes a central passage and common air space with pens on each side of it. Air is ducted into the passage at low level and is drawn out of screened ridge extract fans. Alternatively, the central passage can be doubled so that each side of the house has its own air supply, but increases the floor area by about 25 ft²/pen. As a variation to this layout, the pens can be placed back-to-back and passages can be between the pens and the external walls.

9. *Siting*
Siting a rearing unit has general requirements similar to those for a fattening enterprise (IIIE 9, p. 218). However, the need for regular and frequent supervision is more critical. The unit should be close to the pigman's house. Similarly, disease control also is more critical and the unit should be sited away from other enterprises. Shelter must be provided, especially for any layout which is semi-intensive, relying on open yards or on pasture. Dung removal, unless piped, needs consideration so that the layout is in a suitable relationship for spreading the dung on the fields. It is possible that the dry-sow housing will be sited separately from the farrowing and weaning quarters, though some producers consider that dry stock, farrowing and fattening should all be grouped together (21).

10. *Services*
Services required are similar to those for a fattening enterprise (IIIE 10, p. 219). In addition, reference has been made, 4*d* above, to the possible inclusion of close-circuit television for observation. Drainage needs careful detailing to ensure hygienic conditions with minimum risk of cross-infection. Stalls or pens should drain, for preference, into slatted channels leading into external slurry tanks.

11. *Costs*
Simple huts and arks, providing shelter, can cost under £15 each, and farm-erected farrowing huts with simple construction may only cost £15–£20 for materials (22). However, most farrowing huts will cost between £30 and £100, generally averaging around £50–£60 including a run. Obviously, those which are more expensive may include additional space, insulation and fittings and, generally, an allowance of £60–£80 per farrowing hut should be allowed to include a

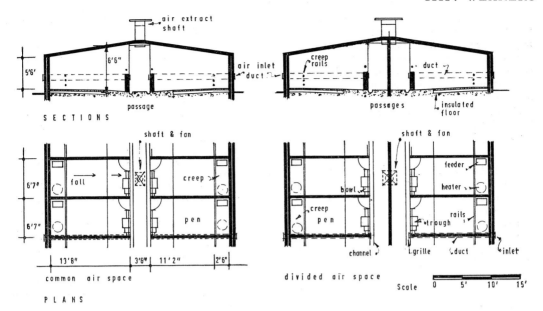

Fig. 115. Combined farrowing and weaning pens

reasonable standard of design and fittings. This is considerably less than permanent accommodation, being as little as one-half, or even one-quarter, of the cost of intensive farrowing houses. However, both the value of the land used for the extensive system of rearing and of the additional labour required should be considered. Simple farrowing rails, which can be placed in a pen and be removed after farrowing, might cost less than £15 per set. Thus, since most heaters cost only £1–£5 and feeders under £10, a run of farrowing pens, fully equipped and based on the Solari-type layout open at one end, might cost about £80–£90 for each pen plus £20–£30 for equipment. However, an external work yard is also required for cleaning by tractor, on to which the pens can open, and this might increase the cost to nearly £140 per pen. But a cost of about £140 includes accommodation, in this case, both for farrowing and for fattening. Other simple forms of farrowing accommodation might also cost about £120–£150 per pen. Farrowing crates cost £13–£30 each, and one with creep areas, perhaps, £50. A pen, including demountable crate, creeps, insulated flooring and all fittings, could cost £100, and the enclosing house another £50 providing accommodation both for farrowing and for weaning. However, a farrowing house, fully equipped and with artificial ventilation, is unlikely to cost less than £200 per place, and if slatted dung channels are also included the cost may be over £230 per place. Some layouts, with food storage, mechanized feed conveyance and other services, can cost over £250 per place.

As discussed above, 2c, the cost per place is relevant both in relation to the overall size of the farrowing unit, the number of farrowings each year, the period each sow and litter spends in the house and the livewt of the litter at birth and at weaning. Allowing a throughput of 4 litters/place p.a., a cost of £200 per place represents a cost of £7½/litter, but if the building can be used only 3 times p.a., then the cost becomes £10/litter. Similarly, if only 8 piglets per litter are weaned the cost per pig reared is a little under £1 and £1¼ respectively. However, if 10 piglets are reared successfully the cost per pig drops to £¾ and £1 respectively.

In considering the cost of a rearing unit, the other housing in addition to the farrowing and weaning accommodation must be taken into account. Housing a boar might cost about £300–£400, including service area, or for a herd of 25 sows this might represent an annual building cost of about £2 per sow. Dry-sow and gilt yards, including self-feeders, which cost about £7–£12 each, might cost £40–£80 per place or, on average, about £9/place p.a. Since gilts may need yards for at least six months before service and since there may be at least ⅓ of the numbers of a breeding herd again as followers, then a herd of 25 sows with 8 gilts will require at least 4 gilt places. This would represent an additional £1½ per breeding sow. Similarly, a yard for dry sows will be used for about ¾ of each year by each breeding sow, representing a cost of about £6/sow or about £60/place. A dry-sow house might cost up to £100/place.

Thus, additional accommodation to support a breeding sow, above that required for farrowing, might represent on average £10/sow p.a. This should equal, for a sow rearing 20 piglets p.a., a cost of £$\frac{1}{2}$ per pig weaned, provided the throughput and use of accommodation is planned with great efficiency.

It is possible to establish a theoretical capital budget for the two-man unit discussed above, 8a, for a complete rearing unit:

	£
Controlled environment house: 20 crates at £200 each	4000
Controlled environment house: 40 weaning pens at £150 each	6000
Yards for 80 dry sows: at £75 each	6000
Yards for 30 gilts: at £60 each	1800
Boar housing for 4 boars: at £300 each	1200
Storage and utility rooms	1000
	£20,000

Thus, a capital outlay of some £20,000 might be required. Allowing for interest, insurance, some maintenance and depreciation, this might represent an annual building cost of £3000. The latter equals £25 per sow or £12½ per litter. It would be desirable to aim for more than 2 litters/sow p.a. and for above-average litter sizes. Even averaging no more than 10 reared per litter, the cost of the unit per pig reared is about £1¼, which is similar to the examples discussed above for piecemeal development. Labour, including all overheads and allowing for the two men to bear their own relief labour, should be costed at not less than £3000 p.a., that is another £1¼ per pig reared. Thus, the enterprise should be costed at £2½ for accommodation and labour per pig reared, to which must be added the food costs, stock depreciation, veterinary expenses and other overheads. If these average £3½/pig reared, which may be considered low, then the weaners must sell at over £6 each to show a profit. However, if 2⅛ litters/sow are obtained, averaging 11 piglets reared/litter, the throughput is increased from 2400 weaners p.a. to just over 2800 p.a. On this basis the cost of accommodation and labour will be reduced to approximately £2⅛/weaner sold.

12. References

(1) 'Breeding by computer'. *Pig Farming*, pp. 41–3 (June 1963).

(2) 'A.I. far from A.1'. *Pig Farming*, p. 27 (September 1963).

(3) SMITH, A. K. 'Pig Mortality'. *Farmers Weekly*, 13th March 1964, pp. 91–2 and five subsequent weeks; also, 'Producers headaches'. *Pig Farming*, p. 73 (June 1963).

(4) CHARLTON, R. 'Hysterectomy: a short cut to better pigs?' *Farmers Weekly*, p. 113 (30th November

1962)'; SAINSBURY, D. W. B. 'Health in the herd'. Ref. a, p. 37.

(5) RIDGEON, R. F. 'Profitable pigs—aim for 16 weaners a year'. *Farmers Weekly*, p. 91 (8th June 1962).

(6) Ref. 6.

(7) PHELPS, A. 'Accommodating dry sows'. *Farmbuildings*, pp. 53–9 (Spring 1964).

(8) 'Farm Building developments in the N.E. of Scotland'. North of Scotland College of Agriculture (1964).

(9) KING, J. W. B. 'Role of the boar. Pig Feeding'. *Farmers Weekly Supplement*, p. xii (7th February 1964).

(10) FISHWICK, V. C. *Pigs: their breeding, feeding and management*. Crosby Lockwood, p. 45 (1961).

(11) LAURENCE, H. 'Pig policies at Pimperne'. *Farmers Weekly*, pp. 90–3 (24th April 1964).

(12) PHELPS, A. 'Wean by weight not by age'. *Pig Farming*, p. 33 (June 1963).

(13) Ref. a, p. 28.

(14) Ref. a, p. 179.

(15) SAINSBURY, D. W. B. 'Healthier and cheaper: farrowing huts and arks'. *Pig Farming*, pp. 36–43 (June 1964).

(16) SAINSBURY, D. W. B. 'Restrict to save: aids to farrowing'. *Pig Farming*, pp. 43–5 (February 1964) and Ref. 2, p. 75.

(17) Ref. c, p. 7.

(18) SAINSBURY, D. W. B. 'Fair do's for all: Sow feeding stalls'. *Pig Farming*, pp. 49–51 (April 1964).

(19) SAINSBURY, D. W. B. 'Cut your piglet losses: infrared heaters'. *Pig Farming*, pp. 65–7 (January 1964).

(20) PRINCE-SMITH, W. R. 'Comfort in the Labour wards'. *Pig Farming*, pp. 75–7 (July 1963).

(21) Ref. d, p. xliii.

(22) STEVEN, K. 'My £15 farrowing ark'. *Pig Farming*, p. 57 (April 1963).

SELECTED REFERENCES

a. SAINSBURY, D. W. B. *Pig housing*. Farming Press (1963).

b. FISHWICK, V. C., revised HICKS, N. *Pigs: their breeding, feeding and management*. Crosby Lockwood (1961).

c. *Manual of Modern Pig Housing*. Vitamealo Advising Service (1962).

d. 'Purpose in pigs'. *Farmers Weekly Bulletin* (3rd May 1963).

e. 'Pig feeding'. *Farmers Weekly Supplement* (7th February 1964).

f. MINISTRY OF AGRICULTURE. *Housing of Pigs*. Revised edition (1962).

g. TUITE, P. J. *Specialised Pig Housing*. Dublin Agriculture Institute (1963).

h. AGRICULTURAL RESEARCH COUNCIL. *Bibliography of Farm Building Research Part 1 Buildings for pigs* (1945–58) and Supplement (1958–62).

i. THOMSON, J. M., WALKER-LOVE, J. & FORSYTH, R. J. *Replanned Farrowing Facilities for Auchincruive*. H.M.S.O. (1960).

IIIG Mutton and Lamb

1. *Activity*

a. Production of mutton and lamb is subject to seasonal variations, and, unlike other meat, it is doubtful whether it will ever be marketed at a constant level throughout the year. Home production rose from under $\frac{1}{5}$ M tons in 1958 to over $\frac{1}{4}$ M tons in 1961, with imports averaging rather more than $\frac{1}{3}$ M tons p.a. In the same period the number of ewes in the United Kingdom at the June census rose from 10·3 M to 11·5 M. In spite of the size of the mutton and lamb trade, investment in permanent sheep buildings is small, though in recent years opinion with regard to their economic value has changed. This is reflected by there being no reference to permanent buildings within the *Farmers Weekly Supplement* on 'Sheep husbandry' published in 1958, whereas their 1962 *Supplement*, 'A shepherd's guide', gave details for in-wintering hoggs.

Within the next few years it is probable that housing will be developed both for wintering ewe-hoggs and for fattening lambs, not only in upland districts but also in the south and lowlands. Widespread investment in intensive fattening houses is unlikely, though this might be encouraged by the rapidly expanding supermarket trade for prepacked meats throughout the year. It is worth noting that, in experimental work during the last decade at the Boots' Thurgarton Priory Farm, breeding ewes have been permanently housed with good lambing percentages of up to 175 and with increased fleece yields (1). Moreover, in France 90 per cent of the 6 M breeding ewes are winter housed, though this is attributable partly to such factors as autumn lambing and lack of shepherds (2).

b. Sheep, though a natural enterprise in most upland districts, can be a successful undertaking on many lowland farms either as a principal enterprise or as a flying flock maintained for a limited period. In fact, many farmers hesitate between beef and mutton production, and non-intensive dairy producers may have a flock as a subsidiary enterprise. However, good shepherding is a very skilled job. Sheep production techniques have been summarised (3):

i. Early fat-lamb production, with most lambs sold before May.

ii. Light or heavy fat-lamb production, for summer sales.

iii. Rearing store lambs, for autumn sales.

iv. Fat-lamb production from flying flocks.

v. Fat-lamb production from intensive grazing.

vi. Fattening hoggets off grass and roots, from autumn stores.

vii. Upland farming, producing gimmers for breeding and store lambs for fattening on lowland farms.

viii. Arable flocks, mainly for specialized ram breeding.

c. With intensive sheep production the winter management can be difficult, in order to save grazing and to give better attention to the stock, unless winter housing is adopted. Stocking rates in hill districts may be as low as 1 ewe/10 acres or as high as 5 ewes/acre on lowland farms, or even 8 ewes + lambs/acre with forward creep grazing on very good grass for intensive early summer fattening. Profitability depends on:

i. High lambing rate per 100 ewes of over 150 per cent, by having a good proportion of twins and triplets. (Experimental lambing at Nottingham University's farm has proved satisfactory yielding 3 lambings/ewe/2 yr.)

ii. Rapid livewt gain of lambs after birth to reach 70–80 lb livewt from 10–12 lb at birth in 80–100 days, with a daily livewt gain of 0·75–1·0 lb.

iii. Minimum mortality—frequently 12 per cent lamb crop dies in first month, or over 15 per cent in severe weather; with over 5 per cent shearling ewes and nearly 10 per cent 3-crop ewes annual losses.

iv. Good food conversion rates of under 5 : 1.

v. Reduced labour, perhaps a winter-lambing flock of 300–400 ewes/man, or with 1000 ewes/man on extensive systems (4).

2. *Managerial requirements*

a. Winter housing, to be economic, has to be constructed cheaply, perhaps within £3–£5/place. In many cases temporary winter housing is formed from straw bales. This has the advantage of flexibility. However, at £5/place the depreciated cost is £$\frac{3}{4}$/ewe for permanent housing, and this might prove cheaper than the handling cost for bales in a temporary yard, which, in any case, does not provide any cover for the sheep, except in the case of straw and tarpaulin shelters for lambing.

b. Winter housing should include storage for the winter rations. The latter may be self-fed or rationed silage, hay, roots or combinations of these fodders, but usually contains a proportion of concentrates. At least one layout is based on feeding haylage from a hermetically sealed tower silo (5). Experiments at the East Riding Institute have shown that it can be economic to fatten lambs with various concentrate rations plus no more than $\frac{1}{2}$ lb hay/day, a conversion of 5 : 1 being obtained (6). The conversion ratio, the cost of food and the price of lamb are critical factors. However, it is probable that further research into sheep nutrition will eventually show that winter housing is desirable, as with other stock. Experiments at the Drayton Experimental Husbandry Farm have compared indoor housing at 12 ft²/ewe with out-wintering on grass at one acre/4$\frac{1}{2}$ ewes (7):

	Indoor	Out-wintered
Wt on 9th Dec., lb	152	152
Wt after lambing, lb	159	169
Lambing percentage per cent	188	186
Lamb birthweights, lb	9·9	11·5
Hay fed, cwt	3·5	2·5
Concentrates fed, lb	57	57

Though out-wintering gave heavier lambs at birth, the in-wintered lambs were only a day or two behind in weight by the fat stage. With *ad lib.* hay for the in-wintered ewes, an extra cwt/ewe was consumed, though restricted feeding might not have proved adverse. In-wintering saved labour as well as rested the pastures.

c. Silage can be an important fodder for in-wintered in-lamb ewes, but its quality must be sufficient both for maintenance and for the prospective lamb crop. This was shown by experiments at Leeds University, when 3 groups of 10 ewes were fed from different silo stores (8):

	Silo-barn	Open pit	Tower
Dry matter, per cent	21·1	17·5	18·6
Crude protein, per cent	14·6	11·8	19·5
Crude fibre, per cent	29·5	41·4	30·0
Acidity, pH	4·5	5·03	5·12
Av. daily consumption, lb	21·1	11·9	14·6
Av. daily d.m. consumed, lb	2·56	2·10	2·72
Av. livewt gain 15th December–23rd February, lb	19	6	17

Further experiments showed that the silage should have a d.m. content of at least 25 per cent, with 17 per cent crude protein and a pH of 4$\frac{1}{2}$, and that additional concentrates are required prior to lambing.

d. Ewe housing may be combined with a paddock for day-time exercise and, therefore, less covered space is required than with total housing.

Experiments have shown that outdoor exercise is not essential (7). When housed, fattening lambs are normally kept indoors throughout the winter months, though occasionally they are let out on dry days. In most districts the housing period for ewe and lamb will be from early December to April or May. If the lambs are born around the end of January not only should they reach 80 lb livewt by May, when the peak prices begin to decline, but the critical last 6–8 weeks of the ewe's pregnancy will be under supervision indoors.

3. *Production techniques*

a. Strawed yards with both concreted floors and slatted floors can be satisfactory. However, straw allowances may amount to one bale/4 ewes/wk, or perhaps 150 T/100 ewes per winter. The cost of handling and littering straw has the same disadvantage as with other classes of stock (IIIB 2b, p. 184). Alternatively, about $\frac{1}{4}$ ft of sawdust and shavings can be used as bedding over $\frac{1}{4}$ ft of ground limestone on a concrete base. Slats, particularly in upland districts, will justify their cost, being satisfactory both for ewes and lambs.

b. Though research at the Liscombe Experimental Husbandry Farm has shown that self-feeding silage is satisfactory with good silage (9), manual feeding into troughs is practised generally both for silage and hay. Self-feeding, as with other livestock, may not be the best rationing method for large units, due to wastage, uncontrolled consumption and labour requirements in managing the silage face. As previously mentioned, one farm has haylage in a tower (5), the haylage being blown from the tower into a hopper supplying a 1 ft-wide chain conveyor (modelled on a dung-scraper), which operates in a trough $\frac{3}{4}$ ft deep around a slatted open yard, 187 ft × 32 ft, for 400 ewes.

c. Food requirements for sheep have been given (10):

Lamb livewt, lb	60	80	100	120
d.m./wk, lb	14·5	17·9	20·4	22·9

Ewe in-milk, 160 lb livewt : 40 lb d.m./wk

In the 8 weeks before lambing a ewe should receive each day about 3–3$\frac{1}{2}$ lb d.m./100 lb livewt (11) and this, for example, might equal over the period 7 lb concentrates plus 7 lb hay, with additional silage or roots.

4. *Work routines*

Work requirements for in-wintering are not easy to assess. As with any livestock, feeding is important and, with the exception of self-feeding silage or concentrates and the rare exception of mechanized feeding, most units are based on the manual rationing into troughs. Therefore, housing should be based normally on a central feed passage to take a trolley, though some units are based on a tractor and trailer for handling feed. Littering, unless slats are used, can be time consuming. However, it is the stockmanship and veterinary work which will require unstinted attention, and lambing within a concentrated period will cause a peak labour demand. Dipping, etc., is discussed in IIG (p. 149). Though 400 ewes/man may be winter housed, $\frac{1}{2}$ man day/lowland winter store has been given as the requirement, which would limit the flock to about 250 stores (12). Other sources quote $\frac{1}{2}$ hr/day for a 200-hogg unit (11).

5. Design data

a. Slatted Floors

Floor area requirements for lambs on slats have been given (13):

Welsh Mountain lambs	$4\frac{1}{2}$ ft^2
Swaledale lambs	5 ft^2
Scotch Blackface lambs	$5\frac{1}{2}$ ft^2

or an allowance of $5\frac{1}{2}$ ft^2 for small sheep and $6\frac{1}{2}$ ft^2 for large breeds, with a 3-acre daytime run/200 sheep (11). However, for permanent housing of the fattening lamb, 12 ft^2 should be allowed, perhaps with 18 ft^2 for yearlings, or 14–16 ft^2 for ewe and lamb. Slats should be in hardwood, $1\frac{1}{2}$ in. wide ($1\frac{1}{4}$–3 in. have proved satisfactory) tapering to the bottom, being perhaps $1\frac{1}{2}$ in. deep, set $\frac{5}{8}$ in. apart and supported on joists, usually 4 in. $\times$ 2 in. at $1\frac{1}{2}$-ft centres in panels 8 ft long and resting on 6 in. $\times$ 4 in. beams between concrete block piers (Fig. 116). The depth of the slatted floor to the sub-floor, to form a slurry pit, might be only 1–$1\frac{1}{2}$ ft, for night housing, or 3 ft for permanent lamb housing. The sub-floor should be of concrete with a slope to drain urine to a catch pit, though on a free-draining site only a well-rammed stone-dust floor might be used. The slatted floor should be removed for cleaning, though on a steep site it might be possible to have a tractor access at low

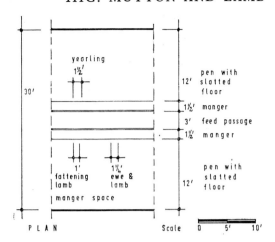

Fig. 117. Manger space/head of sheep

level at one end. The slats should be parallel to the entrance door to give a solid appearance as the hoggs approach.

b. Strawed Yards

Floor areas are normally more generous for straw than for slats, perhaps being as much as 50 per cent greater. There should be a concreted area in front of the troughs.

c. Mangers or Racks

An allowance of 1–$1\frac{1}{4}$ ft.R of manger/lamb should be allowed. Hay racks may be above the manger or they may be suspended above the lying area from the roof, allowing the sheep to move under them. If no silage is fed, the racks will suffice. Self-feed concentrate hoppers, if used, should be based on 2 in./lamb of feed face. Feed passages should be 3–4 ft wide, or 7 ft wide for tractor and trailer, though if self-unloading trailers are used in the future, 9–10 ft might be required. Mangers may be $1\frac{1}{2}$ ft wide. Thus a building of 30 ft internal span might hold 2 sheep/ft.R, at a density of 15 ft^2/head, with a 3-ft passage down the centre (Fig. 117).

d. Self-fed Silage

In-lamb ewes can self-feed at an allowance of $\frac{1}{3}$ ft.R silage face/ewe, preferably through a 4-ft-high barrier with vertical uprights $\frac{3}{4}$ ft apart (9). Therefore, the clamp should not be much more than 5 ft high. Other details conform to silo designs for cattle. At 10 lb silage/ewe/day, about 5 cwt/ewe will be required during 8 wks prior to lambing, that is about 10 ft^3/ewe.

e. Walls

Hollow block walls should be used to 4 ft above the

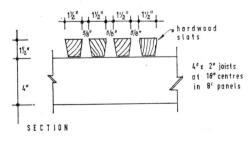

SECTION

Fig. 116. Slats

slat floor level, with 6 ft timber cladding above. The sheep should enter through a sliding door, perhaps 8 ft wide. If a ramp is required to reach the floor, it should be movable, with grip battens, and inclined at 30 deg.

f. Temperature
The internal temperature should be akin to the external temperature, but free from draughts. However, in France temperatures of 15° C (60° F) have been quoted as desirable (2). Ample ventilation should be provided.

g. Water
Water should be provided *ad lib.*

6. *Equipment*
Equipment is limited principally to the slatted floor panels, feeding mangers and racks, water troughs and ramps for access.

7. *Environmental control*
a. Ventilation should be based on a through air-flow from eaves to ridge above the sheep. In a sheltered site the upper part of the wall can be slatted or perforated below the eaves or, preferably, be formed as opening shutters to allow for variation in the air flow. For lamb sheds, an allowance of 8 ft²/15 ft.R of wall has been quoted (13). The outlet should be of at least equal area at the ridge and can be formed by having an open ridge, the roof sheeting on the two slopes almost meeting, but with no capping. This may allow a small amount of dry drift snow to penetrate. Alternatively, a flashing piece can form an upstand, having a capping about $\frac{1}{3}$ ft above the upstand, the sheets being set about $\frac{1}{4}$ ft apart. Roof insulation and controlled ventilation is not used. Pneumonia is a risk in housing sheep and this could be caused by poor ventilation (14).

b. Natural lighting should be provided and should be set high in the walls at an allowance of 8 ft²/100 ft² floor area. Rooflights can be used, but may become obscured by snow.

c. Artificial lighting is essential, and might be based on a 150-W bulb/15 ft.R of building, placed over the feed passage. Good lighting should be provided in the food store. A few hogg units may have no electricity.

8. *Layout*
a. Though many converted buildings are used for sheep and, therefore, internal layouts vary, the layout should be based, as with other livestock production units, on a central feed passage with a food store at one end, there being the additional need for access for the sheep and for tractor access for cleaning under the slats. A sick bay is desirable (Fig. 118).

b. Various kinds of traditional shelters can be formed, including a circular stell, partly open at the top, which is available as a prefabricated unit, perhaps allowing 4 ft² covered area plus 3 ft² open area/hogg, with an 8-ft-wide door in the side and sheep pop-holes, and with curved corrugated steel walls and flat steel sheet roofs, erected on a dwarf foundation wall base. The floor can be limestone, sand or saw-dust (Fig. 119) (15).

9. *Siting*
The unit can be sited near the farmstead or in relation to a few acres of grazing for day-time use. Since supervision, particularly during lambing, and hand-feeding are normal requirements, the unit should be near the shepherd's house. A dry, preferably sloping, site and a hard road access are desirable. In upland districts some hogg units are well away from a farmstead. However, water and electricity should be available, and fodder, whether silage or hay, plus concentrates, have to be carted to the unit's store. With silage, when also used for cattle, the silo-barn may be sited for both enterprises. Prevailing winds, natural shelter and snow-drifts must be considered.

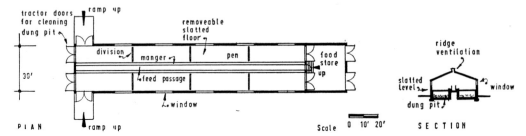

Fig. 118. House for 320 fattening lambs or 200 yearlings

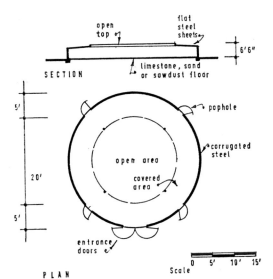

```
open                    flat
top                     steel
                        sheets

SECTION                 limestone, sand
                        or sawdust floor

                        pophole

        open area       corrugated
                        steel
        covered
        area

    entrance
    doors

PLAN            Scale   0   5'  10'  15'
```

Fig. 119. Circular stell

10. Services

The water supply must be protected from frost. This can be achieved by having a well-lagged stand-pipe and tap, with short lengths of hose for filling the troughs, emptied after use. Care must be taken that any run-off from the slurry under a slatted floor does not enter a watercourse. Roof water should be drained clear of the building.

11. Costs

Slatted floors normally cost £1½–£2/place and may be fitted into an existing building. Rough timber framed and clad units, with slatted floors, and cheap block lower walling, might cost £4–£5 per place, though units used in conjunction with grazing paddocks, being smaller, may cost only £3¾–£4 per place. A stell shelter might cost £2–£2½/place. At £5/place a cost of £¾/ewe or lamb should be allowed. The capital cost must be judged in relation to the reduced labour cost for winter management, including the use of vehicles to outlying places for inspection, the easier life for the shepherd, the possibility of increased throughput and reduced mortality, the improved value of grassland which is not winter grazed and the possibility of better conversion ratios and gain in livewt/day. Insufficient evidence has been collected concerning the value of these benefits.

12. References

(1) 'When the flock comes in'. *Farmers Weekly*, pp. 99–101 (15th March 1963).
(2) 'Sheep the inside story'. *Farmer and Stockbreeder*, pp. 100–1 (14th March 1961).
(3) DEXTER, K. & BARBER, D. *Farming for Profits*, p. 182. Penguin. (1961).

(4) *Farmers Weekly Almanack*, p. vii (21st December 1962).
(5) GOMERY, D. 'Focus on the tower silo'. *Dairy Farmer*, pp. 28–31 (January 1963).
(6) HURST, D. *Farmers Weekly*. 'Intensive Lambs fed to pay'. p. 107 (16th March 1963).
(7) GOMERY, D. *Dairy Farmer*, 'New ways with sheep'. pp. 43–4 (August 1962).
(8) BOAZ, T. G. & DALTON, D. C. *Farmers Weekly*. 'Inwintering and the unborn lamb'. p. 85 (7th December 1962).
(9) WILLCOCK, J. M. *Dairy Farmer*. 'New ways with sheep'. pp. 44–5 (August 1962).
(10) 'Off the grass'. *Farmers Weekly Supplement* (14th September 1962).
(11) *Farmers Weekly Supplement*. (See Selected References.)
(12) STURROCK, F. G. 'Planning Farm Work'. Bulletin No. 172. Ministry of Agriculture. p. 6 (1960).
(13) WILLIAMS, L. J. *Agriculture*. 'Lamb Wintering Sheds'. (May 1959).
(14) LONG, D. 'Inwintering sheep'. *Farmers Weekly*, pp. 107–15 (29th June 1962).
(15) SOUTAR, D. 'A stell for sheep'. *Farmers Weekly*, pp. 78–9 (14th December 1962).

SELECTED REFERENCES
a. 'A Shepherd's Guide'. *Farmers Weekly Supplement* (10th August 1962).
b. 'Sheep Equipment Leaflet: notes on housing for hoggs'. North of Scotland College of Agriculture (1962).
c. SIMPSON, I. G. 'Economic aspects of sheep production on the lowland farm: results of a Yorkshire survey'. Department of Agriculture, Leeds (May 1962).

IIIH. Poultry and Eggs

By D. W. B. Sainsbury, M.A., B.Sc., Ph.D., M.R.C.V.S.

Introduction

Poultry keeping is developing from its traditional place in agriculture as predominantly a large number of small enterprises on general farms into a limited number of specialist units containing large groups of birds kept under highly intensive systems. Indeed, poultry are now kept more intensively and in larger groups than any other species of livestock. It hardly needs to be stressed, therefore, that in these circumstances correct housing and management are critical factors in the maintenance of good production and in the control of disease.

In this section poultry housing will be dealt with under four headings:

A. The environmental conditions required by poultry.
B. A brief survey of the practical methods of achieving the correct conditions, including ventilation and insulation.

C. The systems used in practice for brooding young chicks, for rearing layers and for broiler or other meat producers.

D. Equipment.

A. *The environmental conditions required by poultry*
The environmental factors of importance to poultry include temperature, humidity, air movement and ventilation rates, and lighting.

a. Temperature
More information is available on the temperatures required by poultry than on any other environmental factor. At the beginning of the chick's existence 30° C (55° F) is the optimum for the egg-holding room prior to incubating. Incubation should be carried out at 37° C (99° F), and the temperature should be lowered 1·1° C (2° F) in the hatcher. The correct brooding temperature for the day-old chick is 35° C (95° F) with a gradual reduction of the order of nearly 3° C/wk (5° F) (Fig. 120). With 'broilers' in particular the house temperature should be kept up between 15° C (60° F) and 20° C (70° F), as in this way the chicks are encouraged to leave the restricted area under the brooder and appetite and growth are stimulated, while the possibility of respiratory infection may be lessened.

After the first four to five weeks the optimum temperature continues to fall more slowly, the ideal for the adult still being as high as 13° C (55° F). There is no evidence, however, to suggest that it is worthwhile to house the birds at a constant temperature—indeed, the evidence is rather the reverse: some changes in temperature stimulate appetite and resistance to disease, and do not harm egg yield or size, but temperatures below 5° C (40° F) and above 30° C (85° F) must be avoided where possible.

b. Humidity
The R.H. of the air is a very important factor in the egg-holding room, and about 80 per cent is correct for maximum hatchability (Fig. 121). Artificial means of humidifying the air are necessary to maintain this, such as water pans or mist sprays. During incubation the humidity is still critical, and while 60 per cent is satisfactory during the first stages, it should rise by 10 per cent in the hatcher. A similar humidity is good for the early feathering. After this early period the bird itself is unlikely to be directly affected by normal humidity conditions, though in badly ventilated and constructed houses extreme dampness has disastrous effects on the fabric of the building and on the litter. Such conditions will promote the spread of disease, particularly via the litter.

In practice, it is satisfactory if the humidity in the poultry house can be kept to a maximum of 70 per cent in the winter.

c. Air Movement and Ventilation Rates
All poultry houses must be ventilated, but it is vital that the system used be designed to prevent

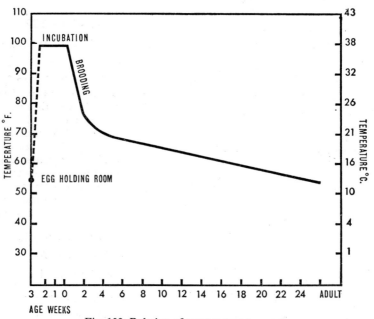

Fig. 120. Relation of temperature to age

93: INTENSIVE BREEDING HOUSE: DEEP LITTER

A timber-framed and clad house is divided internally into compartments with studding mesh. In the foreground wood shavings form a deep litter. Internal wall and ceiling surfaces are smooth. Air-inlet flaps in the wall are open, as is the outlet chimney in the ridge. The lights have reflector shades which increase efficiency and reduce dust deposit. [SEE PAGE 245] Courtesy of Dr. Sainsbury.

94: PORTABLE GAS BROODER

Either electricity or gas can be used to provide warmth for the brooders. Gas can be provided easily from cylinders and portable heaters with reflectors and with a flexible gas supply pipe, as shown, are economical and safe. [SEE PAGE 249] Courtesy of Dr. Sainsbury.

95: BROILER HOUSE

Mr. R. Barnes, Wigton, Nr. Kirkbride, Cumberland

    External view of timber clad broiler house resting on concrete dwarf walls. This is typical of many intensive poultry buildings of 30–40 ft span with a completely controlled environment. Along the side walls of the house are large baffled air inlets in plywood. There are two inlets on each side to each of the ridge fan extractor units. Walls and roof are insulated. [SEE PAGE 244] Courtesy of Farmers Weekly.

96: DEEP LITTER HOUSE

Cobb's stock farm, Happisburgh, Norfolk

    Internal view of a deep litter poultry house divided into sections. The deep litter section includes a continuous feeder and a raised, slatted area covers a droppings pit and suspended drinker. Down the centre of the house is an access passage. The house is timber framed with insulated walls and roof, artificial fluorescent lighting and controlled ventilation. [SEE PAGE 245] Courtesy of Farmers Weekly.

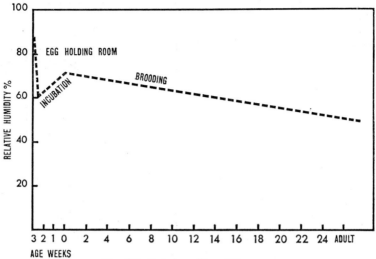

Fig. 121. Relation of humidity to age

draughts. It is most important to stress the great difference between the minimal ventilation required in the winter, when it is necessary to conserve all available heat, and the maximum requirements of summer, when it is required to keep the temperature down as low as possible. In a later section the method used to ensure the correct ventilation rate will be described, but it may be as well to mention here that this is based specifically on the needs of the birds. The arrangement of correct ventilator and fan capacity in a building depends on the number and weight of the stock in the house and cannot be based on the house size and capacity without these other factors being known (Fig. 122).

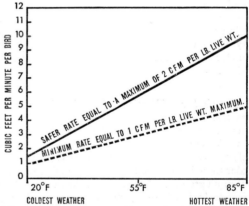

Fig. 122. Ventilation rates in relation to temperature and weight

d. Light

Light frequency, intensity and total duration affect growth and egg production. Intensity is the least important factor, and birds can thrive within a very wide range. For example, light may vary between 0·1 and 100 f.c. intensity without it having any effect on growth, and it may vary between 0·5 and 38 f.c., at least without any effect on egg production. However, to control cannibalism and feather pecking, and also the activity of the birds, dim conditions may therefore be justified for broilers and layers under intensive conditions.

Total hours of light are also important. It is correct to have almost a twenty-four-hour lighting period for day-old chicks, decreasing as the birds grow (Fig. 123). The development of sexual maturity may be delayed by decreasing the hours of light gradually during the rearing period. This régime ensures that full somatic development takes

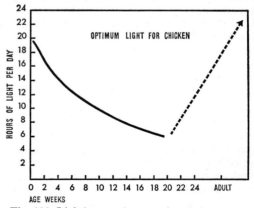

Fig. 123. Lighting requirements in relation to age

place before laying commences and that not only are more eggs laid, but these are of better size and more even quality.

Also shown in recent years has been the benefits on egg production of gradually increasing the lighting period during production. This is shown graphically in Fig. 123. The increasing increments of light act as a constant stimulus to the ovaries throughout the laying period. Thus complete control of light is required by more and more poultry farmers who wish to make use of this modern knowledge, and increasing numbers of birds are reared and lay in completely artificially lighted houses. In practice, artificial lighting is applied most cheaply by the use of standard tungsten-bulb fittings at 10–15-ft intervals. In laying houses 75- or 60-watt bulbs may be used, and in broiler and brooder houses 60-, 40- and 25-watt bulbs as required. White, red and blue bulbs can be interchanged as necessary, red being used to lessen the chances of cannibalism, and blue being the most useful colour for catching the birds when ready for market, since birds are virtually blind at the blue end of the spectrum, and sit quietly on the floor. However, in practice the easiest way to control behaviour and light intensity is to use an automatic intensity regulator which can alter the intensity at will by the turn of a switch.

B. Practical consideration of poultry-house construction

The summary just given of the environmental conditions required by poultry shows that a reasonably fine control of the environment is justified in order to maintain conditions capable of producing optimum growth and production. Further, modern practice in the industry utilizes increasingly the so-called 'controlled-environment' house. This is a logical practical step forward resulting from the knowledge of the conditions required for optimum production, and it is enabling the industry to house its stock on very near 'industrial' lines. Nevertheless, the problems that occur with such large units are very great, and probably the most difficult are those in connection with controlling and preventing disease.

a. The Construction of the House

The basis of a well-constructed house is a good standard of thermal insulation of the surfaces (see Vol. 2). While it is vital that all surfaces are equally well insulated, the floor warrants some separate consideration in view of its great importance in disease and litter control. Earth floors may be considered satisfactory under slats, where the soil conditions are right for drainage as the birds have no contact with the ground. However,

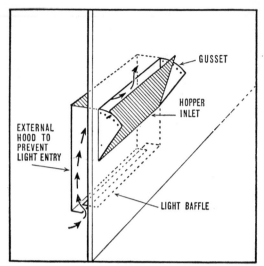

Fig. 124. Baffled air inlet

in the case of built-up litter systems it is a considerable advantage to have a concrete floor incorporating a damp-proof course. In such cases the litter stays drier and is therefore less likely to constitute a health risk. The evidence accumulates that with intensive poultry houses, particularly where young stock is concerned, a 'build-up' of diseases ranging from parasites to E. coli bacterial infection may take place in the soil and be difficult to control.

b. Ventilation

In controlled-environment poultry houses mechanically operated ventilation is essential. In others, and particularly with narrow-span buildings up to 20–30 ft wide, natural ventilation may still be satisfactory. General principles, as given elsewhere, apply to poultry, but one or two additional points may be made.

Air-inlet design is an important feature. In a poultry house with birds on the floor the walls will normally be 5–6 ft high. The inlets are of hopper type with the internal flap hinged at the bottom to give well-baffled air entry in cold weather when the flap is partially closed; in warm weather the flap can be progressively opened to give unobstructed and direct entry of air (Fig. 124). The inlets should be placed with the top at least 1 ft below the eaves and purlins, or other horizontal obstructions on the ceiling should be concealed to prevent the air rebounding to the ground, producing draughts at floor level and causing an unequal distribution of birds. To prevent entry of light where this is required, a hood is placed on the outside containing a 'light-trap' (Fig. 124). A baffle is also placed under the outlet ventilator to prevent entry of light at this point. All ventilators should be of insulated construction to prevent cooling of the air and condensation. Mechanical systems of conventional type are based on the scheme outlined here, with fans placed at the base of outlet chimneys in the ridge, in effect assisting the natural arrangement and ensuring it functions at all times.

The arrangement outlined above is suitable for most broiler, brooder and laying houses with the birds on the floor. In battery houses further problems arise, however, owing to the birds being kept at various heights within the house, and due to the difficulty of bringing the fresh air into the central cages when three or more lines of cages are installed. The methods of overcoming this problem are:

i. To instal two lines of inlets, one 1 ft below the eaves and the other $2\frac{1}{2}$ ft from the floor.
ii. To use underfloor ducting to bring the correct percentage of air to the central cages. The underfloor ducts are usually made approximately 2 ft wide and 1 ft deep and run transversely across the building at 10 ft centres, though the actual shape and size will clearly depend on the number of birds housed.

c. Rearing Systems for Layers and Breeders
i. Single stage. The simplest system, and one which at present is gaining in popularity is the single-stage intensive method. In this the birds may be reared on built-up litter from day-old until they are ready to enter the laying quarters at 16–20 wks of age. With this arrangement there is the opportunity for the birds to be reared without any check from movement and settling into new quarters, and also resistance to parasitic diseases such as coccidiosis is built up gradually. It can thus be claimed to be the ideal system from the husbandry point of view. Floor-space allowances may be as little as $1\frac{1}{3}$ ft²/bird for light breeds and light hybrids and up to 2 ft² for heavy breeds, the maximum figure being required for broiler breeders.

Alternatives to the all deep-litter house are:

i. The use of houses with part deep-litter and part slats or wire. Or
ii. total covering with slats or wire. In these cases the floor area per bird may be reduced by about one-third.

The all deep-litter floor is the customary way also to rear broilers during their 9–10 wk growth period that takes them from day-old ($1\frac{1}{2}$ oz) to finishing weight (4 lb). The softness of well-managed and correctly 'working' deep-litter is necessary for a good grading carcass.

Single-stage rearing can also be carried out successfully in purpose-made pullet-rearing batteries in which the birds are initially brooded and then, by means of extensions, the area is enlarged to satisfy the increasing demands of the growing birds. Following this period the birds should be allocated to wire or slatted floors or batteries, but not deep-litter, as there would be a possibility of poor resistance to parasitic infections. There is no doubt that all the single-stage intensive systems require extremely careful hygiene, nutrition and management in order to minimize the considerable risk of vices and disease, particularly as units are often large, running into thousands for pullet replacement and tens of thousands for broilers. It may be said in their favour that they obviate the management difficulties inseparable from the more usual multi-stage systems and also greatly simplify the range of equipment and housing needed.

ii. *Multi-stage: Intensive.* There are a number of systems that brood the birds in one house and carry on after the period of artificial heating in a different form of accommodation. A popular arrangement of this type is based on the tier brooder which is suitable for the first 3–5 wks of life. Tier brooders have the advantage that they can be kept in many forms of adapted and non-specialist buildings, but the period birds are kept in them should be as brief as possible, as room for exercise is limited and the birds will thrive better if they can be moved to more spacious quarters. The tier brooder consists of two or three hover compartments, one above the other, with runs attached in front. The base is of wire, and droppings trays are provided underneath. A suitable size of tier brooder is 9 ft × 3 ft taking 50 chicks to 4 wks of age. With tier brooding the concentration of chicks is greater than with any other system, and management and disease problems can, in consequence, be considerable. Careful ventilation and some insulation of the building must be provided. The brooders in themselves offer an obstruction to the free passage of air, and it is also more difficult to bring in fresh air evenly to all tiers. The brooders should be arranged across the building if possible to cause as little obstruction as possible, and air inlets should be arranged at two heights in the walls as with battery laying cages, the lower $2\frac{1}{2}$ ft from the ground and the higher 1 ft below the eaves. Extraction will be by ridge ventilator, preferably fan assisted. If the brooders run lengthwise down the house, however, and there are more than two rows underfloor ducts to the centre cages are necessary.

With intensive rearing the birds may go on to any other system, for example to wire-floored carry-on cages, slatted floors or deep-litter. It is generally advisable to avoid changing the type of flooring too frequently, as not only are there increased hazards from parasitic diseases, such as coccidiosis, but a major change may cause a prolonged check in growth. A recent innovation which has much to commend it is to keep the chicks in tier brooders for 6 wks and then put them straight into the laying cages, which are specially designed to facilitate easy feeding by the young birds.

iii. *Multi-stage: indoors to outdoors.* A number of systems involving a period outdoors are popular with a diminishing number, who consider there are advantages in the 'grower-stage' if the birds have access to grass. These systems are as follows:

a. The first stage is on floor or in tier brooders. Thence the birds go to haybox brooders at 3–4 wks. The haybox consists of a small enclosed compartment 3 ft × 3 ft and a run in front approximately 6 ft long. No artificial heat is used, as the chicks own heat is conserved by packing straw above their heads. The sleeping-quarters and runs are made with solid wooden sides, but the floor is of wire, and also the roof of the run. While no one questions the healthy nature of this system and its ability to produce hardy and vigorous stock, it is a relatively expensive arrangement, both from the points of view of capital, maintenance and labour, and it requires highly skilled management at all times. In effect, it introduces a middle stage between brooding and rearing which may be considered superfluous; it also introduces another 'check', and the chicks are on this form of accommodation only a short time. Normally, the units are moved over a field, but it is also a practice to use them as a static unit, and one popular way is to mount them on straw bales, new bales being used each season.

b. After the haybox stage the customary arrangement is to move birds to *Range Shelters*, and here they can stay from 8 wks to point of lay. This is a cheap and light form of housing. The dimensions are usually 8 ft × 6 ft × 5 ft high to ridge and $2\frac{1}{2}$ ft to eaves. Such a unit will take 60 growers to point of lay. The usual construction for the roof is either galvanized iron or felt on wire, while the floor is of slats or wire, together with skids for moving it over the ground. The sides are covered with wire netting, and the large overhang on the roof protects the stock from wind and rain.

Alternative housing systems to the range shelter are the Sussex Night Ark and the Apex Hut, for birds reared on range. The Sussex Night Ark is a hut 6 ft × 3 ft with a slatted floor and solid walls and roof, while the Apex Hut, as its name implies, is of triangular cross-section of dimension 6 ft × 5 ft. Both are more expensive than the Range Shelter and have no advantages to offer.

Some farmers prefer to rear their birds in smaller confined groups but still give them the benefit of grass. In these circumstances the fold unit is the ideal method. A fold unit consists of a hut measuring some 6 ft × 4 ft with a run in front extending 12 ft in length. It will take 20–25 pullets to point of lay. Fold units should be moved daily in order to be sure that the birds do not build up infection from parasites and bacteria in their own droppings.

d. Broilers
Probably no type of livestock has a more standardized method of housing than broilers. Almost invariably the birds are reared from day-old to 63–70 days of age in 'controlled environment' housing in one stage and on built-up litter. The typical broiler house is of 5,000–10,000-bird capacity, rectangular in shape and 37–45 ft wide. The birds are kept at a density of between 0·65 and 1 ft²/head, the lower densities being permissible when the housing is good and ventilation is planned on a satisfactory basis for the number of birds housed.

The usual brooding systems rear the chicks in groups of 1000, feeding being either by tubular feeders or by automatic trough feeders. Watering is by either circular or trough-type automatic drinkers. With the continual throughput of young stock, hygienic construction of the house is most important, and inner linings of impervious and smooth unobstructed materials are essential. Also, since much artificial heat is applied, good thermal insulation of the surfaces is essential and a *U*-value of 0·1 is advised. This is equivalent to 2 in. of glass or mineral wool. A concrete floor is likewise an almost essential part of healthy broiler production, though one that is often neglected. Without this, infections in the soil may build up to unmanageable proportions.

e. Systems for Layers
The trend with laying stock, as with growers, is towards a great intensification of housing and methods. Fewer and fewer birds are kept under the old-established extensive and semi-extensive systems, and over 80 per cent of layers are maintained intensively on deep-litter, slatted floors or cages. The houses now popular are the so-called 'controlled environment' buildings; that is, control is exercised in some degree over all the environmental factors—viz. temperature, humidity, light, air movement and ventilation.

C. *The systems*
a. Extensive and Semi-extensive
Certain of the traditional systems, nevertheless, still remain in some measure and may be examined critically.

i. *Free range.* Keeping layers on free range still has a place on some farms. Under such systems the housing is simple and cheap, but any real environmental control is impossible.

ii. *Movable colony house.* This is a popular house on skids or wheels, holding 40 to 50 birds and measuring about 10 ft × 8 ft. The hut has a solid wooden base and is fitted with perches, droppings boards and nests.

iii. *Slatted-floor house.* This is basically similar to the Movable Colony House, the all-over slatted floor enabling a heavier concentration of stock; for example, a hut of 8 ft × 6 ft will hold 60 birds comfortably. The hut will have skids or wheels and be fitted with nests, broody coop, troughs and drinkers.

These systems are healthy, but have serious disadvantages in that the birds are at the mercy of the elements and winter production can be particularly poor. No advantage can be taken of artificial-light stimulation by increasing the hours of light. Largely the same disadvantages may be said for the Fold Unit, though environmental control of the birds is better.

iv. *The fold unit.* This consists of a covered-in roost with slatted floor measuring about 5 ft × 5 ft × 3½ ft high and with a totally enclosed run in front about 12 ft long. The whole unit is built rigidly to withstand daily moving across the ground. It has a capacity for 25–30 birds. While the birds will benefit from the advantages inherent in keeping stock in small groups, of moving birds to fresh ground daily and keeping them in fairly good control, the cost is out of proportion with the return and it is a system of diminishing popularity.

v. *Fixed pen with outside runs.* The fixed house with single or alternative runs is a system much used by the domestic poultry keeper, but has little to commend it and is mentioned in passing only because numbers of these units remain in use, due to its great popularity in the past. A typical unit consists of 50 birds kept in a house 8 ft × 8 ft with two runs each 30 ft × 30 ft, the birds alternating between these at six-month intervals. The cost of such a system is high both in capital and labour, yet the climatic control over the birds is poor. Even when alternating between two runs a certain build-up of disease may occur, as the area the birds run over is limited.

b. Intensive Housing: Deep Litter

The first completely successful method of housing layers intensively was the 'built-up' or 'deep-litter' system, which was re-introduced to Britain after the last war. It has undergone many changes since then, but remains as a basically satisfactory system, though of rather high capital cost (see Appendix E to section: p. 249). The system keeps birds on a built-up litter of wood shavings which may be supplemented in part, or replaced, by peat moss or straw. It is kept to a depth of about 1 ft.

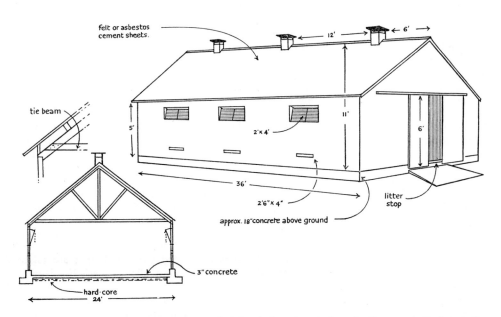

Fig. 125. A type of deep-litter house. Air inlets below the windows leading to ventilation shaft
From Leonard Robinson's *Modern Poultry Husbandry*

Movable perches were used in the first designs, and also drinkers and feeders that could be moved around the house so that droppings and water splashing were so far as possible distributed evenly. Under this system in its original form as described, birds require 3–4 ft² of floor space each, if the litter is to 'work' properly, that is, bacterial decomposition will keep it warm and in a 'friable' state (Fig. 125). A sounder proposition economically is to have a slatted area over a droppings pit for perching and roosting which may also take the food and water troughs. With the food and water sited over the slatted area a high proportion of the droppings go into the pit underneath and the density of stocking can be increased, the litter receiving proportionally less of the excreta. With the nest boxes suitably disposed around the house, feeding and egg collection can be combined in a single movement round the house, though often automatic feeding leaves egg collection as the only 'chore'. With a system of deep-litter combined with a droppings pit in roughly equal proportions, 2 ft²/bird is sufficient for heavy breeds and 1½ ft² for light breeds.

Basically a variation of the deep-litter house, the *Hen Yard* was introduced just after the deep-litter system as a cheap alternative particularly suited to the arable farmer who has abundant straw and a number of old and redundant buildings of questionable strength. It fails to give full climatic control and will not produce the highest egg yields. On the other hand, these disadvantages must be balanced against the very low capital cost of the system which can be as little as £¼ a bird. One of the problems that has occurred with this system has been heavy intestinal worm infestation in the birds, the viability of the eggs being enhanced under the wet conditions prevailing at certain times of the year. Plenty of straw and good drainage are essential in controlling this danger. Certain figures have been given to show that as good a profit may be obtained per bird from this system as some of those that fashion has preferred lately, but the hen yard does demand a degree of skill in management that more popular systems partially avoid.

The construction is simple. It is based on any existing shed, and in front of this is built an uncovered deeply strawed yard. The birds are usually given 1½–2 ft² of covered space and 3–4 ft² of uncovered. Some drinkers and feeders will be placed in the uncovered area while the nests and the remainder of the food and water troughs will be placed in the covered area. It is preferable if the enclosed area is entirely covered with wire or slats on which may be placed sufficient feeders and water for all the birds in severe weather, but an alternative is to have two-thirds slats and one-third litter. If the nest boxes are placed so that the birds have to walk across the slats to enter them cleaner eggs are produced. The production of dirty eggs is often a severe drawback with the hen yard.

As the system is primarily intended to make use of existing open-fronted cattle yards, cart sheds and so on, the problem must be tackled of avoiding draughts and cold winds. Both the yard and the house benefit from a solid front to a height of 2–3 ft: a cheap way of providing this is to use corrugated sheets placed horizontally. It then depends on the height of the eaves and the overhang on the roof whether further protection is necessary. If the eaves are no more than 5 ft and the overhang 2 ft or more no further protection may be required, but usually these requirements are not satisfied and a simple front may be constructed of straw bales and polythene or 'window-lite'. A reasonably free circulation of air must nevertheless be allowed in the house, or damp litter and condensation problems may result. There is no doubt that some form of cheap insulation of the roof is always justified as an aid to keeping the birds warm and the litter in good condition. The insulation can be achieved by placing a glass-wool mat on wire and polythene to form a false ceiling.

The general disadvantages to the system are relatively poor environmental control, though artificial lighting is possible, and heavy usage of straw, 15–25 T/1000 is a reasonable quantity to expect with an uncovered yard.

A straw-yard conversion will cost approximately 9s./bird, and for an equivalent cost or slightly more, a similar building could be converted to a slatted-floor or deep-litter unit. For this reason it is difficult to justify the use of a straw yard, but nevertheless it still has its advocates, and particularly by those who prefer a more 'natural' environment for their birds.

c. Intensive Housing: Slatted-floor System

The slatted- or wire-floored system for layers represents the most concentrated method of housing layers on the floor, at a density down to 1 ft²/bird. Buildings with these false floors have become popular for several reasons. There are no problems of caked and wet litter, and parasites thereon. Birds can be housed more densely, labour needs and housing costs are far less, and clean eggs are readily produced. In such buildings automatic methods of feeding and watering are particularly economical and justified in large units (Fig. 126). The floors are built either of slats or welded wire mesh that are raised 2½ ft above the floor to allow a year's build-up of dung. The slats or wire are made in sections that are easily removed to allow mechanical removal of the dung. Slats are usually made 1¼ in. wide at the top tapering to 1 in. at the base and with a 1 in. gap between. The frames are made of 6 in. × 1½ in.

timber lengthwise with 4 in. × 1½ in. crosspieces at 2–2½ ft centres. Wire floors are of 3 in. × 1 in. mesh, 10 or 12 s.w.g. and galvanized, the frame being similar to that for slats. 2 in. × 2 in. perches may be fixed across the sections at 1¼-ft centres on top of the mesh to give added strength and to help in a uniform distribution of the birds.

Because of the great concentration of birds correct ventilation and insulation are vital. Houses taking up to 5000 birds are quite common, but should be divided into units by simple wire partitions of not more than 500.

d. The Layout for Floor-laying House

It is important that all the equipment in a floor-laying house should be considered in site and position so that the various chores associated with management—feeding and egg collection being the major ones—can be easily carried out.

In a small building taking up to 500 layers a service room may be placed at one end of the house and the nests so placed that collection is made from this room, the nests forming the upper part of the dividing wall between the house and the service room.

In larger buildings with automatic feeding the more usual arrangement is to have a central service passage and nests on either side so that a quick collection of the eggs is easily made.

With hand feeding it is preferable to have the nests against the wall and an overhead monorail and conveyor are placed round the house adjoining the nests. The conveyor can then be used to collect the eggs and to take the food to the tubular or trough feeders which are placed on the opposite side towards the centre of the house. When this design is used in a deep-litter house a central droppings pit is installed, and on this would be placed the bulk of the waterers to minimize the effect of splashing. It may be argued, however, that it is better if the birds walk across the slats before they enter the nest box, as this will keep their feet cleaner and produce a cleaner egg. With this arrangement in a wide-span building, a centre passage would be used with nest boxes on each side and droppings pit immediately adjoining. There are, however, those who prefer the droppings pit at the side of the house, as it is easier constructionally and makes a rather 'cleaner' design. The usual pattern for this is to have droppings pit one side, central deep-litter area and nests adjoining a passage at the other side. This passage will also take the food trolley where hand feeding is practised.

There are alternative layouts, but it must always be foremost in mind to reduce the heavy chores associated with floor layers—that is, egg collection and feeding. The house will usually be cleaned out annually and for this to be easily done the slats, perches and divisions should be easily demountable and end doors should be sufficiently large to allow tractor entry. Mechanical methods of daily cleaning under the droppings pit with conveyor belt or scraper are used but have not proved popular due to the high capital cost of such units. There is no advantage hygienically. The area beneath the slats or the droppings pit is unventilated and virtually a dead area out of contact with the birds.

e. Laying Batteries

The maintenance of birds in cages three or four tiers high has been popular for thirty years, but has recently taken on a new lease of life due to the breeding of small birds which can be kept housed much more densely than hitherto. Whereas one bird per laying cage was the normal practice until a year or two ago, three or more birds per cage are now generally accommodated, at a greatly reduced cost (Fig. 127). For example, a hand-feeding hand-operated set-up with four birds to a cage can be installed for as little as 16*s.* a bird, and this established the multi-bird cages as the cheapest method of housing layers. With a multi-bird cage

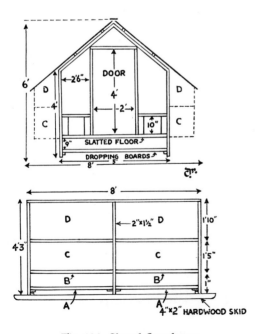

Fig. 126. Slatted-floor house

A. Droppings board. B. Slatted floor. C. Food hopper. D. Nest box. From Leonard Robinson's *Modern Poultry Husbandry*

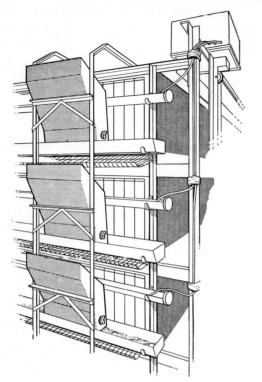

Fig. 127. Laying battery with automatic hopper feeding. From Leonard Robinson's *Modern Poultry Husbandry*

operation: cleaning may be by hand or mechanically operated plastic or proper belts beneath the cage, or by scraper on metal or glass. Feeding may be by hand, or by hand or mechanically operated moving hoppers filling up a continuous trough line. The moving cafeteria blocks of food and water troughs have gone out of fashion, particularly as they are unsuitable for multi-bird cages. There has, in fact, recently been a return to simpler design where mechanical problems are minimized or non-existent. One of the most popular types hand-feeds and hand-cleans each cage individually and, though labour costs are higher, the cages are so much cheaper that with good organization and once-weekly cleaning, the job can be contracted out economically.

An entirely new approach to battery housing is the 'Californian Cage', which is already popular in America, Australia, Africa and warmer climates. With this design the cages are in two tiers, which are staggered one behind the other and the droppings fall through directly to the ground and need be removed only once a year. The cages are of low cost, and feeding can be easily effected with a travelling hopper and continuous trough.

From the point of view of disease control, cages have both advantages and disadvantages. The very heavy concentration of birds is clearly a risk, but on the credit side there are considerable advantages in the individual attention and culling that is possible, particularly with single-bird cages. With 'endless-belt' cleaning of cages there is a grave risk of easy spread of bacterial diseases. Fowl typhoid, for example, has been known to spread rapidly when birds in the lower tiers can peck at the belt above. With this type of cleaning device a brush and disinfectant cleaner should be fitted.

D. *Equipment*
a. Feeders

An essential to the good management of intensive poultry houses is the correct disposal and area of drinking, feeding, and nesting space. Most of the standards are unfortunately empirical, but appear to be generally 'conservatively' satisfactory, so that with these followed it is possible to be reasonably certain that sufficient space is provided.

Several basic forms of feeders are used, both hand-operated and automatic. The space requirements for trough feeders are:

Wks old	
1–4	1 in. per bird,
4–10	2–3 in. per bird,
10–20	3–4 in. per bird.

Tubular feeders (1–1¼ ft dia.)

1–4	one per 35 birds,
4–10	one per 25 birds,
10–20	one per 20 birds.

system, the total floor area per bird may be no more than ⅔ ft² (the following sizes of cages are used— single-bird cage 11–12 in. frontage, for the light hybrid, 14–15 in. for single heavy bird or two hybrids, and 17–18 in. for two heavier crosses or three light hybrids). Thus the overall floor and air space is very low compared with other systems, and the need for perfect environmental control is acute.

It is probably truer with batteries than with any other system that the layout should be planned around the ventilation system. The usual arrangement is to place batteries lengthwise down the house so that they tend to act as a barrier to the air flow across the building. With two rows of cages side inlets and ridge extraction can still be used, but with more than two rows underfloor ducting of air to the centre rows of cages must be provided. An alternative can be to have the cages arranged *across* the house which should be as near square in shape as possible. Arranged in this fashion they do not interrupt the air flow, and underfloor ducting is not necessary.

There are several types of battery on the market with the following variations in features and

Automatic feeders are generally of the trough type with a continuous-chain conveyor taking the food through metal troughs from a storage bin that serves 1, 2, 3, or 4 outlets. A less-popular arrangement is to have a pipeline delivery which operates by conveying feed in a closed pipeline to existing tube or trough feeders of any type on any type of floor. There is also an oscillating type of trough conveyor in which feed from a master bin moves along a gently oscillating line of troughing.

As important as the actual trough space is the distribution of feeders, which should ensure that a bird is always in close proximity to the food. This is particularly important in the early days of life: many chicks die due to starvation or dehydration from failing to find water or food.

b. Drinkers
Poultry drinkers should be automatic, easy to clean, free from excessive splashing and not liable to flood. The amount of trough space recommended is:

1–12 wks	$\frac{1}{2}$ in. per bird,
12-Adult	1 in. per bird.

Water consumption is:

	gal per 100 birds
Day-old–2 wks	$\frac{3}{4}$–1
Wks old	
2–6	$1\frac{1}{2}$–2
6–10	3
10–20	4

The main types of drinkers include those with ball valves, or polystyrene floats, weight-controlled valves and small individual low-pressure gravity valves operating as contact with the bird's beak and used in battery cages only. An alternative arrangement is to use 3-in. guttering, metal or plastic, which runs the length of the house and has water trickling through it continuously.

c. Nest Boxes
The requirements are extremely difficult to satisfy all at once in any particular design. The hen requires privacy and quiet, and will prefer a soft floor, though the nests must be easily accessible, well ventilated and clean. The nests may be of single type—one bird to a nest—or community—taking 12 birds or so. Collection of eggs is a major chore, and the nests must always be sited to make movement minimal. They must also be sited so that hens are never far from any nest. The usual practice in the common long and narrow poultry house is to have lines of nests placed longitudinally through the house. With individual nests, 1 ft³, 5 birds are allowed to one nest; with community types 12 ft² are sufficient for 100 birds.

E. *Appendix*
Egg production with different systems

	Eggs/ bird (dozen)	Food/ bird (lb)	Food conversion	Food cost/ doz. at $3\frac{1}{2}d$. lb
				s. d.
Free range	14	120	8·6	2 6
Intensive (unmodified no fans or insulation)	17	110	6·5	1 10
Intensive (insulated and fan ventilated)	20	95	4·8	1 $4\frac{1}{2}$

Fig. Showing the advantages of the Intensive System of housing poultry under ideal environmental control. (N.A.A.S. figures.)

Stocking density and comparative costs of housing with different systems

System	Square feet of floor space per bird	Minimum cost per bird
Layers		£ s. d.
Deep litter	3	2 0 0
Deep litter and slats in ratio 2 to 1	2	1 10 0
Deep litter and slats in ratio 1 to 2	$1\frac{1}{2}$	1 0 0
All slats or welded mesh	1	17 6
Multi-bird battery cages and house	$\frac{1}{2}$	15 0
Rearing		
Tier brooders	36 in.² at 3 wks	18 0
Floor rearing	1–2 ft²	15 0 to 1 10 0
Haybox brooder	50 in.² to 8 wks plus run	8 0
Sussex night ark	70 in.² to point of lay plus pasture	10 0
Range shelter	100 in.² to point of lay plus pasture	7 0
Fold units	100 in.² plus pasture	15 0

Bibliography

Agricultural Research Council. A Bibliography of Farm Buildings Research, 1945–58 and 1958–61, Part III. Buildings for Poultry, (1960) (1963).

BARRETT, H. G. & PRINGLE, E. M. 'The Effect of Environment on the Growth and Feed and Water Consumption of Chickens'. *J. Nutr.*, **37**, 153 (1951).

BLOUNT, W. P. *Diseases of Poultry*. Bailliere, Tindall & Cox (1947).

BRITISH OIL AND CAKE MILLS POULTRY ADVISORY DEPARTMENT. *Insulating Poultry Buildings* (1962).

FOX, S. *Electricity and the Influence of Light upon Poultry Husbandry*. London Electrical Development Association, No. 2005 (1961).

GRAY, H. E. *Farm Service Buildings*. McGraw-Hill (1955).

MITCHELL, H. H. & KELLEY, M. A. R. 'Estimated Data on the Energy, Gaseous and Water Metabolism of Poultry'. *J. Agric. Res.*, **47**, 735 (1933).

OSBALDISTON, G. W. & SAINSBURY, D. W. B. (1963). 'Control of the Environment in a Poultry House'. Parts I, II and III. *Vet. Rec.*, **75**, 159, 193 and 223.

Poultry Handbook, Poultry World (1955).

Practical Poultry Keeping, Poultry World (1955).

Rearing the Laying Pullet. Farmers Weekly Publication (1963).

ROBINSON, LEONARD. *Modern Poultry Husbandry*, 5th edn. Crosby Lockwood (1961).

SAINSBURY, D. W. B. & OSBALDISTON, G. W. 'Poultry Housing and Husbandry'. Paper at British Veterinary Association Congress (1963).

STURKIE, P. D. *Avian Physiology*. Comstock (1954).

interest on the capital, insurance of the building and a small amount of maintenance, then: (Pt. I. Ch. I. p. 4.)

$$\text{Annual Building Cost} = \frac{\text{Capital Cost} \times 150 \text{ per cent}}{10}$$

The Annual Building Cost is important when considering the annual budget for a farm and should be added to the other overheads or production costs such as labour, machinery, stock, seeds, fertilizers, feed and general management expenditure. While the *weight* of an animal is important the *quality* of the meat produced is equally important.

APPENDIX

Livestock Buildings as an Investment

Each livestock enterprise, except for extensive farm systems, needs a building in which the animals may be born and weaned or in which they may be fattened. In addition to the livestock building, in which the animals are housed and fed, storage buildings may be required for such things as food, bedding or manure. Moreover, in some cases, other buildings may be needed for processing materials, either for the preparation of the livestock rations or for the preparation of the commodity for sale, such as in a milking parlour where the milk is extracted and cooled.

No matter how many different buildings or parts of buildings are required for one enterprise, their total capital cost should be assessed in relation to the saleable commodity as part of the production costs. Rearing and fattening enterprises should always be costed separately even if a producer fattens his own rearing stock. In the latter case, the farmer should 'sell' his youngstock to the fattening unit.

It is not sufficient to consider the capital cost in relation to the animal or to the number of 'animal places' provided in a layout. In breeding units, the cost should be assessed in relation to each calf or piglet weaned and sold. In fattening enterprises the cost must be related to the increase in liveweight attained within the buildings.

As discussed previously, the life of a farm building should be depreciated, generally, over ten years. Allowing for 6 per cent compound

IIIA. Milk Production

Since cows calve once a year and since their milk is yielded, as far as the National Milk Records are concerned, within 305 days, it is relatively easy to establish the herd average yield. If experiments to increase the calving rate to more than once per cow per year should prove successful, then herd averages would have to be re-assessed. It is not difficult to relate the cost per cow place to the number of gallons produced. Capital expenditures for dairy layouts, depending on management policy, vary for the most part between £80 and £200 per cow place. Most herd averages—at least for herds justifying expenditure on new layouts of more than £80 per cow place—will be between 800 and 1200 gal. See chart at foot of page.

IIIB. Beef Production

In beef fattening enterprises two factors, other than capital cost, are important when considering the buildings as part of the investment:

a. The net livewt increase from calf to finished animal.

b. The fattening period.

Much of modern beef production is concentrated on producing an animal ready for slaughter at some 8–10 cwt, though some may be slaughtered

Cost of buildings per gal of milk produced

Capital cost per cow place		£80	£100	£120	£140	£160	£180	£200
Annual Building Cost		£12	£15	£18	£21	£24	£27	£30
Herd average:		Cost per gal produced in pence						
800 gal	3·6	4·5	5·4	6·3	7·2	8·1	9·0	
1000 „	2·9	3·6	4·3	5·0	5·7	6·4	7·1	
1200 „	2·4	3·0	3·6	4·2	4·8	5·4	6·0	

at lighter or heavier weights. For convenience, these limits may be taken as 900–1100 lb. For intensive fattening systems, the aim may be to produce a calf ready for fattening at 3 months of age weighing 200 lb. Thus, the net livewt increase during fattening would be 700–900 lb. The fattening period varies tremendously between intensive and extensive management systems. However, the following might be considered a general guide for intensive or semi-intensive systems:

Net livewt increase, lb	Period fattened, months
700	9–15
800	12–18
900	15–21

Capital expenditure on buildings may vary from £40–£140 per beef place. It is true that some layouts can cost less than £40 per place and some, including complete environment control and mechanization for handling feed and slurry, more than £140 per place. More expensive buildings may reduce other production costs, such as labour or food intake.

Two assumptions are made in the table below:

a. If rest pens are provided, a proportion of the cost of these extra places is reflected in the capital cost per beef place.

b. The building is kept in constant use, perhaps on the basis of batches of calves being bought and fattened stock sold each month. However, should stock be fattened to slaughter weight in 9 months, then the house remains empty for 3 months, the cost per lb livewt gain would have to be assessed on the 12-month period. This, for an investment of £100 per place, the cost per lb livewt gain would be increased by 1s. 4d. Some producers use the house for pig fattening during intervals when there are no beef animals present.

IIIC. Calf Production

Though cows may have twin, or even triplet, calves, most cows produce only one calf each year. However, the number of calves per cow is less important than the calving policy when considering the economics of calf housing. If all the calves are born within a short season, then each calf place will be used only once a year. Alternatively, if calving occurs throughout the year, as many as four calves per calf place may be reared annually, though three will normally be nearer the maximum due to failures in the calving dates. Accommodation for calves may include both a rearing and a nursing house or yards for multi-suckling. In either case, the capital cost should be considered in relation to each calf reared or, preferably, to each lb of calf reared per place. Mortality may account for 20 per cent of the calves born, but with good housing and management should not be greater than 15 per cent. Obviously, if mortality can be reduced to 10 per cent the value of the investment will be considerably improved. Costs of good calf housing may be some £40–£80 per calf place. The latter cost might include a bull pen.

The weight of the calf at the end of the calf-house period is as important as the number of calves reared in relation to those born. Sturdy stock may justify more expensive buildings—as previously stated, calves which are fat will not be as valuable as those which are well developed. With intensive beef production, the aim may be to attain calves weighing 200 lb at 3 months, thus allowing a throughput of 4 calves per place each year. If only 3 calves per place are reared the cost per lb of calf increases. Similarly, if the calf weight is taken to 250 lb the economics of the investment change. If 250-lb weights can be reached in 4 months, which is very unlikely, then 3 calves per place p.a. may be reared. However, it is more likely to take 5–5½ months to attain weights of 250 lb and, on this basis, the throughput might be reduced to 2 calves/place p.a.

Cost of buildings per lb livewt gain

Capital cost per beef place		£40	£60	£80	£100	£120	£140
Annual Building Cost		£6	£9	£12	£15	£18	£21
Period, months	Gain, lb	Cost per lb livewt gain in pence					
9	700	1·5	2·3	3·1	3·9	4·7	5·5
12	700	2·1	3·1	4·1	5·1	6·1	7·1
	800	1·8	2·7	3·6	4·5	5·4	6·3
15	700	2·6	3·9	5·1	6·4	7·6	8·9
	800	2·3	3·4	4·5	5·6	6·7	7·8
	900	2·0	3·0	4·0	5·0	6·0	7·0
18	800	2·7	4·0	5·4	6·8	8·1	9·4
	900	2·4	3·6	4·8	6·0	7·2	8·4
21	900	2·8	4·2	5·6	7·0	8·4	9·8

Cost of buildings per calf reared

	£40	£50	£60	£70	£80
Capital cost per calf place	£40	£50	£60	£70	£80
15% mortality allowance*	£46	£57·5	£69	£80·5	£92
Annual Building Cost	£6·9	£8·6	£10·4	£12·1	£13·8

Throughput:

	£40	£50	£60	£70	£80
1 calf place p.a.	£6·9	£8·6	£10·4	£12·1	£13·8
2 ,, ,, ,,	3·5	4·3	5·2	6·1	6·9
3 ,, ,, ,,	2·3	2·9	3·5	4·0	4·6
4 ,, ,, ,,	1·7	2·2	2·6	3·0	3·5
10% mortality allowance*	£44	£55	£66	£77	£88
Annual Building Cost	£6·6	£8·3	£9·9	£11·6	£13·0

Throughput:

	£40	£50	£60	£70	£80
1 calf place p.a.	£6·6	£8·3	£9·9	£11·6	£13·0
2 ,, ,, ,,	3·3	4·2	5·0	5·8	6·5
3 ,, ,, ,,	2·2	2·8	3·3	3·9	4·3
4 ,, ,, ,,	1·7	2·1	2·5	2·9	3·3

Cost of buildings per lb calf reared

Capital cost per calf place			£40	£50	£60	£70	£80
Mortality* %	Throughput, calves p.a.	Calf wt, lb	Cost per lb calf produced in pence				
15	4	200	0·6	0·7	0·8	0·9	1·0
	3	200	1·0	1·2	1·4	1·6	1·8
	3	250	0·7	0·9	1·1	1·3	1·5
	2	250	1·7	2·1	2·5	2·9	3·3
10	4	200	0·6	0·7	0·8	0·9	1·0
	3	200	0·9	1·1	1·3	1·5	1·7
	3	250	0·7	0·9	1·0	1·2	1·4
	2	250	1·6	2·0	2·4	2·8	3·1

* For example: if a farmer has 60 cows and 30 calf in the autumn and 30 in the spring he will need 30 calf places: if he spends £40 per calf place the building will cost £1,200: however, when assessing the cost per calf, the depreciated capital cost is £6 per place and, with each place used twice p.a., the cost per calf is £3; but some of the calves go and die on him, so he has fewer to sell and it is too late to buy another cow to get another calf to replace one that dies: thus, each calf reared per place has to carry those places which have no value each year due to mortality: at 10 per cent mortality this becomes £3·3 as the building cost for each calf successfully reared.

IIIC. Heifer Production

Some calves will be retained as replacements for a dairy herd. The period during which housing will be required for the heifers, from the end of the calf period until they join the dairy herd, will vary. In many cases they will be kept without the provision of new buildings. However, winter housing accommodation, on the basis of one place for each heifer, might cost £40–£80 per place.

Cost of building per heifer

Capital cost per heifer place	£40	£50	£60	£70	£80
Annual Building Cost	£6	£7·5	£9	£10·5	£12

IIID. Veal Production

Veal calves are fattened from about 80 lb livewt at 4 days to 200–240 lb within 10–12 weeks. This represents a livewt increase of 120–160 lb. Mortality should average around 5 per cent and throughput should be about 4 calves per place p.a. Housing may cost £22–£30 per calf place.

Cost of buildings per lb livewt gain

Capital cost per calf place	£22	£24	£26	£28	£30
5% mortality allowance	£23·1	£25·2	£27·3	£29·4	£31·5
Annual Building Cost	£3·5	£3·8	£4·1	£4·4	£4·7

Throughput 4 calves/place p.a.:

Livewt gain/calf:	Cost per lb livewt gain in pence				
120 lb	7·0	7·6	8·2	8·8	9·4
140 lb	6·0	6·5	7·0	7·5	8·0
160 lb	5·3	5·7	6·1	6·6	7·0

APPENDIX

IIIE. Pig Production

Pig production, basically, may include porkers, or baconers or heavy hogs reaching finishing weights of 140 lb, 200 lb and 260 lb respectively within 13 weeks, 18 weeks or 22 weeks. Since the pig house should be rested for 3 weeks between batches, 16, 21 or 25 weeks are required per batch. On the basis of these fattening periods, the piglets may enter the house at, perhaps, an average weight of 45 lb. Thus, production throughput might be based on the following:

	Porker	Baconer	Heavy hog
lb livewt increase	95	155	215
Weeks in house plus rest	16	21	25
Av. livewt gain:			
lb/wk/place	6	7·4	8·6
lb/yr/place	312	385	447

Generally, houses cost £10–£25 per place. Therefore, it is possible to express the cost of the house in relation to the livewt produced.

If fattening takes an additional 2 wks to reach finishing wts per batch, throughput of the livewt gain will drop to 260, 348 and 416 respectively per lb year/place. However, the cost per lb livewt gain would have to be taken to two places of decimals before this would make an appreciable difference.

Cost of buildings per lb livewt gain

Capital cost per place	£10	£15	£20	£25
Annual Building Cost	£1·5	£2·3	£3·0	£3·8

Cost per lb livewt gain in pence

Porker	1·2	1·8	2·3	3·0
Baconer	1·0	1·4	1·9	2·4
Heavy hog	0·8	1·2	1·6	2·0

IIIF. Weaner Production

The cost of buildings for weaner production should be related to the livewt reared. Sows may rear less than 9 pigs on average per litter, but 8–14 weaned piglets should be considered. Since space will be provided adequate for large litters of more than 18 piglets, mortality will not affect the capital cost of the buildings, unlike in calf production, but only the economics of the investment. The average piglet weight may be taken as 45 lb at 8 weeks. However, the costs given below would vary if the average piglet weight varied. Costs of farrowing and weaning accommodation may vary between £180 and £260 per sow place, especially if boar pens and dry sow housing is reflected in the cost per sow place. Farrowing accommodation should be used 4 times a year, but in many cases may be used only thrice.

Cost of buildings per piglet reared

Capital cost per sow/place	£180	£200	£220	£240	£260
Annual Building cost	£27	£30	£33	£36	£39

Cost per litter

Throughput:					
3 litters/place p.a.	£9	£10	£11	£12	£13
4 ,, ,,	£6·8	£7·5	£8·3	£9·0	£9·8

Cost per piglet reared at 3 litters/place p.a. in shillings

Size of litter reared:					
8 piglets	22·5	25·0	27·5	30·0	32·5
10 ,,	18·0	20·0	22·0	24·0	26·0
12 ,,	15·0	16·8	18·4	20·0	21·8
14 ,,	12·9	14·3	15·7	17·1	18·6

Cost per piglet reared at 4 litters/place p.a. in shillings

Size of litter reared:					
8 piglets	17·0	18·8	20·8	22·5	24·0
10 ,,	13·6	15·0	16·6	18·0	19·6
12 ,,	11·3	12·5	13·8	15·0	16·3
14 ,,	9·8	10·7	11·8	13·0	14·2

The average wt of the piglets, before fattening, will affect the value of the investment of the rearing house. If an average of 10 piglets per sow are reared and the average piglet/wt is increased from 40 lb to 50 lb, then the cost per lb reared will be reduced by about 1d. to 1½d.

Cost of buildings per lb piglet reared: average of 10 piglets per litter

Capital cost per sow place		£180	£200	£220	£240	£260
Throughput	Piglet weight		Cost per lb livewt reared in pence			
3 litters/place p.a.	Av. 40 lb	5·4	6·0	6·6	7·2	7·8
	,, 50 ,,	4·3	4·8	5·3	5·8	6·2
4 litters/place p.a.	,, 40 ,,	4·1	4·5	5·0	5·4	5·9
	,, 50 ,,	3·2	3·6	4·0	4·3	4·7

IIIG. Mutton Production

Winter housing for ewes or hoggs may be provided from lamb wt at about 80 lb at 14 weeks to about 160 lb before slaughter. This gives a maximum livewt increase of 80 lb per ewe place annually. Capital costs may vary between £3 and £5 per ewe place.

Cost of buildings per lb livewt gain

	£3	£4	£5
Capital cost per ewe place	£3	£4	£5
Annual Building Cost	£0·45	£0·6	£0·75

Cost per lb livewt gain in pence

60 lb gain/place p.a.	1·8	2·4	3·0
80 lb gain/place p.a.	1·4	1·8	2·3

IIIG. Lamb Production

The number of lambs reared per ewe will affect the investment in winter rearing quarters. About 1½ lambs per ewe is a reasonable average, but this may be considered both too low and too high, within a range of 1–2 lambs per ewe. The aim should be to reach a livewt of 80 lb at the end of lambing, which may coincide with the end of the winter housing period. Costs of housing per ewe place may be kept to £4–£6. Mortality during the lamb period should be kept to under 15 per cent, preferably to 10 per cent.

Though reduced mortality makes little real difference to the cost of each lb of lamb reared, there will be more important differences in relation to other overheads.

Cost of buildings per lb lamb reared

	£4	£5	£6
Capital cost per ewe place	£4	£5	£6
15% mortality allowance	£4·6	£5·75	£6·9
Annual Building Cost	£0·69	£0·86	£1·04

Lambing rate	Lamb wt	Cost per lb lamb produced in pence		
100 per cent	80 lb	2·1	2·6	3·0
150 ,,	,,	1·4	1·7	2·0
200 ,,	,,	1·1	1·3	1·5

10% mortality allowance	£4·4	£5·5	£6·6
Annual Building Cost	£0·66	£0·83	£0·99

Lambing rate	Lamb wt	Cost per lb lamb produce in pence		
100 per cent	80 lb	2·0	2·5	3·0
150 ,,	,,	1·3	1·7	2·0
200 ,,	,,	1·0	1·3	1·5

INDEX

Several of the index entries have been placed within brackets; in these cases the entry refers back to the preceding non-bracketed entry.

INDEX

INDEX

INDEX

Get 'em!
RIGHT NOW!

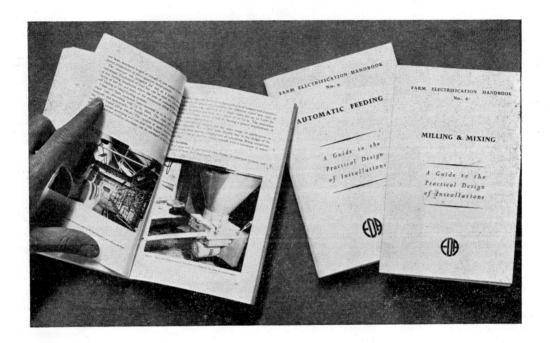

They'll show you
how to save time. How to use manpower better.
And look after your stock better. And cut
your production costs. And increase your income.
And they're **FREE!**

Where from? From your Electricity Board, Electrical Contractor or Agricultural Machinery Dealer. Or you can fill in and post this coupon.

Get 'em! RIGHT NOW!

Top: Cambridge Farm Buildings

•

Centre: Barn and Cattle Yard

•

Below: Sawston Building and Silos in course of erection

Whatever the individual need of your farm, there is a Simplex building to cover it at the most economic cost. A special feature of this design is their adaptability to your requirements. Please write for details. Dept. F.B.A.

MAKE MINE A **Simplex** MILKING MACHINE

Simplex GRAIN SYSTEMS

 Simplex OF CAMBRIDGE | MODERN FARMING EQUIPMENT

Tel.: Sawston 3281 (8 lines)   *A Member of the GEC Group of Companies*